Basic Network Theory

McGraw-Hill Electrical and Electronic Engineering Series

Frederick Emmons Terman, *Consulting Editor*
W. W. Harman and J. G. Truxal, *Associate Consulting Editors*

Ahrendt and Savant · Servomechanism Practice
Angelakos and Everhart · Microwave Communications
Angelo · Electronic Circuits
Angelo · Electronics: BJT's, FET's, and Microcircuits
Aseltine · Transform Method in Linear System Analysis
Atwater · Introduction to Microwave Theory
Beranek · Acoustics
Bracewell · The Fourier Transform and Its Application
Brenner and Javid · Analysis of Electric Circuits
Brown · Analysis of Linear Time-invariant Systems
Bruns and Saunders · Analysis of Feedback Control Systems
Carlson · Communication Systems: An Introduction to Signals and Noise in Electrical
    Communication
Chen · The Analysis of Linear Systems
Chen · Linear Network Design and Synthesis
Chirlian · Analysis and Design of Electronic Circuits
Chirlian · Basic Network Theory
Chirlian and Zemanian · Electronics
Clement and Johnson · Electrical Engineering Science
Cunningham · Introduction to Nonlinear Analysis
D'Azzo and Houpis · Feedback Control System Analysis and Synthesis
Eastman · Fundamentals of Vacuum Tubes
Elgerd · Control Systems Theory
Eveleigh · Adaptive Control and Optimization Techniques
Feinstein · Foundations of Information Theory
Fitzgerald, Higginbotham, and Grabel · Basic Electrical Engineering
Fitzgerald and Kingsley · Electric Machinery
Frank · Electrical Measurement Analysis
Friedland, Wing, and Ash · Principles of Linear Networks
Gehmlich and Hammond · Electromechanical Systems
Ghausi · Principles and Design of Linear Active Circuits
Ghose · Microwave Circuit Theory and Analysis
Glasford · Fundamentals of Television Engineering
Greiner · Semiconductor Devices and Applications
Hammond · Electrical Engineering
Hancock · An Introduction to the Principles of Communication Theory
Harman · Fundamentals of Electronic Motion
Harman · Principles of the Statistical Theory of Communication
Harman and Lytle · Electrical and Mechanical Networks
Harrington · Time-harmonic Electromagnetic Fields
Hayashi · Nonlinear Oscillations in Physical Systems

Basic Network Theory

Paul M. Chirlian

Professor of Electrical Engineering

Stevens Institute of Technology

McGraw-Hill Book Company

New York   St. Louis   San Francisco   Toronto   London   Sydney

Basic Network Theory

To

Barbara, Lisa, and Peter

Preface

This undergraduate college-level text on introductory electric circuits is to be used in basic electric circuits courses by students who have had an elementary course in differential and integral calculus. The purpose of a modern introductory circuits course is to provide the electrical engineering student with the basic tools with which to analyze the circuits and systems he will encounter. Such a course is a prerequisite not only for advanced circuit courses, but also for such courses as those in electronic circuits and control systems. A basic circuits course should include techniques for the analysis of nonlinear and time-varying systems as well as detailed studies of linear time-invariant systems.

After completing a basic circuits course or sequence, the student should be familiar with time-domain analysis not only by classical means but also by Laplace transform and state-variable techniques. The latter method is especially important for nonlinear and time-varying circuits and for analysis to be done by computers. These techniques should be introduced early so that the student can apply them to many problems. For instance, network theory and twoport circuits should be analyzed on a Laplace transform basis. State variables should be available to solve nonlinear electronics problems and control system problems. The Laplace transform should be used in the study of linear electronic circuits. Sinusoidal-steady-state solutions follow very simply from the Laplace transform, and such a development has the advantage of being rigorous without tending to confuse the student.

The use of integrated circuits places special emphasis upon distributed-parameter systems. These should also be introduced at an early stage.

In Chapter 1 and part of Chapter 2 electric field concepts are discussed solely to provide the reader with an idea of the foundations of electric circuit theory. *However, the fundamental purpose of the book is to provide the reader with an understanding of the basic procedures used to analyze electric networks and systems; thus the field approach is not used in the remainder of the book.*

The fundamental ideas of electric circuits are presented in Chapter 1. The concepts of voltage and current are obtained from electromagnetic field theory, and field concepts are then used to introduce circuit elements. Nonlinear and time-varying resistance, inductance, capacitance, and mutual inductance are presented here; power, energy, and elementary realizability theory are discussed; distributed parameters are introduced. Some basic notation is also discussed. *Most of this chapter will be a review for students who have had a good first physics course. For such students the chapter should be assigned reading, but most of the material need not be discussed in classroom lectures.*

In Chapter 2 Kirchhoff's laws are developed from the basic field laws. The general limitations of these laws are discussed (for example, the continuity equation is developed). The assumptions of circuit theory are presented, and then Kirchhoff's laws are applied to the solution of simple network problems using branch currents and voltages. Simple equivalent circuits are presented so that interchange of sources and combination of elements can be performed. The important ideas of dependent generators are introduced.

The fundamental ideas and theorems of network topology are presented in Chapter 3. These are used in a development of procedures for loop, nodal, and cut-set analyses (topology is used in later chapters for such things as state-variable analysis of networks). Dependent generators are again considered here. Loop, nodal, and cut-set analyses are applied to nonlinear and time-varying networks, and procedures for the solution of simultaneous equations are given. Matrices, matrix operations, and determinants are also discussed here.

Chapter 4 presents classical methods for the solution of linear differential equations. Initial conditions are discussed thoroughly here in terms of network theory, and the responses of some typical networks are presented. The concept of negative resistance is introduced, and the solution of simultaneous linear differential equations is presented.

The Laplace transform is discussed in Chapter 5. The $0-$ rather than the $0+$ form is used here, and it is demonstrated that, when used properly, the $0-$ form is in fact often less difficult and tedious to use than the $0+$ form. Toward the end of the chapter impulse functions are introduced, and the advantages of the $0-$ form are clearly pointed out. The Laplace transform is applied to the solution of electric networks by means of transformed networks with initial-condition generators. Partial-fraction expansion is introduced, the concept of general impedance is presented, and a general change-of-source theorem is given. Poles and zeros are introduced and applied to a discussion of stability and stability tests. Impulses are discussed, and then the impulse and step responses are given and related. Laplace transform theorems, such as time shift, semiperiodic functions, initial value, and convolution, are discussed, and network response is related to impulse response.

The sinusoidal-steady-state solution of networks is presented in Chapter 6. The concept of a sinusoidal-steady-state solution is discussed. It is derived from the Laplace transform solution. This leads to a clear introduction of the concept of phasors. Phasor algebra is reviewed. Loop, nodal, and cut-set analyses are presented. Impedance and the change-of-source theorem are discussed on a sinusoidal-steady-state basis. Average power is discussed. Amplitude and phase, polar, and Bode plots are presented. The concept of resonance and the substitutions and approximations made in the analysis of these circuits are discussed in detail. Ideal and practical transformers are considered, and the equivalent circuits of a practical transformer are given. Distributed-parameter systems are analyzed, and infinite and terminated transmission lines are discussed. These results are applied to RC lines and to distributed integrated circuits.

State variables are discussed in Chapter 7, and state equations are defined. A procedure for writing state-variable equations for linear, nonlinear, and time-varying networks is presented, and techniques for the solution of these equations are discussed. State variables are also applied to nonlinear oscillators and stability. The equations of state of networks are related to their topology.

In Chapter 8 twoport networks are discussed. The network parameters, including the scattering parameters, are presented, and the useful idea of characteristic functions is introduced. The immittance and transfer functions of networks are discussed in terms of the network parameters. The use of linear equivalent circuits for electronic devices is presented, and some transistor circuits are analyzed. A twoport distributed-parameter network is thoroughly analyzed as a twoport. The concept of twoports is extended to n-ports.

Network theorems are presented in Chapter 9. To provide as much generality as possible, Laplace transforms and state variables are used here. The superposition theorem, the substitution theorem (introduced in Chapter 7), Thévenin's and Norton's theorems, the reciprocity principle, the compensation theorem, duality, mechanical analogs, and network transformations are presented in as general a way as possible, and their limitations are stressed. For instance, it is shown that the load in Thévenin's theorem can be nonlinear, and it is stressed that a network and its Thévenin equivalent circuit are equivalent only for external conditions.

In Chapter 10 signal-flow graphs are defined and related to simultaneous equations. Techniques are given for the solution and simplification of signal-flow graphs and for drawing the signal-flow graph of a network on the basis of its topology. The solution of state-variable equations by analog-computer procedures is discussed in this chapter. This topic is not included earlier because of the ease with which analog-computer diagrams can be represented by means of signal-flow graphs.

The Fourier series and Fourier integral are discussed in Chapter 11. The Fourier series is introduced, and the truncated Fourier series is then discussed. The periodic-steady-state solution of networks is presented. The Fourier integral is then developed and applied to the solution of network problems. Convolution is presented, and the relationship between the Fourier and Laplace transforms is discussed.

I would like to express my grateful thanks to Dr. John Truxal for his many valuable comments and discussions.   I also thank Dr. Ronald Rohrer for his valuable comments.

Loving and heartfelt thanks are again due my wife Barbara, who not only provided me with continuous encouragement and saw to it that my time was free from interruptions, but who also typed the rough draft and final draft of this manuscript and corrected the punctuation, spelling, and grammar.

Paul M. Chirlian

Contents

Chapter 6.   The Sinusoidal Steady State

Chapter 7. *State Space*

Chapter 8. *Twoport Networks*

Chapter 9. *Network Theorems*

Chapter 10. *Signal-flow Graphs*

Chapter 11.   Fourier Series and Fourier Integral

Electromagnetic Fields and Circuit Concepts

1

In this book we shall discuss the procedures used to analyze electric circuits. Although these analysis techniques are general and can be applied to disciplines other than networks, they are fundamental to all electric circuits and systems and hence are indispensable to the electrical engineer. We shall begin in this chapter with the most fundamental aspects of electric circuits. The material is developed from a discussion of electric fields. Most of the remainder of the book *does not* use this field-theory approach; it is included here to provide an idea of the origins of circuit theory.

Many of the topics discussed in this chapter will be a review for the reader. They are included only to reinforce the ideas of the fundamental concepts of network theory. Often this material need not be included in classroom lectures.

1

1-1   Electric charge and Coulomb's law

All atoms comprise a nucleus and electrons which travel about the nucleus. In an equilibrium state the atom is said to be *uncharged* or *neutral*. However, if one or more electrons are removed from it, then the atom is said to be *positively charged*. A *negative charge* is associated with the *electrons*, while a *positive charge* is associated with the *protons*, which are contained in the nucleus. It has been known since early Grecian times that forces existed between charged bodies. Indeed, it was because of these forces that the concept of charge was developed. If an object is positively charged, it will *attract* one that is negatively charged and will *repel* another that is positively charged. Because the operation of all electrical devices is based on the motion of these charges and/or the forces between them, it is important for us to obtain quantitative information about charges and their motion.

In this book we shall use the mks (meter, kilogram, second) system of units. This system is commonly used by electrical engineers and results in convenient numerical values. No matter what system of units is used, however, the fundamental ideas are the same. The basic unit of charge is the *coulomb*, which represents the charge of 6.242×10^{18} electrons; that is, a single electron has a charge of -1.602×10^{-19} coul. The minus sign is used to indicate that the electron is *assigned* a negative charge.

Coulomb discovered that the force between two charged bodies was proportional to the product of their charges and inversely proportional to the square of the distance between them, that is, the force on a charge q_1 in the presence of another charge q_2 is

$$\mathbf{f} = \frac{q_1 q_2}{4\pi \epsilon r^2} \, \mathbf{U}_r \tag{1-1}$$

where $\mathbf{f}$ is the force in newtons, q is the charge in coulombs, and r is the distance in meters. The quantity ϵ, called the *permittivity*, depends upon the medium between the charges, that is, it has been found experimentally that the force is a function of the medium between the charges. ϵ is expressed in units of newton-meters squared per coulomb squared. In a vacuum the value of ϵ to be used in Eq. (1-1) is 8.85×10^{-12} newton-m²/coul². The quantity 4π is included by convention and can be omitted if the value of ϵ is modified. Note that $\mathbf{f}$ is a vector quantity; that is, it has both a magnitude and a direction. The magnitude is given by $q_1 q_2 / 4\pi \epsilon r^2$. The direction of the vector is given by the unit vector $\mathbf{U}_r$. Its magnitude is unity and its direction points from q_2 toward q_1. In this book vectors will be designated by boldface sans serif letters, as shown. Lightface sans serif will be used for the magnitudes of these vectors.

A force will be exerted upon a single charge in a region where there is more than one fixed charge. This can be considered to be the sum of the forces due

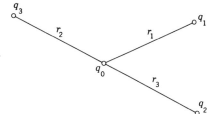

Fig. 1-1   A charge in the presence of others.

to the individual charges.   For instance, consider Fig. 1-1.   The force on q_0 is

$$\mathbf{f} = \frac{q_0 q_1 \mathbf{U}_1}{4\pi\epsilon r_1^2} + \frac{q_0 q_2 \mathbf{U}_2}{4\pi\epsilon r_2^2} + \frac{q_0 q_3 \mathbf{U}_3}{4\pi\epsilon r_3^2} \qquad (1\text{-}2)$$

The unit vector $\mathbf{U}_j$ points from q_j to q_0.   If we did not know the location and magnitudes of the charges, we could still determine that q_0 experienced a force. To *explain* this, we say that there is a field, called an *electric field*, which interacts with q_0.   If the charges do not change as a function of time, the field is called an *electrostatic field*.   The electric field, which is a vector, is defined as the force on a unit (positive) charge (it is assumed that the unit charge does not disturb the location of the other charges).   For instance, in Fig. 1-1 the electric field is given by

$$\mathbf{e} = \frac{q_1 \mathbf{U}_1}{4\pi\epsilon r_1^2} + \frac{q_2 \mathbf{U}_2}{4\pi\epsilon r_2^2} + \frac{q_3 \mathbf{U}_3}{4\pi\epsilon r_3^2} \qquad (1\text{-}3)$$

The units of electric field are newtons per coulomb (we shall see other ways of expressing this unit subsequently).

We may not know the location of the charges that produce the electric field. However, we can move a small "test charge" q_0 into the region in question and determine the force on it.   The electric field is then given by

$$\mathbf{e} = \frac{\mathbf{f}}{q_0} \qquad (1\text{-}4)$$

In general, when a charge is moved in an electric field, *work* is done.   Let us calculate this work in some specific cases.   For instance, in Fig. 1-2 the electric field $\mathbf{e}$ is assumed to be everywhere constant in both magnitude and direction.   Such a field is called a *uniform field*.   A charge q_0 is to be moved from point a to point b.   The component of force along line ab is

$$\mathbf{f}_{ab} = q_0 e \cos \theta \qquad (1\text{-}5)$$

Thus the work or energy expended in moving the charge from a to b is

$$w = -q_0 e \cos \theta \mathbin{|} \qquad (1\text{-}6)$$

where $\mathbin{|}$ is the length of the line ab and e is the magnitude of $\mathbf{e}$.   To avoid conflict with the many other meanings usually assigned to the letter l, in this

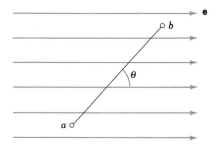

Fig. 1-2 A path in a uniform electric field.

book the magnitude of the length vector will be designated by the lightface sans serif | and its complete vector by the boldface sans serif **|** (see below). The minus sign indicates that the field actually does work on the charge.

Now let us consider a more general problem. Suppose that the electric field is not uniform, that is, that its magnitude and direction vary from point to point. Moreover, we need not assume that the path is a straight line. Such a situation is illustrated in Fig. 1-3. One procedure for determining the work done in moving the charge from point a to point b would be to approximate the path by straight-line segments, as shown. These should be short enough that the path is well approximated and also that the electric field can be considered uniform over any one segment. Thus the work done in moving a charge q_0 over any one segment is given approximately by Eq. (1-6). If we break the path into n segments of length Δl, then the total work, expressed in joules, is given

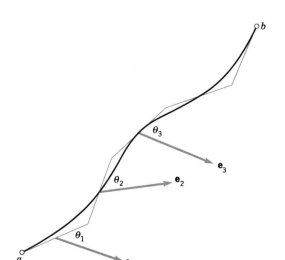

Fig. 1-3 A curved path in a nonuniform electric field.

approximately by

$$w \approx -q_0 \sum_{k=1}^{n} e_k \cos \theta_k \, \Delta l \tag{1-7}$$

In the limit, as Δl approaches zero, the result becomes exact. This is *defined* as a *line integral*. It is written as

$$w = -q_0 \int_a^b e \cos \theta \, dl \tag{1-8}$$

where e is the magnitude of the electric field as a function of position and θ is the angle between the electric field and the tangent drawn to the path as a function of position. It should be emphasized that the integral of Eq. (1-8) is simply *defined* as the limit of the sum of Eq. (1-7).

Let us now discuss a matter of notation. The product of the magnitude of two vectors and the cosine of the angle between them occurs very often in a variety of physical problems. For instance, in Fig. 1-4 we might require $\mathbf{f}_1\mathbf{f}_2 \cos \theta$. The notation for this product is

$$\mathbf{f}_1 \cdot \mathbf{f}_2 = \mathbf{f}_1\mathbf{f}_2 \cos \theta \tag{1-9}$$

The dot placed between the two vectors indicates the operation of Eq. (1-9) and is called a *vector dot product*, or simply a *dot product*. In this compact notation we can write Eq. (1-8) as

$$w = -q_0 \int_a^b \mathbf{e} \cdot dl \tag{1-10}$$

Note that dl represents a vector of differential length whose direction is tangent to the curve of Fig. 1-3.

It has been determined *empirically* that if there are no time-varying fields (that is, all charges are at rest), then the work done in moving a test charge from one point to another is independent of the path taken. For instance, if we were to choose a different path from point a to point b in Fig. 1-3, then the work as evaluated by Eq. (1-8) or (1-10) would be the same. This is analogous to the situation in a gravitational field where the work done in moving a mass between two points is independent of the path taken.

We can use this result to derive another one. Consider Fig. 1-5. The work done in moving a test charge from point a to point b along path 1 is equal to that done moving it from point a to point b along path 2. Thus the work

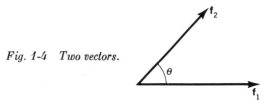

Fig. 1-4   Two vectors.

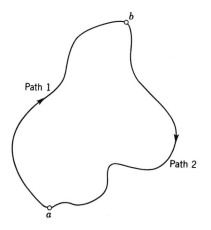

Fig. 1-5   Two paths in a time-invariant field.

done in moving the test charge q_0 from point b to point a along path 2 must be the negative of that done in moving q_0 from point a to point b along path 1 [in Eq. (1-8) we interchange the limits when the direction is changed]. Hence the net work in moving from a to b and back to a is zero. *In general, we can state that if there are no charges in motion (except the test charge), then the work done in moving the test charge around a closed path is zero.* This is symbolically written as

$$q_0 \oint \mathbf{e} \cdot d\mathbf{l} = 0 \tag{1-11}$$

The circle on the integral sign indicates a closed path (at times an arrow is included to indicate the path direction). Since q_0 is constant, we can state that

$$\oint \mathbf{e} \cdot d\mathbf{l} = 0 \tag{1-12}$$

These results are analogous to those in gravitational fields, that is, the work done in moving a mass around a closed path in such a field is zero. We shall see that Eq. (1-12) is modified when time-varying fields are present.

1-2   Voltage and current

The work done or the energy expended in moving a charge between two points in a time-invariant field is independent of the path taken between the points. It is convenient to *normalize* this energy, or to express it in terms of a unit test charge. Note that if positive energy is required to move a charge between two points, then the test-charged body has acquired some *potential energy.* This is lost when the test charge travels back to its original position. Again, note that the same is true of the motion of a mass in a gravitational field. In an electrostatic field we shall define the normalized energy required to move a unit charge from point a to point b as the *voltage between points a and b,* or the *difference of electric potential between points a and b.* Thus, from Eq. (1-10),

$$v_{ab} = -\int_a^b \mathbf{e} \cdot d\mathbf{l} \qquad (1\text{-}13)$$

The units of v_{ab} are joules per coulomb;

$$\frac{1 \text{ joule}}{1 \text{ coulomb}} = 1 \text{ volt}$$

From Eq. (1-13) the units of electric field are volts per meter. Note that the units of voltage are energy per unit charge, and *not* force. Note also that a voltage is defined *between two points*.

A voltage can be set up by placing charged bodies in space. Most electrical devices require the controlled flow of charge from one point to another. Fixed charges could not be used to establish the voltage here, since they would soon become neutralized by the moving ones. Practical voltages can be established electrochemically with batteries or electromagnetically with generators. These devices establish a difference of electric potential even though there is a flow of charge through them. It is assumed that the reader has a basic familiarity with these devices, and their operation will not be discussed here. The symbols for a battery and a voltage generator and some symbolic notation that will be used throughout the book are illustrated in Fig. 1-6. Plus and minus signs and/or an arrow will be associated with voltage. The arrow points from the minus to the plus (note that this is opposite to the direction of the electric field). If a positive charge is moved (external to the generator) from the minus side to the plus side, positive work is done. Figure 1-6b shows a general symbol for an ideal voltage generator (or battery). The letter V (or v) indicates the voltage it produces, and plus and minus signs are as before. To reiterate, a positive charge, external to the generator, will undergo a force that tends to move it from the positive terminal to the negative terminal, and, of course, a negative charge will experience a force in the opposite direction.

The voltage between a and b, V_{ab}, is called a positive-voltage *drop* if terminal a is positive with respect to terminal b. This is the situation shown in Fig. 1-6b. We can also speak of voltage *rises*. As a rise, V_{ab} would be positive if terminal a were negative with respect to terminal b. Unless otherwise stated, we shall consider voltage *drops* in this book.

If a copper wire is connected to the terminals of a generator, the electric

Fig. 1-6   (a) The symbol for a battery; (b) a general symbol for a voltage generator.

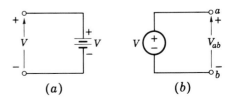

(a)   *(b)*

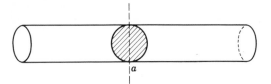

Fig. 1-7   A section of a wire in which there is charge flowing.

field set up by the generator will exert forces upon the electrons and protons within the wire.   The protons are all in the nucleus of the copper atoms and will not move to any extent.   Many of the electrons are closely bound to their nuclei and remain near them.   However, there are also many electrons that are liberated from their atoms by the thermal excitation of the ambient temperature. These are called *free electrons*.   When the electric field of the generator interacts with these electrons, they flow from the negative terminal of the generator to the positive one.   The motion of these electrons is quite complex.   There are numerous "collisions" between them and the copper atoms.   The electrons do not accelerate continuously, as they would under the influence of an electric field in a vacuum, but flow at an essentially constant speed.   This relatively low speed is called the *drift velocity*.   We shall discuss this drift velocity in greater detail in Sec. 1-5.   The flow of charges constitutes an *electric current*. The amount of current in a wire depends upon the number of electrons passing a point per unit time.   The unit usually used for current is the ampere, defined as

$$1 \text{ ampere} = \frac{1 \text{ coulomb}}{1 \text{ second}} \tag{1-14}$$

By *convention*, the charge of an electron is negative.   Thus, if an electron moves from right to left, we have a *positive current* from left to right.   It would have been more convenient if electrons had been assigned a positive charge.   However, it is extremely difficult to change a convention that dates back hundreds of years, and actually, once the idea of charge flow is understood, the convention causes no trouble.

Consider Fig. 1-7, which represents a section of a wire in which there is charge flowing.   If Δq represents the total charge in coulombs flowing past point a in Δt sec, then the current is given approximately by

$$i \approx \frac{\Delta q}{\Delta t} \quad \text{amp} \tag{1-15}$$

This is only an approximate current, since Δq may vary with time.   To make this result accurate we must choose Δt very short.   In the limit, as Δt approaches zero, we obtain

$$i = \frac{dq}{dt} \tag{1-16}$$

Note that i can be a function of time.   Alternatively, if we wish to find the total charge that has flowed past point a in the time ranging between 0 and T sec, we have

$$q = \int_0^T i \, dt \qquad (1\text{-}17)$$

This result is obtained by integrating both sides of Eq. (1-16).

We have assumed thus far that the potentials are essentially independent of time and that the flow of charge is at a constant velocity.   In general, the preceding discussion holds even for time-varying conditions if the time variations are slow.   However, if the variations in the potential and the acceleration of the flowing charges is high, *radiation* will result.   Considerable energy will actually leave the system, and the previous results must be modified.   In Chap. 2 we shall discuss these effects more completely.   We shall also see what is meant by "slow variations."

1-3   Energy and power

Let us now consider the flow of charge in response to an electric field applied by a generator.   A simple diagrammatic representation is shown in Fig. 1-8. This is actually a simple *electric circuit*.   The generator produces a time-invariant, or *direct*, voltage of V volts.   In general, we shall use E or V to designate a voltage.   (The letter E is often used to represent a voltage.   It stands for *electromotive force* or emf.   This terminology is poor, since voltage is *not* a force.)   Let us assume that in response to this voltage a current of I amp results in the wire.   In this book we shall use *capital letters* for *time-invariant* quantities and *lowercase letters* for *time-varying* ones.   Equations (1-10) and (1-13) show that the net energy expended (or work done) in moving a charge of Q coul through a potential difference of V volts is

$$W = QV \qquad (1\text{-}18)$$

If the flow of charge took place from time t_1 to time $t_1 + T$, then, substituting Eq. (1-17), we have

$$W = V \int_{t_1}^{t_1+T} I \, dt = VIT \qquad (1\text{-}19)$$

Fig. 1-8   A representation of a very simple electric circuit; the wire is not an ideal conductor.

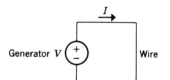

Generator V Wire

where I is the current in the wire. This energy is supplied mechanically by the generator (or chemically by a battery).

Now let us assume that the potential and the current vary slowly with time. In this case we write the voltage as v and the current as i. Consider an interval of time Δt which is short enough that the voltage and current can be considered constant in this interval. The net energy supplied by the generator in the time Δt is given approximately by Eq. (1-19) as

$$\Delta w \approx v \int_{t_1}^{t_1+\Delta t} i \, dt \tag{1-20}$$

but Δt is short enough that i can be considered a constant there. Thus

$$\Delta w \approx vi \int_{t_1}^{t_1+\Delta t} dt = vi \, \Delta t$$

or, equivalently,

$$\frac{\Delta w}{\Delta t} \approx vi \tag{1-21}$$

This result is only approximately correct, since v and i may vary in the interval Δt. However, in the limit, as Δt approaches zero, Eq. (1-21) becomes completely accurate. Hence

$$\frac{dw}{dt} = vi \tag{1-22}$$

But dw/dt is defined as the power. Hence

$$p = \frac{dw}{dt} = vi \tag{1-23}$$

Or, alternatively, the total energy supplied by the generator in the time between 0 and T sec is

$$w = \int_0^T p \, dt = \int_0^T vi \, dt \tag{1-24}$$

The statements concerning radiation at the end of Sec. 1-2 also apply here.

1-4 Resistance and conductance

Let us again consider the circuit of Fig. 1-8. The generator produces a constant direct voltage. If a copper wire is connected across the terminals of the generator, a current I results. Now let us discuss some experiments that can be performed. We can replace the copper wire by one of the same size made of silver and then by one made of Nichrome. In each case a direct current will result, but the currents in all three cases will be different.

Now let us return the copper wire to the generator; if we *change the direct voltage* to another constant one, the current will change. If the temperature of the copper wire is held constant, we find that the current is proportional to the applied voltage.   Thus we can write

$$I = \frac{V}{R} \tag{1-25}$$

where R is a constant of proportionality.   It is called the *resistance* and its units are ohms, where

$$1 \text{ ohm} = \frac{1 \text{ volt}}{1 \text{ ampere}}$$

Equation (1-25) is called *Ohm's law*.   We shall see that the resistance depends upon the material and its dimensions.

If the direct-voltage generator is replaced by one that varies slowly with time, Eq. (1-25) is still valid.   In this case we write

$$i = \frac{v}{R} \tag{1-26}$$

From Eq. (1-23) we see that the power supplied by the generator is

$$p = vi = i^2 R = \frac{v^2}{R} \tag{1-27}$$

This power is dissipated by the resistance in the form of heat.   The total energy supplied by the generator in the time between t_1 and t_2 is

$$W = \int_{t_1}^{t_2} p \, dt \tag{1-28}$$

It is often convenient to work with the reciprocal of resistance, called the conductance G,

$$G = \frac{1}{R} \tag{1-29}$$

The unit of conductance is the mho (ohm spelled backwards).

As another experiment, consider a region of nonzero conductivity and assume that an electric field has been established there by a generator (for simplicity consider this region to be the inside of a wire).   The cross section of such a region is shown in Fig. 1-9.   Let **E** be the electric field in the material.   It may

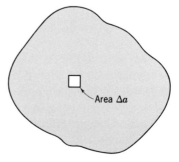

Fig. 1-9   A cross-sectional area of a conductor.

Area Δa

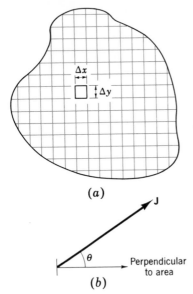

Fig. 1-10   (a) A cross-sectional area of a conductor showing small subareas; (b) the angle between the current density and a vector drawn perpendicular to a subarea.

vary as a function of position over the cross section, so let us consider an area Δa which is small enough that **E** can be considered constant there.   It has been found experimentally that the current through this area is proportional to the electric field (perpendicular to the area) and the magnitude of the area.   The constant of proportionality is called the *conductivity* σ.   Thus

$$I_{\Delta a} \approx \sigma \mathsf{E}\, \Delta a \tag{1-30}$$

$$\frac{I_{\Delta a}}{\Delta a} \approx \sigma \mathsf{E} \tag{1-31}$$

If we let Δa become differentially small, then Eqs. (1-30) and (1-31) become exact.   In this case $I_{\Delta a}/\Delta a$ is defined as the *current density* **J**.   Its units are amperes per square meter.   The current density is a vector; its direction, in simple cases, is the same as that of **E**.   Hence

$$\mathsf{J} = \sigma \mathsf{E} \tag{1-32}$$

This relation is called *Ohm's law in point form*.   The units of σ are mhos per meter.   Equation (1-32) can be used to calculate the current density at any point.

Let us now obtain the total current through an area.   Consider the cross-sectional area of Fig. 1-10a.   Assume for the time being that the current density **J** is everywhere constant over the area and that it makes an angle θ with a perpendicular drawn to the area, as shown in Fig. 1-10b.   Then the current through the area is

$$I = JA \cos \theta \tag{1-33}$$

where A is the total area. The $\cos\theta$ term reflects the fact that the current through a right cylindrical wire is defined by the charge which flows through a cross-sectional area perpendicular to the surface of the wire. For instance, in Fig. 1-11, which represents a conductor, the total current is constant at all points along the wire. Assume that the current density is also constant everywhere in the wire. Now consider the three cross-sectional areas shown. Their areas differ, although the magnitude of $\mathbf{J}$ is constant on them. To obtain the correct current we must include the $\cos\theta$ term of Eq. (1-33).

Suppose $\mathbf{J}$ is not constant in Fig. 1-10. To calculate I we can divide the area into many small areas, as shown in Fig. 1-10a. These should be small enough so that on each of them $\mathbf{J}$ can be considered constant. The current through each of these areas can then be found from Eq. (1-33). The sum of all these currents gives the total current through the area,

$$I \approx \sum_x \sum_y \mathbf{J} \cos\theta \, \Delta x \, \Delta y \qquad (1\text{-}34)$$

Note that $\mathbf{J}$ and θ are functions of position. In the limit, as Δx and Δy approach zero, this summation becomes the double integral

$$I = \iint_a \mathbf{J} \cos\theta \, dx \, dy \qquad (1\text{-}35)$$

where Eq. (1-35) is *defined* as the limit of Eq. (1-34) and is called a *surface integral*. We can write $dx \, dy$ as d_a. In addition, we can define any area as

Fig. 1-11　A right cylindrical conductor; cross-sectional areas are shown.

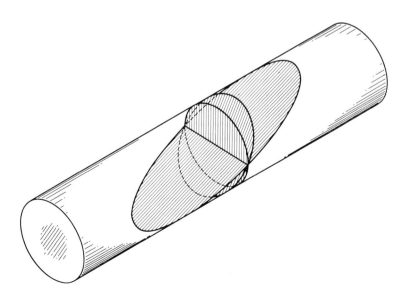

a vector whose magnitude is the magnitude of the area and whose direction is perpendicular to the area.   Then, using the notation of Eq. (1-9), we have

$$I = \iint_a \mathbf{J} \cdot d\mathbf{a} \tag{1-36}$$

or, substituting Eq. (1-32),

$$I = \iint_a \sigma\mathbf{E} \cdot d\mathbf{a} \tag{1-37}$$

Let us now consider that we have a right cylindrical conductor of (perpendicular) cross-sectional area A and total length l.   We shall assume that the current density within the conductor is parallel to its sides and everywhere constant.   Thus the same assumption is made for the electric field.   Then from Eq. (1-33) we have

$$I = JA$$

Substituting Eq. (1-32), we have

$$I = \sigma A\mathbf{E} \tag{1-38}$$

Equation (1-13) shows that if an electric field $\mathbf{E}$ is constant and parallel to a straight line, then the potential difference between two points a distance l m apart on that line is

$$V = \mathbf{E}l$$

(note that the magnitude of $\mathbf{E}$ is used here).   Substituting in Eq. (1-38), we have

$$I = \frac{\sigma a}{l} V \tag{1-39}$$

Comparing this with Eq. (1-25), we obtain

$$R = \frac{l}{\sigma A} = \rho \frac{l}{A} \tag{1-40}$$

where ρ, called the *resistivity*, is the reciprocal of the conductivity.   The units of ρ are ohm-meters.   The value of ρ will vary from one material to another. If it is very low (on the order of 10^{-9} to 10^{-8} ohm-m), then the material is called a *conductor*.   If ρ is very much higher (on the order 10^{-3} ohm-m or larger), then the material is called an *insulator*.   Some typical values for ρ are 1.724×10^{-9} ohm-m for copper and 1.610×10^{-9} ohm-m for silver.   Note that R is directly proportional to the length of the conductor and inversely proportional to its area.

Usually, wires are circular.   At times, to reduce arithmetic, l in Eq. (1-30) is expressed in feet and A is expressed in circular mils (1 circular mil is the area of a circle 0.001 in. in diameter).   The units of ρ are, then, ohm–circular mils

Fig. 1-12   *The symbol for resistance; the value in ohms is given by R.*

per foot. The resistivity of copper is 10.37 ohm–circ mil/ft. Note that A is given by the square of the diameter of the wire in mils.

It is often convenient to represent circuit elements by symbols. The one used for resistance is shown in Fig. 1-12.

1-5   Conductivity

As mentioned in the last section, conductivity (or resistivity) is a function of the material used. Let us discuss this matter in some additional detail. We shall use a classical discussion here to provide the reader with a feeling for the physical phenomenon. Quantum-mechanical procedures can also be used; these will give slightly different results. The thermal energy supplied to *any* material at a temperature greater than 0°K will allow some of the electrons to escape from their atoms and impart random motion to them. These electrons can then wander through the material or move under the influence of an applied electric field. Such electrons are called *free electrons.* In a good conductor at usual room temperatures there is a copious supply of free electrons. However, in an insulator there are very few free electrons at room temperature. The energy required to liberate electrons from the nuclei of their atoms determines whether a material is a conductor or an insulator.

In conductors electrons are available for conduction even at a temperature of 0°K. Some materials, called *superconductors,* exhibit the property of losing all resistance at very low temperatures. The presence of a strong enough magnetic field causes their resistance to become nonzero. The theory of superconductivity is beyond the scope of this chapter.

Now let us consider a conductor with a very large supply of free electrons and determine its conductivity. Ohm's law in point form states that

$$\mathbf{J} = \sigma\mathbf{E} \tag{1-41}$$

We shall assume that the electric field has been set up by an external generator and is constant throughout the conductor. The free electrons move under the influence of this field. In free space the force on the electrons would be given by Eq. (1-4). Hence the acceleration would be given by

$$\mathbf{A} = -\frac{\mathbf{E}q_e}{m} \tag{1-42}$$

where q_e is the *magnitude* of the charge of the electron and m is its mass (9.107 × 10^{-31} kg). In a conductor a similar relation can be assumed. However, to obtain correct numerical results we must make some adjustments in the values of q_e and m. These adjusted values are termed *effective mass* and *effective charge.*

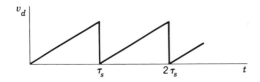

Fig. 1-13   The drift velocity of a free electron in a conductor, under the influence of an applied electric field.

Another factor to be considered in a conductor is that the free electrons do not continuously increase their velocity, as they would in free space, because they are *scattered* by the thermal motion of the atoms in the lattice structure of the conductor.   In addition, lattice imperfections will also scatter the free electrons.   These scatterings lead to ohmic resistance.   In a very simple sense, we can think of the scatterings as collisions of the electron with the lattice structure.   Such "collisions" deflect the electron and often cause it to reverse direction.   It can be considered that, *on the average*, the velocity of an electron after it is scattered is zero.   *It should be emphasized that this entire discussion is statistical in nature, and we are only speaking of things on the average.* Then, on the average, in a conductor the magnitude of the velocity of a free electron under the influence of an electric field will be as shown in Fig. 1-13. The motion of the free electrons in a conductor under the influence of an applied electric field is termed *drift*, and the velocity of this motion is called *drift velocity*.   If we call the average time between scatterings of the free electrons τ_s, a free electron will accelerate essentially as though it were in free space for τ_s sec, and then its velocity will fall to zero (see Fig. 1-13).   The average drift velocity V_d is then one-half its maximum value.   Thus from Eq. (1-42) we have

$$V_d = -\frac{1}{2}\frac{\mathbf{E}q_e}{m}\tau_s \tag{1-43}$$

The current density is given by the product of V_d, $-q_e$, and the average density of the free electrons; that is, if there are n electrons/m³, all moving at a velocity V_d, then the number of coulombs per second passing through a unit area would be given by $-nq_e V_d$ or, equivalently, by

$$\mathbf{J} = \frac{n\mathbf{E}q_e{}^2}{2m}\tau_s \tag{1-44}$$

If we compare this with Eq. (1-41), we obtain

$$\sigma = \frac{nq_e{}^2\tau_s}{2m} \tag{1-45}$$

Since q_e and m are relatively constant, we see that the conductivity is directly proportional to the density of the free electrons in the material and to the average time between scatterings.

The average drift velocity of the free electrons is usually much less than 1 m/sec.   Electric energies can propagate along wires at the velocity of light.

These two statements are not contradictory, since the mechanism which sets up the drift can propagate at the velocity of light even though the electron's drift is slow drift can be set up over the entire length of a long wire very quickly.

In general, if the speed of an electron increases, the time between scatterings will decrease. Thus it may appear that τ_s is a function of the drift velocity. However, it essentially is not. In general, τ_s is a function of the *total* velocity of the electron, but, in addition to drift, the electrons have a component of velocity due to thermal excitation v_r. In general,

$$v_r \gg v_d$$

so that the overall magnitude of the electron's velocity will be essentially v_r. Thermally excited electrons will travel in straight lines between scatterings. The *electron mean free path* L_m is the average length of these paths and is given by the product of the electron's velocity and the time τ_s,

$$L_m = v_r \tau_s \tag{1-46}$$

Substituting in Eq. (1-44), we obtain

$$\sigma = \frac{1}{\rho} = \frac{n q_e{}^2 L_m}{2 m v_r} \tag{1-47}$$

The quantity L_m is often used in discussing the conductivity of a material.

In Sec. 1-4 it was implied that conductivity is independent of the dimensions of the material. In general this is true, unless one of the cross-sectional dimensions becomes very small (for instance, if the conductor becomes very thin). The electron mean free path is much smaller very near the surface of a conductor than it is within its bulk because of the greater concentration of imperfections at the surface. With thick conductors this is unimportant, because there are large areas far removed from the surface which have large values of L_m. These provide paths for conduction with high σ. As a result, the high-resistance (low-conductivity) areas very near the surface are essentially "bypassed," However, if the conductor is extremely thin, then the entire material is "close to the surface," and the conductivity is reduced. This effect does not become noticeable until the thickness falls below 10^{-6} to 10^{-7} m.

1-6   Nonlinear and time-varying resistance

Often we can assume that resistance is independent of time and the voltage across it or the current through it. However, there are times when this is not true. If the resistance is a function of the voltage across it or the current through it, then it is termed *nonlinear* or a *nonlinear resistance*. All resistances are to some extent nonlinear. The power that is dissipated in them due to the current through them [see Eq. (1-27)] causes a rise in temperature. This in

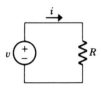

Fig. 1-14   *A simple circuit.*

turn increases the number of free electrons available for conduction, and also increases the lattice vibrations and reduces the electron mean free path. These effects [see Eq. (1-47)] can lead to either a rise or a fall in the conductivity depending on the predominant effect.

In conductors those electrons with the highest energy levels are free electrons even if the temperature is extremely low, and an increase in temperature above room temperature does not substantially increase the number of free electrons. In good conductors the conductivity usually falls with an increase in temperature, while in insulators or semiconductors it rises. In the latter case most "high-energy" electrons are bound to their atoms even at room temperature, and an increase in temperature can greatly increase the number of free electrons. There are other situations involving electronic devices where the resistance is a function of voltage or current. These also result in nonlinear resistances.

In many instances the variation of resistance with voltage and current is so small that we can neglect it. However, there are some circumstances in which it must be considered. To determine the behavior of a nonlinear resistance experimentially we can apply a direct voltage and then measure the resulting current. The resistance can be obtained from the relation

$$R = \frac{V}{I} \tag{1-48}$$

If we repeat these measurements with different values of voltage, we can plot a curve of resistance versus voltage or current. It is possible to approximate this curve by an equation. Alternatively, the resistance as a function of voltage or current can be derived through physical arguments. In Sec. 3-8 nonlinear resistance will be discussed in much greater detail.

To demonstrate a simple calculation with a nonlinear resistance, let us assume that we have a resistance characterized by

$$v = (10 + 2i^2)i \qquad \text{volts}$$

where i is expressed in amperes. If, in Fig. 1-14, this represents the resistor R and $v = 12$ volts, then

$$i = \frac{12}{10 + 2i^2}$$

or

$$2i^3 + 10i - 12 = (i - 1)(2i^2 + 2i + 12) = 0$$

There is only one real root of this equation, so

$$i = 1 \text{ amp}$$

If there is more than one real solution to such an equation, then there is more than one possible current. Only one current can exist at any one time, and in such a case the circuit may be unstable and jump back and forth between the solutions. Or it may choose one solution over the other, depending upon the history of the circuit (for instance if $i = 1$ and 3 amp are possible solutions and the current is increasing from zero, it may stop at 1 amp).

As another example, suppose we wish the current through the given R to be

$$i = 10 \sin \omega t \qquad \text{amp}$$

that is, we want the current to vary sinusoidally with time. We must now determine the voltage that will produce this current. From Eq. (1-26) we have

$$v = iR = 10 \sin \omega t [10 + 2(10 \sin \omega t)^2]$$

$$= 100 \sin \omega t + 2{,}000 \sin^3 \omega t \qquad \text{volts}$$

Thus the voltage will vary in a relatively complex fashion. We shall consider nonlinear circuits in much greater detail in Sec. 3-8 and Chap. 7. In Sec. 3-8 we shall also discuss incremental resistance whereby, under certain circumstances which often occur in electronic devices, nonlinear resistances can be treated as linear ones. The discussion of incremental capacitance in Sec. 1-8 lays the groundwork for this discussion.

Circuit elements can be made to vary as a function of time. For example, consider the variable resistor diagrammatically illustrated in Fig. 1-15. The arrowhead of terminal b represents a contact that slides over the resistor, enabling us to vary the length of the resistance. Hence the resistance between terminals b and a (or c) can be varied. This very simple type of variable resistor is called a *potentiometer* (other, more complex variable resistors can be obtained with electronic devices). If the arm b of the resistor is moved as a function of time, then the resistance between a and b will also be a function of time. This is called a *time-varying resistor*. In contrast, resistors which are not functions of time (although they may be nonlinear) are called *time-invariant resistors*. As an example, let us assume that the resistor of Fig. 1-14 is given by

$$r = 1 + 0.5 \sin \omega t \qquad \text{ohms}$$

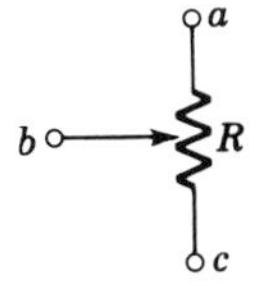

Fig. 1-15   The symbol for a variable resistor.

where a lowercase letter is used to indicate a time-varying quantity.   If

$$e = 10 \text{ volts}$$

then

$$i = \frac{10}{1 + 0.5 \sin \omega t}$$

The subject of time-varying circuits will be considered in greater detail in Chap. 7.

The reader should not assume from the foregoing discussion that most circuit analysis deals with nonlinear and/or time-varying networks.   There is often a need to study linear time-invariant circuits.

1-7   Capacitance

We have seen that charge will flow in a resistance which is placed across a difference of potential.   However, resistance is not the only circuit parameter that we must consider.   For instance, the circuit configuration of Fig. 1-16 consists of two irregularly shaped conductors connected to a voltage generator. For the sake of simplicity let us assume that all the conductors have zero resistance; hence the voltage drop in them will be zero (we assume that all the currents are finite).   Thus the voltage between point 1 and point 2 will be equal to v [note from Eqs. (1-12) and (1-13) that the sum of the time-invariant voltage around any closed path will be zero].   The electric-potential difference between points 1 and 2 is due to the electric field set up in the regions between them by the charges on conductors a and b.

To clarify this, let us describe the sequence of events that occur when the

Fig. 1-16   *Two conductors connected to a voltage generator.*

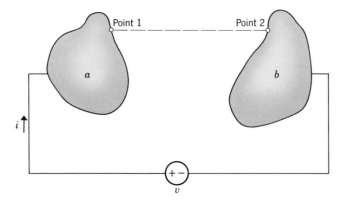

generator is connected to conductors a and b. Initially conductors a and b are neutrally charged, and there is no electric field between them. At this point an electric field is set up within the conductors by the generator. This causes a net flow of electrons from conductor a to conductor b, setting up the required electric field in the space between them. When an equilibrium has been reached the field within the conductors becomes zero (because of the charge unbalance), and the charge flow ceases. If v represents a direct voltage, then the flow of charge will drop to zero as equilibrium is reached. The charge transferred will distribute itself over the surface of the conductors.

Let us consider that the voltage v is changed to a new (constant) value. For simplicity, assume that it is multiplied by a constant k. The electric field in the space between conductors a and b will be multiplied by k, but will be otherwise unchanged; that is, its direction and *relative* magnitude will be unchanged. For instance, if when the applied voltage is v, the electric field is $\mathbf{E}$, then the electric field when the applied voltage is kv will be $k\mathbf{E}$. Note that $\mathbf{E}$ is a function of position, but k is not. The charge transferred from conductor b to conductor a will also be multiplied by the same constant. Thus the voltage difference between conductors a and b will be proportional to the charge transferred between these conductors,

$$v_{ab} = \frac{q}{C} \tag{1-49}$$

where v_{ab} is the voltage drop from conductor a to conductor b and q is the net positive charge transferred to conductor a from conductor b (actually, the flow of charges consists of electrons leaving conductor a and flowing to conductor b). The constant of proportionality C is called the *capacitance*. Its units are farads:

$$1 \text{ farad} = \frac{1 \text{ coulomb}}{1 \text{ volt}}$$

At times it is convenient to work with the reciprocal of capacitance, called the *elastance* D,

$$D = \frac{1}{C} \tag{1-50}$$

The unit of elastance is the daraf (farad spelled backwards).

Equation (1-49) relates the voltage drop across the capacitance to the transferred charge. It is usually desirable to relate voltage and current. If we substitute Eq. (1-17) into Eq. (1-49), we obtain

$$v = \frac{1}{C} \int i \, dt \tag{1-51}$$

We have replaced the definite integral of Eq. (1-17) by an indefinite one. This represents the *total* charge on the capacitor for its *entire existence* as a function of time (including any charge present when the capacitor was formed).

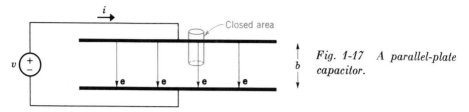

Fig. 1-17   A parallel-plate capacitor.

We could write

$$q(t) = \int i \, dt = q_{-\infty} + \int_{-\infty}^{0} i \, dt + \int_{0}^{t} i \, d\tau = q_0 + \int_{0}^{t} i \, d\tau \tag{1-52}$$

where $q_{-\infty}$ is the charge ("transferred") present when the capacitor is formed. The second integral represents the positive charge transferred from conductor b to conductor a from the time that the capacitor was formed up to an arbitrary starting time $t = 0$. Thus q_0 represents the charge transferred at $t = 0$. Equation (1-52) gives q as a function of t, written $q(t)$. Note that the variable of integration has been changed from t to τ in the last integral. This is to avoid confusion. It is poor practice to use the same symbol for both a variable of integration and for one of the limits (τ is called a *dummy variable*, since any letter could be used as the variable in the definite integral without changing its value).

Another useful result can be obtained by differentiating both sides of Eq. (1-51). This yields

$$i = C \frac{dv}{dt} \tag{1-53}$$

To develop some further understanding of capacitance, consider the capacitor shown in Fig. 1-17. Here the conductors of the capacitor are not irregular shapes, but are parallel plates. If the spacing b between the plates is small in comparison with their linear dimension, then the electric field can be considered to lie only in the region between the plates, to be constant there, and to be perpendicular to the plates. This situation is illustrated in Fig. 1-17. In addition, we can assume that the transferred charge distributes itself uniformly over the plates. To simplify the analysis of this configuration let us define a new vector, the electric displacement $\mathbf{d}$. This is related to the electric field intensity by

$$\mathbf{d} = \epsilon \mathbf{e} \tag{1-54}$$

The units of $\mathbf{d}$ are coulombs per square meter. In addition, we shall make use of an experimentally determined result called *Gauss' law*, which states

$$\oint_{a} \mathbf{d} \cdot d\mathbf{a} = q \tag{1-55}$$

That is, for any closed area the surface integral [see Eqs. (1-34) and (1-35)] of **d** over this area is equal to the charge enclosed.

To illustrate the use of this law and to study the parallel-plate capacitor, let us consider the closed area shown in Fig. 1-17. We have

$$\oiint \mathbf{d} \cdot d\mathbf{a} = \underset{\substack{\text{upper} \\ \text{surface}}}{\iint} \mathbf{d} \cdot d\mathbf{a} + \underset{\text{cylinder}}{\iint} \mathbf{d} \cdot d\mathbf{a} + \underset{\substack{\text{lower} \\ \text{surface}}}{\iint} \mathbf{d} \cdot d\mathbf{a} \qquad (1\text{-}56)$$

From Eq. (1-54) we see that **d** is constant and perpendicular to the plates in the region between the plates. It is zero elsewhere. The first integral is zero because **d** is zero outside the region between the plates. The second integral is zero because **d** is parallel to the sides of the cylinder. Thus there is no component of **d** perpendicular to that area. If the area of the lower surface has a magnitude a_1, then, since **d** is constant and perpendicular to this area, we have

$$\underset{\substack{\text{lower} \\ \text{surface}}}{\oiint} \mathbf{d} \cdot d\mathbf{a} = a_1 \mathbf{d} = a_1 \epsilon \mathbf{e} \qquad (1\text{-}57)$$

If q is the total charge transferred to the upper plate and A is its area, then the charge contained within the closed area is $q a_1/A$. Substitution in Eq. (1-55) yields

$$\mathbf{e} = \frac{q}{\epsilon A} \qquad (1\text{-}58)$$

Since the electric field is constant and perpendicular to the plates, the voltage between the plates is given by [see Eq. (1-13)]

$$v = eb = q \frac{b}{\epsilon A} \qquad (1\text{-}59)$$

Comparing this with Eq. (1-49), we obtain for the capacitance

$$C = \frac{\epsilon A}{b} \qquad (1\text{-}60)$$

Thus the capacitance of a parallel-plate capacitor varies directly with the area of (one of) the plates and inversely with the distance between them. The quantity ϵ plays an important role. Materials used for the medium between the plates of capacitors are usually insulators. Their permittivity may be close to that of vacuum (such as air) or it may be many times that of air. It is often desirable to express the permittivity of a material in terms of the permittivity of free space, ϵ_0. We can write

$$\epsilon = k\epsilon_0 \qquad (1\text{-}61)$$

The quantity k is dimensionless. It is called the *dielectric constant* or *relative permittivity*. Dielectrics with high dielectric constants are used to produce large capacitors in relatively small volumes.

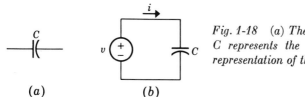

Fig. 1-18   (a) The symbol for a capacitor, where C represents the capacitance; (b) a symbolic representation of the circuit of Fig. 1-17.

(a)   (b)

Equation (1-60) was specifically derived for the parallel-plate capacitor and does not apply for other configurations.   However, some of the general concepts gained from Eq. (1-60) do apply.   We shall not derive these results, but shall merely state them.   The capacitance is a linear function of the permittivity of the dielectric (or insulator).   If the capacitor is formed of conductors of arbitrary shape, as in Fig. 1-16, then the capacitance is reduced if the separation between them is increased.   If the surface area of the conductors is increased, but the spacing between them is held constant, the capacitance will increase.

Finally, let us determine the current i in Fig. 1-17 if

$$v = V_{\text{max}} \cos \omega t$$

that is, the voltage varies sinusoidally.   Substituting in Eq. (1-53), we obtain

$$i = -\omega V_{\text{max}} \sin \omega t \qquad (1\text{-}62)$$

Note that the current is also sinusoidal.   As the frequency is reduced to zero, the current also becomes zero.   Note that the voltage and current are not in phase; that is, they pass through their zero and maximum points at different times.   We shall discuss sinusoidal currents and voltages further in Chap. 6.

The symbol for a capacitor is shown in Fig. 1-18a.   Figure 1-18b is a diagrammatic representation of the circuit of Fig. 1-17.   The farad is a very large unit, and capacitance is usually expressed in microfarads (μf), which is 10^{-6} farad, or picofarads (pf), which is 10^{-12} farad.

1-8   Time-varying and nonlinear capacitance

We have assumed thus far that capacitance is a constant which is independent of time and/or voltage or current.   This is not always the case.   In this section we shall consider capacitors that vary with time and/or applied potential.

Time-varying capacitors

A *time-varying capacitor* is one whose capacitance can be made to vary as a function of time.   For instance, if b, the spacing between the plates of the parallel-plate capacitor of Fig. 1-17, is made to vary as a function of time, then [see Eq. (1-60)] the capacitance will vary.   In analyzing this case we cannot just replace the constant C in all the relations of the last section by one which is a function of time. Consider Eq. (1-49), the fundamental definition of capacitance. Rewriting it, we have

$$q = cv \tag{1-63}$$

where q is the charge transferred from one plate of the capacitor to another and v is the voltage drop across the capacitor. A lowercase c has been used for capacitance, since it can be a function of time.

Now let us obtain the relation between voltage and current. Equation (1-16) gives the fundamental relation between current and charge, and if we substitute Eq. (1-63) into Eq. (1-16), we obtain

$$i = \frac{d(cv)}{dt} \tag{1-64}$$

If c is constant, then Eq. (1-64) reduces to Eq. (1-53). Note that Eq. (1-64) *cannot* be obtained from Eq. (1-53) by substituting the time-varying c for the constant one. If we use the rule for the differentiation of a product, Eq. (1-64) becomes

$$i = c\frac{dv}{dt} + v\frac{dc}{dt} \tag{1-65}$$

Now let us express the voltage in terms of the current. The total charge transferred from one plate of the capacitor to another is still given by [see Eq. (1-52)]

$$q = \int i\, dt$$

Then, substituting in Eq. (1-63), we obtain

$$v = \frac{1}{c}\int i\, dt \tag{1-66}$$

Note that this relation has the same *form* as that of the time-invariant one.

As an example, consider the circuit of Fig. 1-18b, where

$$c = C_{max}(\cos \omega_1 t + 1)$$
$$v = V_{max} \cos \omega_2 t$$

Then the current is given by Eq. (1-64). Substituting in this relation, we obtain

$$i = -\omega_2 C_{max} V_{max}(\cos \omega_1 t + 1)\sin \omega_2 t - \omega_1 C_{max} V_{max} \sin \omega_1 t \cos \omega_2 t$$

Nonlinear capacitance

Thus far we have assumed that the permittivity of the dielectric of a capacitor is a constant. At times, however, the permittivity will change as a function of the applied electric field. In this case the capacitance will be a function of the applied voltage [see Eq. (1-60)] and will be called a *nonlinear capacitance*. Other types of capacitors that employ semiconductors are also nonlinear.

The analysis of a nonlinear capacitor can at times be made similar to that of a time-varying one. In a nonlinear capacitor the capacitance varies as a function of the applied voltage. Consider a linear time-varying capacitor whose capacitance varies such that it is equal to the nonlinear one on an instantaneous basis. This capacitance would act exactly the same as the non-linear one. Hence we can use Eq. (1-64) for the time-varying capacitor to analyze the nonlinear one. In this case c is a function of v, and not an arbitrary function of time. We shall use the relation

$$\frac{dc}{dt} = \frac{dc}{dv}\frac{dv}{dt}$$

Then for a nonlinear time-invariant capacitor Eq. (1-65) becomes

$$i = \left(c + v\frac{dc}{dv}\right)\frac{dv}{dt} \tag{1-67}$$

Note that c and dc/dv are functions of v and must be evaluated, on an instantaneous basis, at the actual instantaneous value of v.

Equation (1-66) is also applicable here. Actually, the simple procedure that we shall discuss here is often a cumbersome procedure for analyzing non-linear capacitors. In Sec. 3-8 and Chap. 7 we shall consider better ones.

As an example, let us assume that

$$c = C(1 + kv)$$

Then, if $v = V_{\max} \cos \omega t$, we have

$$i = -\omega C V_{\max}(1 + 2kV_{\max} \cos \omega t) \sin \omega t$$

If k becomes zero, then the capacitor becomes a linear one and the relation reduces to that of Eq. (1-62).

Nonlinear capacitors occur very often in semiconductor devices. Frequently in these cases the applied potential consists of the sum of a large constant term and a small time-varying one. If we wish to find the current in response to the small time-varying voltage, we can make approximations which simplify the results. A typical curve of charge versus voltage in a nonlinear capacitor is shown in Fig. 1-19. If the capacitor were linear, then this curve would be a straight line passing through the origin.

Suppose the applied voltage is

$$v = V_0 + v_1 = V\left(1 + \frac{v_1}{V}\right) \tag{1-68}$$

with

$$|V_0| \gg |v_1|_{\max} \tag{1-69}$$

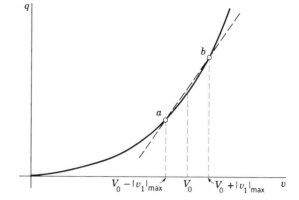

Fig. 1-19 A curve of charge versus voltage in a nonlinear capacitor.

where $|v_1|_{max}$ is the maximum magnitude of v_1. If v_1 is small enough, then we can approximate the curve of q versus v by the dashed straight line in the figure [this is the reason for the restriction of relation (1-69)]. Note that we need only use the curve of q versus v over the range of operation of the capacitor. Thus the approximation need only be valid between points a and b in Fig. 1-19. Then for the approximate curve we can write

$$q = k_1 + kv \tag{1-70}$$

where k_1 and k are constants. The value of k should be chosen equal to dq/dv evaluated at $v = V_0$. Substituting in Eq. (1-63), we have

$$C = k + \frac{k_1}{v} \tag{1-71}$$

To obtain an expression for the current we substitute Eqs. (1-71) and (1-68) into Eq. (1-67). This yields

$$i = k\frac{dv}{dt} \tag{1-72}$$

Now compare this with Eq. (1-53), which applies to a linear time-invariant capacitor. If we let $C = k$, we see that the relations are exactly the same. We can use the relation for a linear capacitor here, because we have represented the charge-vs.-voltage curve of the nonlinear capacitor by a straight line; that is, we have "linearized" the nonlinear capacitor. If we restrict the region of operation (see Fig. 1-19), such approximations are often very good, and the approximate results of Eq. (1-72) can be very accurate. From Eq. (1-72), we can say that if the changes of voltage characterized by relations (1-68) and (1-69) are small enough, the capacitance of this circuit can be considered linear and is given by

$$C = \frac{dq}{dv}\bigg|_{v=V_0} \tag{1-73}$$

This is called the *incremental capacitance*, since it is applicable only when the voltage varies in small increments about an applied potential. Note that the capacitance we use in such approximations is *not* the ratio of charge to voltage, but is the *slope* of the charge-vs.-voltage curve.

We can use an alternative but equivalent approach to derive these results. Let us expand the curve of q versus v in a Taylor series about V_0:

$$q = Q_0 + \left.\frac{dq}{dv}\right|_{v=V_0} v_1 + \frac{1}{2!}\left.\frac{d^2q}{dv^2}\right|_{v=V_0} v_1^2 + \cdots$$

where $v_1 = v - V_0$. The term Q_0 is the value of q when $v = V_0$. If $|v_1|$ is small enough that

$$\left|\frac{dq}{dv}v_1\right| \gg \left|\frac{1}{2!}\frac{d^2q}{dv^2}v_1^2 + \cdots\right| \tag{1-74}$$

then we can write

$$q = Q_0 + \left.\frac{dq}{dv}\right|_{v=V_0} v_1 = Q_0 - \left.\frac{dq}{dv}\right|_{v=V_0} V_0 + \left.\frac{dq}{dv}\right|_{v=V_0} v$$

This is exactly the same as Eq. (1-70), where

$$Q_0 - \left.\frac{dq}{dv}\right|_{v=V_0} V_0 = k_1 \qquad \left.\frac{dq}{dv}\right|_{v=V_0} = k$$

Note that V_0 is a constant, so k_1 will also be a constant. Thus the development of the incremental capacitance following Eq. (1-70) can be used here also. A Taylor series expansion is often used to linearize a nonlinear problem when there are small changes in the variables. For this reason, we have illustrated this alternative procedure.

1-9   Ampère's law and Faraday's law

In addition to the electric field there is another important field to be considered. When there is current in a wire, a force will be exerted on any magnet in the vicinity. In addition, if two wires in the same vicinity are each carrying a current, then forces will be exerted upon both of them. To *explain* this force we say that a current sets up a *magnetic field* which interacts with the other currents (including the internal currents of the magnet).

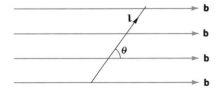

Fig. 1-20   A section of wire of length l in a uniform magnetic field.

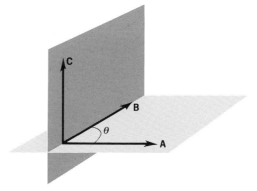

Fig. 1-21   A vector cross product.

Consider a hypothetical experiment in which we have a straight wire of length ǀ carrying a direct current I in a magnetic field **b**, as shown in Fig. 1-20. It has been found experimentally that there is a force on the wire which is proportional to the current, the magnetic field, and sin θ.   The direction of the force is perpendicular to the plane defined by the wire and the uniform magnetic field.   Its direction is the one in which a right-handed screw would move if it were turned from ǀ to **b** through the angle θ.   Thus we can write

$$\mathbf{f} = I|\mathbf{b}\sin\theta\mathbf{U}_f \tag{1-75}$$

where $\mathbf{U}_f$ is a unit vector that points in the direction of the force.   The magnetic field is represented by the vector **b**, called the *magnetic flux density* and expressed in newtons per ampere-meter, volt-seconds per square meter, or webers per square meter.

It is convenient to develop a shorthand notation to represent Eq. (1-75). To do this we introduce the idea of a *vector cross product*.   Consider Fig. 1-21. The cross product of the vectors **A** and **B** is **C**, or

$$\mathbf{C} = \mathbf{A} \times \mathbf{B} = \mathsf{A}\mathsf{B}\sin\theta\mathbf{U}_c \tag{1-76}$$

where $\mathbf{U}_c$ is a unit vector that is perpendicular to the plane defined by the vectors **A** and **B** and points in the direction in which a right-handed screw would move if it were turned from **A** to **B** through θ.   Note that if the order of the vectors in the cross product is changed, the direction of the resultant vector shifts by 180°.   Hence

$$\mathbf{A} \times \mathbf{B} = -\mathbf{B} \times \mathbf{A} \tag{1-77}$$

We have now mentioned two vector products, the dot product [see Eq. (1-9)] and the cross product.   Note that the dot product results in a scalar quantity (that is, it is not a vector), while the result of the cross product is a vector.

We can now rewrite Eq. (1-75) as

$$\mathbf{f} = I\mathbf{l} \times \mathbf{b} = -I\mathbf{b} \times \mathbf{l} \tag{1-78}$$

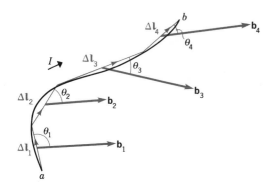

Fig. 1-22   A wire carrying current in a magnetic field.

where $\mathbf{l}$ is a vector whose length is l and whose direction is the same as that of the wire.   The vector $\mathbf{l}$ also points in the direction of positive current.

Suppose we have a curved wire in a magnetic field which is not uniform, as illustrated in Fig. 1-22.   To compute the force on the wire we divide it into n segments of length Δl.   These should be short enough so that the magnetic field can be considered constant over any one segment, and also short enough so that the wire is accurately described by the straight-line segments.   Then the total force on the wire is approximately equal to the sum of the forces on the individual segments, or

$$\mathbf{f} \approx \sum_{k=1}^{n} I \, \Delta\mathbf{l}_k \times \mathbf{b}_k \tag{1-79}$$

In the limit, as Δl becomes differentially small, this relation becomes accurate and reduces to the line integral

$$\mathbf{f} = I \int_a^b d\mathbf{l} \times \mathbf{b} = -I \int_a^b \mathbf{b} \times d\mathbf{l} \tag{1-80}$$

where the minus sign is introduced because we have interchanged the order of the cross product.   Note that Eq. (1-80) is *defined* as the limit of Eq. (1-79).

If there are two conductors near each other, and each is carrying current, then forces will be exerted on each of them.   In this case we consider that one of the currents sets up a magnetic field which interacts with the other current, and vice versa.   To determine the magnetic field set up by the current we make use of an experimentally determined law called *Ampère's law*.   Consider that we have a very short length of wire Δl carrying a current I in a uniform homogeneous medium, (see Fig. 1-23).   The point where the magnetic field is to be determined is P; r is the distance from P to the segment of wire; and $\mathbf{U}_r$ is a unit vector that points from the wire to point P.   It is assumed that Δl is small enough so that the magnitude of r and the direction of $\mathbf{U}_r$ are essentially constant over the entire segment.   The vector $\Delta\mathbf{l}$ points in the same direction as the current.   Then we find that

$$\mathbf{b} = -\frac{\mu I \mathbf{U}_r \times \Delta\mathbf{l}}{4\pi r^2} \tag{1-81}$$

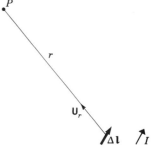

*Fig. 1-23 The quantities used to calculate the mag-
netic field at a point P.*

where μ is a constant which depends upon the medium.   It is called the *permea-
bility* and is expressed in volt-seconds per ampere-meter.   For free space
$\mu = 4\pi \times 10^{-7}$.   There is another vector, called the *magnetic intensity* **h**,
which is related to the magnetic flux density by

$$\mathbf{b} = \mu\mathbf{h} \tag{1-82}$$

where **h** is in amperes per meter.   The most fundamental form of Ampère's
law relates **h** to the current.   From Eqs. (1-81) and (1-82) we see that this is

$$\mathbf{h} = -\frac{I\mathbf{U}_r \times \Delta\mathbf{l}}{4\pi r^2} \tag{1-83}$$

If we have a long length of wire and wish to determine the magnetic field
at a point, we break the wire into n segments of length $\Delta\mathbf{l}$, as shown in Fig. 1-24.

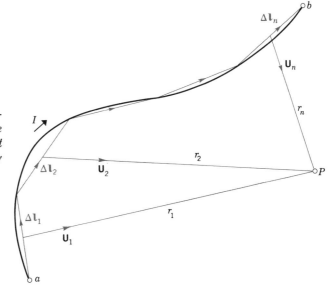

*Fig. 1-24 The quanti-
ties used to calculate the
magnetic field at a point
when the field is set up by
a long wire.*

Then the sum of the magnetic fields from each of these segments gives the total magnetic field as

$$\mathbf{h} \approx -I \sum_{k=1}^{n} \frac{\mathbf{U}_k \times \Delta \mathbf{l}_k}{4\pi r_k^2} \tag{1-84}$$

Note that this represents a sum of vector quantities, and the rules of vector addition must be used. In the limit, as $\Delta \mathbf{l}$ approaches zero, this relation becomes exact, and

$$\mathbf{h} = -I \int_a^b \frac{\mathbf{U}_r \times d\mathbf{l}}{4\pi r^2} \tag{1-85}$$

where this line integral is *defined* as the limit of Eq. (1-84).

One other concept we must consider is the *magnetic flux* through an area. Consider Fig. 1-10, but now assume that the vector is $\mathbf{b}$ instead of $\mathbf{J}$. The magnetic flux through the small area $\Delta x \, \Delta y$ is defined as

$$\Delta \phi = \mathbf{b} \cos \theta \, \Delta x \, \Delta y = \mathbf{b} \cdot d\mathbf{a} \tag{1-86}$$

where $d\mathbf{a}$ is a vector of magnitude $\Delta x \, \Delta y$ whose direction is perpendicular to the area. Thus, by analogy with Eqs. (1-34) and (1-35), we can write

$$\phi = \iint_a \mathbf{b} \cos \theta \, dx \, dy \tag{1-87}$$

$$\phi = \iint_a \mathbf{b} \cdot d\mathbf{a} \tag{1-88}$$

where ϕ is called the *magnetic-flux density*. Its units are volt-seconds or webers. Note that the relationship between ϕ and $\mathbf{b}$ is exactly analogous to the relationship between current and current density. The flux ϕ is not a vector.

The relations we have developed are valid if the currents, and hence the magnetic fields, vary slowly with time. If the variation is slow enough, then all we need do is substitute a time-varying current for the constant one. We shall discuss this further in Sec. 1-14.

If the magnetic field varies with time, then some of our previous electric field relations must be modified. We previously stated that no work is done in moving a test charge around a closed path in an electric field [see Eqs. (1-11) and (1-12)]. In a changing magnetic field, however, this is no longer true, and we must generalize Eq. (1-12). An experimentally determined law called *Faraday's law* is used to do this.

Consider the closed path in Fig. 1-25. This path defines not only a line $\mathbf{l}$, but also a set of areas of which $\mathbf{l}$ is the perimeter. One such area is the plane of the page enclosed by the path. Other areas need not lie in the page (for example, the one illustrated in Fig. 1-25). It is an experimentally determined fact that the magnetic flux through all areas which have $\mathbf{l}$ as their perimeter

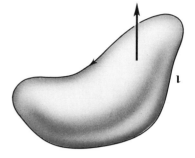

Fig. 1-25   A closed path and an area defined by it.

will be constant.   This is analogous to the fact that the current through any cross-sectional area of a conductor is constant.   Let us call the magnetic flux ϕ.   Then Faraday's law states that

$$\oint_l \mathbf{e} \cdot d\mathbf{l} = -\frac{d\phi}{dt} \tag{1-89}$$

Thus [see Eq. (1-13)] the voltage drop around a closed path is not necessarily zero, but depends upon the rate of change of the magnetic flux enclosed by the path.   This is essential to the operation of all electric generators and, as we shall see in the next section, to a parameter called *inductance*.

Let us clarify the sign in Eq. (1-89).   If we consider that the positive direction of the line integral is in the direction shown in Fig. 1-25, then the positive direction of the area is indicated by the arrow (if the area is the plane of the paper, then the arrow is perpendicular to it and points toward the reader).   If the direction of the line integral is reversed, then the positive direction of the area will be reversed.

1-10   Inductance

If the magnetic flux passing through a closed loop changes as a function of time, then a voltage drop will occur around that loop [see Eqs. (1-89) and (1-13)]. In this case voltage is said to be *induced* in the loop.   If the closed loop is a conductor, then the induced voltage will result in a current.   This phenomenon is utilized in electric generators.   There the magnetic field is set up by a current that is isolated from the loop.   Conversely, the current in a wire can set up a magnetic field which induces a voltage in the *same* wire.

Consider the closed loop which consists of the wire and generator shown in Fig. 1-26.   We shall evaluate Eq. (1-89) over the dashed path through the center of the wire and the generator.   In the body of the conductor the electric field is given by Eq. (1-41).   The evaluation of $\int \mathbf{E} \cdot d\mathbf{l}$ across the generator just yields the voltage rise of the generator $-v$.   Hence, substituting in Eq. (1-89),

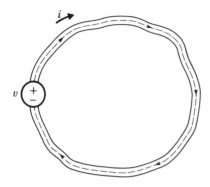

Fig. 1-26   A loop of wire connected to a generator. The dashed line shows the path of integration.

we obtain

$$-v + \int \frac{\mathbf{J}}{\sigma} \cdot d\mathbf{l} = -\frac{d\phi}{dt} \tag{1-90}$$

where ϕ is the total flux through the area defined by the path of integration. To simplify the relation let us assume that the conductor is ideal, so that $\sigma = \infty$. Then, assuming that the current density is finite, we obtain

$$v = \frac{d\phi}{dt} \tag{1-91}$$

The voltage drop of the generator is exactly equal to the voltage induced in the wire caused by the time variation of the flux.   If we had not assumed that σ was infinite in Eq. (1-90), then an iR term (see Sec. 1-4) would have been added to the right-hand side of Eq. (1-91).   Note that if $\mathbf{J}$ were infinite in Eq. (1-90), then the magnetic field and hence ϕ, would also be infinite, and Eq. (1-91) would not be satisfied with finite v.   Therefore our assumption of finite $\mathbf{J}$ is valid.

Now consider a multiturn loop of wire connected to a generator, as shown in Fig. 1-27.   For simplicity we shall again assume that the conductivity is infinite.   Equation (1-91) is still applicable here.   Now ϕ represents the magnetic flux through the rather complex area defined by the dashed line.   The flux through the area is termed the flux that links the coil and is called the *flux linkage*.   The magnetic field that produces this flux is proportional to the current i in the coil.   Hence we can write

$$\phi = Li \tag{1-92}$$

where L is a constant of proportionality called the *inductance*.   The unit of inductance is the henry:

$$1 \text{ henry} = \frac{1 \text{ weber}}{1 \text{ ampere}}$$

If we substitute Eq. (1-92) into Eq. (1-91) and assume that L is constant, we obtain

$$v = L \frac{di}{dt} \tag{1-93}$$

Alternatively, we can solve Eq. (1-93) for the current. This yields

$$i = \frac{1}{L} \int v \, dt \tag{1-94}$$

At times it is desirable to work with the *reciprocal inductance* Γ,

$$\Gamma = \frac{1}{L} \tag{1-95}$$

The units of Γ are *reciprocal henrys* ("henry" spelled backward would be difficult to pronounce).

The actual calculation of the inductance of a coil is relatively complex, and we shall not go into it here. However, let us state a relation for the inductance of a multiloop coil such as that shown in Fig. 1-27. Consider that b is the radius of the wire and that there are N circular turns, each of radius R. If $R/b \gg 1$, then the inductance of such a coil is approximately[1]†

$$L \approx N^2 R \mu \left(\ln \frac{8R}{b} - 2 \right) \tag{1-96}$$

The actual formula is not important here. However, note that in general the inductance is proportional both to μ and to the square of the number of turns. In addition, as the radius of the coil increases, the inductance will also increase.

† Superscript numerals are keyed to the references at the end of the chapter.

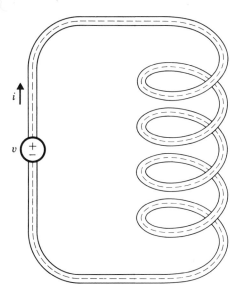

Fig. 1-27 A multiturn loop of wire connected to a generator. The dashed line
shows the path of integration.

Fig. 1-28   The symbol for inductance.

Let us now calculate the current in an inductance if the applied voltage is

$$v = V_{max} \cos \omega t$$

Substitution in Eq. (1-94) yields

$$i = \frac{V_{max}}{\omega L} \sin \omega t \tag{1-97}$$

Note that the current varies inversely with frequency and is not in phase with the voltage.   The symbol for inductance is shown in Fig. 1-28.

1-11   Mutual inductance

If two or more coils are in close proximity, then the flux set up by any one coil will link all of them.   Thus the voltage induced in any one coil will be a function of the currents in all the coils.   For instance, consider the two coils shown in Fig. 1-29.   If i_2 is zero, then the total flux linking coil 1 is proportional to i_1. Similarly, if i_1 is zero, then the flux linking coil 1 is proportional to i_2.   If neither i_1 nor i_2 is zero, then the flux is the sum of the fluxes calculated on an individual basis; that is,

$$\phi_1 = L_1 i_1 + M_{12} i_2 \tag{1-98}$$

where L_1 and M_{12} are constants of proportionality. L_1 is the inductance of

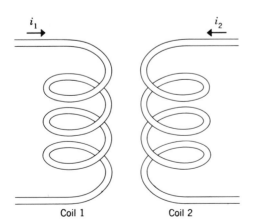

Fig. 1-29   Two coupled coils.

Coil 1   Coil 2

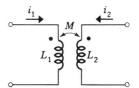

Fig. 1-30   *The symbol for a pair of coupled coils.*

coil 1. M_{12} is called the *mutual inductance*, since it relates the flux linkages of one coil to the current in another.   The units of mutual inductance are henrys. The voltage induced in coil 1 is

$$v_1 = \frac{d\phi_1}{dt} = L_1 \frac{di_1}{dt} + M_{12} \frac{di_2}{dt} \tag{1-99}$$

Similarly, the flux that links coil 2 is

$$\phi_2 = M_{21}i_1 + L_2 i_2 \tag{1-100}$$

and the voltage drop across the coil is

$$v_2 = M_{21} \frac{di_1}{dt} + L_2 \frac{di_2}{dt} \tag{1-101}$$

L_1 and L_2 are the inductances of the coils themselves; they are called *self-inductances*.

It can be shown that

$$M_{12} = M_{21} \tag{1-102}$$

(we shall demonstrate this in Sec. 1-13).   Thus, the mutual inductance between a pair of coils is often indicated by the letter M with no subscripts.

It is possible that when i_1 and i_2 are both positive, the magnetic field set up by i_1 near coils 1 and 2 may buck that set up by i_2, with the result that the net flux linking the coils may decrease because of the mutual inductance.   In this case $M = M_{12} = M_{21}$ will have a negative numerical value.

The symbol for a pair of coupled coils is shown in Fig. 1-30.   The dots are symbols which indicate whether the magnetic fields set up by the coils aid or buck each other.   If both currents are into the dotted terminals (or both are out of the dotted terminals), then the fields aid each other, and the mutual-inductance terms have a positive sign (for example, $M \, di_1/dt$).   However, if one current enters a dotted terminal and the other leaves the dotted terminal, then the mutual-inductance terms will be negative (for example, $-M \, di_1/dt$; note that di_1/dt itself may be negative).

More than two coils can be coupled by mutual inductance.   For instance, Fig. 1-31 represents three coupled coils.   Note that three pairs of differently shaped dots are used—one pair to indicate the sign of the mutual-inductance terms for each pair of coupled coils.   The voltages v_1, v_2, and v_3 indicate the

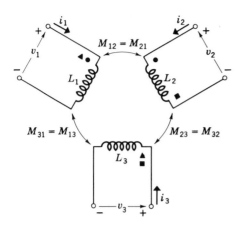

Fig. 1-31   Three coupled coils.

terminal voltages of the coils.   In this case we have

$$v_1 = L_1 \frac{di_1}{dt} + M_{12} \frac{di_2}{dt} + M_{13} \frac{di_3}{dt}$$

$$v_2 = M_{21} \frac{di_1}{dt} + L_2 \frac{di_2}{dt} - M_{23} \frac{di_3}{dt} \qquad (1\text{-}103)$$

$$v_3 = M_{31} \frac{di_1}{dt} - M_{32} \frac{di_2}{dt} + L_3 \frac{di_3}{dt}$$

where $M_{ij} = M_{ji}$.   In general, by extending this procedure we can write the equations for any number of coupled coils.

1-12   Time-varying and nonlinear inductance

Time-varying inductance

If the inductance of a circuit element is made to vary as a function of time, then it is called a *time-varying inductance*.   The analysis of such an element is very similar to that for the time-varying capacitor (the reader is advised to reread Sec. 1-8 before proceeding).   The terminal voltage of an inductance is given by Eqs. (1-91) and (1-92).   Combining these, we obtain

$$v = \frac{d(li)}{dt} \qquad (1\text{-}104)$$

where we have used a lowercase l for inductance, since it can be a function of time.   If we apply the rule for the derivative of a product, we obtain

$$v = l \frac{di}{dt} + i \frac{dl}{dt} \qquad (1\text{-}105)$$

If l is time-invariant, then Eq. (1-105) reduces to that of Eq. (1-93). Note that Eq. (1-105) *cannot* be derived from Eq. (1-93) simply by replacing the constant L by a time-varying term. Solving Eq. (1-104) for li and manipulating, we can write the current in terms of the voltage. Thus

$$i = \frac{1}{l} \int v \, dt \tag{1-106}$$

Note that this has the same *form* as Eq. (1-94) for the time-invariant case.

Now let us extend this analysis to the case where we have a time-varying mutual inductance. Consider that we have the pair of coupled coils represented in Fig. 1-30. The flux which links coils 1 and 2, respectively, is

$$\phi_1 = l_1 i_1 + m i_2 \tag{1-107a}$$

$$\phi_2 = m i_1 + l_2 i_2 \tag{1-107b}$$

where lowercase letters indicate time-varying quantities. Substituting each of these into Eq. (1-91), we obtain

$$v_1 = \frac{d}{dt}(l_1 i_1) + \frac{d}{dt}(m i_2) \tag{1-108a}$$

$$v_2 = \frac{d}{dt}(m i_1) + \frac{d}{dt}(l_2 i_2) \tag{1-108b}$$

or, alternatively,

$$v_1 = l_1 \frac{di_1}{dt} + m \frac{di_2}{dt} + i_1 \frac{dl_1}{dt} + i_2 \frac{dm}{dt} \tag{1-109a}$$

$$v_2 = m \frac{di_1}{dt} + l_2 \frac{di_2}{dt} + i_1 \frac{dm}{dt} + i_2 \frac{dl_2}{dt} \tag{1-109b}$$

This analysis can be extended in a similar way to any number of coupled coils.

Nonlinear inductance

At times the permittivity μ of the space surrounding the wires of an inductance is not constant, but is a function of the magnetic field. Thus it will be a function of the current of the inductance. In this case [see Eq. (1-96)] the inductance will also be a function of the current and is called a *nonlinear inductance*. Just as with a nonlinear capacitance, we can study a nonlinear inductance by treating it as a linear time-varying one with an instantaneous inductance equal to that of the actual nonlinear one. This will not lead to the best analysis procedure (analysis procedures are discussed in Sec. 3-8 and Chap. 7), but it is useful in relating nonlinear inductors to time-varying ones. This illustrates the fact that the inductance varies with current. Then Eqs. (1-105) and (1-106) can be used to analyze the nonlinear inductance. However, now the inductance is a function of the current, and not an independent function of time. Thus we have

$$\frac{dl}{dt} = \frac{dl}{di}\frac{di}{dt} \qquad (1\text{-}110)$$

Substituting in Eq. (1-105), we obtain

$$v = \left(l + i\frac{dl}{di}\right)\frac{di}{dt} \qquad (1\text{-}111)$$

Note that l and dl/di are functions of i. Thus these terms must be evaluated on an instantaneous basis, at the actual instantaneous value of i.

For a circuit containing mutual inductance the problem becomes somewhat more complex. The value of μ, and hence the inductances, will generally depend upon all the currents. Thus, for two coupled coils,

$$\frac{dl_1}{dt} = \frac{\partial l_1}{\partial i_1}\frac{di_1}{dt} + \frac{\partial l_1}{\partial i_2}\frac{di_2}{dt} \qquad (1\text{-}112a)$$

$$\frac{dm}{dt} = \frac{\partial m}{\partial i_1}\frac{di_1}{dt} + \frac{\partial m}{\partial i_2}\frac{di_2}{dt} \qquad (1\text{-}112b)$$

$$\frac{dl_2}{dt} = \frac{\partial l_2}{\partial i_1}\frac{di_1}{dt} + \frac{\partial l_2}{\partial i_2}\frac{di_2}{dt} \qquad (1\text{-}112c)$$

Substituting in Eqs. (1-109a) and (1-109b), we obtain

$$v_1 = \left(l_1 + i_1\frac{\partial l_1}{\partial i_1} + l_2\frac{\partial m}{\partial i_1}\right)\frac{di_1}{dt} + \left(m + i_2\frac{\partial m}{\partial i_2} + i_1\frac{\partial l_1}{\partial i_2}\right)\frac{di_2}{dt} \qquad (1\text{-}113a)$$

$$v_2 = \left(m + i_1\frac{\partial m}{\partial i_1} + i_2\frac{dl_2}{\partial i_1}\right)\frac{di_1}{dt} + \left(l_2 + i_1\frac{\partial m}{\partial i_2} + i_2\frac{\partial l_2}{\partial i_2}\right)\frac{di_2}{dt} \qquad (1\text{-}113b)$$

This notation is lengthy, and at times it is more convenient to write this relation in terms of the flux linkages. For instance, if ϕ_1 and ϕ_2 are the flux linkages of coils 1 and 2, respectively, then

$$v_1 = \frac{d\phi_1}{dt} = \frac{\partial\phi_1}{\partial i_1}\frac{di_1}{dt} + \frac{\partial\phi_2}{\partial i_2}\frac{di_2}{dt} \qquad (1\text{-}114a)$$

$$v_2 = \frac{d\phi_2}{dt} = \frac{\partial\phi_2}{\partial i_1}\frac{di_1}{dt} + \frac{\partial\phi_2}{\partial i_2}\frac{di_2}{dt} \qquad (1\text{-}114b)$$

Equations (1-114) are much more compact than Eqs. (1-113). They are equivalent, so that

$$\frac{\partial\phi_1}{\partial i_1} = l_1 + i_1\frac{\partial l_1}{\partial i_1} + i_2\frac{\partial m}{\partial i_1} \qquad (1\text{-}115a)$$

$$\frac{\partial\phi_1}{\partial i_2} = m + i_2\frac{\partial m}{\partial i_2} + i_1\frac{\partial l_1}{\partial i_2} \qquad (1\text{-}115b)$$

$$\frac{\partial\phi_2}{\partial i_1} = m + i_1\frac{\partial m}{\partial i_1} + i_2\frac{\partial l_2}{\partial i_1} \qquad (1\text{-}115c)$$

$$\frac{\partial\phi_2}{\partial i_2} = l_2 + i_1\frac{\partial m}{\partial i_2} + l_2\frac{\partial l_2}{\partial i_2} \qquad (1\text{-}115d)$$

where all quantities are expressed on an instantaneous basis; for instance, l_1 is a function of i_1 and i_2, which are functions of time.

If the current through a single inductance consists of a time-invariant term plus a small time-varying one (for example, $I_0 + i_1$), and we are interested in only the varying component of voltage, then we can use an analysis which exactly parallels that of Eqs. (1-68) to (1-74) for the nonlinear capacitor. Voltages and currents are now interchanged. In addition, capacitance is replaced by inductance. The details are left to the reader. Then for incremental components we have

$$v = L \frac{di}{dt}\bigg|_{i = I_0} \tag{1-116}$$

where L is *not* the ratio of flux linkages to current, but is the slope of the flux-linkage-vs.-current curve evaluated at the point where $i = I_0$. Thus L is called the *incremental inductance*.

1-13   Power and energy: circuit elements

Let us now consider the power and energy associated with the circuit elements we have discussed.

Resistance

From Eq. (1-27) we see that the instantaneous power dissipated in a resistance of R ohms is

$$p = vi = \frac{v^2}{R} = i^2 R \tag{1-117}$$

where v and i are the instantaneous voltage across and the current through the resistance, respectively. In a resistance all this power is dissipated as heat. If the voltage applied to the resistance is zero before time $t = 0$, then at time T the net energy supplied to the resistance is

$$w = \int_0^T p \, dt = R \int_0^T i^2 \, dt = \frac{1}{R} \int_0^T v^2 \, dt \tag{1-118}$$

If R is nonlinear or time varying, then it cannot be removed from within the integral sign. If we wish to obtain the energy dissipated by the resistance for all its past history up to time T, then Eq. (1-118) becomes

$$w = \int_{-\infty}^T p \, dt \tag{1-119}$$

Capacitance

Let us now compute the power and energy supplied to a linear time-invariant capacitor. We shall again assume that the voltage and current are functions of time and write them as $v(t)$ and $i(t)$.   Then the instantaneous power supplied to the capacitor is

$$p(t) = v(t)i(t) \tag{1-120}$$

Substituting Eq. (1-53), we obtain

$$p(t) = Cv(t)\frac{dv(t)}{dt} \tag{1-121}$$

Thus the energy supplied to the capacitor between $t = 0$ and $t = T$ is

$$w = \int_0^T Cv(t)\frac{dv(t)}{dt}\,dt \tag{1-122}$$

which can be written as

$$w = \int_{v(0)}^{v(T)} Cv(t)\,dv(t) \tag{1-123}$$

Note that the upper limit of integration is now $v(T)$ [that is, the value of $v(t)$ at $t = T$], and the lower limit is $v(0)$.   Carrying out the integration of Eq. (1-123), we obtain

$$w = \tfrac{1}{2}C[v^2(T) - v^2(0)] \tag{1-124}$$

Let us assume that the capacitor was uncharged at $t = 0$, that is, that $v(0) = 0$.   Then Eq. (1-124) becomes

$$w = \tfrac{1}{2}Cv^2(T) \tag{1-125}$$

Note that the energy depends only upon the value of the voltage at time T. It does *not* depend upon the waveform of $v(t)$ at other times.   Equation (1-125) represents the energy supplied to the capacitor starting from any uncharged state.

Now suppose that a capacitor is connected into the circuit of Fig. 1-18b and that the voltage v across the capacitor is varied as shown in Fig. 1-32.   That is, the voltage increases from 0 to a value $V_{\max}$ at $t = T_1$, and then falls to zero and remains there for all $t > T_2$.   The energy [see Eq. (1-125)] will rise from 0 to $\tfrac{1}{2}CV_{\max}^2$ and then *fall back to zero*.   The energy is zero for all $t > T_2$, so there has been no net energy into the capacitor.   That is, there is a net flow of energy into the capacitor for $0 \leq t < T_1$, and then the capacitor supplies energy back to the generator for $T_1 \leq t \leq T_2$.   Thus, in contrast to a resistor, the capacitor does not dissipate energy in the form of heat, but simply stores it in the electric field set up between its plates.   If the generator voltage falls off, the capacitor then returns the energy to the generator.   If the generator is mechanically driven, it actually runs as a motor during those times when the capacitor is supplying energy, that is, the generator takes electrical energy from the capacitor and supplies mechanical energy through its drive shaft.

Let us consider the power supplied to the capacitor [see Eq. (1-121)]. When $v(t)$ is increasing the power will be positive and when $v(t)$ decreases the

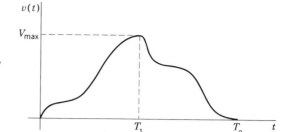

Fig. 1-32 An arbitrary voltage, which is a function of time.

power will be negative; that is, the capacitor is supplying power to the external circuit. Although the power can become negative, the energy can never be negative. Note that the $[v(t)]^2$ term will always be positive. The capacitor can absorb energy, store it, and at a later time supply it to the external circuit, but it can never supply more energy than it has received.

It is sometimes convenient to write Eq. (1-124) in terms of the charge. Substituting Eq. (1-49) into Eq. (1-124), we obtain

$$w = \frac{q^2(T) - q^2(0)}{2C} \tag{1-126}$$

Inductance

If $v(t)$ is the voltage across an inductance and $i(t)$ is the current through it, then the instantaneous power supplied to it is

$$p(t) = v(t)i(t)$$

Substituting Eq. (1-93), we obtain

$$p(t) = Li(t)\frac{di(t)}{dt} \tag{1-127}$$

If $i(0)$ is the current at $t = 0$ and $i(T)$ is the current at some later time T, then the net energy supplied to the inductor between $t = 0$ and $t = T$ is

$$w = \int_0^T p(t)\, dt = \int_{i(0)}^{i(T)} Li(t)\, di(t) = \tfrac{1}{2}L[i^2(T) - i^2(0)] \tag{1-128}$$

If the current at $t = 0$ is zero, then

$$w = \tfrac{1}{2}Li^2(T) \tag{1-129}$$

This represents the total energy supplied to the inductor at time T.

The energy supplied to the inductor at any time depends upon only the magnitude of the current, and not upon its past history. If $i(T)$ becomes zero, then the energy supplied to the inductor becomes zero. As in the case of the capacitor, the inductor can take energy from a circuit, store it, and then return it to the circuit. The inductor does not dissipate power in the form of heat,

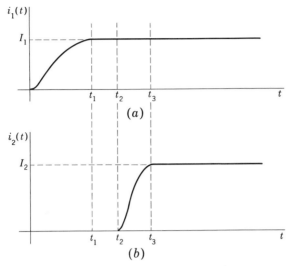

Fig. 1-33   (a) $i_1(t)$; (b) $i_2(t)$.

but stores it in its magnetic field.   Energy is taken from the circuit to set up the magnetic field, and when the field collapses, the energy returns to the circuit.   We can express the stored energy in terms of the flux linkages.   Substitution of Eq. (1-92) into Eq. (1-129) yields

$$w = \frac{1}{2L} \phi^2(T) \tag{1-130}$$

Let us now discuss the energy stored by a pair of coupled coils.   We shall compute the energy stored in the coils of Fig. 1-30 when $i_1 = I_1$ and $i_2 = I_2$; that is, we shall consider that i_1 and i_2 are zero at $t = 0$ and then are increased arbitrarily to I_1 and I_2, respectively.   As for the simple inductance, we shall assume that the energy is stored in the magnetic field and so does not depend upon the past history of the currents.   Thus we can assume that the current has any waveforms which finally reach I_1 and I_2.   For convenience let us use the currents shown in Fig. 1-33; that is, $i_1(t)$ increases arbitrarily from zero at $t = 0$ to I_1 at $t = t_1$ and remains constant thereafter.   The current $i_2(t)$ is zero until $t = t_2 > t_1$; it then increases arbitrarily until $t = t_3$, where $i_2(t) = I_2$, and then remains constant.   The voltages across the coils are given by Eqs. (1-99) and (1-101).

For $0 \leq t \leq t_2$, $i_2(t) = 0$.   Hence

$$v_1 = L_1 \frac{di_1}{dt}$$

Thus the energy supplied in this time interval is

$$w_1 = \int_0^{t_2} L_1 i \frac{di_1}{dt}\, dt = L_1 \int_0^{I_1} i_1\, di_1 = \tfrac{1}{2} L_1 I_1^2 \tag{1-131}$$

Since $i_2(t) = 0$ for $0 \leq t < t_2$, there is no power supplied to the terminals of coil 2. For $t > t_2$, $i_1(t)$ is constant; hence $di_1/dt = 0$, and [see Eqs. (1-99) and (1-101)]

$$v_1(t) = M_{12} \frac{di_2}{dt}$$

$$v_2(t) = L_2 \frac{di_2}{dt}$$

Thus the energy supplied to the entire circuit for $t_2 \leq t \leq t_3$ is

$$w_2 = \int_{t_2}^{t_3} M_{12}I_1 \frac{di_2}{dt} dt + \int_{t_2}^{t_3} L_2 i_2 \frac{di_2}{dt} dt \qquad (1\text{-}132a)$$

or, equivalently,

$$w_2 = M_{12}I_1 \int_0^{I_2} di_2 + L_2 \int_0^{I_2} i_2 \, di_2 \qquad (1\text{-}132b)$$

Integration yields

$$w_2 = M_{12}I_1 I_2 + \tfrac{1}{2} L_2 I_2{}^2 \qquad (1\text{-}132c)$$

The total energy supplied to the coupled coils for $0 \leq t \leq t_3$ is $w_1 + w_2$. Hence

$$w = \tfrac{1}{2} L_1 I_1{}^2 + M_{12}I_1 I_2 + \tfrac{1}{2} L_2 L_2{}^2 \qquad (1\text{-}133)$$

The energy stored is equal to the sum of the energies that would be stored by the coils themselves plus a term $M_{12}I_1 I_2$, which is due to the mutual inductance.

We can use the previous development to prove Eq. (1-102), that is, that $M_{12} = M_{21}$. Let us again compute the energy stored in the coupled coils, but with the waveforms of the currents changed somewhat. Assume that $i_2(t)$ increases from zero to I_2 in the time range $0 \leq t \leq t_1$ and remains constant thereafter, and that $i_1(t)$ is zero until $t_2 > t_1$ and then increases to I_1 at $t = t_3$. This analysis essentially parallels our previous one (the details are left to the reader). In this case

$$w = \tfrac{1}{2} L_1 I_1{}^2 + M_{21}I_1 I_2 + \tfrac{1}{2} L_2 I_2{}^2$$

The final currents used in deriving this and Eq. (1-133) are identical, so the magnetic fields will be the same. We assume that the stored energies in each case will be equal. Comparing the relations, we see

$$M_{12} = M_{21}$$

which is the result that we wished to prove.

The energy stored in a pair of coupled coils cannot be negative. If it were, then the law of conservation of energy would be violated, since the coils would supply net energy to the circuit. Equation (1-133) looks as though it could be negative since M_{12}, I_1, and/or I_2 can be negative. In fact the value of M is restricted so that the energy cannot become negative. Let us determine this restriction. To aid us in this we shall make use of a constant called the *coefficient of coupling*, defined as

$$k = \frac{M}{\sqrt{L_1 L_2}} \tag{1-134}$$

Note that k can be either positive or negative.

Substituting into Eq. (1-133), we obtain

$$w = \tfrac{1}{2} L_1 I_1{}^2 + k \sqrt{L_1 L_2} \, I_1 I_2 + \tfrac{1}{2} L_2 I_2{}^2$$

This must always be positive. The only time this expression could be negative is if $k \sqrt{L_1 L_2} I_1 I_2$ were negative. Let us assume that k, I_1, or I_2 is of the correct sign to cause this. Then

$$w = \tfrac{1}{2} L_1 I_1{}^2 - |k \sqrt{L_1 L_2} \, I_1 I_2| + \tfrac{1}{2} L_2 I_2{}^2 \geq 0$$

or, equivalently,

$$(\sqrt{\tfrac{1}{2} L_1} \, I_1 - \sqrt{\tfrac{1}{2} L_2} \, I_2)^2 + (1 - |k|) \sqrt{L_1 L_2} \, |I_1 I_2| \geq 0 \tag{1-135}$$

This must be nonnegative for *all* I_1 and I_2. The first term will never be negative, since it is a square. However, with an appropriate choice of I_1 and I_2 it can be made zero. Thus, if relation (1-135) is to be nonnegative for all I_1 and I_2, the last term cannot be negative; that is,

$$1 - |k| \geq 0$$

or, equivalently,

$$|k| = \frac{|M|}{\sqrt{L_1 L_2}} \leq 1 \tag{1-136}$$

Hence the maximum magnitude of mutual inductance is limited.

We have discussed the energy supplied to resistors, capacitors, and inductors. There are two different situations represented here. The energy supplied to capacitors or inductors can, at a later time, be returned to the circuit. This is called a *lossless network*, and inductors and capacitors are called *lossless elements*. The energy supplied to a resistor, however, is converted into heat and leaves the circuit; for this reason resistors are called *lossy elements*. We can never construct elements that are completely lossless. The wire used to make an inductor has some resistance, which dissipates power when there is current through it. In analysis procedures, therefore, an actual inductance is often approximated by an ideal one in series with a resistance. In addition, if the inductor has an iron core, it will be heated if the current through the inductor varies with time. This dissipation of heat is called *core loss*. In analysis procedure, resistors are placed in series and/or shunt with the inductor to approximate the actual coil. The power dissipated in these resistors should equal that dissipated in the coil.

In a capacitor the resistance of the interconnecting wires and plates is usually small enough that it can be neglected. However, many times there are power losses in the dielectric which cannot be ignored. When a dielectric is subjected to a rapidly changing electric field, it is heated. This is called *dielectric loss*. It occurs when molecules are subjected to (electric) forces which have rapidly changing directions. The energy for this heating is supplied electrically. Since only a resistance can dissipate power, the dielectric loss causes the capacitor to act as if a resistance were associated with it. In analysis procedures a resistor placed in parallel with an ideal capacitor is usually used to approximate an actual capacitor.

At times actual circuit elements must be considered as distributed parameters. This is discussed in Sec. 1-14.

Nonlinear capacitors

We have considered the energy stored in a linear capacitor. Let us now extend the analysis to a nonlinear capacitor. In analyzing a nonlinear capacitor we can usually express the charge stored (on one plate) as a function of the applied voltage,

$$q(t) = f[v(t)]$$

If the charge is a linear function of the voltage, then the capacitor is linear. The capacitance is the constant of proportionality [see Eq. (1-49)]. The current into the capacitor is given by

$$i(t) = \frac{dq(t)}{dt} = \frac{df[v(t)]}{dt}$$

The instantaneous power supplied to the capacitor is given by Eq. (1-120). Hence

$$p = v(t) \frac{df[v(t)]}{dt}$$

Therefore the energy supplied to the capacitor between $t = 0$ and $t = T$ is

$$w = \int_0^T v(t) \frac{df[v(t)]}{dt} dt$$

Alternatively, we can write

$$w = \int_0^T v(t) \frac{dq(t)}{dt} dt = \int_{q(0)}^{q(T)} v(t) \, dq(t)$$

We can usually express the voltage across a nonlinear capacitor as a function of the charge stored,

$$v(t) = f_1[q(t)]$$

Substituting into the above equation, we have

$$w = \int_{q(0)}^{q(T)} f_1[q(t)] \, dq(t) = \int_{q(0)}^{q(T)} f_1(q) \, dq$$

Thus the stored energy is equal to the area under the (nonlinear) voltage-vs.-charge curve.

Nonlinear inductors

In most inductors the flux linkages can be expressed as a function of the current,

$$\phi(t) = f[i(t)]$$

The voltage across the inductor is defined by Eq. (1-91). Hence the instantaneous power supplied to the inductor is

$$p = i(t) \, \frac{df[i(t)]}{dt} \, dt$$

Thus the energy supplied between $t = 0$ and $t = T$ is given by

$$w = \int_0^T i(t) \, \frac{df[i(t)]}{dt} \, dt$$

or

$$w = \int_0^T i(t) \, \frac{d\phi(t)}{dt} \, dt = \int_{\phi(0)}^{\phi(T)} i(t) \, d\phi(t)$$

We can usually express $i(t)$ as a function of the flux linkages,

$$i(t) = f_1[\phi(t)]$$

Thus we can write

$$w = \int_{\phi(0)}^{\phi(T)} f_1[\phi(t)] \, d\phi(t) = \int_{\phi(0)}^{\phi(T)} f_1(\phi) \, d\phi$$

1-14   Distributed parameters

We have considered the circuit elements of resistance, inductance, and capacitance to be isolated elements characterized by the relations

$$v = iR$$

$$v = \frac{1}{C} \int i \, dt$$

$$v = L \frac{di}{dt}$$

Isolated elements which can be characterized by equations such as these are

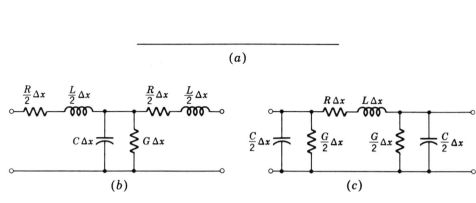

Fig. 1-34 (a) A transmission line; (b) a representation of a small section of this transmission line, where R, L, C, and G are the resistance, inductance, capacitance, and conductance per meter, respectively; (c) an alternate representation.

called *lumped elements.* However, consider the pair of parallel wires, called a
transmission line, shown in Fig. 1-34a. The wires have resistance. In addition, they set up a flux which links them, so they possess an inductance. *In
fact, the wires of any circuit will have an inductance. A capacitance will exist
between any two conductors.* Hence there will be a capacitance between the
wires. Moreover, since the insulating medium between the wires may not
be perfect, there will be a finite resistance between the wires. The importane
fact here is that *all these circuit elements exist simultaneously at all points along
the transmission line.* This is called a *distributed-parameter network,* since the
circuit elements are not isolated, but are distributed along it.

To analyze such a circuit we approximate a small section of it by a network
containing lumped elements. Such a representation for a length Δx is shown
in Fig. 1-34b. The parameters are expressed per unit length. For instance,
R is the resistance of 1 m of the transmission line (that is, the resistance of 2 m
of the wire, because both the upper and lower lines have resistance). Similarly,
C represents the capacitance between two wires 1 m long. The reader may
wonder why the configuration of Fig. 1-34b is chosen, instead of a circuit such as
Fig. 1-34c. Actually, when $\Delta x \to 0$, either of these circuits becomes an accurate
representation. In this case a finite length of transmission line will consist of
an infinite cascade of sections of the type shown in Fig. 1-34b or c.

Although any electric network is in reality a distributed-parameter one,
it can often be represented by lumped constants. Many times detailed measurements cannot demonstrate any flaw in the lumped-constant approach; at
other times, however, distributed parameters must be used. For instance,
electronic devices constructed as integrated systems within a small piece of

silicon at times must be analyzed as distributed parameters. Actual procedures for distributed-parameter analysis will be discussed in Chap. 6 and Sec. 8-9.

1-15 Voltage generators and current generators: notation

Before we discuss network analysis, it would be well to review and clarify some procedures of notation. In addition, we shall discuss the types of generators that may be encountered.

Consider the plus and minus symbols in the voltage generator of Fig. 1-35. If v represents a constant positive voltage, then terminal a will be positive with respect to terminal b. That is, positive work must be done on a positive charge to move it from point b to point a, external to the generator. Hence there will be a voltage drop from terminal a to terminal b.

Now let us complicate the situation by assuming that v is a function of time that changes its polarity; for example,

$$v = V_{\text{max}} \cos \omega t \tag{1-137}$$

Plus and minus signs are still placed on the generator. For those times that Eq. (1-137) is positive, terminal a is positive with respect to terminal b. However, when Eq. (1-137) is negative, then terminal a will be negative with respect to terminal b. The plus and minus signs do not *necessarily* specify the actual generator polarities, but serve as an indication of the polarity of the generator when v is known.

We have discussed generators which supply a stated voltage independent of its terminal connections. Actually, this is an idealization. Any practical generator will have resistance and inductance associated with it. For instance, if a zero resistance were connected to terminals a and b of Fig. 1-35, an infinite current would result [see Eq. (1-26)]. In theory this is possible, but in practice the current would be limited by the inductance and resistance. They also cause a decrease in the terminal voltage when there is any current.

The ideal voltage generator of Fig. 1-35 produces a voltage which is independent of the circuit elements connected to it. Another ideal generator would be one that produces a current which is independent of the circuit elements connected to it. Such a generator, symbolically illustrated in Fig. 1-36, is

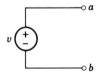

Fig. 1-35   A voltage generator.

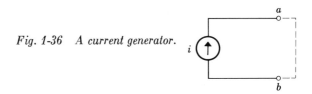

Fig. 1-36   A current generator.

called a *current generator*.   This can be thought of as a voltage generator whose
voltage is adjusted instantaneously so that its current is always equal to i (of
course, we could just as well think of a voltage generator as a current generator
whose current is adjusted instantaneously to produce the correct voltage).
At times a current generator requires infinite voltage, but remember that this
is an idealization.   Practical generators can be represented by an interconnection of an ideal generator and circuit elements.

If i represents a positive constant, then the positive current will be in the
direction of the arrow, that is, from a to b in the external (dashed) wire in
Fig. 1-36 (electrons will flow from b to a).   If i is time-varying, such as

$$i = I_{\max} \sin \omega t \tag{1-138}$$

then when Eq. (1-138) is positive the positive current is in the direction of the
arrow on the current generator (from a to b in the dashed external wire).   For
those times when Eq. (1-138) is negative the positive current is from b to a
in the dashed external wire.   If i is a negative constant, then the current
direction is the same as when Eq. (1-138) is negative.

Sometimes it is desirable to specify the voltage drop between two arbitrary
points in a network—for instance, across the resistor shown in Fig. 1-37.   We
can use the arrow notation introduced previously.   If v is a positive constant,
then terminal a, toward which the arrow points, will be positive with respect
to terminal b.   If v is a negative constant, with the arrow and plus-minus signs
as they are in Fig. 1-37, then point a is negative with respect to point b.   If v
is a time-varying quantity such as that given in Eq. (1-137), then point a will
be positive (or negative) with respect to point b when Eq. (1-137) is positive
(or negative).   At times, instead of using arrows, the voltage drop between two

Fig. 1-37   Symbols for voltage and current.

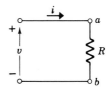

points is indicated by appending two subscripts to v.   For instance, the voltage drop from a to b in Fig. 1-37 could be indicated as

$$v_{ab}$$

The voltage v_{ab} has the same meaning as v with an arrow; that is, if the arrow were drawn, it would point toward the first subscript.   This notation is called the *double-subscript notation*.

Often in analyzing a network the voltage is unknown.   In this event its polarity is assumed, and it is labeled as in Fig. 1-37.   If the calculated value of the voltage is a positive constant, then its polarity is as marked (terminal a positive with respect to terminal b).   If the calculated value of v turns out to be negative, then point a is negative with respect to point b.   If v is a time-varying quantity, such as Eq. (1-137), then the polarity of the actual voltage will be as discussed following Eq. (1-137).   If the calculated voltage is

$$v = -V_{max} \cos \omega t \tag{1-139}$$

then point a will still be positive (or negative) with respect to point b when Eq. (1-139) is positive (or negative) [note that the minus sign causes Eq. (1-139) to be negative (or positive) at different times from Eq. (1-137)].

The notation for current is similar to that for voltage.   If i is to be calculated, then an assumed direction for i is picked.   If the calculated i is either a positive constant or positive on an instantaneous basis, then the current is in the direction of the arrow (the electron flow is in the opposite direction).   If the calculated current is negative, then the positive current is opposite to the direction of the arrow.

REFERENCE

[1] S. Ramo and J. R. Whinnery, "Fields and Waves in Modern Radio," 2d ed., p. 261, John Wiley & Sons, Inc., New York, 1953.

BIBLIOGRAPHY

Clement, P. R., and W. C. Johnson: "Electrical Engineering Science," chaps. 1–4, McGraw-Hill Book Company, New York, 1960.

Close, C. M.: "The Analysis of Linear Circuits," chap. 1, Harcourt, Brace & World, Inc., New York, 1966.

Manning, L. A.: "Electrical Circuits," chap. 1, McGraw-Hill Book Company, New York, 1966.

Pearson, S. I., and G. J. Maler: "Introductory Circuit Analysis," chaps. 1 and 2, John Wiley & Sons, Inc., New York, 1965.

Van Valkenburg, M. E.: "Network Analysis," 2d ed., chaps. 1 and 2, Prentice-Hall, Inc., Englewood Cliffs, N.J., 1964.

PROBLEMS

1-1. Compute the force on two electrons 1 m apart in free space.

1-2. Compute the force on a 1-coul positive charge placed at point P in Fig. 1-38. The three charges and point P are the corners of a square, and they all lie in a plane. Write the vector in terms of its x and y components and $\mathbf{U}_x$ and $\mathbf{U}_y$, which are unit vectors in the x and y directions, respectively.

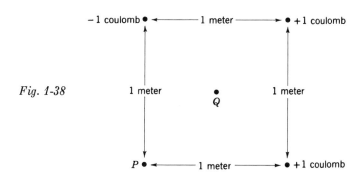

Fig. 1-38

1-3. From the description in Prob. 1-2 compute the electric field at point P in Fig. 1-38.

1-4. Compute the work done in moving a unit positive charge from point a to point b in Fig. 1-39.

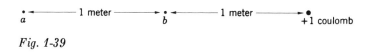

Fig. 1-39

1-5. Compute the work done in moving a unit positive charge around a circle which has a unit negative charge at its center.

1-6. Compute the voltage drop (potential difference) between points a and b in Fig. 1-39.

1-7. Compute the potential difference between points P and Q in Fig. 1-38. Point Q lies at the intersection of the diagonals of the square.

1-8. The current in a wire is 1 amp and does not vary with time. Compute the net total charge that flows past a point in 1 min. How many electrons does this represent?

1-9. The voltage across a circuit element is $v = 10 \sin 5t$ volts and the current through it is $i = 5 \sin (5t + \pi/4)$ amp. Compute the instantaneous power supplied to the circuit elements.

1-10. Compute the energy supplied to the circuit element of Prob. 1-9 between $t = 0$ and $t = 1$ sec.

1-11. The voltage across a circuit element is $e = 1 \cos \omega t$ volt, and the current through it is $i = 1 \sin \omega t$ amp. Compute the energy supplied to the circuit between $t = 0$ and $t = \pi/2\omega$ sec.

1-12. Repeat Prob. 1-11, but now compute the energy supplied to the circuit between $t = 0$ and $t = 2\pi/\omega$ sec.

1-13. A generator whose voltage is $v = 10 \sin t$ volts is connected across a 5-ohm resistor. Compute the current through the resistor, the instantaneous power dissipated in it, and the energy supplied to the resistor in 1 sec.

1-14. A circular wire has a cross section whose radius is 1 cm. The magnitude of the current density through the central portion of the wire, whose radius is 0.25 cm, is 1,000 amp/m, and the magnitude of the current density elsewhere in the wire is 500 amp/m. The direction of the current density is parallel to the direction of the wire. Compute the current in the wire.

1-15. Compute the resistance of a round copper wire whose radius is 1 mm and whose length is 100 cm.

1-16. Repeat Prob. 1-15 for a silver wire.

1-17. Compute the resistance of a round copper wire whose length is 100 ft and whose diameter is 0.01 in.

1-18. A nonlinear resistance has a resistance given by $R = 10 + i^2$, where i is the current through the resistance. A voltage of 11 volts is connected across this resistance. What is the resulting current?

1-19. A time-varying resistance is given by $r(t) = 10 + 5 \sin 2t$ ohms. The current through this resistance is $i(t) = 3 + 1 \sin 2t$ amp. Compute the voltage across the resistance and the instantaneous power dissipated in it.

1-20. The capacitor of Fig. 1-18b has a capacitance of 1 μf. The current through this capacitance is constant at 1 amp. It is applied at $t = 0$ and is constant thereafter. Compute the voltage necessary to produce this current. What practical problems would we encounter in actually constructing this voltage generator?

1-21. A 1-μf capacitor has a difference in potential across its plates of 1 volt. How many electrons have been transferred from one plate to another?

1-22. A parallel-plate capacitor has plates 1 cm² in area and 0.1 mm apart. The dielectric is air, with a dielectric constant of approximately unity. Compute the capacitance of the capacitor.

1-23. Report Prob. 1-22, but now assume that the insulator has a relative dielectric constant of 100.

1-24. In the circuit of Fig. 1-18b the value of C is 1 μf and $v = 1 - e^{-t} + \sin 2t$ volts. Compute the current through the capacitor.

1-25. Repeat Prob. 1-24, but now use $v = 1 + e^{-10^9 t} + \sin 10^9 t$.

1-26. A capacitance varies in accordance with the expression $C = 0.1(1 + e^{-10^6 t})$ μf. The voltage across the capacitor is $v = 100 \sin 10^7 t$ volts. What is the current into the capacitor?

1-27. The capacitance of a nonlinear capacitor is given by $C = C_0 - C_1 v + C_2 v^2$, where v is the voltage across the capacitor. If $v = V_{max} \sin \omega t$, what is the current into the capacitor?

1-28. The charge-vs.-voltage curve of a capacitor is given by $q = k_1 v^2$. If $v = V_{max} \sin \omega t$ what is the current into the capacitor?

1-29. For the capacitor in Prob. 1-28 the voltage is given by $v = V_0 + V_{max}$ sin ωt. Determine the current in response to the time-varying portion of this voltage. Assume that V_{max} is small enough so that a "linearization approximation" can be made.

1-30. Repeat Prob. 1-29, but do not make any approximations.

1-31. The current through a 1-henry inductance is given by $i = 1 - e^{-t}$. What is the voltage across the inductance? Now repeat this problem, but assume that the current through the inductance is $i = -e^{-t}$. Compare this answer with the previous one.

1-32. Write the relationship that gives the voltage-current relations for the coupled coils of Fig. 1-40. How do these change if the position of one of the dots is reversed?

Fig. 1-40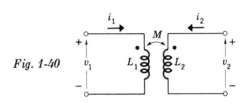

1-33. In Fig. 1-31

$L_1 = 10$ henrys

$L_2 = 5$ henrys

$L_3 = 5$ henrys

$M_{12} = 3$ henrys

$M_{23} = 1$ henry

$M_{31} = 1$ henry

and the currents are

$i_1 = 10$ sin ωt amp

$i_2 = 5$ sin $2\omega t$ amp

$i_3 = 3$ sin $3\omega t$ amp

Compute v_1, v_2, and v_3.

1-34. An inductance is given by $L(2 + \sin \omega_1 t)$. The current through the inductance is $i = I_{max} \sin \omega_2 t$. What is the voltage across it?

1-35. A pair of time-varying coupled coils is characterized by the relations

$L_1 = 2 + \sin \omega_1 t$ henrys

$L_2 = 3 + \sin \omega_2 t$ henrys

$M = 0.1(1 + e^{-at})$ henrys

If the currents are

$$i_1 = I_{max} \sin \omega_3 t$$
$$i_2 = I_0 e^{-bt}$$

compute the voltage drops across the coils.

1-36. An inductor has an inductance given by $L = 1 + a_0 i$. If the current through the inductance is $i = I_{max} \sin \omega t$, compute the voltage across the inductance.

1-37. The flux-linkage-vs.-current curve for an inductor is given by $\phi = a_1 i + a_2 i^2$. If the current through the inductance is $i = I_{max} \sin \omega t$, compute the voltage across the inductance.

1-38. For the inductor in Prob. 1-37 let $i = I_0 + I_{max} \sin \omega t$. Determine the time-varying component of voltage across the inductor. Assume that I_{max} is small enough so that a "linearization approximation" can be made.

1-39. Repeat Prob. 1-38, but now do not assume that I_{max} is small.

1-40. The pair of coupled coils of Fig. 1-40 is characterized by the relations

$$\phi_1 = i_1{}^2 + 0.1 i_2{}^2$$
$$\phi_2 = 0.1 i_1{}^2 + i_2 + i_2{}^2$$

If the currents are

$$i_1 = I_{1,max} \sin \omega_1 t$$
$$i_2 = I_{2,max} \sin \omega_2 t$$

what are the voltage drops v_1 and v_2 across the coils?

1-41. The current through a 10-ohm resistor is $10 + 15 \sin t$ amp. What is the energy supplied to the resistor from $t = 0$ to $t = 1$ sec?

1-42. The voltage across a 1-μf capacitor is 100 volts. What is the energy stored in the electrostatic field of the capacitor?

1-43. A 1-μf capacitor has 0.1 coul of charge transferred from one plate to the other. The capacitor is then disconnected from any external circuit. Assume that the charge now remains the same for all time. The plates of the capacitor are then physically moved apart until the capacitor becomes a 0.5-μf capacitor. What work is required to do this?

1-44. A 1-μf capacitor is connected to a voltage generator that produces 1 volt for all times. The generator is disconnected, and the plates of the capacitor are then moved apart so that the capacitor becomes a 0.5-μf capacitor. How much work is required to do this?

1-45. Repeat Prob. 1-44, but now assume that the voltage generator is not removed. Note that the voltage across the capacitor will remain constant. In addition, a current through the generator will occur; this should be taken into account.

1-46. The current through a 1-henry coil is 1 amp. What is the energy stored in the magnetic field of the coil?

1-47. For the coupled coils in Fig. 1-40 $L_1 = L_2 = 1$ henry and $M = 0.5$ henry. If $i_1 = 10$ amp and $i_2 = -2$ amp, what is the energy stored in the magnetic field?

1-48. For the coupled coils of Fig. 1-40 $i_1 = i_2 = 10$ amp and $L_1 = L_2 = M = 1$ henry. Without changing the currents, the coils are moved apart so that $M = 0.5$ henry. Compute the work required to move the coils apart.

1-49. Repeat Prob. 1-48, but now assume that $i_2 = -10$ amp.

1-50. A 5-henry coil is coupled to a 2-henry coil by a mutual inductance M. What is the largest value that M can have if this configuration is not to violate the law of conservation of energy?

1-51. For the coupled coils of Fig. 1-31 show that $M_{12} = M_{21}$, $M_{23} = M_{32}$, and $M_{13} = M_{31}$.

1-52. For the coupled coils of Fig. 1-31 derive the limitations on the mutual inductances.

Kirchhoff's Laws and Elementary Circuit Analysis

We have characterized electric circuit elements by equations which relate the voltage across them to the current through them. These are often called *terminal* voltages and currents, since they involve the measurement of voltages and currents at the (external) terminals of the elements. We must now develop techniques that can be used to analyze networks made up of the arbitrary interconnections of many circuit elements and generators. If we know the circuit configuration, the element values, and the voltages and/or currents produced by the generators, then we should be able to find the currents through all the circuit elements and the voltages across them. In this chapter we shall develop laws which are fundamental to the analysis of all electric circuits and apply them to a simple type of electric circuit analysis. In the next chapter we shall apply these laws to more powerful and practical techniques of circuit analysis.

2-1 Kirchhoff's voltage law

Let us now develop a law that can be used to establish relationships among some of the voltage drops in a network. The fundamental relation we shall use here is the experimentally determined Faraday's law, which is expressed in Eq. (1-89) as

$$\oint_l \mathbf{e} \cdot d\mathbf{l} = -\frac{d\phi}{dt} \tag{2-1}$$

This states that the line integral of the electric field around any closed path is equal to the negative of the rate of change of magnetic flux linking the path. Now let us write Eq. (2-1) in terms of voltage drops along the path. As an example we shall use the path shown in Fig. 2-1. We can rewrite Eq. (2-1) as

$$\int_a^b \mathbf{e} \cdot d\mathbf{l} + \int_b^c \mathbf{e} \cdot d\mathbf{l} + \int_c^d \mathbf{e} \cdot d\mathbf{l} + \int_d^a \mathbf{e} \cdot d\mathbf{l} = -\frac{d\phi}{dt} \tag{2-2}$$

where it is understood that each of the line integrals is taken along a segment of the path of Fig. 2-1. Then, substituting Eq. (1-13), we obtain

$$v_{ab} + v_{bc} + v_{cd} + v_{da} = \frac{d\phi}{dt} \tag{2-3}$$

The path and voltage drops chosen are arbitrary. We can therefore infer a general result from Eq. (2-3): *the sum of the voltage drops around any closed loop is equal to the rate of change of flux linking that loop.* This statement will be

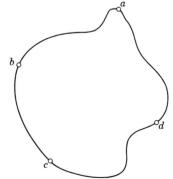

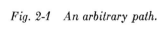

Fig. 2-1 An arbitrary path.

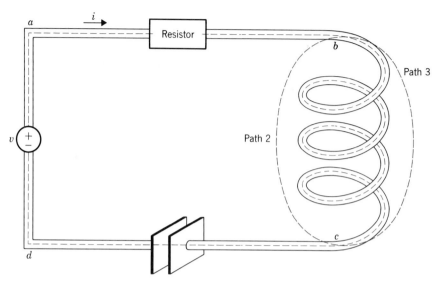

Fig. 2-2   A simple electric circuit.

called the *generalized Kirchhoff's voltage law.*   If there is no flux linking the loop, we have a special case of this law that is important in circuit analysis: *the sum of the voltage drops around a closed loop is equal to zero.*   This is called *Kirchhoff's voltage law.*

Let us study both forms of Kirchhoff's voltage law and see how they are applied to electric circuit analysis.   To do this we shall consider an electric circuit made up of a voltage generator, a resistor, a capacitor, and an inductor, as shown in Fig. 2-2, and then generalize our results.   Except for the voltage generator, no symbols are used here.

Let us evaluate Eq. (2-1) for this circuit.   The path of integration is shown by the dashed line.   If we make no approximations whatsoever, then this is an extremely complex problem, because the fields of the various circuit elements exist at all points in space.   For instance, in evaluating $\int \mathbf{e} \cdot d\mathbf{l}$ through the turns of the inductance we must take into account not only the magnetic field of the inductor, but also the electric field of the capacitor that exists there. In addition, there is a field at the inductor due to the electric field set up by the resistance.   In general, in the vicinity of any one circuit element we have the fields due to all of them.

When practical circuit elements are used, we can usually assume that their fields do not interact.   For instance, almost all of the capacitor's electric field is in the space between the plates, and any electric field external to the capacitor is negligible.   Similarly, it is usually assumed that the magnetic field set up by the inductor is important only in the region of the inductance.   If we proceed in this fashion, then we can consider that the potential difference across any one circuit element is due only to that element itself. That is, the results of Chap. 1 can be used to calculate the potential *drops* across each element. For instance, to evaluate the integral from a to b we can use Eq. (1-32):

$$\int_a^b \mathbf{e} \cdot d\mathbf{l} = \int_b^a \frac{\mathbf{J}}{\sigma} d\mathbf{l} \tag{2-4}$$

The voltage drop v_{ab} is thus proportional to the current. The constant of proportionality is the resistance [see Eq. (1-26)]. Hence

$$\int_a^b \mathbf{e} \cdot d\mathbf{l} = iR \tag{2-5}$$

where we have assumed that the conductivity of the wire, except in the resistive block, is infinite. Since the current density is finite, $\mathbf{e}$ is zero within the infinite-conductance wire. This is true even in the wire of the inductance. Thus we have

$$\int_b^c \mathbf{e} \cdot d\mathbf{l} = 0 \tag{2-6}$$

The integral from c to d is essentially that given by integrating the electric field between the plates of a capacitor. Then (see Sec. 1-7)

$$\int_c^d \mathbf{e} \cdot d\mathbf{l} = \frac{1}{C} \int i \, dt \tag{2-7}$$

where C is the capacitance of the capacitor. The integral from d to a will be the voltage *rise* of the generator, $-v$; thus

$$\int_d^a \mathbf{e} \cdot d\mathbf{l} = -v \tag{2-8}$$

Hence, substituting in Eq. (2-1), we obtain

$$-v + iR + \frac{1}{C} \int i \, dt = -\frac{d\phi}{dt} \tag{2-9}$$

where ϕ is the flux linked by the dashed path of Fig. 2-2. The flux is proportional to the current, so we can substitute Eq. (1-92) into this expression. This yields

$$-v + iR + \frac{1}{C} \int i \, dt + L \frac{di}{dt} = 0 \tag{2-10}$$

The inductance L actually represents the inductance of the entire circuit; that is, flux linkages are set up by the current in all parts of the circuit. In many instances the flux linkages set up by the current in the coil are so much greater than the other flux linkages that we can disregard the others. Of course, the inductance L is not then the inductance of the complete circuit, but only that of the coil. However, if the approximation above is valid, the difference between the two inductances is negligible.

In our discussion of Kirchhoff's voltage law it is convenient to speak of voltage drops. Let us consider Eq. (2-10) in these terms. The first three terms are the voltage drops defined by Eqs. (2-5), (2-7), and (2-8). However, the fourth term comes about from the flux linkages of the complete path and is not a voltage drop across a specific element [note that Eq. (2-6) yields zero]. Hence it is desirable to use a different approach that will produce a voltage drop for the inductance term.

In Fig. 2-2 we replace the path from b to c through the coil by the one labeled path 2. Then, to obtain the contribution of the line integral along path 2, we consider the line integral consisting of path 2 and the original path through the *wire of the coil.* This yields

$$\int_{b}^{c} \mathbf{e} \cdot d\mathbf{l} + \int_{c}^{b} \mathbf{e} \cdot d\mathbf{l} = -\frac{d\phi}{dt} \qquad\qquad (2\text{-}11)$$
$$\text{wire} \qquad\quad \text{path 2}$$

The first integral is zero [see Eq. (2-6)], and the second one is just the voltage drop $-v_{bc}$. The flux linked by this path is the same as the flux that links the entire circuit if we assume that only the flux set up by the coil is important and that this flux essentially resides within, or extremely close to, the coil. Thus we can write

$$v_{bc} = L\frac{di}{dt} \qquad\qquad (2\text{-}12)$$

Thus, if the path is chosen properly, we can represent the $L\,di/dt$ term as a voltage drop. That is, we can consider Eq. (2-10) to be the sum of voltage drops when the path from b to c is not taken through the coil, but is taken instead along path 2. In this case we assume that v_{bc} is given by Eq. (2-12) and the coil's magnetic flux does not link the path.

In general, any path from one terminal of the coil to the other (from b to c) which does not link the flux of the coil can be used. For example, visualize the coil and its flux as being enclosed in a box through which the path of integration cannot pass. Thus the dashed path 3 in Fig. 2-2 can also be used. It may seem that if we use path 3 instead of path 2, the flux linkages will be different. However there is no difference if all the magnetic field is within a box enclosing the coil and the path does not cut through the box. The magnetic field vectors will be such that when all are drawn, they will form a closed curve. If they are all enclosed within the box, and the closed path is outside the box, then for any area defined by the path any flux set up by one magnetic field vector will be canceled by the flux set up by another magnetic field vector.

In general, all circuit elements can be considered as being enclosed in boxes, with the path of integration taken around them, as in Fig. 2-3. In practice, this is usually the case since the boxes are often the physical covers of the elements, and we cannot get inside them to make measurements. If all magnetic fields are enclosed within the boxes, then any allowable path of integration (see Fig. 2-3) will *not* link any magnetic flux. Also, the allowed paths

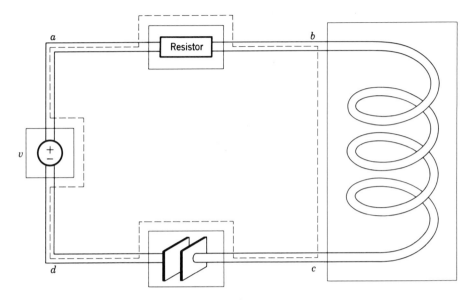

Fig. 2-3   Enclosed circuit elements and a path.

between the terminals of the elements will define the voltage drops across them.   Hence we can state that *the net sum of the voltage drops around any closed loop will be zero.*   Then we have

$$V_{da} + V_{ab} + V_{bc} + V_{cd} = 0 \qquad (2\text{-}13)$$

or

$$-v + iR + L\frac{di}{dt} + \frac{1}{C}\int i\,dt = 0 \qquad (2\text{-}14)$$

We can state this expression in another way: *the voltage drop between any two points is independent of the path by which it is measured.*

We have considered a specific circuit.   However, we can use the same arguments and discussions in obtaining restrictions on the voltage drops in any other circuit.   Thus we can generalize all the preceding discussion to arbitrary network configurations.

In considering mutual inductance we follow the same procedure; that is, the coupled coils and their fields are all assumed to be enclosed in a box through which a path of integration cannot pass.   The voltage drops across the coils then will be those given by Eqs. (1-99) and (1-101).

Many times our assumption that the fields set up by the circuit elements can be enclosed in imaginary boxes is a good approximation.   However, there are times when it is not.   In general, as the frequencies of the circuit generators are increased, the approximation becomes poorer.   If the generators produce voltages of the form (see Sec. 6-1 for a discussion of sinusoidal waveforms)

$$v = V_{\max} \sin 2\pi f t \qquad\qquad (2\text{-}15)$$

then the frequency of this voltage is f. In free space a sinusoidally varying electric field will have a wavelength given by

$$\lambda = \frac{c}{f} \qquad\qquad (2\text{-}16)$$

where c is the velocity of light in free space. $c = 3 \times 10^8$ m/sec. If the circuit dimensions are considerably less than 0.1λ, then the approximations are usually valid. Moreover, no appreciable amount of energy will be radiated from such a small circuit.

When the circuit elements cannot be isolated into single elements, but all exist simultaneously at all points, then the distributed parameters discussed briefly in Sec. 1-14 must be used. We shall discuss distributed elements in much greater detail in Secs. 6-22 to 6-25.

2-2   Kirchhoff's current law

In this section we shall develop a law that relates certain currents in an electric network. This law, in conjunction with Kirchhoff's voltage law, forms the basis of electric circuit analysis. In this development we shall make use of a relation between current density and charge density. Before proceeding further, however, let us discuss the concept of a *charge density*.

Consider a volume such as that shown in Fig. 2-4. Assume that there are charges fixed in space, which are distributed throughout the volume. Now consider the small volume labeled ΔV. If the charge contained within this volume is q_V, then we define the charge density as

$$\rho_V = \lim_{\Delta V \to 0} \frac{q_V}{\Delta V} \qquad \text{coul/m}^3 \qquad\qquad (2\text{-}17)$$

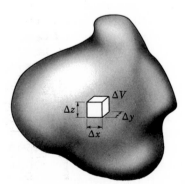

Fig. 2-4   A volume enclosed by an area.

Note that charge density is analogous to mass density. Let us assume that the charge density is known throughout a large volume. If we want to know the charge contained in the entire volume, we can divide it into small volumes $\Delta V = \Delta x\, \Delta y\, \Delta z$. These volumes should be small enough so that the charge density can be considered constant within any one of them. Then the charge in a small volume is

$$q_V = \rho_V\, \Delta x\, \Delta y\, \Delta z \tag{2-18}$$

Note that ρ_V is a function of position. To obtain the charge within the entire volume we add the charges contained in the individual ones,

$$Q \approx \sum_x \sum_y \sum_z \rho_V\, \Delta x\, \Delta y\, \Delta z \tag{2-19}$$

In the limit, as Δx, Δy, and Δz approach zero, this relation becomes exact and can be written as a *volume integral,*

$$Q = \iiint_V \rho_V\, dx\, dy\, dz = \iiint_V \rho_V\, dV \tag{2-20}$$

Note that the integral of Eq. (2-20) is just *defined* as the limit of Eq. (2-19).

Now we can relate the charge density within a closed area (i.e., an area enclosing a volume) to the current through the area. For instance, consider Fig. 2-4. Assume that a current density **J** exists at the surface of the area. Then there is a net current into the volume of

$$i = \oint_a \mathbf{J} \cdot d\mathbf{a} \tag{2-21}$$

If i is not zero, then the charge contained within the volume will change with time (for example, if i is constant at 1 amp, then the charge within the volume will increase at the rate of 1 coul/sec). Thus we can write

$$\iint_a \mathbf{J} \cdot d\mathbf{a} = \frac{d}{dt} \iiint_V \rho_V\, dV \tag{2-22}$$

The last integral represents q, the unbalance of charge carriers contained within the volume. We can write Eq. (2-22) as

$$i = \frac{dq}{dt} \tag{2-23}$$

In other words, *the net current through any closed area is equal to the rate of change of charge within that area.* We shall call this statement the *generalized Kirchhoff's current law.*

In electric circuits it is often found that charge will not accumulate at a point in conductors. This is because the force on the electrons due to such an accumulation causes them to flow almost immediately from the accumulation. In this case q, the unbalance of carriers, will be essentially zero. Thus we can

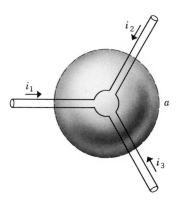

a *Fig. 2-5   The junction of three conductors.*

write Eqs. (2-22) and (2-23) as

$$i = \oint_a \mathbf{J} \cdot d\mathbf{a} = 0 \tag{2-24}$$

or, *the net current through any closed area is equal to zero.*   This is called *Kirchhoff's current law* and is generally used in network analysis.

Let us now determine when the simpler form of Kirchhoff's current law can be used.   We shall use Gauss' law [stated in Eq. (1-55)], which relates the charge enclosed within an area to the electric displacement **d** at the surface of the area.   Substituting Eq. (1-55) into Eq. (2-22), we obtain

$$\oint_a \mathbf{J} \cdot d\mathbf{a} = \frac{d}{dt} \oint_a \mathbf{d} \cdot d\mathbf{a} \tag{2-25}$$

In general, **d** will be such that the order of differentiation and integration can be interchanged, and we can write

$$\oint_a \mathbf{J} \cdot d\mathbf{a} = \oint_a \frac{d\mathbf{d}}{dt} \cdot d\mathbf{a} \tag{2-26}$$

From Eq. (1-54) we see that $\mathbf{d} = \epsilon\mathbf{e}$ where **e** is the electric field intensity.   If **e** and its derivative are negligible on the area, the right-hand side of Eq. (2-26) becomes zero and Eq. (2-25) reduces to Eq. (2-24).   Then the simpler form of Kirchhoff's current law can be applied.   Thus the simple form can be used if the electric field intensity can be neglected on the area in question.

If we assume, as discussed in the last section, that the fields associated with circuit elements are confined in boxes and if we do not let the area of integration pass through them, and if we further assume that the electric field is zero in any connecting wires, then we can always use the simpler form of Kirchhoff's current law.   To illustrate this, consider Fig. 2-5, which shows the junction of several wires.   It is assumed that these are externally connected to circuit elements and/or generators.   Usually, the conductivity of these wires can be considered to be infinite.   Hence the electric fields in them will be zero. Since we have assumed that all the fields are confined within the boxes around the elements, then the electric field will be zero everywhere on the (dashed) area. Thus we can write for Fig. 2-5

$$i = \oint_a \mathbf{J} \cdot d\mathbf{a} = 0 \tag{2-27}$$

The only place where there is charge flowing through the area is in the wires. Hence we have

$$i = i_1 + i_2 + i_3 = 0 \tag{2-28}$$

We can make the area a as small as we desire as long as the junction is completely included. In general this discussion is applicable to any junction of conductors. Hence we can write Kirchhoff's current law in the following form: *the net current into any junction is zero.*

Let us consider the generalized form of Kirchhoff's current law given by Eq. (2-26). The left-hand side of this equation has the dimension of a current, so the right-hand side must also have such a dimension. However, *at the area in question* there is no flow of charge associated with

$$\oint_a \frac{d\mathbf{d}}{dt} \cdot d\mathbf{a}$$

Thus it is not an ordinary current. To indicate this we call

$$\oint_a \frac{d\mathbf{d}}{dt} \cdot d\mathbf{a}$$

the *displacement current*. Then $d\mathbf{d}/dt$ is called the *displacement-current density*.

As an illustration of the use of displacement current, consider the parallel-plate capacitor shown in Fig. 2-6. The closed area in question is the flattened

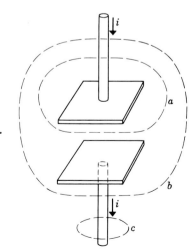

Fig. 2-6　A parallel-plate capacitor.

spherical one designated a, which cuts through the dielectric of the capacitor. Let us now evaluate Eq. (2-26). The only place that **J** is not zero on this area is where it cuts through the wire carrying the current i. Hence

$$i = \oint_a \mathbf{J} \cdot d\mathbf{a} \tag{2-29}$$

We shall assume that the electric field is completely confined to the space between the plates of the capacitor and is given by Eq. (1-58). In this region, then,

$$\mathbf{d} = \frac{q}{A} \, \mathbf{U} \tag{2-30}$$

and is zero elsewhere. In Eq. (2-30) q is the net charge delivered to the upper plate of the capacitor, A is its area, and **U** is a unit vector which points from the positively charged plate to the negative one. Since $\mathbf{d} \neq 0$ only on that portion of area a that lies between the plates, and we have chosen a such that it is parallel to the plates there, the right-hand side of Eq. (2-26), after substitution of Eq. (2-30), yields

$$\oint_a \frac{d\mathbf{d}}{dt} \cdot d\mathbf{a} = \frac{1}{A} \iint_{\substack{\text{area between} \\ \text{plates}}} \frac{dq}{dt} \mathbf{U} \cdot d\mathbf{a} = \frac{dq}{dt} \frac{1}{A} \iint_{\substack{\text{area between} \\ \text{plates}}} \mathbf{U} \cdot d\mathbf{a} \tag{2-31}$$

However, the last integral just yields the area between the plates, since **U** is perpendicular to this area (note that q is not a function of position and can be removed from the integral). Then, substituting Eqs. (2-29) and (2-31) into Eq. (2-26), we obtain

$$i = \frac{dq}{dt} \tag{2-32}$$

which is the fundamental definition of current [see Eq. (1-16)]. Thus the actual current dq/dt into the area is exactly equal to the displacement current dq/dt leaving the area. In each case q is the charge in the upper plate.

If we do not take the area through the dielectric, but use areas such as b or c, then the electric field will be zero on the area, and the displacement current will be zero. This is usually the case when we analyze electric networks, since we do not cut through components. Note that we can state the generalized Kirchhoff's current law as follows: *the net current (including displacement current) into a closed area is zero.* If we apply Kirchhoff's current law to area b, we see that the current into the upper plate of the capacitor is always equal to that leaving the lower plate. Thus, if we do not consider the internal behavior, we see that a capacitor acts as though charge "flows through" it.

The preceding discussion is applicable to conductors, generators, and usual circuit elements, where the charge carriers are free electrons. In general, the free electrons remain as mobile charge carriers.   However, with semiconductors the situation is somewhat different.   Here the free electrons are continuously being generated thermally; that is, there is thermal energy supplied to the valence electrons that are bound to their molecules.   This gives them sufficient energy to escape and become free electrons.   In addition, the free electrons continuously lose energy and become valence electrons.   Thus we can define a *generation rate* g_n for the formation of free electrons and a *recombination rate* r_n for the recapture of the free electrons.   If n represents the density of the free electrons, these rates are given by

$$g_n = \left. \frac{dn}{dt} \right|_{\substack{\text{due to generation} \\ \text{of free electrons}}} \tag{2-33}$$

and

$$r_n = \left. \frac{dn}{dt} \right|_{\substack{\text{due to recombination} \\ \text{of free electrons}}} \tag{2-34}$$

When regeneration and recombination are considered, Eq. (2-22) must be modified as

$$\oint_a \mathbf{J} \cdot d\mathbf{a} + \iiint_V (g_n - r_n) q_e \, dV = \frac{d}{dt} \iiint_V \rho_V \, dV \tag{2-35}$$

where q_e is the charge of an electron $(-1.602 \times 10^{-19} \text{ coul})$.   That is, the net rate of change of charge density within the volume is equal to the current through the area enclosing the volume (first integral on the left) plus the net generation of (positive) charge carriers within the volume.   Note that the generation of a positive-charge carrier is equivalent to the recombination of a free electron.   Note also that ρ_V is negative when there are electrons present.

It may seem that the number of free electrons and holes is equal, but the addition of impurities to the semiconductor will upset this balance and create many times more free electrons than holes, or vice versa (for example, if the impurity atom has one more valence electron than the semiconductor material, then it can become a free electron without causing a hole to be formed).

Actually, Eq. (2-35) does not tell the complete story.   There are two types of charge carriers in semiconductors.   One is the free electron, and the other is called the *hole*.   When a free electron is generated, a vacancy is created in the valence bond between a pair of atoms.   A bound electron from an adjacent atom can move into this vacancy, and in this way, the vacancy can move throughout the entire semiconductor.   This constitutes the *motion of a hole*.   This motion actually consists of the motion of many free electrons, but semiconductor devices can be analyzed by considering the hole as a positive charge of the same magnitude as that of the electron and with a mass approximately equal to that of the electron.

It may seem that the number of free electrons and holes is equal, but the addition of impurities to the semiconductor will upset this balance and create many times more free electrons than holes, or vice versa (for example, if the impurity atom has one more valence electron than the semiconductor material, then it can become a free electron without causing a hole to be formed).

Equation (2-35) can be written only for the free electrons as

$$\oint_a \mathbf{J}_n \cdot d\mathbf{a} + \iiint_v (g_n - r_n)q_e \, dv = \frac{d}{dt} \iiint \rho_n \, dv \tag{2-36}$$

where $\mathbf{J}_n$ is the electron current density and ρ_n is the electron charge density. Another equation is then written for the holes:

$$\oint_a \mathbf{J}_p \cdot d\mathbf{a} + \iiint_v (g_p - r_p)q_p = \frac{d}{dr} \iiint \rho_p \, dv \tag{2-37}$$

where $\mathbf{J}_p$ and ρ_p are the hole current and charge densities and

$$q_p = 1.602 \times 10^{-19} \text{ coul}$$

The subscript n indicates that a quantity refers to free electrons, and the subscript p refers to holes. Equations (2-36) and (2-37) are called the *continuity equations for free electrons and holes in integral form.*

Often in the analysis of electric circuits we represent semiconductor devices by *equivalent circuits* which contain ordinary circuit elements and generators. In this case we analyze a circuit with "ordinary" elements, and Kirchhoff's current law can be applied in its simple form.

An example of the application of Kirchhoff's laws will be given in the next section.

2-3 Branch-current analysis

Let us now apply Kirchhoff's laws to the analysis of electric circuits. The method discussed in this section is somewhat cumbersome in comparison with others that we shall study in Chap. 3, but it is a fundamental procedure, and an understanding of it will aid in the study of other analysis techniques. This method will enable us to determine the current through and the voltage across all the circuit elements of a network when we are given its configuration, the element values, and the voltage-generator values. The unknowns will be the currents in the elements and in the generators and the voltage drops across the elements. For the time being we shall assume that all generators are voltage generators. In the next section we shall consider current generators.

Let us study some elementary circuits and see how Kirchhoff's laws are applied to them. Consider Fig. 2-7. Here we have several branches connected to a common point. A *branch* is a part of a circuit containing just one element or generator. The connection point of the branches is called a *node*. The first step in the analysis procedure is to assign currents to each branch. This is done in Fig. 2-7. Note that these currents are *unknowns;* thus their values are assigned as letters and their direction is assumed. If the chosen

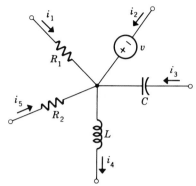

Fig. 2-7 Branches connected at a node. Note that this is just a part of a circuit.

direction is wrong, then the calculated current will be a negative number. To avoid confusion, once a direction is assigned, it should *not* be changed even if a current turns out to be negative. The negative value and the arrow indicate the true direction of the current.

Once the current values have been assigned to all the branches connected to a node, we can apply Kirchhoff's current law at this node. The algebraic sum of all the currents entering a node is zero (the currents drawn entering the node are taken as positive, while those drawn leaving the node are taken as negative). Thus in Fig. 2-7 we have

$$i_1 + i_2 + i_3 - i_4 + i_5 = 0$$

Note that the minus sign is associated with i_4 because it has been chosen as leaving the node.

In a complex electric circuit we can write equations of this type at every node. For instance, consider Fig. 2-8. We write the Kirchhoff's current-law equation for each node in turn:

$$i_1 - i_4 = 0 \tag{2-38a}$$
$$-i_2 - i_3 + i_4 = 0 \tag{2-38b}$$
$$i_2 - i_5 = 0 \tag{2-38c}$$
$$i_5 - i_6 = 0 \tag{2-38d}$$
$$i_6 - i_7 = 0 \tag{2-38e}$$
$$i_3 + i_7 + i_8 = 0 \tag{2-38f}$$
$$-i_1 - i_8 = 0 \tag{2-38g}$$

It may appear that Eqs. (2-38) represent seven equations that can be used in the solution for the unknown currents. Actually, only six of these equations can be used, because only six of them are *linearly independent*. The seventh one can be obtained by appropriate combinations of the other six, so it provides no new information. For instance, Eq. (2-38*f*) can be obtained by taking the

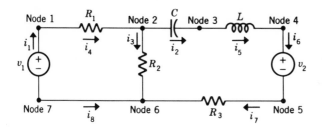

Node 1 R_1 Node 2 C Node 3 L Node 4

i_1 i_4 i_3 i_2 i_5 i_6

v_1 (+−) R_2 v_2 (+−)

Node 7 i_8 Node 6 R_3 i_7 Node 5

Fig. 2-8 Branch currents in a complete network.

negative of the sum of all the other equations. If any one of Eqs. (2-38) is eliminated, the remaining six equations will be linearly independent. *In general, if we have a network containing N nodes, then we can only obtain N − 1 independent Kirchhoff's current-law equations.* These may be written at any N − 1 nodes of the network. An alternative way of stating this is that *if Kirchhoff's current law is satisfied at N − 1 nodes of an N-node network, then it will automatically be satisfied at the Nth node.* Thus an equation written about the Nth node will not supply any new information.

Let us discuss these statements further. Consider the Nth node of the network and draw a volume about it which encloses no other node. If Kirchhoff's current law is not satisfied at the Nth node, then the net current through this volume will not be zero. The current into the remainder of the network [the (N − 1)-node subnetwork outside the volume] will also be the current through the volume and thus will not be zero. Now assume that Kirchhoff's current law is satisfied at N − 2 nodes of the (N − 1)-node subnetwork. It will have to be violated at the (N − 1)st node. The current entering N − 2 nodes equals the current leaving them; thus the net current entering these nodes is zero. However, the net current entering the entire subnetwork is not zero. This can be true only if the net current entering the (N − 1)st node is not zero [if it were zero, then the net current entering the entire (N − 1)-node subnetwork would have to be zero]. In other words, if Kirchhoff's current law is violated at one node of a network, then it must be violated at at least one other node. Thus, if Kirchhoff's current-law equations are written for N − 1 nodes, and the currents into these nodes are required to obey this law, then the currents into the Nth node must automatically satisfy it. Hence, in writing Kirchhoff's current-law equations, in an N-node network we obtain only N − 1 independent equations.

There are some simplifications that we can use in writing these equations. For instance, in Fig. 2-8

$$i_1 = i_4 = -i_8 \tag{2-39a}$$

$$i_2 = i_5 = i_6 = i_7 \tag{2-39b}$$

These can be obtained from Eqs. (2-38*a*) and (2-38*g*) and from Eqs. (2-38*c*), (2-38*d*), and (2-38*e*), respectively. Inspection of Fig. 2-8 shows that Eqs.

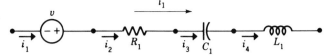

Fig. 2-9   A series connection of branches.

(2-39) are true.   For instance, Eq. (2-39*b*) must be true, since these currents are in branches wherein the "beginning" of one is connected only to the "end" of the other.   If there are *only two branches at any one node*, then the current entering one branch must equal that leaving the preceding one.   This is called a *series connection of branches*.   Another series connection is illustrated in Fig. 2-9.   If we apply Kirchhoff's current law at each node of this figure, we obtain

$$i_1 = i_2 = i_3 = i_4 \tag{2-40}$$

To avoid an unduly large number of unknowns and equations, we can replace these four currents by a single one.   This is done in Fig. 2-9, which also shows a single current i_1.   The number of unknown currents chosen in Fig. 2-8 can be greatly reduced by recognizing the series branches and choosing only one unknown current in each.   Such a simplification is shown in Fig. 2-10.

Remember that if two branches are connected at a node where *there are no other branches*, then the two branches are in series and the currents in them are the same.   In Fig. 2-10 the only nodes that can be used to obtain Kirchhoff's current-law equations are nodes 2 and 6 (the other node equations have been "used" to equate the currents in the series branches).   At nodes 2 and 6 we have

$$i_1 - i_2 - i_3 = 0 \tag{2-41a}$$
$$-i_1 + i_2 + i_3 = 0 \tag{2-41b}$$

These are dependent [Eq. (2-41*b*) is the negative of Eq. (2-41*a*)], so that we have one equation to relate the three unknowns.

In general, Kirchhoff's current law will not provide sufficient information to solve for the unknowns, and we must also use Kirchhoff's voltage law in network analysis.   We shall assume that all the fields are confined within the

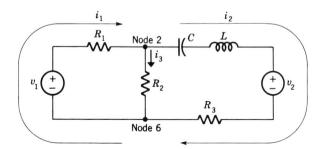

Fig. 2-10   A modification of Fig. 2-9 with the currents in series branches chosen equal.

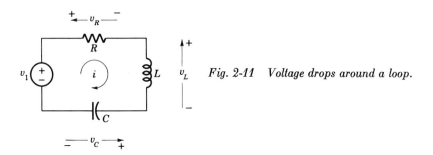

Fig. 2-11   *Voltage drops around a loop.*

cases of the circuit elements, and thus use the form of Kirchhoff's voltage law which states that the sum of the voltage drops around any closed path is equal to zero.

For example, for the very simple circuit of Fig. 2-11, if we write the voltage drops around the loop, we have

$$-v_1 + v_R + v_L + v_C = 0 \qquad\qquad (2\text{-}42)$$

Note that we have arbitrarily assigned letters to the voltages of the circuit elements; these are unknown quantities. The polarity of the voltage is also assigned. It may appear that Kirchhoff's voltage law does not supply any additional information about the unknown currents, but merely adds additional unknown voltages. However, the voltage drop across a circuit element can be related to the current through it even if both are unknown. For instance, for resistors, capacitors, and inductors [see Eqs. (1-26), (1-51), and (1-93)], we have

$$v = Ri \qquad\qquad (2\text{-}43a)$$

$$v = \frac{1}{C} \int i \, dt \qquad\qquad (2\text{-}43b)$$

$$v = L \frac{di}{dt} \qquad\qquad (2\text{-}43c)$$

Let us use these equations to write Eq. (2-42) in terms of the unknown current of Fig. 2-11. Since all the branches are in series, there is then just one unknown current here, which we have labelled i. The assumed voltage drop, polarities, and the assumed direction of current have been chosen compatibly. Note that when the assumed current *enters* a circuit element (not a generator) *that end* of the element is assumed to be at a *positive* voltage with respect to the other end. In general, i and the voltage drop can be negative. This means that the current and voltage (possibly on an instantaneous basis) can have a direction or polarity the opposite of that indicated (for a further discussion of this see Sec. 1-15). Then, substituting Eqs. (2-43) into (2-42),

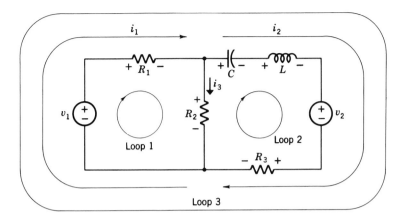

Fig. 2-12 Loops in a network.

we obtain

$$v_1 = Ri + L\frac{di}{dt} + \frac{1}{C}\int i\,dt \tag{2-44}$$

where we have assumed that v_1 is a known quantity. This is an integral-differential equation which can be solved for i.

In this chapter and the next one we shall consider an electric circuit problem to be solved if its integral-differential equations are obtained. In subsequent chapters we shall discuss techniques for actually solving these equations, but for the time being we shall just discuss procedures for obtaining the equations.

Let us now write Kirchhoff's voltage-law equations for the somewhat more complex circuit of Fig. 2-12, which is another version of the circuit of Fig. 2-10. The plus and minus signs across each element indicate the (assumed) polarity produced by the assumed current through the element. Now let us write the sum of the voltage drops around the marked loops 1, 2, and 3. We shall use Eqs. (2-43) to write the voltage drops across the circuit elements. Thus

$$-v_1 + R_1 i_1 + R_2 i_3 = 0 \tag{2-45a}$$

$$-R_2 i_3 + \frac{1}{C}\int i_2\,dt + L\frac{di_2}{dt} + v_2 + R_3 i_2 = 0 \tag{2-45b}$$

$$-v_1 + R_1 i_1 + \frac{1}{C}\int i_2\,dt + L\frac{di_2}{dt} + v_2 + R_3 i_2 = 0 \tag{2-45c}$$

These three equations are not linearly independent. For instance, Eq. (2-45c) can be obtained by adding Eqs. (2-45a) and (2-45b). In general, the determination of the number of Kirchhoff voltage-law equations and the allow-

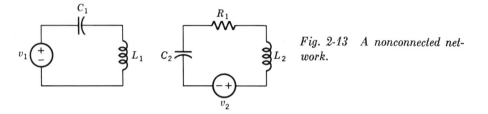

Fig. 2-13   A nonconnected network.

able choice of loops is a complex one. We shall discuss this fully at the beginning of the next chapter. For the time being, let us restrict ourselves to simple networks which meet the following requirements:

1. The networks can be drawn without the wires (or circuit elements) crossing over each other. Such networks are called *planar*, since they can actually be constructed in a single plane.

2. The network consists of only one part; that is, any two nodes on the network can be connected by the branches of the network. For instance, in Fig. 2-8 nodes 1 and 5 are connected by the branches consisting of R_1, R_2, and R_3. Such a network is called *connected*. Figure 2-13 shows a *nonconnected* network.

These concepts will be discussed in greater detail and formalized in Chap. 3.

If conditions 1 and 2 are met, then a simple procedure can be used to choose an appropriate set of loops. The branches of the network enclose subareas. The set of branches that encloses one subarea is considered a valid loop, known as a *windowpane loop* (since the configuration of the branches appears similar to a window). In Fig. 2-12, for instance, loops 1 and 2 are the windowpane loops. These are not the only valid set of loops (in fact, loops 1 and 3 could also have been used); however, this is a simple procedure for choosing loops.

As we shall discuss in the next chapter, it is not always desirable to choose such simple loops. For the time being, however, we can state that if the network has B branches and N nodes, then $B - N + 1$ independent voltage-law equations will exist and can be found by using the windowpane loops. For instance, consider the equivalent Figs. 2-12, 2-10, and 2-8. In Fig. 2-8 there are eight branches and seven nodes; thus there are two independent voltage-law equations. In Fig. 2-10 there are three branches and two nodes; and we again calculate two independent Kirchhoff's voltage-law equations. Since the two networks are the same, we expect the number of independent equations to be the same. This result is also substantiated by Eqs. (2-45).

If we combine Eqs. (2-41*a*), (2-45*a*), and (2-45*b*), we obtain three simultaneous equations with three unknowns (in general, there are B unknown branch currents, and we can write $N - 1$ current-law equations and $B - N + 1$ voltage-law equations). These can be used to solve for the currents in the network:

$$i_1 - i_2 - i_3 = 0 \tag{2-46a}$$

$$-v_1 + R_1 i_1 + R_2 i_3 = 0 \tag{2-46b}$$

$$-R_2 i_3 + \frac{1}{C} \int i_2 \, dt + L \frac{di_2}{dt} + v_2 + R_3 i_2 = 0 \tag{2-46c}$$

If we use the first of these to eliminate i_3 from the remaining ones, we obtain

$$v_1 = (R_1 + R_2)i_1 - R_2 i_2 \tag{2-47a}$$

$$-v_2 = -R_2 i_1 + (R_2 + R_3)i_2 + L \frac{di_2}{dt} + \frac{1}{C} \int i_2 \, dt \tag{2-47b}$$

These equations can then be solved for i_1 and i_2. Equation (2-46a) can be used to obtain i_3, and then Eqs. (2-43) can be used to calculate the voltage drop across each element. We shall defer the actual solution of these equations to subsequent chapters.

The procedure we have discussed is called the *branch-current method* for the solution of an electric circuit. To further clarify it let us discuss an additional example. Consider the network of Fig. 2-14. We have chosen the unknown currents in each branch. In each set of series-connected branches only one current has been chosen. The windowpane loops along which Kirchhoff's voltage law will be considered are marked. Their directions are also shown; these directions are chosen arbitrarily.

Fig. 2-14   A somewhat more complex electric network.

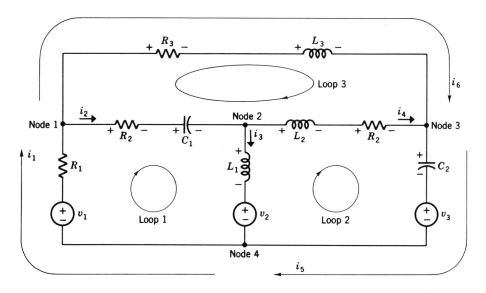

Let us apply Kirchhoff's current law to nodes 1, 2, and 3.   This yields

$$i_1 - i_2 - i_6 = 0 \qquad\qquad\qquad (2\text{-}48a)$$

$$i_2 - i_3 - i_4 = 0 \qquad\qquad\qquad (2\text{-}48b)$$

$$i_4 + i_6 - i_5 = 0 \qquad\qquad\qquad (2\text{-}48c)$$

We now apply Kirchhoff's voltage law to loops 1, 2, and 3.   This yields

$$-v_1 + R_1 i_1 + R_2 i_2 + \frac{1}{C_1} \int i_2\, dt + L_1 \frac{di_3}{dt} + v_2 = 0 \qquad (2\text{-}49a)$$

$$-v_2 - L_1 \frac{di_3}{dt} + L_2 \frac{di_4}{dt} + R_2 i_4 + \frac{1}{C_2} \int i_5\, dt + v_3 = 0 \qquad (2\text{-}49b)$$

$$R_3 i_6 + L_3 \frac{di_6}{dt} - R_2 i_4 - L_2 \frac{di_4}{dt} - \frac{1}{C_1} \int i_2\, dt - R_2 i_2 = 0 \qquad (2\text{-}49c)$$

Note that the generator "polarities" are *given* by the plus and minus signs and do not depend upon the current.   However, the polarities of the voltage drops across the other circuit elements do depend upon the assumed direction of the current.   The positive terminal is the one in which the assumed current enters, as shown in Fig. 2-14.   This is in contrast to the voltage generators, whose polarities and voltages are independent of current (the significance of these polarity markings was discussed in Sec. 1-15).   Equations (2-48) and (2-49) supply six linearly independent equations with six unknowns which can be used to solve for the unknown currents and voltages.

As a final example we shall consider the circuit with mutual inductance shown in Fig. 2-15.   Let us apply Kirchhoff's current law.   The current in all the branches of loop 1 (v, R, L_1, and C_1) must be the same, since they all are

Fig. 2-15   A mutual-inductance-coupled circuit.

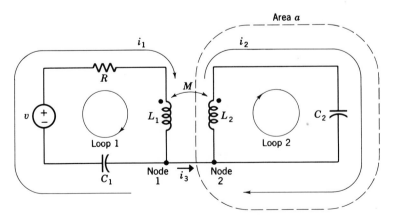

in series. From an examination of node 1 it is *not* obvious that this is true. However, the current in C_1 must equal that in v, which must equal that in R, which, finally, must equal that in L_1. Thus at node 1 we have

$$i_1 - i_1 - i_3 = 0 \qquad\qquad (2\text{-}50)$$

This yields

$$i_3 = 0 \qquad\qquad (2\text{-}51)$$

This could have been deduced from Kirchhoff's current law as stated following Eq. (2-24), that is, that the net current through any closed area is equal to zero. Consider area a. The net current through it is i_3. Thus Eq. (2-51) is verified. There are then two unknown currents, and we can write two Kirchhoff's voltage-law equations:

$$-v + Ri_1 + L_1\frac{di_1}{dt} + \frac{1}{C_1}\int i_1\,dt - M\frac{di_2}{dt} = 0 \qquad\qquad (2\text{-}52a)$$

$$-M\frac{di_1}{dt} + L_2\frac{di_2}{dt} + \frac{1}{C_2}\int i_2\,dt = 0 \qquad\qquad (2\text{-}52b)$$

The voltage drops due to mutual inductance are given by Eqs. (1-99) and (1-101). Note that i_2 induces a voltage in coil 1 and that i_1 induces a voltage in coil 2.

To review, according to the dot convention, when an assumed current enters a dotted terminal on one coil, then on the other coil the dotted terminal is assumed positive with respect to the nondotted one (positive polarity is taken in the sense of the conventions of Sec. 1-15). If a current leaves a dotted terminal, the converse is true.

Equations (2-52) can now be solved for the unknown currents and voltages.

The procedure we have discussed in this section is a general one. In the next chapter we shall discuss procedures that are far more convenient to use.

2-4 Simple equivalent circuits

Analysis of an electric circuit is often simplified if we can replace one element or group of elements by some other element or group of elements. This must be done without changing any of the currents or voltage drops in the *remainder* of the circuit. Let us see how this substitution can be accomplished. The effect of an element on the circuit is represented by the relation between its terminal current and terminal voltage. For instance, in Fig. 2-14, if we were to replace C_1 by a different circuit element whose terminal voltage was related to the current through it by

$$v = \frac{1}{C_1}\int i\,dt \qquad\qquad (2\text{-}53)$$

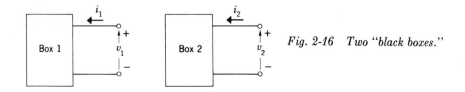

Fig. 2-16   Two "black boxes."

then the circuit equations would be exactly the same as Eqs. (2-48) and (2-49), and all the currents and voltages in the circuit would be unchanged. Such a new element is then said to be *equivalent* to the original one. Alternatively, the new element and the old elements are said to be *equivalent circuits*.

Let us illustrate this in another way. Suppose we have two circuit elements, such as those in Fig. 2-16, which are encased so that we cannot see them. We often state that such elements are enclosed in *black boxes*. In general, we can express the voltage across any such elements as functions of the current entering them

$$v_1 = f_1(i,t) \tag{2-54a}$$

$$v_2 = f_2(i,t) \tag{2-54b}$$

where the term t indicates that the circuits may be time-varying. Note also that the functions need not be linear. If

$$f_1(i,t) = f_2(i,t) \tag{2-55}$$

then the two black boxes will be equivalent, since their terminal voltage-current relations are the same under any external electric measurement that we make. For example, if one of these boxes is an element in an electric network, then the branch-current-analysis relations will be unchanged if we switch boxes. One fact should be emphasized: the two boxes are identical *as far as external measurements are concerned, but their internal behavior may be very different*. We shall subsequently see examples that will clarify this point.

Let us consider the circuit of Fig. 2-17, which consists of a voltage generator $v(t)$ in series with a resistor R. The (t) is included to emphasize that $v(t)$ is a function of time. This circuit has voltage-current characteristics which often approximate those of actual voltage generators. It consists of an ideal generator (whose voltage is independent of its current) in series with a resistance. The voltage $v_1(t)$ is the terminal voltage of the circuit, and $i_1(t)$ is its terminal

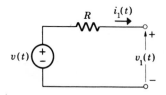

Fig. 2-17   A voltage generator whose characteristics approximate an actual one.

current [if $i_1(t) \neq 0$, it is assumed that this network is connected to another circuit]. If we apply Kirchhoff's voltage law to the loop, we obtain

$$v_1(t) = v(t) - Ri_1(t) \qquad (2\text{-}56)$$

Thus we see that the terminal voltage of this generator falls off as the current through it is increased. This is in contrast to the ideal voltage generator $v(t)$, whose voltage is independent of the current through it.

Now let us consider the practical current generator shown in Fig. 2-18 and obtain the relation between its terminal voltage and terminal current. Applying Kirchhoff's current law to node 1, we obtain

$$i(t) - i_1(t) - i_2(t) = 0 \qquad (2\text{-}57)$$

The voltage across R is $v_1(t)$. Hence

$$i_2(t) = \frac{v_1(t)}{R} \qquad (2\text{-}58)$$

Substituting in Eq. (2-57) and manipulating, we obtain

$$i_1(t) = i(t) - \frac{v_1(t)}{R} \qquad (2\text{-}59)$$

and we see that the terminal current of the practical generator is a function of the output voltage. If R approaches an open circuit (infinite resistance), then $i_1(t) = i(t)$, and the generator becomes an ideal current generator, that is, one whose terminal current is independent of its terminal voltage. Manipulating Eq. (2-59), we obtain

$$v_1(t) = Ri(t) - Ri_1(t) \qquad (2\text{-}60)$$

Compare this with Eq. (2-56), which relates the terminal voltage and current of the voltage generator of Fig. 2-17. If the ideal current generator and ideal voltage generators of Figs. 2-17 and 2-18, respectively, are related by

$$i(t) = \frac{v(t)}{R} \qquad (2\text{-}61)$$

then Eqs. (2-60) and (2-58) will be identical. In this event the relation between the terminal voltage and current for Figs. 2-17 and 2-18 will be the same, and these two networks will be equivalent circuits. That is, if the circuit of Figs.

Fig. 2-18   A current generator whose characteristics approximate an actual one.

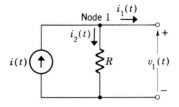

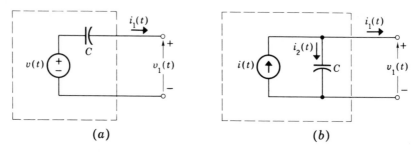

Fig. 2-19   (*a*) *A voltage generator with a series capacitor;* (*b*) *a current generator with a shunt capacitor.*

2-17 and 2-18 are enclosed in black boxes, if the resistors are equal, and if Eq. (2-61) is satisfied, then there is no external electrical measurement that can be made to tell these two circuits apart.   Note that the internal conditions, however, are *not* equivalent.   For instance, consider Figs. 2-17 and 2-18, where $i_1(t) = 0$.   No power will be dissipated in the resistor of Fig. 2-17, while i^2R will be dissipated in that of Fig. 2-18.

In the last section we discussed an analysis procedure which did not take current generators into consideration.   In analyzing a network that contains a current generator shunted by a resistance, we can replace the current generator by a voltage generator in series with a resistance and then proceed as before. Suppose that as part of the analysis we want to know the current through R of Fig. 2-18.   If we replace Fig. 2-18 by Fig. 2-17, then the current through R of Fig. 2-17 is *not* the same as the current through R of Fig. 2-18 (remember that these circuits are equivalent only for *external* conditions).   However, $v_1(t)$ and $i_1(t)$ will be the same for either network.   Thus, if Fig. 2-17 was used in the calculations and we want to find $i_2(t)$ of Fig. 2-18, we determine $v_1(t)$ from Fig. 2-17, substitute it in Fig. 2-18 [or Eq. (2-58)], and then calculate i_2; that is, *once the terminal conditions are obtained,* they can be used to solve for *conditions in the original network.*

The element associated with the current and/or voltage generator need not be a resistance.   For instance, in Fig. 2-19 the element is a capacitor. Applying Kirchhoff's voltage law to Fig. 2-19*a*, we obtain

$$v_1(t) = v(t) - \frac{1}{C} \int i(t) \, dt \tag{2-62}$$

Similarly, applying Kirchhoff's current law to Fig. 2-19*b*, we have

$$i_1(t) = i(t) - i_2(t) = i(t) - C \frac{dv_1(t)}{dt} \tag{2-63}$$

Integration of both sides of Eq. (2-63) yields

$$v_1(t) = \frac{1}{C}\int i(t)\,dt - \frac{1}{C}\int i_1(t)\,dt \tag{2-64}$$

Comparison shows that Eqs. (2-63) and (2-64) are identical if

$$v(t) = \frac{1}{C}\int i(t)\,dt \tag{2-65}$$

Thus Figs. 2-19a and b will be equivalent if the two capacitors are equal and Eq. (2-65) is satisfied. For instance, if

$$v(t) = V_{max}\sin \omega t$$

then

$$i(t) = -\frac{V_{max}}{\omega C}\cos \omega t$$

We can obtain a similar equivalence if an inductance is associated with the generator. Such circuits are shown in Fig. 2-20. Analyzing these, we obtain for Fig. 2-20a

$$v_1(t) = v(t) - L\frac{di_1(t)}{dt} \tag{2-66}$$

and for Fig. 2-20b

$$v_1(t) = L\frac{di(t)}{dt} - L\frac{di_1(t)}{dt} \tag{2-67}$$

Thus Figs. 2-20a and 2-20b will be equivalent if the inductors are equal and

$$v(t) = L\frac{di(t)}{dt} \tag{2-68}$$

If a current generator is shunted by a single element, it can be made equivalent to a voltage generator in series with that element, and vice versa.

Fig. 2-20 (a) A voltage generator with a series inductor; (b) a current generator with a shunt inductor.

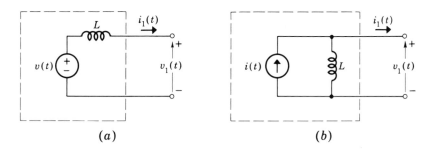

                            (a)   *(b)*

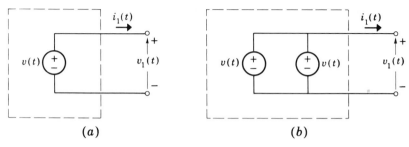

Fig. 2-21   (a) A voltage generator; (b) a circuit equivalent to (a).

Suppose that now more than one element is associated with the generator. Before we consider this, let us derive a simple equivalent circuit that will aid us. Consider Fig. 2-21.   In either of these diagrams we have

$$v_1(t) = v(t) \tag{2-69}$$

independent of $i_1(t)$.   The current $i_1(t)$ will depend only upon the voltage $v(t)$ and the external circuit.   If either of the black boxes of Fig. 2-21 is connected into a circuit, then the branch-current equations will be the same.   Thus the circuits are equivalent.   Therefore we can connect one (or more) voltage generators in parallel with a voltage generator without disturbing the remainder of the circuit, as long as all the voltages are equal.

Let us extend this result.   Consider a voltage generator with three elements connected to it (see Fig. 2-22a).   We can replace the single voltage generator by three equal ones whose terminals are connected together as illustrated in Fig. 2-22b.   Now consider the current i_1 in the conductor between points a and b in Fig. 2-22b.   Assume that the conductor between points a and b has a resistance of R_1 ohms.   We write Kirchhoff's voltage law around the loop *abde;* this yields

$$-v(t) + R_1 i_1(t) + v(t) = 0 \tag{2-70}$$

or

$$i_1(t) = 0 \tag{2-71}$$

Equation (2-71) will be true for any nonzero value of R_1 no matter how small it is.   Thus, if we assume that R_1 is arbitrarily small, we still obtain that $i_1(t) = 0$.   *If the current in a circuit element is zero, then that element can be removed without disturbing the remainder of the network.*

Let us discuss this statement.   Kirchhoff's current-law equation for any node of this zero-current branch will be unchanged if this branch is removed, since only a zero will be "subtracted" from one side of the equation.   The (zero) current in the branch will not affect Kirchhoff's current-law equations at other nodes, so all the current-law equations will be unchanged if the branch is removed. The voltage-law equations will also be unchanged if the branch is removed, since there would be no voltage drop across this element (between its nodes) whether the branch is there or not. Since the circuit equations will be unchanged if zero-current branches are removed, the connection between points a and b, and also that between b and c, can be removed from Fig. 2-22b. The circuit of Fig. 2-22c results. These three individual voltage generators can now be converted into current generators by the method previously discussed, as shown in Fig. 2-22d.

Now let us discuss the case where more than one element is associated with a current generator. First we need a very simple equivalence. Consider Figs. 2-23a and b. Each of these circuits actually represents a device that produces a current $i(t)$ in the external circuit, independently of what that circuit is. The terminal voltage will depend just upon the current and the external circuit. Thus for each circuit the terminal voltage $v(t)$ will be the same if the external circuit is the same. Since the terminal currents are also the same, the external conditions of these circuits are equivalent. This discussion could apply to any number of equal current generators in series.

Fig. 2-22 (a) A voltage generator with three elements connected to it; (b) a circuit equivalent to (a) for conditions external to the generator; (c) another equivalent circuit; (d) a circuit with current generators that is equivalent to (a), (b), and (c) for external conditions.

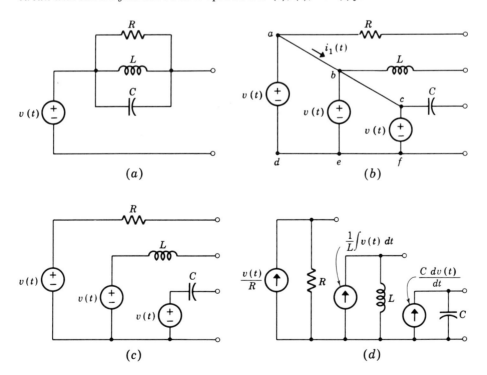

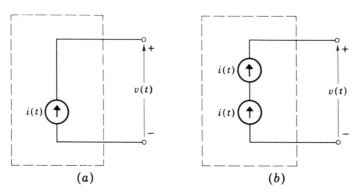

Fig. 2-23   (a) A current generator; (b) a circuit equivalent to (a).

Now look at the circuit of Fig. 2-24a, which consists of current generators connected to a network. If a connection is made from point *a* to any node within the network, as shown in Fig. 2-24b, *none* of the voltages or currents through any of the elements of the network will be changed. This can be seen by writing Kirchhoff's current law about node *a* of Fig. 2-24b which yields

$$i(t) - i(t) - i_1(t) = 0$$

or

$$i_1(t) = 0 \tag{2-72}$$

If the current in a branch is zero, then it can be added to or removed from a network without disturbing conditions within the network [see the discussion following Eq. (2-71)]. Now let us use Figs. 2-23 and 2-24 to replace the current generator of Fig. 2-25a by voltage generators. As a first step we use the equivalent circuit of Fig. 2-23 and replace the current generator by three

Fig. 2-24   (a) A current generator connected to a network; (b) a circuit equivalent to (a).

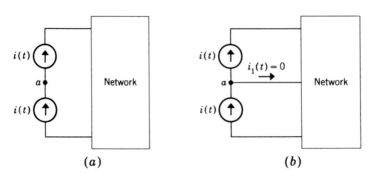

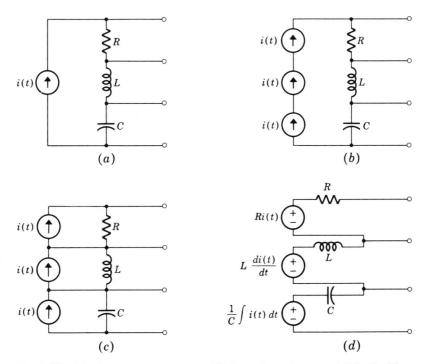

Fig. 2-25   (a) *A current generator with three elements connected to it; (b) a circuit equivalent to (a) for conditions external to the generator; (c) another equivalent circuit; (d) a circuit with voltage generators that is equivalent to (a), (b), and (c) for external conditions.*

equal current generators (see Fig. 2-25*b*) and then use the equivalence of Fig. 2-24 to make the connections of Fig. 2-25*c*. There are now three current generators, each with a single element connected across it. Each of these "generators" can then be converted to a voltage generator; this is shown in Fig. 2-25*d*.

Figures 2-22 and 2-25 show three circuit elements associated with the generators. These procedures can be extended to any number of elements.

We have discussed equivalent circuits for generators. Now let us consider some simpler equivalent circuits that are often quite convenient.

Series connections

When several elements of the same kind are connected as series branches, they can be combined into a single element. As before, this equivalence is valid only for the external circuit. Consider the resistances of Fig. 2-26*a*, which are connected in series (note that no other connections can be made at nodes 1

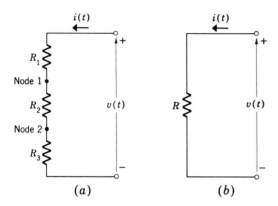

Fig. 2-26 (a) A series connection of resistances; (b) a single resistance that is equivalent to (a) if $R = R_1 + R_2 + R_3$.

and 2).   The current through each resistance is $i(t)$.   Thus, writing Kirchhoff's voltage law, we obtain the terminal voltage-current relations for this combination of resistances,

$$v(t) = R_1 i(t) + R_2 i(t) + R_3 i(t) = (R_1 + R_2 + R_3)i(t) \qquad (2\text{-}73)$$

In Fig. 2-26b the terminal voltage-current relations are

$$v(t) = Ri(t) \qquad (2\text{-}74)$$

If we set

$$R = R_1 + R_2 + R_3 \qquad (2\text{-}75)$$

then Eqs. (2-73) and (2-74) will be the same.   Thus Figs. 2-26a and 2-26b will have the same terminal voltage-current relations and will be equivalent.   In general, *the resistance equivalent to a series connection of resistances will be equal to the sum of the individual resistances.*

Now consider the series connection of inductances shown in Fig. 2-27.

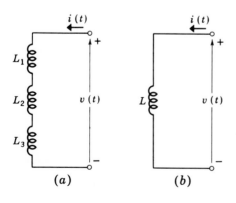

Fig. 2-27 (a) A series connection of inductances; (b) a single inductance that is equivalent to (a) if $L = L_1 + L_2 + L_3$.

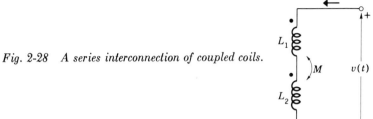

Fig. 2-28   *A series interconnection of coupled coils.*

Writing Kirchhoff's voltage law for each of these circuits in turn, we obtain

$$v(t) = L_1 \frac{di(t)}{dt} + L_2 \frac{di(t)}{dt} + L_3 \frac{di(t)}{dt} = (L_1 + L_2 + L_3) \frac{di(t)}{dt} \qquad (2\text{-}76a)$$

$$v(t) = L \frac{di(t)}{dt} \qquad (2\text{-}76b)$$

Then Figs. 2-27a and b will be equivalent if

$$L = L_1 + L_2 + L_3 \qquad (2\text{-}77)$$

In general, *the inductance equivalent to a series connection of inductances is equal to the sum of the inductances.*

As a further example, consider the series connection of two inductances shown in Fig. 2-28. These are also coupled by mutual inductance. Both these coupled coils contain the same current. From Eqs. (1-99) and (1-101) we have

$$v(t) = L_1 \frac{di(t)}{dt} + M \frac{di(t)}{dt} + M \frac{di(t)}{dt} + L_2 \frac{di(t)}{dt} = (L_1 + L_2 + 2M) \frac{di(t)}{dt}$$
$$(2\text{-}78)$$

Comparison of this with Eq. (2-76b) for Fig. 2-27b gives us the equivalent inductor

$$L = L_1 + L_2 + 2M \qquad (2\text{-}79)$$

If the winding of one of the inductances is reversed (the position of one of the dots will be changed), M is replaced by $-M$ in Eq. (2-79). However, the equivalent inductance cannot be negative, so we shall always have $L_1 + L_2 \geq 2M$ [see Eq. (1-136)].

Now consider the series interconnection of capacitors shown in Fig. 2-29a. Kirchhoff's voltage-law equations for Figs. 2-29a and b give us

$$v(t) = \left(\frac{1}{C_1} + \frac{1}{C_2} + \frac{1}{C_3} \right) \int i(t)\, dt \qquad (2\text{-}80)$$

$$v(t) = \frac{1}{C} \int i(t)\, dt \qquad (2\text{-}81)$$

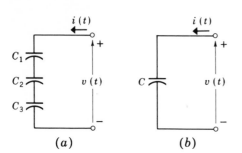

Fig. 2-29 (a) A series interconnection of capacitors; (b) a single capacitance that is equivalent to (a) if $1/C = 1/C_1 + 1/C_2 + 1/C_3$.

Thus Figs. 2-29a and b will be equivalent as far as external conditions are concerned if

$$\frac{1}{C} = \frac{1}{C_1} + \frac{1}{C_2} + \frac{1}{C_3} \tag{2-82}$$

In general, *the capacitance equivalent to a series interconnection of capacitors will be equal to the reciprocal of the sum of the reciprocals of the individual capacitances.*

It is often convenient to use reciprocal capacitance or elastance here [see Eq. (1-50)]. Substituting in Eq. (2-82), we obtain

$$D = D_1 + D_2 + D_3 \tag{2-83}$$

In general, *the elastance equivalent to a series interconnection of capacitors will be equal to the sum of the individual elastances.*

Parallel interconnections

Two (or more) branches connected to the same pair of nodes are said to be in *parallel.* For instance, in Fig. 2-30a three resistances are connected in parallel. Let us obtain the single resistance which is equivalent to Fig. 2-30a. Such an equivalence is shown in Fig. 2-30b. If we apply Kirchhoff's current law to

Fig. 2-30 (a) A parallel interconnection of resistors; (b) a resistance that is equivalent to (a) if $1/R = 1/R_1 + 1/R_2 + 1/R_3$.

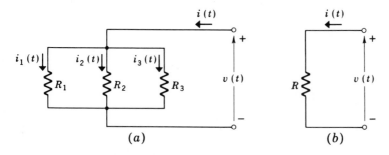

node 1 of Fig. 2-30a, we have

$$i(t) = i_1(t) + i_2(t) + i_3(t)$$

The voltage across each resistance is $v(t)$. Thus

$$i(t) = \left(\frac{1}{R_1} + \frac{1}{R_2} + \frac{1}{R_3}\right) v(t) \tag{2-84}$$

The voltage-current relation for Fig. 2-30b is

$$i(t) = \frac{1}{R} v(t) \tag{2-85}$$

Thus the two circuits are equivalent if

$$\frac{1}{R} = \frac{1}{R_1} + \frac{1}{R_2} + \frac{1}{R_3} \tag{2-86}$$

In general, *if several resistances are connected in parallel, they are equivalent to a single resistance which is the reciprocal of the sum of the reciprocals of the individual resistances.*

When resistors are connected in parallel, it is often convenient to use conductance [see Eq. (1-29)]. If we substitute, Eq. (2-86) becomes

$$G = G_1 + G_2 + G_3 \tag{2-87}$$

Thus to obtain the equivalent conductance, we need only take the sum of the individual conductances.

Now consider Figs. 2-31a and b. These will be equivalent if

$$\frac{1}{L} = \frac{1}{L_1} + \frac{1}{L_2} + \frac{1}{L_3} \tag{2-88}$$

The details of this development are similar to the preceeding ones and are left to the reader.

It is often convenient to use reciprocal inductance [see Eq. (1-95)] when

Fig. 2-31   *(a) A parallel interconnection of inductors; (b) an inductance that is equivalent to (a) if $1/L = 1/L_1 + 1/L_2 + 1/L_3$.*

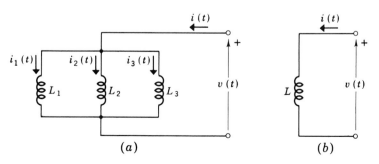

(a)   (b)

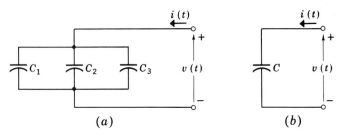

*Fig. 2-32   (a) A parallel interconnection of capacitors; (b) a
capacitance that is equivalent to (a) if $C = C_1 + C_2 + C_3$.*

inductors are paralleled.   In this case

$$\Gamma = \Gamma_1 + \Gamma_2 + \Gamma_3 \tag{2-89}$$

In general, *if several inductors are connected in parallel, they are equivalent to a
single inductor whose inductance is equal to the reciprocal of the sum of the reciprocals
of the inductances of the individual ones.*

Proceeding in a similar manner, we see that the parallel connection of
capacitors of Fig. 2-32a is equivalent to Fig. 2-32b if

$$C = C_1 + C_2 + C_3 \tag{2-90}$$

In general, *if several capacitances are connected in parallel, they are equivalent to a
single one which is equal to the sum of the individual capacitances.*

2-5   Dependent generators

So far we have discussed ideal voltage and current generators whose voltages
or currents were specified functions of time.   For instance, the voltage generator
v_1 [or, equivalently, $v_1(t)$] of Fig. 2-14 produces the voltage $v_1(t)$ independently
of any external conditions; that is, the time function $v_1(t)$ is specified independently of the network to which the generator is connected.   Similarly, the
current generator $i(t)$ of Fig. 2-18 produces a specified current $i(t)$ independently
of the external conditions.   These generators are called *independent generators,*
since their currents or voltages are independent of the network to which they
are connected.

In analyzing circuits which contain transistors or other electronic devices
we often replace such devices by circuits that contain voltage generators whose
voltages are independent of the current through them but *are* functions of a
voltage or a current at some other part of the network.   Similarly, we often
use a current generator whose current is independent of the voltage across it

but is a function of the current or voltage at some part of the network.   Such generators are called *dependent generators* or *controlled sources.*

    Examples of dependent generators are shown in Fig. 2-33.   The first of these is called a *transfer-voltage-controlled source* or *voltage-controlled voltage source*, since its voltage is a function of another voltage, $v_1(t)$, at some point in the network.   That is, the voltage generator $\mu v_1(t)$ is connected to two nodes of a network.   Nodes a and b are two other nodes of the network, and $v_1(t)$ is proportional to the voltage drop between these (other) nodes.   The second dependent generator is called a *current-controlled voltage source* or *transresistance-controlled source*, since its voltage is proportional to a current in some branch of the network.   The constant of proportionality has the dimensions of a resistance (this gives rise to the term *transresistance*, a combination of "transfer" and "resistance").   The last two generators of Fig. 2-33 are current generators.   The first of these is called a *current-controlled current source* or *transfer-current-controlled source*, since its current is proportional to a current in a branch of the network.   The last dependent generator is called a *voltage-controlled current source* or *transconductance-controlled source*, since the generator current is proportional to a voltage between two nodes of the network.   The

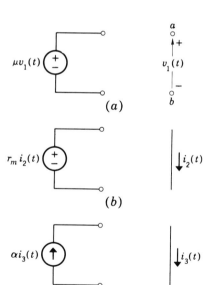

Fig. 2-33   Controlled sources: (a) transfer voltage; (b) transresistance; (c) transfer current; (d) transconductance.

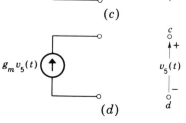

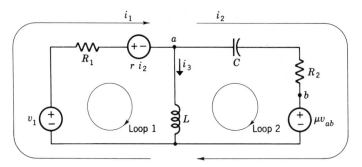

Fig. 2-34   A circuit that contains two dependent generators.

constant of proportionality has the dimensions of a conductance. We have assumed that the dependent generator is controlled from a "remote" part of the network, but this need not be the case. The controlling part of the network can be adjacent to the generator (for example, the current of a trans-conductance-controlled source may be a function of the voltage across its terminals).

To illustrate the analysis of networks containing controlled sources we shall use Fig. 2-34. This circuit contains two dependent voltage generators and one independent voltage generator. The voltage produced by the dependent generators depends only upon the specified values (ri_2 and μv_{ab}), and not upon *any other* circuit conditions. The Kirchhoff's current-law equation about node a is

$$i_1 - i_2 - i_3 = 0 \tag{2-91}$$

Kirchhoff's voltage-law equations around loops 1 and 2 are

$$-v_1 + R_1 i_1 + ri_2 + L \frac{di_3}{dt} = 0 \tag{2-92a}$$

$$-L \frac{di_3}{dt} + \frac{1}{C} \int i_2 \, dt + R_2 i_2 + \mu v_{ab} = 0 \tag{2-92b}$$

Note that the voltage drops for the dependent generators are written just as though they were independent generators; their given voltages (ri_2 and μv_{ab}) are written just as though they were completely independent of the circuit conditions. However, they are unknown quantities.

The dependent generators are expressed as functions either of the network currents or of the voltages. In the branch-current method the currents are the unknowns. Thus, if the dependent generator is a transresistance-controlled source, it will be a function of an existing unknown current and will not add an additional unknown to the simultaneous equations. However, the transfer-voltage-ratio-controlled source does introduce another unknown (v_{ab}), so another equation is required. We must express v_{ab} in terms of known quantities and/or the unknown currents. This can be done by summing the voltage drops between nodes a and b,

$$v_{ab} = \frac{1}{C} \int i_2\, dt + R_2 i_2 \tag{2-93}$$

Then Eqs. (2-91) to (2-93) can be used to solve for the unknown currents of the network.

In the foregoing analysis we considered dependent voltage generators. If dependent current generators had been given, we could have replaced them by equivalent voltage generators (and vice versa) and followed the procedures of Sec. 2-4. In subsequent chapters we shall consider dependent generators in greater detail.

2-6   Some general comments

In this chapter we have presented some fundamental laws for analyzing electric networks. Many of the networks used in the examples are better suited for explaining the subject than they are as actual engineering circuits. However, the laws they illustrate form the basis of the analysis and design of practical networks. Television, radio, and control systems for satellites are all analyzed by procedures based on Kirchhoff's laws. Circuits can also be set up to help the human body when some of its functions are impaired. For instance, many lives have been prolonged by an electric *pacemaker* implanted in the body to send electric impulses to the heart when parts of the nervous system do not function properly.

In succeeding chapters we shall examine further fundamental procedures for analyzing electric systems. Often the reader will not have sufficient information to permit a thorough discussion of practical circuits, but it should be remembered that all the procedures discussed are applied to the analysis and design of these circuits. The modern computer has removed much of the tedium of network analysis, but it has not replaced the need for a thorough understanding of analysis procedures—an understanding that is necessary if the computer is to be made to function properly.

BIBLIOGRAPHY

Balabanian, N.: "Fundamentals of Circuit Theory," chaps. 1 and 2, Allyn and Bacon, Inc., Boston, 1961.

Brenner, E., and M. Javid: "Analysis of Electric Circuits," chaps. 5 and 6, McGraw-Hill Book Company, New York, 1959.

Clement, P. R., and W. C. Johnson: "Electrical Engineering Science," chap. 4, McGraw-Hill Book Company, New York, 1960.

Friedland, B., O. Wing, and R. Ash: "Principals of Linear Networks," chaps. 1 and 4, McGraw-Hill Book Company, New York, 1961.

Close, C. M.: "The Analysis of Linear Circuits," chap. 1, Harcourt, Brace & World, Inc., New York, 1966.

Manning, L. A.: "Electrical Circuits," chap. 2, McGraw-Hill Book Company, New York, 1966.

Pearson, S. I., and G. J. Maler: "Introductory Circuit Analysis," chap. 2, John Wiley & Sons, Inc., New York, 1965.

Van Valkenburg, M. E.: "Networks Analysis," 2d ed., chaps. 2 and 3, Prentice-Hall, Inc., Englewood Cliffs, N.J., 1964.

PROBLEMS

2-1. The flux linking the path shown in Fig. 2-1 is $\phi = \phi_{max} \sin \omega t$ webers. Compute $V_{ab} + V_{bc} + V_{cd} + V_{da}$.

2-2. Repeat Prob. 2-1, but now assume that $\phi = 0$.

2-3. Discuss why the circuit of Fig. 2-3, and most electric circuits, can be analyzed with the form of Kirchhoff's voltage law that states that the sum of the voltage drops around any closed loop is equal to zero.

2-4. Discuss the reason that any electric circuit consisting of a closed loop (such as Fig. 2-3) will always exhibit some inductance. Indicate when this inductance can be ignored.

2-5. A sphere of radius 1 cm has 1 coul of charge uniformly distributed through it. What is the charge density within the sphere?

2-6. A sphere of radius 2 cm has a density within it of $\rho_V = 1,000$ coul/m^3 for points between $r = 0$ and $r = 1$ cm and $\rho_V = 5,000$ coul/m^3 elsewhere. Compute the total charge contained within the sphere.

2-7. In Fig. 2-5 the area a is a sphere of radius 1 cm. The electric field intensity at the surface of the sphere has a magnitude of e volts/m and is everywhere perpendicular to the surface of the sphere (pointing out). The sphere is in vacuum. The current density in each of the wires in 100,000 amp/m^2, and each wire is a right circular cylinder with a radius of 1 mm. Compute the total current due to charge flow into area a.

2-8. If the generalized Kirchhoff's current law is not to be violated in Prob. 2-7, then what must be the value of e?

2-9. In most electric circuit problems what would be the value of e (see Prob. 2-7), and what relation would exist between i_1, i_2, and i_3 in Fig. 2-5? Are the conditions in Prob. 2-7 typical?

2-10. Discuss why most electric circuits can be analyzed with the form of Kirchhoff's current law that states that the net current into any closed area is equal to zero.

2-11. Write Kirchhoff's current-law equations for every node except one for the network of Fig. 2-35.

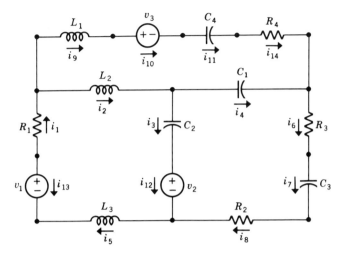

Fig. 2-35

2-12. Repeat Prob. 2-11, but now choose only one unknown current for each set of branches in series.

2-13. Write a set of simultaneous equations that can be used to solve for the currents in all the elements of Fig. 2-36. Define only one unknown current in each set of series branches.

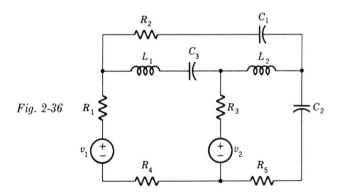

Fig. 2-36

2-14. If we want to know only the current in R_3 in Fig. 2-36, we would have to solve the same set of simultaneous equations as in Prob. 2-13. Explain why.

2-15. Repeat Prob. 2-13 for the network of Fig. 2-37.

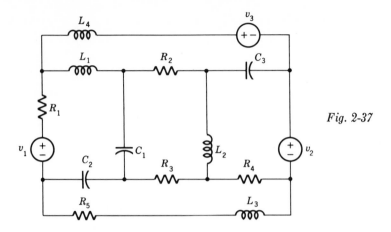

Fig. 2-37

2-16. Obtain a voltage-generator circuit that is equivalent (as far as external conditions are concerned) to the current-generator circuit of Fig. 2-38.

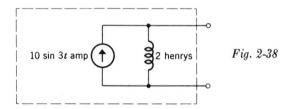

Fig. 2-38

2-17. The voltage- and current-generator circuits of Prob. 2-16 are *not* equivalent *internally*. Explain why.

2-18. Repeat Prob. 2-16 for the circuit of Fig. 2-39.

Fig. 2-39

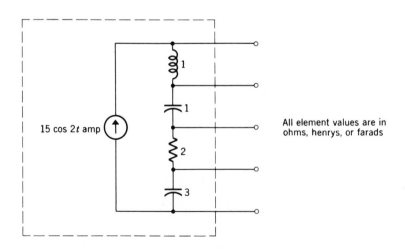

All element values are in ohms, henrys, or farads

2-19. Obtain a current-generator circuit that is equivalent (as far as external conditions are concerned) to the voltage-generator circuit of Fig. 2-40.

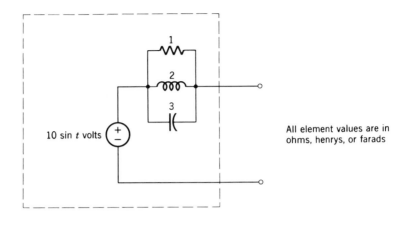

Fig. 2-40

2-20. Repeat Prob. 2-19 for the circuit of Fig. 2-41.

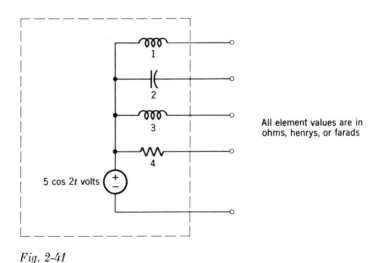

Fig. 2-41

2-21. Perform a branch-current analysis to solve for the current in resistor R_1 of the circuit of Fig. 2-42. "Replace" the current generator by a voltage generator. Choose only one unknown current in each series branch.

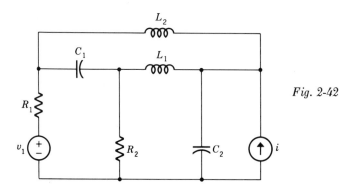

Fig. 2-42

2-22. Repeat Prob. 2-21 for the circuit of Fig. 2-43.

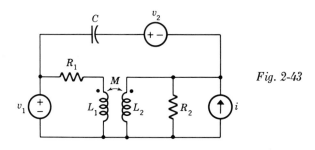

Fig. 2-43

2-23. Obtain a single resistance that is equivalent to the circuit of Fig. 2-44.

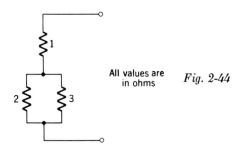

All values are in ohms   *Fig. 2-44*

2-24. Obtain a single capacitance that is equivalent to the circuit of Fig. 2-45.

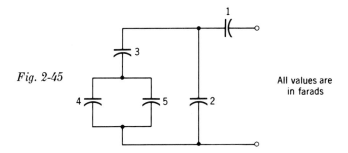

Fig. 2-45

All values are
in farads

2-25. Obtain a single inductance that is equivalent to the circuit of Fig. 2-46. What are the largest and smallest values that this inductance can have? Express these in terms of L_1, L_2, L_3, and L_4.

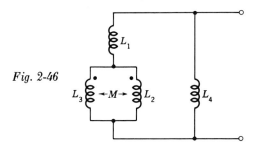

Fig. 2-46

2-26. Obtain a circuit consisting of a single resistance, inductance, and capacitance in series that is equivalent to Fig. 2-47.

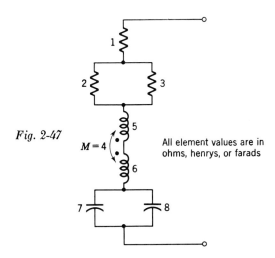

Fig. 2-47

$M = 4$

All element values are in
ohms, henrys, or farads

2-27. Obtain a set of simultaneous equations that can be used to solve for the current in L_2 of Fig. 2-48.

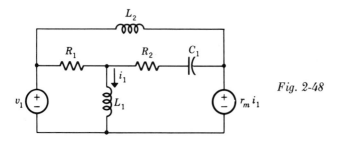

Fig. 2-48

2-28. Repeat Prob. 2-27 for the circuit of Fig. 2-49.

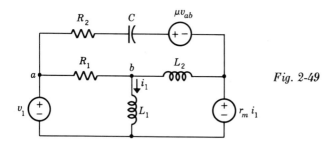

Fig. 2-49

2-29. Repeat Prob. 2-27 for the circuit of Fig. 2-50, but convert the current generator to a voltage generator.

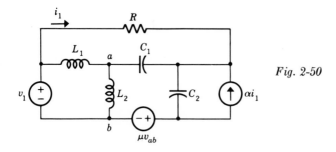

Fig. 2-50

2-30. Repeat Prob. 2-27 for the circuit of Fig. 2-51.

Fig. 2-51

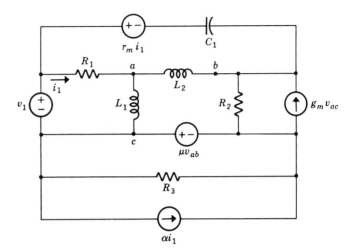

Basic Network Topology and Mesh, Nodal, and Cut-set Analysis

3

In this chapter we shall formalize some of the concepts of electric circuit analysis presented in Chap. 2 so that we may develop further methods of network analysis that will be much less tedious to apply than the branch-current method. In fact, the methods we shall develop here are the basic tools of network analysis. We shall begin with a discussion of network topology, which will supply us with a fundamental insight into general network analysis.

3-1　Network topology

For a formal study of network analysis we make use of a concept called *network topology*. We shall study networks as interconnections of branches, initially without considering the elements themselves. This will enable us to identify such things as a valid set of loops in a branch-current analysis, and also to develop less tedious analysis procedures. The connection between network topology and network analysis may not be immediately obvious. However, we shall see eventually how this material applies to network analysis.

Often the tedious details of the analysis are carried out by a computer. In this event it is especially important that the engineer understand the theoretical fundamentals of any analysis procedure if he is to apply it to a new system.

Let us start by considering the topological elements that we shall use. The fundamental element is the *branch*. A branch is just a directed line segment, that is, a line segment to which we have assigned a direction. Branches are usually numbered. A typical branch is shown in Fig. 3-1. The endpoint of a branch is called a *node* (or *vertex*). A branch is said to be *incident* upon its nodes if the nodes are its endpoints. These definitions are compatible with the ones developed in Chap. 2. Note that the branch in Fig. 3-1 does not necessarily represent a zero-resistance conductor, but is a branch of a circuit; it could represent a resistor, an inductor, a capacitor, or a generator. We shall not bother to draw the element at this time, because here we are studying general concepts of circuit configurations.

A collection of branches is called a *network* or *graph*. Branches may be connected to one another only at their nodes. Some typical network configurations are shown in Fig. 3-2. The networks of Figs. 3-2a and b are equivalent; note that some of the branches are of different length or are curved, but otherwise the figures are the same. For instance, Fig. 3-2c is a network that can be topologically described by either Fig. 3-2a or b. Remember that each branch can represent a circuit element.

Another useful concept is that of a *path*. It is defined in the following way. Starting at one node in a network, we move along a branch connected to that node until we reach another node; then we "leave" that node along a *different* branch. If we continue this procedure, traversing as many branches as desired, and do not encounter any node more than once, then the set of

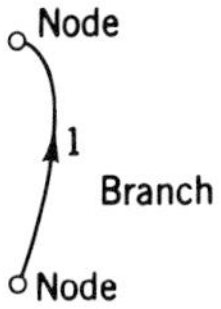

Fig. 3-1　A branch and its nodes.

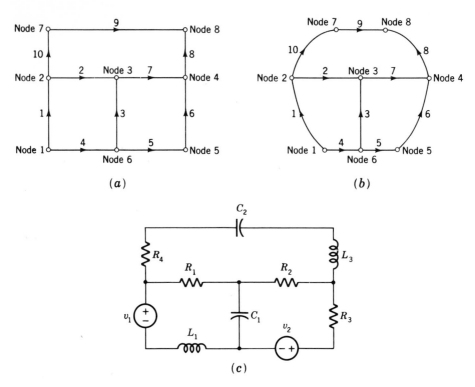

Fig. 3-2   (a) A network; (b) a network that is topologically equivalent to (a); (c) an electric network that can be topologically represented by either (a) or (b).

branches (and nodes) we have traversed constitutes a path.   For instance, in Fig. 3-2, a path would be along branches 10, 9, 8, 7, and 3.   This could be said to be a path from node 2 to node 6.   There are other paths between these nodes, such as branches 2 and 3; or branches 2, 7, 6, and 5; or branches 1 and 4.

If a path exists between every pair of nodes in a network, then the network is said to be *connected*.   For instance, the networks of Fig. 3-2 are connected, since we can find a path that will connect every pair of nodes in the network. Figure 3-3a shows a connected network.   In Fig. 3-3b a *nonconnected* network is illustrated; note that a path cannot be drawn between nodes 1, 2, 3, or 4 and nodes 5, 6, or 7.   The network of Fig. 3-3b can be made a connected one by adding a connecting branch between nodes 4 and 5.   This will not affect any circuit-analysis calculations, since no current can be in that branch.   This can be demonstrated by considering that the set of branches connected to nodes 5, 6, and 7 are enclosed by an area, and then apply Kirchhoff's current law to that area (the net current into any closed area is zero).

We say that the network of Fig. 3-3*b* is in two parts.   In general, if a network is made up of two parts, one branch can be connected from a node of one part to a node of the other part, and no current will be in the branch.   As a result, currents in the rest of the network will not be affected [see the discussion following Eq. (2-71)].   If a network is in three parts, by successive application of this procedure, we can add two branches (which will have no current in them) to form a connected network.   Thus, without disturbing the branch currents, we can "connect" all networks.   For the time being, we shall discuss only connected networks; later we shall generalize these results.

We often speak of a *subnetwork*.   This is just a part of the original network. For instance, in Fig. 3-2 we can say that branches 1, 2, 3, and 7 and their nodes are a subnetwork.   The branches and their nodes that are not in the subnetwork are called the *complement* of the subnetwork.   In Fig. 3-2 branches 4, 5, 6, 8, 9, and 10 and their nodes are the complement.   Note that the subnetwork and complement have some nodes in common.   In this case nodes 1, 2, 4, and 6 are such nodes.   In general, in a connected network a subnetwork will have at least one node in common with its complement.   This can be seen by considering

Fig. 3-3   (*a*) *A connected network;* (*b*) *a nonconnected network.*

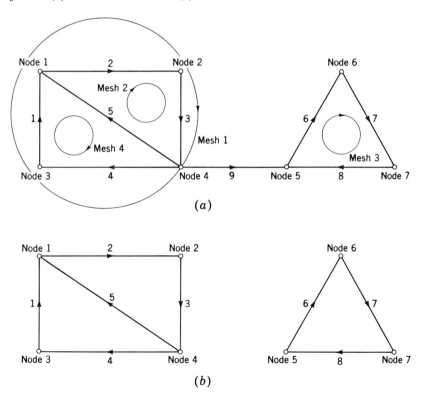

(*a*)

(*b*)

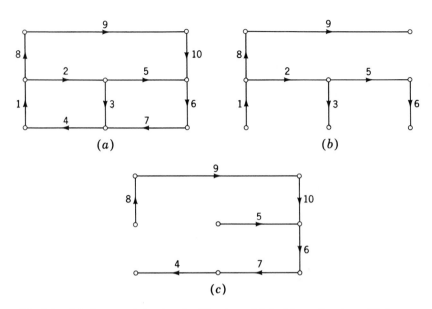

Fig. 3-4   (a) A connected network; (b) a tree of (a); (c) another tree of (a).

that branches are either in the subnetwork or in the complement. If there is not at least one node in common, then the network must be separated into two parts and is not a connected network.

Now let us define a *mesh* or a *loop*. From our studies of the branch-current method we have seen that this is fundamental to network analysis. Starting at a node, for instance, node *a*, we follow the same rules as for tracing a path, but we finally choose a branch which has node *a* as its endpoint; thus node *a* is encountered twice. This is then a closed path which is called a *mesh*. Note that the branches of a mesh form a connected subnetwork. For instance, in Fig. 3-3*a* the following are meshes: branches 1, 2, 3, and 4; branches 2, 3, and 5; branches 1, 4, and 5; and branches 6, 7, and 8. Note that these meshes, or loops, are assigned a direction and number. They will be related to those we used in the branch-current method. We shall also use them to develop a more convenient method of network analysis. Note that in generating a loop, once the starting node (node *a*) is encountered a second time, the procedure stops; thus in Fig. 3-3*a* the paths along branches 1, 2, 3, 4, and 9 and branches 1, 2, 3, 4, 9, 6, 7, and 8 do *not* constitute loops.

A fundamental definition in our study of network topology is the *tree*. A tree is a subnetwork of a connected network which has the following properties: the tree contains *all* the nodes of the original network, and the tree itself is connected; it can contain *no* meshes. Consider the connected network of Fig. 3-4*a*. If we remove branches 4, 7, and 10, the remaining network will be a tree of the original network. Note that it has all the nodes of the original network and is connected, but there are no meshes. A given network may have more than one tree. For instance, Fig. 3-4c is also a tree of this network.

Every connected network has *at least* one tree. We can demonstrate this by developing a construction procedure for the tree. Examine a branch in a connected network. That branch will either be part of one (or more) meshes, or it will not. If it is, then we remove it from the network. The remaining network will still be connected, since the branch was part of a mesh. All nodes will still be in the remaining network. In addition, the network will still be connected, since a path must still exist between what were the two end nodes of the branch. In a mesh there must be two paths between any pair of nodes because a mesh is a closed path. For example, in Fig. 3-5a branch 7 is part of several meshes (one is the mesh consisting of branches 3, 5, 6, and 7). If branch 7 is removed, then the path consisting of branches 3, 5, and 6 will still exist between the nodes of branch 7. Thus these nodes will still remain in the network, and the network will not be broken into two parts. If the chosen branch is not in any mesh, then we leave it. In either case we proceed to another branch, and if this new branch is in any mesh of the modified network, we remove it. As before, the remaining network will contain all the nodes of the original network and will still be connected. For instance, in Fig. 3-5b, branch 10 is part of a mesh, so we remove it; the resultant network is shown in

Fig. 3-5   (a) A connected network; (b) the connected subnetwork formed by removing branch 7; (c) the connected subnetwork formed by removing branch 10 from (b); (d) a tree of (a) formed from (c) by removing branch 4.

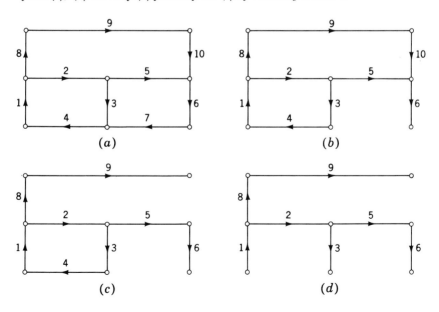

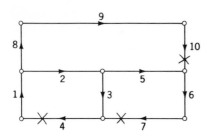

Fig. 3-6   The simplified procedure for obtaining a tree.

Fig. 3-5c.   Now consider a branch of the remaining network, for instance, branch 4.   This is part of a mesh of Fig. 3-5c, so we remove it; the network of Fig. 3-5d results.

If we test every branch of this network, we see that none of them lies in a mesh.   This is a connected network and contains all the nodes of the original network but no meshes; hence it is a tree.   In general, with an arbitrary network we repeat this procedure with every branch.   Eventually a connected subnetwork containing all the nodes and no meshes must result.   Thus we have obtained a tree of the network and have demonstrated that each connected network has at least one tree.   This procedure will generate a tree even if the network is not planar (i.e., cannot be drawn in a plane).

The procedure for obtaining a tree that we have just illustrated does not require redrawing the network, as was done in Fig. 3-5.   We can draw the network once, and merely place cross marks on the "removed" branches.   For instance, in Fig. 3-6, where we have redrawn the network of Fig. 3-5a, we shall obtain the same tree.   Branch 7 lies in a mesh, so "remove" it by placing a cross on it.   Then we pick a branch in the remaining network, for instance, branch 10, and if it lies in a mesh, we "remove" it by placing a cross on it. Repeating this procedure with the rest of the network, we "remove" branch 4.   The resulting network contains no (uncrossed) branches that are in a mesh.   Thus in Fig. 3-6 the tree consists of the uncrossed branches.   The procedures of Figs. 3-5 and 3-6 are essentially the same; Fig. 3-6 just requires less drawing.

A branch of a tree is called a *tree branch*.   The tree branches of a network are not unique, but depend upon the chosen tree.   For instance, in Fig. 3-6 the tree branches for the tree we have chosen are 1, 2, 3, 5, 6, 8, and 9.   The network branches that are not tree branches are called *chords* or *links*.   These also depend upon the choice of the tree.   In Fig. 3-6 the chords are branches 4, 7, and 10.

Let us now determine the number of tree branches and chords in a connected network that has B branches and N nodes.   If T represents the number of tree branches, then

$$T = N - 1 \tag{3-1}$$

This can be proved by a construction procedure. Assume that we have determined the tree of a network such as that of Fig. 3-6. Now we draw the tree one branch at a time. We start with one branch. So far we have drawn one branch and two nodes. We add another tree branch which has a node that is common to one of the nodes we have already drawn; this will add one more branch and one more node to the diagram. Note that one of the nodes of this added branch is common to one of those of the first branch; also note that both nodes of the new branch cannot be common to the original ones, since this would result in a mesh, which is not allowed in a tree. Now we add another branch, which has a node common to one of the drawn nodes (it cannot have more than one node in common with the drawn nodes, since a mesh would be formed). Thus we have added one more node and one more branch. We continue this procedure until the entire tree is formed. This is always possible, since the tree is connected, and therefore a path can be drawn between any pair of nodes. At each step we add one branch and one node, except at the first step, where we started with two nodes and one branch. Thus there must be one more node than branch, and Eq. (3-1) is proven.

The number of chords plus the number of tree branches must equal the total number of branches in the network. If C is the number of chords

$$C = B - N + 1 \qquad\qquad\qquad (3\text{-}2)$$

Now let us develop a result for trees which we shall apply to network analysis. *Every tree has at least two nodes on which only one tree branch is incident.* To demonstrate this, consider a point in the middle of any tree branch; call this point 1. Starting at point 1, we follow the rules for tracing a path. Since there are no meshes in a tree, we cannot pass any node more than once. There are only a finite number of branches and nodes in a tree, so the procedure of tracing a path cannot continue indefinitely. The only thing that can stop the tracing of this path is if we reach a node that has only one branch incident upon it, so that we cannot leave the node. In this case we have found such a node. Now we return to point 1 and trace a path starting in the other direction. This will locate another node with only one branch incident upon it. The two nodes cannot be the same, since there are no meshes in a tree.

Let us clarify this discussion with an example. In the tree of Fig. 3-5*d*, consider that point 1 lies in the middle of branch 2. Start tracing to the right through branches 2, 5, and 6. At the end of branch 6 the path-tracing procedure must stop, since this node has only one tree branch incident upon it. Now return to point 1 and trace to the left. A typical path consists of branches 2, 8, and 9, and the node at the end of branch 9 is another one with only one branch incident upon it. In Fig. 3-5*d* there are in fact four nodes with only one branch incident on it. Any tree will have *at least two* such nodes.

Up to this point we have considered the configuration of branches and nodes without considering that they might be parts of an electric network. Let us now introduce the concepts of voltages, currents, and Kirchhoff's laws. Suppose we assign a current to each branch. This current is a function of time which may be unknown. To simplify the drawings we shall number the currents to correspond to the branch currents (the current in branch 1 is i_1, and so on), and we shall assume that the positive direction of current is in the same direction as the branch orientation. Therefore it is not necessary to indicate current by a separate arrow. For instance, in Fig. 3-7 the current i_1 in branch 1 is shown by an external arrow and by the symbol i_1. When the branches are numbered and oriented, it is unnecessary to draw the current arrow. We shall also assign voltage drops to the branches, with the positive direction of the drop assumed to be in the direction of the branch. For instance, in Fig. 3-7 the voltage drop from node 1 to node 2, v_{12}, could be written as v_2, since this is a branch that connects nodes 1 and 2; it points from node 1 to node 2. When $v_{12} = v_2$ is positive, then node 1 is positive with respect to node 2. Note that a voltage-defining arrow could be drawn from node 2 to node 1 (see Fig. 1-37). As a further example, in Fig. 3-7, $v_{26} = v_5$, $v_{87} = v_9$, $v_{76} = v_{10}$, and $v_{87} = v_{11}$.

The currents and voltages of a network are not arbitrary, but must be related by Kirchhoff's laws. Kirchhoff's current law is applicable at each node. For instance, in Fig. 3-7

$$i_1 - i_2 - i_8 = 0$$
$$i_2 - i_3 - i_5 = 0$$
$$i_8 - i_9 - i_{11} + i_{12} = 0$$
$$\cdots \cdots \cdots \cdots \cdots$$

In addition, Kirchhoff's voltage law is applicable around every mesh. For instance, in Fig. 3-7

$$v_1 + v_2 + v_3 + v_4 = 0$$
$$v_2 + v_5 - v_{10} - v_9 - v_8 = 0$$
$$v_9 - v_{11} = 0$$
$$v_{11} + v_{12} = 0$$
$$\cdots \cdots \cdots \cdots$$

An implication of Kirchhoff's current law is that all the branch currents are not arbitrary. In fact, we shall see that once certain of the branch currents are specified, *all* of them are uniquely determined in terms of those that are specified. For instance, in Fig. 3-7 a knowledge of i_1 and i_2 uniquely determines i_8. In addition, Kirchhoff's voltage law imposes similar relations upon the voltages. For instance, in Fig. 3-7 $v_9 = v_{11} = -v_{12}$. We shall now discuss the fact that, if Kirchhoff's laws are not to be violated, the tree-branch voltages must uniquely determine all the branch voltages of the network and the chord branch currents must uniquely determine all the branch currents in the network.

Consider the statement that *the tree-branch voltages of a network uniquely*

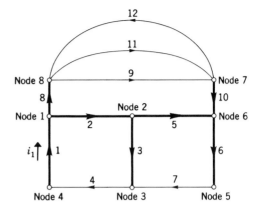

Fig. 3-7   A   connected   network.   A tree is shown by the heavy branches.

determine all the branch voltages.   According to Kirchhoff's voltage law, the sum of the voltage drops around any closed loop is equal to zero.   In other words, the voltage drop between any two points is independent of the path along which it is measured (see Sec. 2-1).   For instance, in Fig. 3-7

$$v_1 + v_2 + v_3 + v_4 = 0$$

or, equivalently,

$$v_4 = -(v_1 + v_2 + v_3) = v_{34} \qquad (3\text{-}3)$$

Now let us assume that all the tree-branch voltages of a network are specified. Since a tree is a connected subnetwork and contains *all* the nodes of the network, there must be a path in the tree between any two nodes.   Hence the voltage drop between any two nodes can be established by summing the voltage drops in the tree path between these nodes.   For instance, in Fig. 3-7, where a tree is shown by the heavy lines, we can express the voltage drop across the chords as functions of the tree-branch voltage drops:

$$v_4 = -v_1 - v_2 - v_3 \qquad (3\text{-}4a)$$

$$v_7 = v_3 - v_5 - v_6 \qquad (3\text{-}4b)$$

$$v_9 = v_{11} = -v_{12} = -v_{10} + v_5 + v_2 - v_8 \qquad (3\text{-}4c)$$

If another tree were chosen, then we could express all the branch voltages in terms of its tree-branch voltages.   From Eq. (3-1) we see that all the branch voltages can be expressed in terms of $N - 1$ voltages, where N is the number of nodes; that is, no more than $N - 1$ branch voltages are independent in a network.   Of course, the $N - 1$ branches must be branches of some tree of the network (note that these voltages are not completely independent, but are determined by the network equations; there are only $N - 1$ unknown voltages in the network).

Let us now relate all the branch currents of a network to the currents in the chords.   We shall demonstrate that *the chord currents uniquely determine all the currents in a network.* We must show that when the chord currents are specified, we can use Kirchhoff's current law to establish the currents in all the tree branches in terms of the chord currents.

We have demonstrated that each tree must have at least two nodes on which there is only one tree branch incident. Thus at one of these nodes there can be only chords and one tree branch. If the chord currents are specified, then the currents in all the branches but one at this node are specified, so we can use Kirchhoff's current law to specify this tree-branch current. Now consider the subnetwork that consists of the tree with the branch whose current we have determined removed from it. This subnetwork will be a connected network, since the "removed" branch had only one node in common with the rest of the tree. For instance, in Fig. 3-7, if branch 6 is removed from the tree, the remaining "subtree" will still be connected. This "subtree" will have all the characteristics of a tree for an $(N - 1)$-node network. Hence it will have two nodes at which only one of its branches is incident. At one such node there will be one branch of the subtree plus chords and/or the original tree branch. The current is known, or has been determined, in all these branches except that of the subtree, and Kirchhoff's current law determines the current in this subtree branch. This procedure is repeated until the current in every tree branch is established. Thus we shall have applied Kirchhoff's current law to determine the current at every node except one (we demonstrated in Sec. 2-3 that if Kirchhoff's current law holds at $N - 1$ nodes of an N-node network, then it will also hold at the Nth node).

Let us illustrate this procedure with Fig. 3-7. We shall specify all the branch currents in terms of the chord currents i_4, i_7, i_9, i_{11}, and i_{12}. Only one tree branch is incident at node 4, so we have

$$i_1 = i_4 \tag{3-5a}$$

Only one tree branch is incident at node 8, so

$$i_8 = i_9 + i_{11} - i_{12} \tag{3-5b}$$

Then, at node 1

$$i_2 = i_1 - i_8 \tag{3-5c}$$

Both i_1 and i_8 are tree-branch currents, but they have been determined in terms of chord currents [see Eqs. (3-5a) and (3-5b)]. Thus, proceeding in this way, we obtain

$$i_3 = i_4 - i_7 \tag{3-5d}$$

$$i_6 = i_7 \tag{3-5e}$$

$$i_{10} = i_9 + i_{11} - i_{12} \tag{3-5f}$$

$$i_5 = i_6 - i_{10} \tag{3-5g}$$

In general [see Eq. (3-2)], in a network of B branches and N nodes there are

only $B - N + 1$ chords.   Thus we can specify only $B - N + 1$ independent
currents in a connected network.

We now have the preliminary groundwork necessary to the development of
general and rather convenient network-analysis procedures.   We shall illustrate one of them in the next section.   We have worked in terms of connected
networks here and have shown that all networks can be "made" connected
without changing any branch currents.   After we have developed the circuit-
analysis procedure, we shall generalize to unconnected networks.

3-2 Loop analysis

We are now in a position to develop a network-analysis procedure that is far
more convenient to use than branch-current analysis.   We shall assume here
that the networks are linear and time invariant.   For the moment let us consider just simplifying branch-current analysis with the results developed in the
last section.   We have seen that in a connected network all the branch currents
can be expressed in terms of the chord currents.   If, instead of choosing all the
branch currents as unknowns, we choose only the chord currents, then we can
express all the branch currents in terms of them.   This would reduce the number of unknowns and make the simultaneous equations less cumbersome.   In
order to express the tree-branch currents in terms of the chord currents, we
must apply Kirchhoff's current law at every node but one.   This is tedious.
We can now develop a procedure called *loop analysis*, or *mesh analysis*, in
which we shall choose currents in such a way that Kirchhoff's current law is
automatically satisfied at every node.

First let us introduce the concept of a *basic mesh*.   Consider that we have a
connected network and have chosen a tree; such a network is shown in Fig. 3-8.
A basic mesh is defined as a mesh which consists of a chord and the path in the
tree between the nodes of the chord.   Such a basic mesh will exist for every
chord.   Consider that the chord has nodes a and b.   There must be a path in
the tree between node a and node b, since the tree is a *connected* subnetwork that

*Fig. 3-8 A connected network.   A tree is
shown by the heavy branches; the basic
meshes are indicated.*

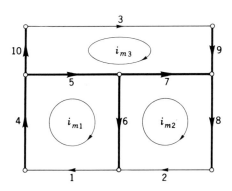

contains *all* the nodes of the network.   This tree path and the chord form a
mesh.   Each chord defines a unique basic mesh, since there is only one path
in the tree between each pair of nodes (if there were more than one tree path,
then the tree would contain a mesh, which is not allowed).   A basic mesh can
be drawn for each chord.   In an N-mesh network there are $B - N + 1$ chords
[see Eq. (3-2)], so $B - N + 1$ basic meshes can be drawn.   This is called the
set of basic meshes.   Note that the basic meshes depend upon the choice of the
tree.   In Fig. 3-8, for example, for the chosen tree the basic meshes consist of
branches 1, 4, 5, and 6, branches 2, 6, 7, and 8, and branches 3, 9, 7, 5, and 10.

Now let us define a *fictitious current* which we shall call a *loop current* or
mesh current.   Assume that the charge carriers do not flow into arbitrary
branches at a node, but flow in continuous loops (or meshes).   Figure 3-8
shows three such mesh currents.   We assume that there is charge which flows
around branches 1, 4, 5, and 6 to form the current i_{m1} and charge which flows
around branches 6, 7, 8, and 2 to form i_{m2}, and so on.   Actually, this does not
happen.   For instance, the charge flowing in branch 1 may eventually flow in
branch 2.   However, by defining loop currents mathematically we obtain a
fictitious current that will enable us to obtain the actual branch currents more
easily.

Let us now discuss how the loop currents are chosen and how the branch
currents are established from them.   We shall subsequently show that these
branch currents satisfy all the conditions that have been imposed upon branch
currents in general, and thus that they and the loop currents are valid.   A
simple choice of loop currents is the assumption that there is one loop current
in each basic mesh.   For instance, Fig. 3-8 shows the loop currents i_{m1}, i_{m2}, and
i_{m3} for the basic meshes of the chosen tree.   We shall see that this procedure
always generates a valid set of loop currents (a valid set of loop currents is one
that establishes a valid set of branch currents).   These loop currents are called
basic-loop currents or *basic-mesh currents*.

We also *define* the current in any branch as equal to the algebraic sum of the
loop currents in it.   In Fig. 3-8 we have

$$i_{b1} = i_{m1} \tag{3-6a}$$

$$i_{b2} = i_{m2} \tag{3-6b}$$

$$i_{b3} = i_{m3} \tag{3-6c}$$

$$i_{b4} = i_{m1} \tag{3-6d}$$

$$i_{b5} = i_{m1} - i_{m3} \tag{3-6e}$$

$$i_{b6} = i_{m1} - i_{m2} \tag{3-6f}$$

$$i_{b7} = i_{m2} - i_{m3} \tag{3-6g}$$

$$i_{b8} = i_{m2} \tag{3-6h}$$

$$i_{b9} = i_{m3} \tag{3-6i}$$

$$i_{b10} = i_{m3} \tag{3-6j}$$

where the subscript b indicates branch current. Note that when the assumed branch-current direction and the assumed loop-current direction are the same, a plus sign is used. If the directions are opposite, a minus sign is used. If a loop current is not in a branch, then it does not contribute to its branch current. In general, the loop and branch currents are instantaneous functions of time, which may be negative (possibly on an instantaneous basis). In this case the current is in a direction opposite the indicated one. As in the case of branch currents, once a choice of loop-current direction is made, it should not be changed.

Let us now demonstrate that the loop currents generate a valid set of branch currents. These must satisfy Kirchhoff's current law at every node, and for a chosen tree the tree-branch currents must be expressible in terms of the chord currents. The loop currents follow the basic meshes. Hence there is one and only one, loop current in each chord. Then the chord currents are independent of each other (they are not related by the loop currents). Note that the chord currents *will* be established from the circuit configuration and thus are related to it. However, we should not be able to specify any one chord current as a function of the others by Kirchhoff's current law. Each chord current defines a loop current, and vice versa [e.g., see Eqs. (3-6)]. Thus the loop currents can be expressed in terms of the chord currents. We can express the tree-branch currents in terms of the loop currents [e.g., see Eqs. (3-6)], so by using loop currents, we can express the tree-branch currents in terms of the chord currents.

Finally, we must demonstrate that the branch currents established by the loop currents satisfy Kirchhoff's current law at every node. The loop currents consist of the flow of charge around a closed loop. Thus any charge that flows into a node flows out of it, automatically satisfying Kirchhoff's current law. This is true regardless of the number of loop currents entering the node. Thus the use of loop currents automatically satisfies Kirchhoff's current law at every node. This is the chief reason that we use loop currents; with loop currents it is *unnecessary to write Kirchhoff's current-law equations.*

To actually establish the value of the loop currents in a particular network we make use of Kirchhoff's voltage-law equations. There are $B - N + 1$ chords [see Eq. (3-2)], so there are $B - N + 1$ unknown loop currents, and we must write $B - N + 1$ Kirchhoff's voltage-law equations to solve for them. A valid set of loops for these equations consists of the loops defined by the loop currents. These will be independent equations, since each one will introduce a new voltage drop (the drop across the chord of the basic mesh). Thus no one can be expressed in terms of the others. In essence, the procedure is to use the branch-current method for each of these loops. However, the branch currents are expressed in terms of the loop currents, so that Kirchhoff's current law need not be applied.

Let us illustrate this procedure with the network of Fig. 3-9, which is topologically equivalent to the network of Fig. 3-8. We have numbered and ori-

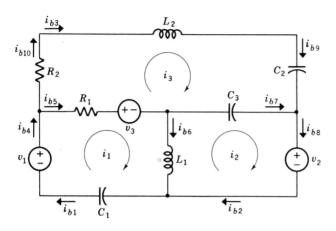

Fig. 3-9   An electric net-work that is topologically equivalent to Fig. 3-8. The branch-current num-bering and orientation are the same as in Fig. 3-8.

ented the branches in the same way as in Fig. 3-8, and the same mesh currents and tree have been chosen.   The loop currents need not be drawn as closed circles so long as the closed loops are clearly understood.   For convenience we have dropped the subscript m from the loop currents.   The branch currents are related to the loop currents by Eqs. (3-6).   Then, using these branch currents and taking the sum of the voltage drops around loops 1, 2, and 3, in turn, we obtain

$$0 = -v_1 + R_1(i_1 - i_3) + v_3 + L_1 \frac{d(i_1 - i_2)}{dt} + \frac{1}{C_1} \int i_1 \, dt \qquad (3\text{-}7a)$$

$$0 = L_1 \frac{d(i_2 - i_1)}{dt} + \frac{1}{C_3} \int (i_2 - i_3) \, dt + v_2 \qquad (3\text{-}7b)$$

$$0 = R_2 i_3 + L_2 \frac{di_3}{dt} + \frac{1}{C_2} \int i_3 \, dt + \frac{1}{C_3} \int (i_3 - i_2) \, dt + v_3 + R_1(i_3 - i_1) \qquad (3\text{-}7c)$$

It is convenient in solving these equations to rewrite them with all the known quantities on the left-hand side, all the terms containing like unknowns grouped together, and all the terms containing unknowns in the same order (the i_1 terms first, and so on).   Equations (3-7) rewritten in this manner are

$$v_1 - v_3 = R_1 i_1 + L_1 \frac{di_1}{dt} + \frac{1}{C_1} \int i_1 \, dt - L_1 \frac{di_2}{dt} - R_1 i_3 \qquad (3\text{-}8a)$$

$$-v_2 = -L_1 \frac{di_1}{dt} + L_1 \frac{di_2}{dt} + \frac{1}{C_3} \int i_2 \, dt - \frac{1}{C_3} \int i_3 \, dt \qquad (3\text{-}8b)$$

$$v_3 = -R_1 i_1 - \frac{1}{C_3} \int i_2 \, dt + R_2 i_3 + L_2 \frac{di_3}{dt} + \frac{1}{C_3} \int i_3 \, dt + R_1 i_3 \qquad (3\text{-}8c)$$

Note that we have far fewer unknowns and equations than we would have with the branch-current method. Since we did not have to make use of Kirchhoff's current law, the number of simultaneous equations has been reduced from six to three.

With some practice equations can be written directly in the form of Eqs. (3-8). We shall consider some rules for doing this. These rules need not be followed for correct results, but they are very convenient. We shall sum the voltage drops around the loops defined by the loop currents and consider a voltage drop positive when it is in the direction of the loop current. The equation for mesh 1 is taken first, that for mesh 2 second, and so on. The terms containing unknowns are written in the numerical order of their subscripts (i_1, i_2, . . .). The left-hand side of the equations consists of the sum of the generator voltage *rises* around the mesh in question (note that a generator whose polarity is such that it represents a voltage rise is recorded as a negative quantity in the sum of the voltage drops).

Now consider the right-hand side of Eqs. (3-8). Each represents the sum of the voltage drops in the elements. The terms containing i_1 in the first equation, i_2 in the second, or i_3 in the third are called the *self-voltage drops;* the others are called *coupled-voltage drops.* Let us consider the self-voltage drops. Every element of any loop will have that loop current in it. The self-voltage drop will be the drop that would result if the loop current were the only current in the elements of the loop. For instance, in loop 1 of Fig. 3-9 this component is

$$R_1 i_1 + L_1 \frac{di_1}{dt} + \frac{1}{C_1} \int i_1 \, dt \tag{3-9a}$$

and in loop 2 of Fig. 3-9 it is

$$L_1 \frac{di_2}{dt} + \frac{1}{C_3} \int i_3 \, dt \tag{3-9b}$$

Let us now consider the coupled-voltage-drop terms. Inspect each element to see if it contains more than one loop current. There is a component of voltage drop due to each of these currents. If the loop current that produces a coupled-voltage drop is in the same direction as the loop current of the mesh in question, then a plus sign is associated with its coupled-voltage-drop component. If the direction of these loop currents is opposite, then a minus sign is used. For instance in loop 1 of Fig. 3-9 consider the voltage drop across R_1. The currents i_1 and i_3 are in opposite directions, so for the coupled-voltage drop we have

$$-R_1 i_3$$

This procedure can be carried out for each element in turn. Then, after

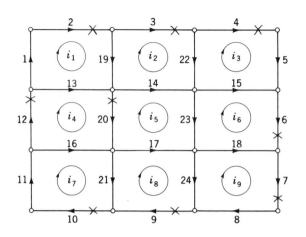

Fig. 3-10 A valid set of meshes that are not basic meshes. The crossed branches are chords of a tree.

systematic application of these rules, equations of the form of Eqs. (3-8) can be written directly, without first having to be written in the form of Eqs. (3-7). Of course, this will require some practice.

We have developed the preceding results in terms of basic meshes, but it is often convenient to use meshes other than basic meshes. For instance, the meshes indicated in Fig. 3-10 can be shown to be a valid set of meshes, although they are not basic meshes for any tree of the network. Each mesh of a basic mesh consists of one (and only one) chord of a tree and each basic mesh has a different chord. Therefore each basic mesh must have at least one branch (the chord) that is not a member of any other basic mesh. In Fig. 3-10 mesh 5 does not have such a branch; hence this mesh is not basic for any tree.

Now let us extend this development to meshes other than basic meshes. We have demonstrated that the chord currents determine all the branch currents. That is, once the chord currents are known, all the branch currents can be found. In addition, no one chord current can be expressed in terms of the others by Kirchhoff's current law, since no node can have only chords incident upon it. Thus, to be valid, a set of loop currents must be such that they can be expressed as functions of the chord currents which are independent of each other. If the equations that express the chord currents in terms of the mesh currents are linearly independent, then the chord currents will be independent. Then, if there are as many loop currents as chord currents, we can solve for the loop currents in terms of the chord currents.

We can express all the branch currents in terms of loop currents. If the loop currents can be expressed in terms of the chord currents, then we can also express the branch currents in terms of the chord currents. Thus a valid set of loop currents will be obtained if we choose $B - N + 1$ loop currents which are related to the chord currents by a set of linearly independent equations (we have not mentioned Kirchhoff's current law here because any branch currents expressed in terms of loop currents must satisfy Kirchhoff's current law).

One procedure for obtaining a valid set of meshes is to choose any $B - N + 1$ loop currents, and then choose a tree and write the set of equations which express the chord currents in terms of the chosen loop currents. If this set of equations is linearly independent, a valid set of meshes has been chosen. If the equations are not linearly independent, then a new set must be tried.

Although the technique that we have described is completely general, it is tedious to apply because it involves a "cut-and-try" procedure. Let us now explore a procedure that is easier to apply. It is not so general, but it is general enough for most instances. This procedure is based on the one for obtaining a tree, discussed in Sec. 3-1 and illustrated in Fig. 3-6. We choose any mesh and its corresponding loop current and cross out one branch of this mesh; then in the remaining network we choose a mesh and its corresponding loop current and cross out any branch of this mesh. If we repeat this procedure until there are no meshes left in the network, a tree of the network will be generated (see Sec. 3-1); that is, the crossed-out branches are the chords, and the remaining ones are tree branches.

Let us now demonstrate that we have $B - N + 1$ loop currents, and the equations relating the loop and chord currents are linearly independent. There will be $B - N + 1$ loop currents, since there is one for each crossed-out branch, which is a chord [see Eq. (3-2)]. Let us, for convenience, call the first loop current i_1 and the first crossed-out branch chord 1 with its current i_{c1}. Chord 1 will contain only i_1; it will contain no other loop currents, since it has been crossed out. Thus $i_{c1} = i_1$ independently of all other loop or chord currents. The second chord will contain i_2 and may also contain i_1. There will be no other loop currents in chord 2, since it was crossed out after i_2 was chosen. Thus i_{c2} will be independent of i_{c1}, since it has a new current i_2 in it. That is, even if $i_{c2} = \pm i_1 + i_2$, i_{c2} will be independent of $i_{c1} = i_1$, since i_2 can be specified independently of i_1. Similarly, each successive chord current will contain a new loop current. Hence we shall not be able to express any chord current in terms of the other chord currents, and a linearly independent set of simultaneous equations has been obtained (note that Kirchhoff's current law cannot be used to relate loop currents, since they automatically satisfy it). Therefore we have obtained a valid set of meshes. To illustrate this procedure with Fig. 3-10, we choose i_1 and cross out branch 2, and then choose i_2 and cross out branch 3. Repeat this procedure with each mesh in turn. The crossed out branches are as shown.

To illustrate the procedure further, let us obtain the loop equations for Fig. 3-9, but with a different set of loops. The network has been redrawn in Fig. 3-11. We choose mesh 1 as shown and cross out the branch containing L_1. Then we choose i_2 as a mesh in the remaining network and cross out the branch containing L_2. The one remaining mesh is that indicated by i_3. If the branch containing C_3 is crossed out, then there are no more meshes in the

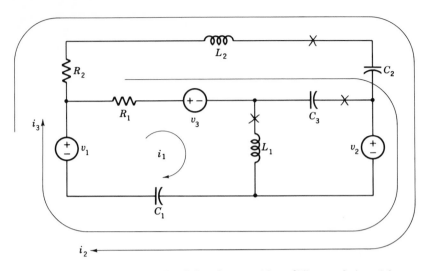

Fig. 3-11   The network of Fig. 3-9 redrawn with a different choice of loop currents.

network.   The loop equations for this network are

$$0 = -v_1 + R_1(i_1 + i_3) + v_3 + L_1\frac{di_1}{dt} + \frac{1}{C_1}\int (i_1 + i_2 + i_3)\,dt \qquad (3\text{-}10a)$$

$$0 = -v_1 + R_2i_2 + L_2\frac{di_2}{dt} + \frac{1}{C_2}\int i_2\,dt + v_2 + \frac{1}{C_1}\int (i_1 + i_2 + i_3)\,dt$$
$$(3\text{-}10b)$$

$$0 = -v_1 + R_1(i_1 + i_3) + v_3 + \frac{1}{C_3}\int i_3\,dt + v_2 + \frac{1}{C_1}\int (i_1 + i_2 + i_3)\,dt$$
$$(3\text{-}10c)$$

Rewriting these equations in a more useful form, we obtain

$$v_1 - v_3 = R_1i_1 + L_1\frac{di_1}{dt} + \frac{1}{C_1}\int i_1\,dt + \frac{1}{C_1}\int i_2\,dt + R_1i_3 + \frac{1}{C_1}\int i_3\,dt$$
$$(3\text{-}11a)$$

$$v_1 - v_2 = \frac{1}{C_1}\int i_1\,dt + R_2i_2 + L_2\frac{di_2}{dt} + \frac{1}{C_2}\int i_2\,dt$$
$$+ \frac{1}{C_1}\int i_2\,dt + \frac{1}{C_1}\int i_3\,dt \quad (3\text{-}11b)$$

$$v_1 - v_3 - v_2 = R_1i_1 + \frac{1}{C_1}\int i_1\,dt + \frac{1}{C_1}\int i_2\,dt + R_1i_3$$
$$+ \frac{1}{C_3}\int i_3\,dt + \frac{1}{C_1}\int i_3\,dt \quad (3\text{-}11c)$$

These equations can be made much more compact if we introduce a *differential operator p*. This is *defined* in the following way: p multiplied by any function means that the derivative of that function is to be taken. For instance,

$$pf(t) = \frac{df(t)}{dt} \tag{3-12}$$

In addition, we define $1/p$ or p^{-1} as an *integral operator*, so that

$$p^{-1}f(t) = \frac{f(t)}{p} = \int f(t)\, dt \tag{3-13}$$

Remember that we have defined the operations of Eqs. (3-12) and (3-13) essentially as a shorthand type of notation. Ordinary algebraic manipulations cannot be performed with p unless they are consistent with the rules for differentiation and integration. With this compact notation we have

$$v_1 - v_3 = \left(R_1 + L_1 p + \frac{1}{C_1 p}\right) i_1 + \frac{1}{C_1 p} i_2 + \left(R_1 + \frac{1}{C_1 p}\right) i_3 \tag{3-14a}$$

$$v_1 - v_2 = \frac{1}{C_1 p} i_1 + \left(R_2 + L_2 p + \frac{1}{C_2 p} + \frac{1}{C_1 p}\right) i_2 + \frac{1}{C_1 p} i_3 \tag{3-14b}$$

$$v_1 - v_3 - v_2 = \left(R_1 + \frac{1}{C_1 p}\right) i_1 + \frac{1}{C_1 p} i_2 + \left(R_1 + \frac{1}{C_3 p} + \frac{1}{C_1 p}\right) i_3 \tag{3-14c}$$

These equations are much easier to write than Eqs. (3-11), and they represent exactly the same thing.

Often we want to obtain the current in a particular element. In this case it is best that the element contain only have one loop current, so that only one unknown need be solved for. To accomplish this we cross out this branch as soon as a loop current is chosen in it.

Let us now write an array of the coefficients of the currents of Eqs. (3-14). Such an array is called a *matrix*. We shall consider many of the details of matrices in Sec. 3-10. The array of the coefficients is

$$\begin{bmatrix} R_1 + L_1 p + \dfrac{1}{C_1 p} & \dfrac{1}{C_1 p} & R_1 + \dfrac{1}{C_1 p} \\[2.5ex] \dfrac{1}{C_1 p} & R_2 + L_2 p + \dfrac{1}{C_1 p} + \dfrac{1}{C_2 p} & \dfrac{1}{C_1 p} \\[2.5ex] R_1 + \dfrac{1}{C_1 p} & \dfrac{1}{C_1 p} & R_1 + \dfrac{1}{C_3 p} + \dfrac{1}{C_1 p} \end{bmatrix}$$

The individual terms are called the *elements* of the matrix. We often write them as a letter with subscripts. The first subscript indicates the row in which the element appears and the second indicates its column. For instance, for the above array,

$$
\begin{bmatrix}
a_{11} & a_{12} & a_{13} \\
a_{21} & a_{22} & a_{23} \\
a_{31} & a_{32} & a_{33}
\end{bmatrix}
$$

$$
=
\begin{bmatrix}
R_1 + L_1 p + \dfrac{1}{C_1 p} & \dfrac{1}{C_1 p} & R_1 + \dfrac{1}{C_1 p} \\[3mm]
\dfrac{1}{C_1 p} & R_2 + L_2 p + \dfrac{1}{C_1 p} + \dfrac{1}{C_2 p} & \dfrac{1}{C_1 p} \\[3mm]
R_1 + \dfrac{1}{C_1 p} & \dfrac{1}{C_1 p} & R_1 + \dfrac{1}{C_3 p} + \dfrac{1}{C_1 p}
\end{bmatrix}
$$

$$(3\text{-}15)$$

Then

$$
a_{11} = R_1 + L_1 P + \frac{1}{C_1 p}
$$

$$
a_{12} = \frac{1}{C_1 p}
$$

. . . .

Note that in the above array

$$
a_{ij} = a_{ji} \qquad i = 1, 2, 3; j = 1, 2, 3 \tag{3-16}
$$

A matrix that satisfies Eq. (3-16) is called a *symmetric matrix*. *If there are no dependent generators, and the rules for writing mesh equations are followed*, then the matrix of the coefficients of the unknown coefficients will always be *symmetric*. Note that a_{ij} is an indication of those elements of loop i which are common to loop j; similarly, a_{ji} indicates the elements of loop j which are common to loop i. The common elements will be the same, and thus $a_{ij} = a_{ji}$. The signs of the elements depend upon whether the two loop currents are in the same direction or in opposite directions. Thus the signs for each element will be the same. Note that if we do not follow the rules for writing mesh equations, this symmetry will not occur. For instance, writing the equations for mesh 3 before mesh 2 will cause Eq. (3-14c) to be the second equation in Eqs. (3-14). As a result, the second and third rows on the right-hand side of Eq. (3-15) will be interchanged, and the symmetry will be gone.

Nonconnected networks

So far we have considered only connected networks. In Sec. 3-1 we noted that all nonconnected networks could be "connected" by adding branches in which there would be no current, and that the addition of these branches would not affect the circuit equations (these branches will never be in a mesh, and

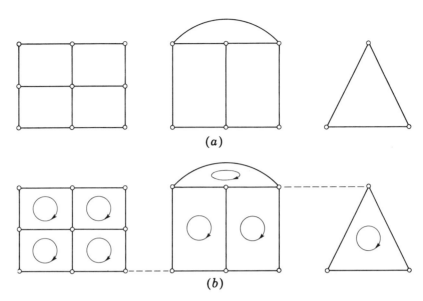

Fig. 3-12   (a) *A nonconnected network;* (b) *the network of* (a) *made connected without changing the circuit equations.*

hence will have no mesh current).   Let us illustrate this with Fig. 3-12 as an example.   Figure 3-12a is nonconnected.   In Fig. 3-12b two (dashed) branches have been added to form a connected network.   Note that no mesh can be formed which contains either of these branches.   Thus there will be no current in them, and they will not alter the circuit equations.   In general, the procedure used to "connect" a network is to add a branch between two of its parts and test to see that this added branch lies in no meshes, then connect another two parts of this modified network and again test that the new added branch lies in no meshes of the modified network.   This procedure is repeated until the network is connected.

One procedure for choosing a valid set of meshes in a nonconnected network is to connect it as indicated and then use the rules for obtaining a valid set of loops in a connected network.   Since no loop currents are in the added branches, we can simplify the rules.   We can consider each separate part as a network, and then draw a valid set of loop currents in each part; the complete set of loop currents will be a valid set for the nonconnected network.

Let us now determine the number of loop currents needed in a network of N nodes and B branches which is in S separate parts.   We can form a connected network by adding $S - 1$ branches.   For a connected network we have $S = 1$, and we add no branches; if the network is in two parts, we add one branch, and so on.   Thus we can form a connected network of N nodes and

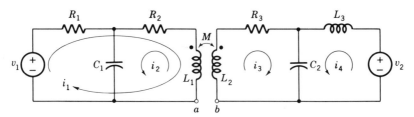

Fig. 3-13   A nonconnected network containing mutual inductance.

B' branches, where

$$B' = B + S - 1 \tag{3-17}$$

Therefore we require $B' - N + 1$ loop currents [see Eq. (3-2)].   Substituting Eq. (3-17), we obtain the number of loop currents L,

$$L = B - N + S \tag{3-18}$$

To illustrate loop analysis in a nonconnected network we shall set up the loop equations for the network of Fig. 3-13.   This will also illustrate the use of loop analysis in a circuit containing a mutual inductance.   A branch can be added between nodes a and b to form a connected network.   A valid set of loop currents is shown.   To make the equations more compact we use the operator notation of Eqs. (3-12) and (3-13); the loop equations are then

$$0 = -v_1 + R_1 i_1 + R_2(i_1 - i_2) + L_1 p(i_1 - i_2) - M p i_3 \tag{3-19a}$$

$$0 = \frac{1}{C_1 p} i_2 + R_2(i_2 - i_1) + L_1 p(i_2 - i_1) + M p i_3 \tag{3-19b}$$

$$0 = M p(i_2 - i_1) + L_2 p i_3 + R_3 i_3 + \frac{1}{C_2 p}(i_3 + i_4) \tag{3-19c}$$

$$0 = \frac{1}{C_2 p}(i_4 + i_3) + L_3 p i_4 - v_2 \tag{3-19d}$$

The mutual-inductance voltage drops are analyzed just as they are in the branch-current method.   If we rearrange Eqs. (3-19), we obtain

$$v_1 = (R_1 + R_2 + L_1 p)i_1 - R_2 i_2 - M i_3 + 0 i_4 \tag{3-20a}$$

$$0 = -R_2 i_1 + \left(R_2 + L_1 p + \frac{1}{C_1 p}\right) i_2 + M i_3 + 0 i_4 \tag{3-20b}$$

$$0 = -M i_1 + M i_2 + \left(L_2 p + R_3 + \frac{1}{C_2 p}\right) i_3 + \frac{1}{C_2 p} i_4 \tag{3-20c}$$

$$v_2 = 0 i_1 + 0 i_2 + \frac{1}{C_2 p} i_3 + \left(\frac{1}{C_2 p} + L_3 p\right) i_4 \tag{3-20d}$$

Note that the matrix of the coefficients still has the symmetry that we have discussed (we write all the unknowns for each equation even if their coefficients are zero).

If branches are added to a nonconnected network to form a connected one, then this network cannot be used to determine the voltage drop between nodes in separate parts of the network. This is discussed and explained in the next section.

3-3   Nodal analysis

In the last section we developed a procedure whereby Kirchhoff's current law was automatically satisfied, and we had only to solve $B - N + 1$ Kirchhoff's voltage-law equations for unknown loop currents [see Eq. (3-2)]. We shall now develop a procedure, called *nodal analysis*, whereby Kirchhoff's voltage law will automatically be satisfied. The unknowns will be voltages, obtained by writing Kirchhoff's current-law equations at $N - 1$ nodes of the network. The reader may wonder why we bother to develop a new procedure. One reason is that in some situations an alternative procedure may be much more convenient to use.

In general, the difficulty in solving a set of n simultaneous equations varies as n factorial; that is, a set of four simultaneous equations requires four times as much work to solve as does a set of three simultaneous equations. Thus if one analysis technique results in fewer unknowns, it is usually much more desirable to use it. In mesh analysis we had $B - N + 1$ unknowns; in nodal analysis there will be $N - 1$ unknowns. One of these numbers may be smaller than the other. For instance, consider Fig. 3-14a. For this network $B - N + 1$ and $N - 1$ are equal, and each procedure entails essentially the same amount of work. In the network of Fig. 3-14b, however, loop analysis will have five unknowns, whereas nodal analysis will require only three unknowns; hence nodal analysis is superior in this case. In the circuit of Fig. 3-14c the converse is true, and loop analysis is superior.

Fig. 3-14 (a) *A network where* $B - N + 1 = N - 1 = 3;$ (b) *a network where* $B - N + 1 = 5$ *and* $N - 1 = 3;$ (c) *a network where* $B - N + 1 = 3$ *and* $N - 1 = 7.$

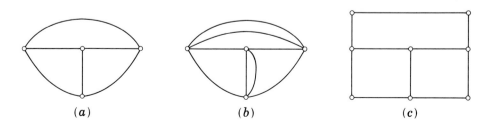

(a)   (b)   (c)

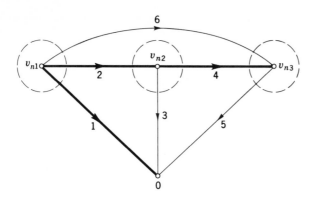

Fig. 3-15   A network illus-trating node voltages. A tree of the network is shown by the heavy lines.

In loop analysis we introduced a fictitious loop current that automatically satisfied Kirchhoff's current law at every node (note that with basic meshes this fictitious current can actually be measured by measuring the chord currents). We shall now introduce fictitious nodal voltages such that when they are used, Kirchhoff's voltage law will be satisfied around every loop (we shall see that these fictitious voltages can be measured directly, although this is not significant in the analysis).

Let us now introduce the concept of a *nodal voltage*. We select any node and enclose it in an area that "cuts" through each branch incident on the node, and through no other ones; such areas are illustrated in Fig. 3-15. We label the interiors of these areas as voltages v_{n1}, v_{n2}, . . . ; in nodal analysis it is convenient to place these voltage labels at the nodes, hence the name node voltage. The Nth node, which is not encircled, is called the *reference node* and is labeled zero. We must now describe a technique for determining the branch voltages in terms of the nodal voltages. We must demonstrate that these branch voltages satisfy Kirchhoff's voltage law around every loop, and that the $N - 1$ branch voltages of any tree of the network are independent of each other (i.e., no one can be specified in terms of the others). We must also demonstrate that the nodal voltages can be expressed in terms of the tree-branch voltages, and hence that all the branch voltages can be expressed in terms of them.

The branch voltages are obtained from the nodal voltages in the following way. The voltage drop of any branch is the algebraic sum of all the nodal voltages through whose closed areas it passes. If the branch is oriented so that it leaves the closed area, then the nodal voltage is added; if the branch is oriented so that it enters the closed area, then the nodal voltage is subtracted. For instance, in Fig. 3-15,

$$v_{b1} = v_{n1} \tag{3-21a}$$

$$v_{b2} = v_{n1} - v_{n2} \tag{3-21b}$$

$$v_{b3} = v_{n2} \tag{3-21c}$$

$$v_{b4} = v_{n2} - v_{n3} \qquad\qquad (3\text{-}21d)$$

$$v_{b5} = v_{n3} \qquad\qquad (3\text{-}21e)$$

$$v_{b6} = v_{n1} - v_{n3} \qquad\qquad (3\text{-}21f)$$

Let us now demonstrate that branch voltages obtained from nodal voltages satisfy Kirchhoff's current law around every loop. The nodal voltages are defined by the closed volumes. Consider "traveling around" the branches that form any closed loop. We must leave any nodal-voltage area we enter, since the loop is closed. Thus the net contribution of the nodal voltages around any closed loop must be zero. For example, consider the loop defined by branches 1, 2, and 3 in Fig. 3-15. The sum of the branch-voltage drops is $v_{b1} - v_{b3} - v_{b2}$. Substituting Eqs. (3-21), we obtain

$$v_{b1} - v_{b3} - v_{b2} = v_{n1} - v_{n2} - (v_{n1} - v_{n2}) = 0$$

Let us demonstrate that for any tree of the network we can specify the tree-branch voltages independently of each other; that is, we must not be able to use Kirchhoff's voltage law to specify any one tree-branch voltage in terms of any other ones, the nodal voltages must be such that we cannot specify one tree-branch voltage in terms of another. We choose a tree branch that is incident on the reference node; let us call it tree branch 1 and let its other node be node 1. The branch voltage of the tree branch is a function only of v_{n1}. Then we choose any other tree branch; let us call it tree branch 2. At least one of its nodes must be different from node 1 or the reference node, since a tree cannot contain a loop. Thus the branch voltage of tree branch 2 is expressed in terms of a "new" nodal voltage which is not a function of v_{n1}; hence it must be independent of the branch voltage of tree branch 1. Now we choose a third tree branch. It must have a node, and hence a nodal voltage, which differs from those of tree branches 1 and 2; otherwise a loop would be formed in the tree. Hence its tree-branch voltage must be independent of the preceding ones. We continue this for each tree branch in turn until we have all the tree-branch voltages. Each will be independent of all the preceding ones. In addition, the tree-branch voltages and the nodal voltages will be equal in number (each tree branch introduces a new nodal voltage). Hence they will be related by a linearly independent set of equations. Thus the nodal voltages can also be expressed in terms of the tree-branch voltages.

Thus we have demonstrated that the branch voltages set up by the nodal voltages satisfy all the requirements imposed upon them, so we can use nodal voltages in circuit analysis and not have to write Kirchhoff's voltage-law equations, since they will automatically be satisfied.

In performing nodal analysis we need not actually draw the closed areas around each node. The effect is the same if we label each node with a nodal voltage and take any branch voltage as the algebraic sum of the nodal voltages of its nodes. The voltage is taken as positive if the branch points away from

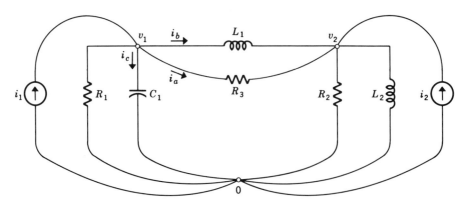

Fig. 3-16   A network with two unknown node voltages.

the node and negative if the branch is oriented toward the node.   In effect
we can always imagine that the imaginary area has been drawn.

Note that the nodal voltage is the actual voltage drop between the node in
question and the reference node.   In traversing a path from any node to the
reference node, we leave the closed area of the node in question, but we *enter
and leave* all other areas.   Thus only the contribution of the nodal voltage in
question appears.   For instance, in Fig. 3-15 we can compute the voltage drop
between node 3 and the reference node by summing the drops in the branches
4, 2, and 1.   This yields

$$v_{n3} + v_{n2} - v_{n2} + v_{n1} - v_{n1} = v_{n3} \tag{3-22}$$

The use of nodal voltages automatically satisfies Kirchhoff's voltage law.
To solve for the $N - 1$ unknown nodal voltages we shall write Kirchhoff's
current-law equations at $N - 1$ nodes of the network.   We have seen (Sec.
2-3) that $N - 1$ independent Kirchhoff's current-law equations can be written
at *any* $N - 1$ nodes of an N-node network.   It is conventional, but not necessary, to omit the reference node in writing these equations.

In nodal analysis it is convenient to work with unknown nodal voltages
and known currents, that is, to use current generators as the independent
generators.   If voltage generators are present in the system, they can be converted to current generators by the techniques of Sec. 2-4.

As an example of this procedure consider the network of Fig. 3-16.   It has
three nodes; hence there are two unknown nodal voltages.   They are labeled
v_1 and v_2, with the subscript n omitted for convenience.   Imagine that the
nodes are enclosed.

Before analyzing the complete circuit, we shall consider the currents in some
of the individual elements.   Let us obtain the current in R_3.   The voltage

drop across it is $v_1 - v_2$, so

$$i_a = \frac{v_1 - v_2}{R_3} = (v_1 - v_2)G_3 \tag{3-23}$$

where we have used conductance for convenience [see Eq. (1-29)]. Now let us obtain i_b through the inductance L_1. From Eq. (1-94) we have

$$i_b = \frac{1}{L_1} \int (v_1 - v_2)\, dt \tag{3-24}$$

Finally, the current through C_1 is given by

$$i_c = C_1 \frac{dv_1}{dt} \tag{3-25}$$

There is only one voltage term here, since C_1 has one of its terminals connected to the reference node.

Now let us apply Kirchhoff's current law to nodes 1 and 2; that is, we shall say that the net current leaving these nodes is equal to zero. To reduce the amount of writing we shall represent differentiation and integration by the operator notation of Eqs. (3-12) and (3-13). Then, applying Kirchhoff's current law at nodes 1 and 2, in turn, we have

$$0 = -i_1 + G_1 v_1 + C_1 p v_1 + \frac{1}{L_1 p}(v_1 - v_2) + G_3(v_1 - v_2) \tag{3-26a}$$

$$0 = \frac{1}{L_1 p}(v_2 - v_1) + G_3(v_2 - v_1) + G_2 v_2 + \frac{1}{L_2 p}v_2 - i_2 \tag{3-26b}$$

Rearranging these equations, we obtain

$$i_1 = \left(G_1 + G_3 + C_1 p + \frac{1}{L_1 p}\right)v_1 - \left(G_3 + \frac{1}{L_1 p}\right)v_2 \tag{3-27a}$$

$$i_2 = -\left(G_3 + \frac{1}{L_1 p}\right)v_1 + \left(G_3 + \frac{1}{L_1 p} + G_2 + \frac{1}{L_2 p}\right)v_2 \tag{3-27b}$$

After these equations have been solved for v_1 and v_2, we can obtain the voltage across each element. Then the current in each branch can be obtained from the voltage drop across it.

The form of Eqs. (3-27) is more convenient for solving for v_1 and v_2. With some practice these can be written directly, without first being written in the form of Eqs. (3-26). There are some rules that will simplify this procedure. It is not essential to follow them, but it is often convenient to do so. First, we write the equations for the nodes in the same order that they are numbered. The right-hand side contains all the terms with unknowns, in numbered order (i.e., the v_1 terms first, v_2 second, and so on). The left-hand side consists of known current generators. Thus the left-hand side of the equation consists of

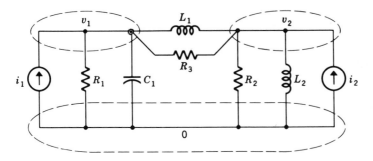

Fig. 3-17   An alternative representation of the network of Fig. 3-15.

the algebraic sum of all the known currents entering the node in question.   The
unknown current leaving a node through an element is "due" to the voltage
drop across the element.   The term containing v_1 in the first equation or v_2 in
the second one is called the *self-current* term; the others are called *coupled
currents*.   At each node the self-current term is the positive sum of all the
currents "due" to the node voltage.   If an element is connected between the
node in question and a node other than the reference node, a coupled term
results.   This is the negative of the current through the element "due" to the
other node voltage.   These rules are helpful in writing equations in the form
of Eqs. (3-27), but even without them, after some practice such equations
can be written directly.

The drawing of Fig. 3-16 is somewhat unconventional.   Usually such a
circuit would be represented by a drawing like that of Fig. 3-17.   Figures 3-16
and 3-17 are equivalent.   Each dashed area of Fig. 3-16 can be considered
to enclose a single node.   Note that only zero-resistance conductors are
enclosed within these areas.   If two or more nodes of a network are *connected
by ideal conductors*, then the voltage drop between these nodes will be zero.
Such points can be considered as one node.   To demonstrate this, consider that
the closed areas can still define nodal voltages as before, and that in addition,
Kirchhoff's current law can be applied to any enclosed areas, as well as to the
nodes.   Hence the nodal-analysis equations will be the same for Figs. 3-16 and
3-17, and they are equivalent.   The dashed curves of Fig. 3-17 are usually
omitted.

To further illustrate nodal analysis, let us consider another, somewhat more
complex example.   The network illustrated in Fig. 3-18*a* is drawn in the conventional way.   Figure 3-18*b* shows the schematic for this network redrawn in
such a way that the individual nodes are clearly defined (after some practice
in solving several of these networks it will not be necessary to redraw the
diagram or enclose the nodes).   Then, writing Kirchhoff's current-law equations for each node in turn and using the operator notation of Eqs. (3-12) and

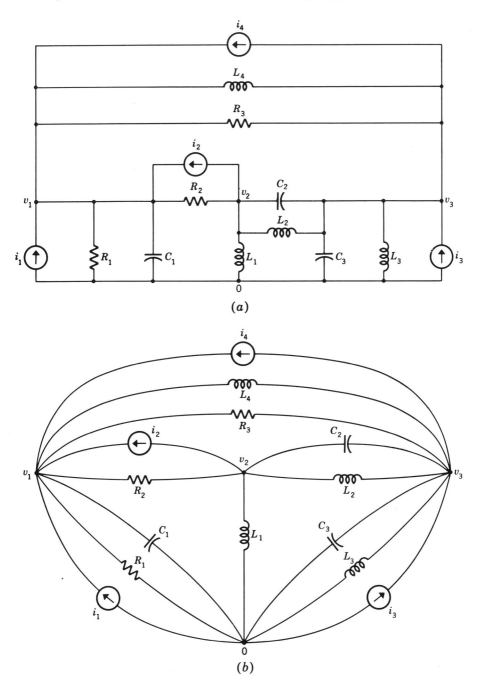

Fig. 3-18 (a) A conventional network diagram; (b) an alternative representation of this network with the nodes clearly indicated.

(3-13), we obtain

$$0 = -i_1 + v_1 G_1 + v_1 p C_1 + G_2(v_1 - v_2) - i_2 + G_3(v_1 - v_3)$$
$$+ \frac{1}{L_4 p}(v_1 - v_3) - i_4 \quad (3\text{-}28a)$$

$$0 = i_2 + G_2(v_2 - v_1) + \frac{1}{L_1 p} v_2 + \frac{1}{L_2 p}(v_2 - v_3) + C_2 p(v_2 - v_3) \quad (3\text{-}28b)$$

$$0 = -i_3 + \frac{1}{L_3 p} v_3 + C_3 p v_3 + C_2 p(v_3 - v_2) + \frac{1}{L_2 p}(v_3 - v_2)$$
$$+ G_3(v_3 - v_1) + \frac{1}{L_4 p}(v_3 - v_1) + i_4 \quad (3\text{-}28c)$$

where $G = 1/R$.   Then, rewriting these equations, we obtain

$$i_1 + i_2 + i_4 = \left(G_1 + G_2 + G_3 + C_1 p + \frac{1}{L_4 p}\right) v_1 - G_2 v_2$$
$$- \left(G_3 + \frac{1}{L_4 p}\right) v_3 \quad (3\text{-}29a)$$

$$-i_2 = -G_2 v_1 + \left(G_2 + C_2 p + \frac{1}{L_1 p} + \frac{1}{L_2 p}\right) v_2 - \left(C_2 p + \frac{1}{L_2 p}\right) v_3 \quad (3\text{-}29b)$$

$$i_3 - i_4 = -\left(G_3 + \frac{1}{L_4 p}\right) v_1 - \left(C_2 p + \frac{1}{L_2 p}\right) v_2$$
$$+ \left(G_3 + C_2 p + C_3 p + \frac{1}{L_2 p} + \frac{1}{L_3 p} + \frac{1}{L_4 p}\right) v_3 \quad (3\text{-}29c)$$

As in the case of loop analysis, we can write a matrix of the coefficients of the unknowns:

$$\begin{bmatrix} a_{11} & a_{12} & a_{13} \\ a_{21} & a_{22} & a_{23} \\ a_{31} & a_{32} & a_{33} \end{bmatrix}$$

$$= \begin{bmatrix} G_1 + G_2 + G_3 + C_1 p + \dfrac{1}{L_1 p} & -G_2 & -\left(G_3 + \dfrac{1}{L_4 p}\right) \\ -G_2 & G_2 + C_2 p + \dfrac{1}{L_1 p} + \dfrac{1}{L_2 p} & -\left(C_2 p + \dfrac{1}{L_2 p}\right) \\ -\left(G_3 + \dfrac{1}{L_4 p}\right) & -\left(C_2 p + \dfrac{1}{L_2 p}\right) & G_3 + (C_2 + C_3)p + \left(\dfrac{1}{L_2} + \dfrac{1}{L_3} + \dfrac{1}{L_4}\right)\dfrac{1}{p} \end{bmatrix} \quad (3\text{-}30)$$

The right-hand side of Eq. (3-30) is a symmetric matrix; that is,

$$a_{ij} = a_{ji} \qquad i = 1, 2, 3; j = 1, 2, 3 \qquad (3\text{-}31)$$

The terms a_{11}, a_{22}, and a_{33} constitute the *principal diagonal* of the matrix. Those terms which are not on the principal diagonal indicate elements that are connected between nodes. For instance, a_{ij} represents elements connected between nodes i and j.   Also, a_{ji} represents the same thing.   Thus Eq. (3-31) results.   In general, if the network contains dependent generators, the symmetry of Eq. (3-31) will not result.

Nonconnected networks

To analyze a nonconnected network we can connect it, as was discussed in Sec. 3-2.   The nodal analysis then proceeds as in a connected network, and we can thus obtain the voltage across and/or the current through each element. However, there is one important fact that must be understood: *the potential difference between nodes in separate parts of a nonconnected network will not affect any of the currents in the network.*   For instance, consider the network topologically illustrated in Fig. 3-19a.   If we add a branch between nodes a and b, as shown in Fig. 3-19b, the network becomes connected.   Since this branch does not lie in any mesh, there will be no loop currents in it if we perform a loop analysis.   No matter what this branch is, then, it will not enter into the loop equations.   Hence it will not affect any of the currents throughout the network.

We have chosen to make this added branch a voltage generator v.   Since it does not enter into the loop equation, as discussed, it will not affect the currents in the network or the voltage drops across any of the elements of the network.   *However, the voltage between nodes in the two separate parts of the network will be a function of v* (for example, consider the voltage drop between nodes a and b).   In general, we shall not be able to determine the potential difference between nodes in separate parts of a network without additional information.   However, since we can determine the voltage drop across any elements of the network, we can determine the potential difference between any nodes in the same part of a network.   Thus in analyzing a nonconnected network we can add branches, which do not lie in meshes, to form a connected

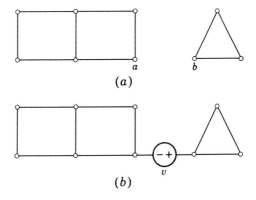

*Fig. 3-19   (a) A nonconnected network;
(b) the network of (a) connected by the
addition of a branch that will not cause
any of the branch currents to change.*

(a)

(b)

network. However, we must not use the results of this analysis to obtain the potential difference between nodes in separate parts of the network.

3-4 Nodal analysis of networks with mutual inductance

It is tedious to apply nodal analysis directly to circuits that contain coupled coils. This is because the mutual-inductance terms are dependent upon the currents in the coupled coils, and these currents are unknown. In addition, the unknowns in nodal analysis are voltages. Thus an expression for these currents in terms of the nodal voltages should be obtained. One convenient way of analyzing these circuits is to replace the coupled coils by equivalent circuits that do not have coupled coils. To demonstrate that these circuits are equivalent we need only show that their circuit equations are the same (see Sec. 2-4). Remember that such equivalencies are valid only for external conditions.

Consider Fig. 3-20, where a pair of coupled coils is illustrated. We have assumed that each coil is connected at one end, as shown. The equations for this circuit are

$$v_1 = L_1 p i_1 + M p i_2 \tag{3-32a}$$

$$v_2 = M p i_1 + L_2 p i_2 \tag{3-32b}$$

where we have used the operator notation of Eqs. (3-12) and (3-13). Now consider the circuit of Fig. 3-20b. Its equations are

$$v_1 = (L_1 - M) p i_1 + M p(i_1 + i_2) \tag{3-33a}$$

$$v_2 = M p(i_1 + i_2) + (L_2 - M)i_2 \tag{3-33b}$$

After simplifying, Eqs. (3-32) result. Thus Figs. 3-20a and b are equivalent circuits, as far as external conditions are concerned. If Fig. 3-20b is used to replace Fig. 3-20a in an analysis, then the v_1 and v_2 that are obtained will be

Fig. 3-20 (a) A pair of coupled coils with a common terminal; (b) a circuit that is equivalent to (a) for external conditions.

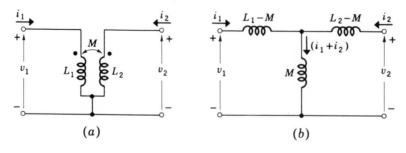

(a)   (b)

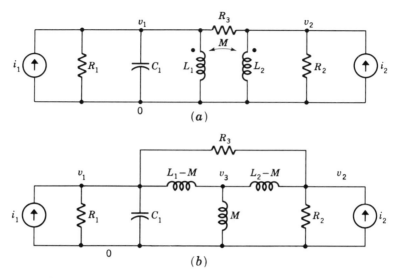

Fig. 3-21 (a) A circuit containing mutual inductance; (b) a circuit that is equivalent to (a) for conditions external to the coupled coils.

the actual voltages across the coils. If the currents are desired, we substitute v_1 and v_2 into Fig. 3-20a or Eqs. (3-32). That is, we use the original circuit to obtain the internal conditions.

If the position of one of the dots in Fig. 3-20a were changed, then M would be replaced by its negative in Fig. 3-20b. The appearance of a negative inductance term does not mean that the law of conservation of energy is violated (see Sec. 1-13), since this negative inductance cannot appear by itself. In Sec. 1-13 we demonstrated the conditions that are imposed upon M by the law of conservation of energy. (Note that at times any *one* of the inductors of Fig. 3-20b can be negative.)

Let us illustrate the use of this equivalent circuit with a nodal analysis of the network of Fig. 3-21a. We replace the coupled coils with the circuit of Fig. 3-20b. Note that another node is added when this is done; the result is Fig. 3-21b. Then, applying nodal analysis, we obtain

$$0 = -i_1 + G_1v_1 + C_1pv_1 + \frac{1}{(L_1 - M)p}(v_1 - v_3) + G_3(v_1 - v_2) \qquad (3\text{-}34a)$$

$$0 = -i_2 + G_3(v_1 - v_2) + \frac{1}{(L_2 - M)p}(v_2 - v_3) + G_2v_2 \qquad (3\text{-}34b)$$

$$0 = \frac{1}{(L_1 - M)p}(v_3 - v_1) + \frac{1}{(L_2 - M)p}(v_3 - v_2) + \frac{1}{Mp}v_3 \qquad (3\text{-}34c)$$

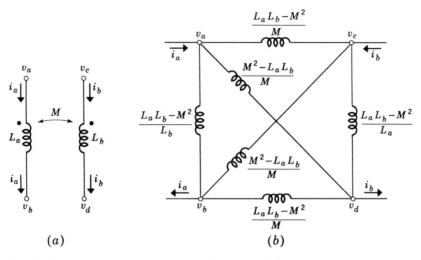

Fig. 3-22   (a) A pair of coupled coils; (b) a circuit that is equivalent to (a) for external conditions.   The values given are inductances in henrys.

Rewriting these equations, we have

$$i_1 = \left[G_1 + G_3 + C_1 p + \frac{1}{(L_1 - M)p} \right] v_1 - G_3 v_2 - \frac{1}{(L_1 - M)p} v_3 \quad (3\text{-}35a)$$

$$i_2 = -G_3 v_1 + \left[G_2 + G_3 + \frac{1}{(L_2 - M)p} \right] v_2 - \frac{1}{(L_2 - M)p} v_3 \quad (3\text{-}35b)$$

$$0 = -\frac{1}{(L_1 - M)p} v_1 - \frac{1}{(L_2 - M)p} v_2$$
$$+ \left[\frac{1}{(L_1 - M)p} + \frac{1}{(L_2 - M)p} + \frac{1}{Mp} \right] v_3 \quad (3\text{-}35c)$$

Let us now consider the coupled coils shown in Fig. 3-22.   They are similar to those of Fig. 3-20a, except that the terminals of the coils are not connected together.   The nodal voltages are marked v_a, v_b, v_c, and v_d.   Assume that these coils are part of a network where these nodal voltages are used.   Before we obtain an equivalent circuit here, let us obtain equations for the current through the coils in terms of their nodal voltages.   We can use these equations directly in a nodal analysis.   From Fig. 3-22 we have

$$v_a - v_b = L_a \frac{di_a}{dt} + M \frac{di_b}{dt} \quad (3\text{-}36a)$$

$$v_c - v_d = M \frac{di_a}{dt} + L_b \frac{di_b}{dt} \quad (3\text{-}36b)$$

Solution of these simultaneous equations for di_a/dt and di_b/dt yields

$$\frac{di_a}{dt} = \frac{L_b}{L_a L_b - M^2}(v_a - v_b) - \frac{M}{L_a L_b - M^2}(v_c - v_d) \tag{3-37a}$$

$$\frac{di_b}{dt} = -\frac{M}{L_a L_b - M^2}(v_a - v_b) + \frac{L_a}{L_a L_b - M^2}(v_c - v_d) \tag{3-37b}$$

Integrating both sides of these equations, we obtain

$$i_a = \frac{L_b}{L_a L_b - M^2}\int (v_a - v_b)\,dt - \frac{M}{L_a L_b - M^2}\int (v_c - v_d)\,dt \tag{3-38a}$$

$$i_b = -\frac{M}{L_a L_b - M^2}\int (v_a - v_b)\,dt + \frac{L_a}{L_a L_b - M^2}\int (v_c - v_d)\,dt \tag{3-38b}$$

and in operator notation this becomes

$$i_a = \frac{L_b}{(L_a L_b - M^2)p}(v_a - v_b) - \frac{M}{(L_a L_b - M^2)p}(v_c - v_d) \tag{3-39a}$$

$$i_b = -\frac{M}{(L_a L_b - M^2)p}(v_a - v_b) + \frac{L_a}{(L_a L_b - M^2)p}(v_c - v_d) \tag{3-39b}$$

An equivalent circuit for these equations is drawn in Fig. 3-22b. Note that its equations are the same as Eqs. (3-39) (note that the negative inductances exist only inside the equivalent circuit; we cannot obtain an external negative inductance). This equivalence is valid for any set of terminals. We shall illustrate the use of this equivalent circuit with the network of Fig. 3-23a. Note that, in relation to Fig. 3-22, $L_1 = L_a$ and $L_2 = L_b$ and

$$v_1 = v_a \tag{3-40a}$$

$$v_2 = v_c \tag{3-40b}$$

$$v_3 = v_d \tag{3-40c}$$

The nodal voltage corresponding to v_b is zero, since its node is chosen to be the reference node. We write the nodal equations in the usual way and obtain

$$i_1 = \left[G_1 + G_2 + \frac{L_2}{(L_1 L_2 - M^2)p}\right]v_1 + \left[\frac{M}{(L_1 L_2 - M^2)p} - G_2\right]v_2$$
$$- \frac{M}{(L_1 L_2 - M^2)p}v_3 \tag{3-41a}$$

$$i_2 = -\left[G_2 - \frac{M}{(L_1 L_2 - M^2)p}\right]v_1 + \left[G_2 + C_2 p + \frac{L_1}{(L_1 L_2 - M^2)p}\right]v_2$$
$$- \left[C_2 p + \frac{L_1}{(L_1 L_2 - M^2)p}\right]v_3 \tag{3-41b}$$

$$-i_2 = -\frac{M}{(L_1 L_2 - M^2)p}v_1 - \left[C_2 p + \frac{L_1}{(L_1 L_2 - M^2)p}\right]v_2$$
$$+ \left[C_2 p + \frac{L_1}{(L_1 L_2 - M^2)p}\right]v_3 \tag{3-41c}$$

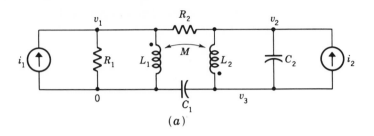

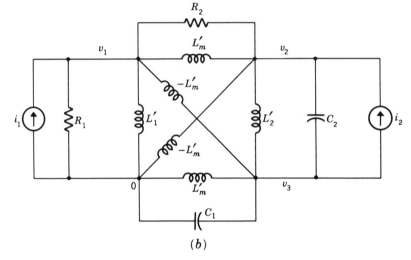

Fig. 3-23   (a) A network containing coupled coils; (b) a network that is equivalent to (a) for conditions external to the coils. $L_1' = (L_1L_2 - M^2)/L_2$, $L_2 = (L_1L_2 - M^2)/L_1$, and $L_m' = (L_1L_2 - M^2)/-M$.

Note that the mutual inductance used here is the negative of that in Fig. 3-22b. This is because the position of one of the dots has been changed.

If more than two coils are coupled, then the current in each of them can be obtained by means of a procedure similar to that used in deriving Eqs. (3-39) and Fig. 3-22b.

3-5   Cut sets and cut-set analysis

If we compare loop analysis and nodal analysis, we see that there is considerably more freedom available in the choice of loops than there is in the choice of nodes. This is because nodal analysis is a special case of another, more general analysis technique called *cut-set analysis*.   This is not to say that nodal analysis is not itself completely general.   Just as basic meshes can be used to analyze a network, but other sets of meshes can also be used, so nodal analysis can always be used to analyze a network, but other *similar* procedures can also be used.

To develop the more general analysis technique we shall define a *cut set*. Let us consider that the networks with which we shall be dealing are connected. Then a cut set is a set of branches which, when removed from a network, splits it into two, and *no more* than two, separate parts; if any one of the branches of the cut set is replaced, the network will be connected again. That is, a cut set consists of the minimum number of branches that split the network into two parts. For the purpose of this discussion we shall consider a node to be a separate part of a network.

To clarify this definition of a cut set consider Fig. 3-24. The simplest cut set in this network is branch 9. When it is removed, the network is split into two separate parts. Another cut set consists of branches 2, 4, and 8. When these are removed, the network is split into two, and only two, parts. In addition, if any one of these branches is replaced, the network will again be connected. Another cut set is branches 1, 2, and 8. One part of the network then consists just of node 2 (this is allowable, since we are considering nodes as separate entities here). Other cut sets are branches 10 and 12, branches 8, 5, and 7, and branches 3, 4, and 7. A set of branches that does *not* constitute a cut set are branches 6, 7, and 9. This is because when they are removed the network is split into *three* parts (one of these is node 4).

Let us now define a *set of basic cut sets* in a connected network. First we must choose a tree. A basic cut set consists of one, and only one, tree branch, plus any chords necessary to break the network into two parts. Such a cut set will always exist. This can be demonstrated by means of a construction procedure. Consider that we have just a tree of the network. Removing any one branch of it will break the remaining subtree into two parts. If it does not, then there must be a path in the subtree between the nodes of the removed branch. This is impossible since that path plus the removed tree branch would be part of a mesh, which is not allowed in a tree. Removing a branch from a tree cannot break it into more than two parts. Note [see the discussion preceeding Eq. (3-17)] that the addition of a branch to a network in S separate

Fig. 3-24   A connected network.

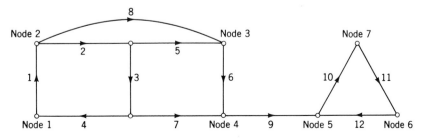

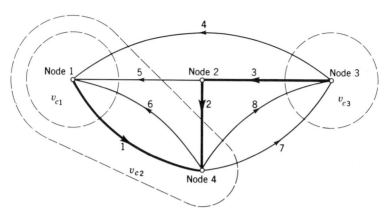

Fig. 3-25   *A connected network.   A tree is shown by the heavy lines, and the basic cut sets are indicated by the dashed lines.*

parts can connect only two of these parts.   Thus the subtree is in only two separate parts.

Now consider that all the chords of the network are removed.   We replace one of them in the network, and if the resulting network is still in two parts, we leave it there.   If replacing the chord causes the network to become connected, then we remove it.   We test each chord in turn, and when we have finished, the network will still be in two parts.   Thus the removed chords plus the original tree branch constitute a cut set.   Note that if any of the branches of this cut set are replaced, the network becomes connected.

As an illustration consider Fig. 3-25.   We remove branch 1 from the tree; then the two parts of the tree are node 1 and the part consisting of branches 2 and 3 and nodes 2, 3, and 4.   Now consider the chords.   If branches 7 and 8 are reconnected to the network, then the network will still be in two separate parts.   However, the addition of any of branches 4, 5, or 6 will cause the network to become connected.   Thus branches 1, 4, 5, and 6 constitute a basic cut set.   This is indicated by the closed area in Fig. 3-25, which cuts these branches and no others.   The closed area completely encloses one of the separated parts of the network, and the other separated part is completely outside it.   The branches of the cut set, which separate these two parts, pass through the area.

We can repeat the previous procedure with each branch of the tree in turn. In Fig. 3-25 the two remaining basic cut sets are branches 2, 4, 5, 7, and 8 and branches 3, 4, 7, and 8.   In an N-node network there are $N - 1$ tree branches, and thus $N - 1$ basic cut sets can be obtained.   All $N - 1$ of these are called a *set of basic cut sets.*

Now let us define *cut-set voltages*.   These are fictitious voltages that are defined in essentially the same way as were the nodal voltages (see Sec. 3-3).

The closed areas used to define them are now the ones used to define the cut sets. The interior of each closed area of Fig. 3-25 is marked with a cut-set voltage (v_{c1}, v_{c2}, or v_{c3}).

We must specify how the branch voltages are obtained from the cut-set voltages and verify that the branch voltages so obtained are valid ones. This procedure is similar to that for nodal analysis (see Sec. 3-3), and some of the details are omitted here. A branch voltage is the algebraic sum of all the cut-set voltages through whose closed area the branch passes. If the branch is oriented so that it leaves the closed area, then the cut-set voltages are taken as positive. If the branch is oriented so that it enters the closed area, then the cut-set voltages are taken as negative. For instance, in Fig. 3-25

$$v_{b1} = v_{c1} \tag{3-42a}$$

$$v_{b2} = -v_{c2} \tag{3-42b}$$

$$v_{b3} = v_{c3} \tag{3-42c}$$

$$v_{b4} = -v_{c1} - v_{c2} + v_{c3} \tag{3-42d}$$

$$v_{b5} = -v_{c1} - v_{c2} \tag{3-42e}$$

$$v_{b6} = -v_{c1} \tag{3-42f}$$

$$v_{b7} = v_{c2} - v_{c3} \tag{3-42g}$$

$$v_{b8} = v_{c2} - v_{c3} \tag{3-42h}$$

Note that a branch voltage may be expressed as a function of more than two cut-set voltages. We must demonstrate that the tree-branch voltages determined from the cut-set voltages are independent of each other, that the tree-branch voltages determine the cut-set voltages, and that the sum of the branch voltages obtained from the cut-set voltages satisfies Kirchhoff's voltage law around any loop.

Each tree branch will be a member of one, and only one, basic cut set. This follows directly from the definition of a basic cut set. Thus each tree-branch voltage will be equal to (plus or minus) its cut-set voltage. Hence the tree-branch voltages will be independent of each other. In addition, because of this (plus or minus) one-to-one correspondence, the tree-branch voltages will determine the cut-set voltages.

Now we need only demonstrate that the tree-branch voltages obtained from cut-set voltages satisfy Kirchhoff's voltage law around every loop. This discussion parallels that of Sec. 3-4, except that cut-set voltages instead of nodal voltages are used. It will not be repeated here.

There are $N - 1$ unknown cut-set voltages. To determine these we make use of $N - 1$ Kirchhoff's current-law equations. We could write these at any $N - 1$ nodes of the network. However, we can also use a somewhat different procedure. We shall utilize the form of Kirchhoff's current law which states that the net current into (or out of) any closed area is zero. The closed

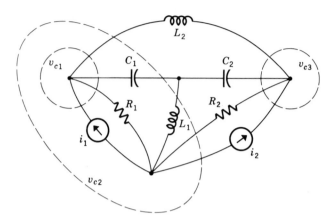

Fig. 3-26   *A network that is topologically equivalent to Fig. 3-25.*

areas that we shall use are those used to define the cut sets.   All the current is in the branches of the network.   The branches that pass through the closed areas are the branches of the cut set defined by the area.   Thus we can state that the algebraic sum of the current through the branches of a cut set is equal to zero.   We designate current in a branch of a cut set as positive if it leaves the closed area defining the cut set and as negative if it enters that closed area.

Let us illustrate this procedure with the circuit of Fig. 3-26.   This circuit is topologically equivalent to that of Fig. 3-25, with the same cut sets.   We shall designate the net sum of currents through a cut set as zero for each cut set in turn.   Note that the voltage drop across each branch is used to determine the current in it.   Then

$$0 = -i_1 + G_1 v_{c1} + C_1 p(v_{c1} + v_{c2}) + \frac{1}{L_2 p}(v_{c1} + v_{c2} - v_{c3}) \tag{3-43a}$$

$$0 = \frac{1}{L_2 p}(v_{c1} + v_{c2} - v_{c3}) + C_1 p(v_{c1} + v_{c2}) + \frac{1}{L_1 p} v_{c2} + G_2(v_{c2} - v_{c3}) + i_2 \tag{3-43b}$$

$$0 = -i_2 + G_2(v_{c3} - v_{c2}) + C_2 p v_{c3} + \frac{1}{L_2 p}(v_{c3} - v_{c1} - v_{c2}) \tag{3-43c}$$

Rewriting these equations, we obtain

$$i_1 = \left(G_1 + C_1 p + \frac{1}{L_2 p}\right) v_{c1} + \left(C_1 p + \frac{1}{L_2 p}\right) v_{c2} - \frac{1}{L_2 p} v_{c3} \tag{3-44a}$$

$$-i_2 = \left(C_1 p + \frac{1}{L_2 p}\right) v_{c1} + \left(G_2 + C_1 p + \frac{1}{L_2 p} + \frac{1}{L_1 p}\right) v_{c2}$$
$$- \left(G_2 + \frac{1}{L_2 p}\right) v_{c3} \tag{3-44b}$$

$$i_2 = -\frac{1}{L_2 p} v_{c1} - \left(G_2 + \frac{1}{L_2 p}\right) v_{c2} + \left(G_2 + C_2 p + \frac{1}{L_2 p}\right) v_{c3} \tag{3-44c}$$

As in the case of nodal analysis, equations of this form are more suitable for solution than those in the form of Eqs. (3-43).   After some practice equations of the form of Eqs. (3-44) can be written directly.   The following rules can prove helpful here.   Write equations for cut sets in the order in which they are numbered, with the terms containing unknowns on the right-hand side in numbered order (the v_{c1} terms first, the v_{c2} terms second, and so on); the left-hand side of the equations then consists of the known currents entering the closed area that defines the cut set in question.   The terms containing v_{c1} in the first equation, v_{c2} in the second equation, and so on, are called the *self-current terms*, and the other unknown terms are called *coupled currents*. For each cut set the self-current terms are those that would exist if the branches of the cut set in question were not members of any other cut sets.   The coupled terms occur when a branch is a member of more than one cut set. The sign of these terms depends upon the relative location of the cut-set defining areas (for example, if the cut-set voltage for which the equation is written and the coupled cut-set voltage add when the branch voltage is computed, then the sign is positive).

Let us now generalize the cut-set-analysis procedure.   It is not necessary to use basic cut sets for a cut-set analysis.   They were used in the example to demonstrate that the number of cut-set voltages equals the number of tree-branch voltages and that the cut-set and tree-branch voltages are related by a linearly independent set of equations.   If we can demonstrate these two facts without using basic cut sets, then the branch voltages obtained from the cut-set voltages will be valid (note that all branch voltages generated by any cut-set voltages satisfy Kirchhoff's voltage law around every loop).   Then, in general, we need only choose any $N - 1$ cuts sets and their cut-set voltages. Choose a tree and write the tree-branch voltages in terms of the cut-set voltages.   If these equations are linearly independent, then a valid set of cut sets has been obtained.   If they are not, then we choose another set of cut sets and try again.   This procedure is tedious.   There is a somewhat less general construction procedure, which is similar to that for construction of a valid set of loops.   First we choose a cut set, and then take any branch of the cut set and "collapse" it; that is, we remove that branch and coalesce its nodes. If any other branches have both their nodes coalesced together by this operation, we remove them as well (these branches are *not* called collapsed).   We choose a cut set in the remaining network and collapse one of its branches, repeating this procedure until only one node exists.   All the nodes will be brought together by the collapsed branches.   Thus the network made up of the collapsed branches will contain all the nodes of the original network.   There will be no loops in this "subnetwork," since each node is brought into it once, and only once, by only one branch.   The subnetwork of the collapsed branches will then be a tree.   Each cut set will contain a "new" tree branch, and there will be a cut set for each tree branch.   Thus the equations relating the tree-branch voltages and the cut-set voltages will be linearly independent, and a valid set of cut sets will have been obtained.

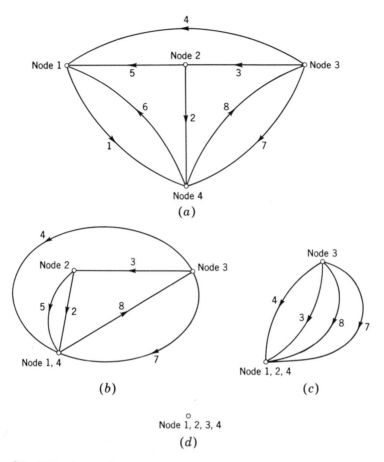

Fig. 3-27   A procedure for the generation of a valid set of cut sets: (a) the original network; (b) the network formed by the collapse of branch 1; (c) the network formed by the collapse of branch 2 of (b); (d) the network formed by the collapse of branch 3 of (c).

This procedure is illustrated in Fig. 3-27.   For instance, in Fig. 3-27a, if we choose the cut set consisting of branches 1, 4, 5, and 6 and then collapse branch 1, Fig. 3-27b results.   Then, in Fig. 3-27b, if we choose the cut set consisting of branches 4, 5, 2, 8, and 7 and then collapse branch 2, Fig. 3-27c results. There is only one cut set here; it is branches 4, 3, 8, and 7.   We collapse one of these branches—for example, branch 3—and the "one-node" network of Fig. 3-27d results.   A valid set of cut sets has been obtained.   The collapsed branches 1, 2, and 3 constitute a tree of the network.   Note that when branch 1 was collapsed, both nodes of branch 6 were brought together.   Hence branch 6 does not appear in Fig. 3-27b.

Let us now demonstrate that an appropriate choice of cut sets will usually be equivalent to nodal analysis. In choosing nodal voltages we originally placed $N - 1$ of the nodes in enclosed areas. The sets of branches cut by each of these areas form a set of cut sets, since each cut set splits the node in question from the rest of the network (see, for instance, Fig. 3-15). These can be shown by the arguments of Sec. 3-3 to be a valid set of cut sets.

A problem can arise in network like that of Fig. 3-24, where there is a branch that does not lie in a mesh. The branches incident on a node of such a branch (for example, node 4) do not constitute a cut set because they split the network into three parts, so in this network nodal analysis is not a special case of cut-set analysis. However, we can alter this situation. We have seen that a branch which is not in a mesh will not affect the circuit equations (see Sec. 3-3), and we can replace it by any other branch without changing the current in or the voltage across any other element. If we replace such a branch by a short circuit, then we can bring its two nodes together to form a single one. For instance, in Fig. 3-24 we can coalesce nodes 4 and 5 without changing any of the currents in or voltages across any of the branches. For the new network the branches incident on any node constitute a cut set, and we can again state that nodal analysis is a special case of cut-set analysis.

Nonconnected networks

We can apply cut-set analysis to nonconnected networks in the same way we applied nodal analysis to these networks. The discussions and limitations of this subject presented in Sec. 3-3 are also applicable here.

The use of cut-set analysis in circuits containing mutual inductance

When cut-set analysis is applied to circuits containing mutual inductance, the equivalent circuit of Fig. 3-20b can be used if the coupled coils have a common terminal. If they do not, then the equivalent circuit of Fig. 3-22b can be used.

3-6 Analysis of networks containing dependent generators

Circuits with dependent generators are usually used in analyzing electronic devices. The application of mesh, nodal, or cut-set analysis to networks that contain dependent generators (see Sec. 2-5) is very similar to the analysis of networks that contain only independent generators. In fact, in writing the equations, we can *initially* treat the dependent generators as though they were independent. However, the voltage or current of the dependent generator is usually expressed as a function of unknown quantities, and additional simul-

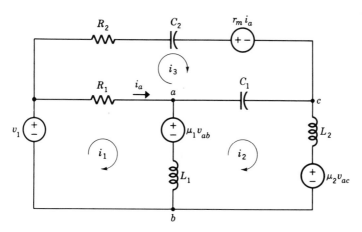

Fig. 3-28   *A three-loop circuit containing dependent voltage generators.*

taneous equations may have to be obtained.   In addition, any unknown dependent-generator terms should be grouped with unknown quantities in the equations.   (The equations will not be wrong if this grouping is not used, but they will not be in the best form for solution.)   It is also convenient to express all the unknowns in terms of loop currents if loop analysis is used, or nodal or cut-set voltages if nodal or cut-set analysis is used.

The analysis of circuits with dependent generators conceptually is the same as that for circuits with independent generators (the reader may find it helpful to review Sec. 2-5 before continuing).   The equations should be arranged in a form that is convenient for solution.

As illustrations of these procedures, let us consider some specific examples. Once the details of these examples are understood, most circuits containing dependent generators can be analyzed.   Consider the loop analysis of the network of Fig. 3-28.   We write the loop equations, at first treating the dependent generators as though they were independent generators.   Thus we have

$$v_1 - \mu_1 v_{ab} = (R_1 + L_1 p)i_1 - L_1 p i_2 - R_1 i_3 \tag{3-45a}$$

$$\mu_1 v_{ab} - \mu_2 v_{ac} = -L_1 p i_1 + \left[(L_1 + L_2)p + \frac{1}{C_1 p} \right] i_2 - \frac{1}{C_1 p} i_3 \tag{3-45b}$$

$$-r_m i_a = -R_1 i_1 - \frac{1}{C_1 p} i_2 + \left[R_1 + R_2 + \left(\frac{1}{C_1} + \frac{1}{C_2} \right) \frac{1}{p} \right] i_3 \tag{3-45c}$$

The terms v_{ab}, v_{ac}, and i_a are unknowns, so we must obtain three additional equations.   It is most convenient to express these in terms of the unknown mesh currents and known quantities:

$$i_a = i_1 - i_3 \tag{3-46a}$$

$$v_{ab} = R_1(i_3 - i_1) + v_1 \tag{3-46b}$$

$$v_{ac} = \frac{1}{C_1 p}(i_2 - i_3) \tag{3-46c}$$

In general, the dependent generators will be functions of branch currents and voltages between nodes. We can always express the branch currents in terms of the loop currents. The unknown voltages are then expressed in terms of loop currents and known quantities. That is, the desired voltage drop is obtained by summing voltage drops between the appropriate pairs of nodes. Note that this desired voltage drop may be obtained by summing over any convenient path between the nodes. For instance, to obtain v_{ab} we have used the path consisting of R_1 and v_1. We could also have used the single branch containing μv_{ab} and L_1 in series to obtain

$$v_{ab} = \mu_1 v_{ab} + L_1 p(i_1 - i_2) \tag{3-47a}$$

Note that v_{ab} appears on both sides of the equation. If $\mu_1 \neq 1$, we can solve this equation and obtain

$$v_{ab} = \frac{L_1}{1 - \mu_1} p(i_1 - i_2) \tag{3-47b}$$

which may be substituted for Eq. (3-46b) if we wish.

Once the dependent generators are expressed in terms of loop currents and known quantities, we substitute for them in the original set of loop equations. These equations are then arranged with all the unknowns grouped on the right-hand side of the equations. For instance, substituting Eqs. (3-46) into Eqs. (3-45) and rearranging, we obtain

$$(1 - \mu_1)v_1 = [R_1(1 - \mu_1) + L_1 p]i_1 - L_1 p i_2 - R_3(1 - \mu_1)i_3 \tag{3-48a}$$

$$\mu_1 v_1 = (-L_1 p + \mu_1 R_1)i_1 + \left[(L_1 + L_2)p + \frac{1}{C_1 p}(1 + \mu_2)\right]i_2$$
$$- \left[\frac{1}{C_1 p}(1 + \mu_2) + R_1 \mu_1\right]i_3 \tag{3-48b}$$

$$0 = -(R_1 - r_m)i_1 + \frac{1}{C_1 p}i_2 + \left[R_1 - r_m + R_2 + \left(\frac{1}{C_1} + \frac{1}{C_2}\right)\frac{1}{p}\right]i_3 \tag{3-48c}$$

These are then three simultaneous equations which can be solved for the mesh currents.

When we consider the solution of simultaneous equations, we shall see that it is very important to separate the known and unknown quantities. Equations in the form of Eqs. (3-45) and (3-46) are often much less desirable to work with then those in the form of Eqs. (3-48). The important idea here is that the

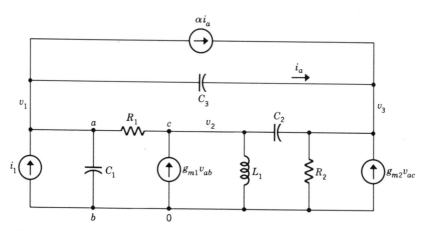

Fig. 3-29   *A three-node circuit containing dependent current generators.*

equations should be arranged so that the known and unknown quantities can be easily recognized and kept separate. Otherwise unknown quantities may be "solved" in terms of other unknowns, which does not result in a real solution.

As a further illustration, let us perform a nodal analysis of the network of Fig. 3-29. We write nodal equations for this network, for the time being treating the dependent generators as though they were independent. This yields

$$i_1 - \alpha i_a = [G_1 + (C_1 + C_3)p]v_1 - G_1v_2 - C_3pv_3 \qquad (3\text{-}49a)$$

$$g_{m1}v_{ab} = -G_1v_1 + \left(G_1 + \frac{1}{L_1p} + C_2p\right)v_2 - C_2pv_3 \qquad (3\text{-}49b)$$

$$\alpha i_a + g_{m2}v_{ac} = -C_3pv_1 - C_2pv_2 + [G_2 + (C_2 + C_3)p]v_3 \qquad (3\text{-}49c)$$

(remember that all points connected by ideal conductors can be treated as a single node). Now let us express the unknowns i_a, v_{ab}, and v_{ac} in terms of known quantities and the unknown nodal voltages. This yields

$$v_{ab} = v_1 \qquad (3\text{-}50a)$$

$$v_{ac} = v_1 - v_2 \qquad (3\text{-}50b)$$

$$i_a = C_3p(v_1 - v_3) \qquad (3\text{-}50c)$$

Substituting in Eqs. (3-49) and rearranging, we obtain

$$i_1 = \{G_1 + [C_1 + C_3(1 + \alpha)]p\}v_1 - G_1v_2 - C_3(1 + \alpha)pv_3 \qquad (3\text{-}51a)$$

$$0 = -(G_1 + g_{m1})v_1 + \left(G_1 + \frac{1}{L_1p} + C_2p\right)v_2 - C_2pv_3 \qquad (3\text{-}51b)$$

$$0 = -[C_3(1 + \alpha)p + g_{m2}]v_1 + (g_{m2} - C_2p)v_2$$
$$+ \{G_2 + [C_2 + C_3(1 + \alpha)]p\}v_3 \qquad (3\text{-}51c)$$

The details for cut-set analysis are very similar to those of nodal analysis and are left to the reader.

In the foregoing examples we have used dependent voltage generators for loop analysis and dependent current generators for nodal analysis. If this is not the case, then current generators and voltage generators can be interchanged by means of equivalent circuits, as discussed in Sec. 2-4.

For either Eqs. (3-48) or (3-51), if we write the matrix which is the array of the coefficients of the unknowns [see Eqs. (3-15) and (3-30)], we see that a symmetrical matrix no longer results. In general, with dependent generators this symmetry may not be present.

3-7   Analysis of networks containing time-varying elements

In this section we shall consider networks containing elements that vary with time. The integral-differential equations for these circuits will be determined by mesh, nodal, or cut-set analysis. There are other techniques that can be used to characterize these circuits, but at this point we shall discuss only those which follow directly from the analysis techniques of this chapter. In Chap. 7 we shall discuss more convenient procedures for analyzing time-varying circuits.

In loop analysis we write the voltage drop across an element in terms of the branch current in it, but we express the branch current in terms of the loop currents. The same procedure is used with time-varying elements, except that expressions for the voltage across the elements in terms of the currents through them are somewhat more elaborate. The expressions for time-varying elements are given in Secs. 1-6, 1-8, and 1-12. The technique for loop analysis of time-varying circuits is essentially the same as that for time-invariant circuits. In writing the loop equations it is best to write the voltage drop across the individual elements first, and then manipulate the equations into a form suitable for solution.

Let us illustrate with a loop analysis of the simple time-varying circuit in Fig. 3-30. The voltage across a time-varying capacitor is given by Eq. (1-66),

Fig. 3-30   A circuit containing time-varying elements. The elements r, c, and l are functions of time whereas R_1 and C_1 are fixed.

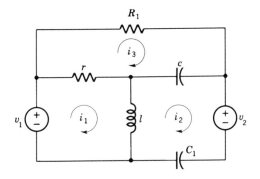

and the voltage across a time-varying inductor is given by Eq. (1-105). The voltage drop across a time-varying resistor is $v = ri$. If we use these equations to write the voltage drop across the time-varying elements and apply mesh analysis to Fig. 3-30, we obtain

$$0 = -v_1 + r(i_1 - i_3) + l\frac{d(i_1 - i_2)}{dt} + (i_1 - i_2)\frac{dl}{dt} \tag{3-52a}$$

$$0 = l\frac{d(i_2 - i_1)}{dt} + (i_2 - i_1)\frac{dl}{dt} + \frac{1}{c}\int (i_2 - i_3)\,dt + v_2 + \frac{1}{C_1}\int i_2\,dt \tag{3-52b}$$

$$0 = \frac{1}{c}\int (i_3 - i_2)\,dt + r(i_3 - i_1) + R_1 i_3 \tag{3-52c}$$

Rewriting these equations, we have

$$v_1 = ri_1 + l\frac{di_1}{dt} + i_1\frac{dl}{dt} - l\frac{di_2}{dt} - i_2\frac{dl}{dt} - ri_3 \tag{3-53a}$$

$$v_2 = -l\frac{di_1}{dt} - i_1\frac{dl}{dt} + l\frac{di_2}{dt} + i_2\frac{dl}{dt} + \frac{1}{c}\int i_2\,dt + \frac{1}{C_1}\int i_2\,dt - \frac{1}{c}\int i_3\,dt \tag{3-53b}$$

$$0 = -ri_1 - \frac{1}{c}\int i_2\,dt + ri_3 + \frac{1}{c}\int i_3\,dt + R_1 i_3 \tag{3-53c}$$

We can apply the operator notation of Eqs. (3-12) and (3-13) to write these equations in a more compact form:

$$v_1 = \left(r + lp + \frac{dl}{dt}\right)i_1 - \left(lp + \frac{dl}{dt}\right)i_2 - ri_3 \tag{3-54a}$$

$$v_2 = -\left(lp + \frac{dl}{dt}\right)i_1 + \left(lp + \frac{dl}{dt} + \frac{1}{cp} + \frac{1}{C_1p}\right)i_2 - \frac{1}{cp}i_3 \tag{3-54b}$$

$$0 = -ri_1 - \frac{1}{cp}i_2 + \left(r + \frac{1}{cp} + R_1\right)i_3 \tag{3-54c}$$

The operator notation could also have been used here to indicate the differentiation of l with respect to time. However, in order to avoid confusion, this has not been done. In the above equations, l, c, and r are known functions of time. These differential equations are somewhat more complex than those we have considered previously because the coefficients of the unknowns are not constant. Note that there is no change in the procedure for obtaining the loop equations when time-varying components are used. The relations for the voltage drops merely become somewhat more elaborate. Actually, these "more elaborate" expressions are *always* used. In the time-invariant case some of the terms become zero.

As a further illustration of the formulation of equations for time-varying networks, let us perform a nodal analysis. Here again, the basic procedure is the same as that for time-invariant elements. However, the currents through

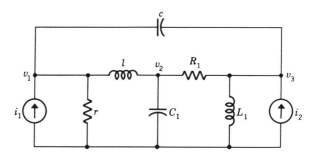

Fig. 3-31   A circuit containing time-varying elements.   The elements r, l, and c are functions of time whereas R_1, L_1, and C_1 are fixed.

the time-varying capacitors and inductors are given by Eqs. (1-65) and (1-106). Consider the network of Fig. 3-31.   Writing nodal equations, we have

$$0 = -i_1 + gv_1 + \frac{1}{l} \int (v_1 - v_2)\, dt + c\,\frac{d(v_1 - v_3)}{dt} + (v_1 - v_3)\frac{dc}{dt} \qquad (3\text{-}55a)$$

$$0 = \frac{1}{l} \int (v_2 - v_1)\, dt + C_1\frac{dv_2}{dt} + G_1(v_2 - v_3) \qquad (3\text{-}55b)$$

$$0 = -i_2 + \frac{1}{L_1} \int v_3\, dt + G_1(v_3 - v_2) + c\,\frac{d(v_3 - v_1)}{dt} + (v_3 - v_1)\frac{dc}{dt} \qquad (3\text{-}55c)$$

where $g = 1/r$.   Rewriting these equations and introducing operator notation, we obtain

$$i_1 = \left(g + \frac{1}{lp} + cp + \frac{dc}{dt}\right)v_1 - \frac{1}{lp}v_2 - \left(cp + \frac{dc}{dt}\right)v_3 \qquad (3\text{-}56a)$$

$$0 = -\frac{1}{lp}v_1 + \left(\frac{1}{lp} + C_1p + G_1\right)v_2 - G_1v_3 \qquad (3\text{-}56b)$$

$$i_2 = -\left(cp + \frac{dc}{dt}\right)v_1 - G_1v_2 + \left(\frac{1}{L_1p} + G_1 + cp + \frac{dc}{dt}\right)v_3 \qquad (3\text{-}56c)$$

If we write the matrix of the coefficients of the unknowns [see Eqs. (3-15) or (3-30)] of either Eqs. (3-54) or (3-56), we see that they are symmetrical. In general, the fact that there are time-varying elements in the network will not alter this symmetry.

Cut-set analysis of a network that contains time-varying elements is essentially the same as nodal analysis, and the details are left to the reader.

3-8   Analysis of circuits containing nonlinear elements: linearization

Let us now consider the mesh, nodal, and cut-set analysis of networks containing nonlinear elements.   In general, we encounter two classes of problems here.   In the first, the voltage across or the current through the nonlinear elements consists of a constant term plus a small time-varying term.   If we are interested only in the time-varying components of the currents and/or voltages in the circuit, and if they are small enough, then the nonlinear elements can be represented by linear incremental elements. Such representations were discussed in Secs. 1-8 and 1-12, where incremental capacitance and incremental inductance, respectively, were derived [see Eqs. (1-73) and (1-116)]. A similar analysis can be used to obtain an incremental resistance. That is, if a resistance is characterized by a nonlinear voltage-vs.-current curve, and its voltage and current vary in small increments about V_0 and I_0, respectively, then the incremental resistance is given by

$$r = \frac{dv}{di}\bigg|_{v = V_0,\ i = I_0} \tag{3-57}$$

(this derivation follows that given in Sec. 1-8).

Electronic devices such as transistor or vacuum-tube circuits are often analyzed in terms of incremental parameters. In this case the voltages or currents consist of a direct component plus a small time-varying quantity. The time-varying components are called the *signal voltages* or *signal currents*, and the direct components are called the *bias voltages* or *bias currents*. The bias voltage across and the bias current through the device specify its *operating point*. Then the signal voltages and currents cause the voltage across and the current through the device to vary slightly about the operating point. For instance, if

$$i = I_0 + I_1 \cos \omega t$$
$$v = V_0 + V_1 \cos \omega t$$

then the operating point is given by V_0 and I_0. The signal components are $I_1 \cos \omega t$ and $V_1 \cos \omega t$.

The voltage-current relations for the *signal components* can be analyzed on a linear basis if the incremental components can be used. For instance, consider Fig. 3-32. The voltage generator consists of a direct generator V_b and a time-varying one v_1. Similarly, the current generator consists of a direct generator I_b and a time-varying one i_1. The resistor R_1, the capacitor C_1, and the inductor L_1 are nonlinear elements. If the values of v_1 and i_1 are small enough that incremental elements can be used (see Sec. 1-8), then the time-varying components of the currents can be obtained from the circuit of Fig. 3-32b. Here all the nonlinear elements have been replaced by linear (incremental) ones, and only the time-varying generators are included. That is, *in so far as the signal components are concerned*, we have *linearized* the circuit, and all we need do is perform a linear circuit analysis. Figure 3-32b can be called a *linear equivalent circuit* or *linear model* of Fig. 3-32a. That is, it can be used to calculate the effect of small changes (signal components) in the generator voltages and/or currents. Note that this linear model *cannot* be used to calculate the currents due to V_b or I_b. In general, such a model can

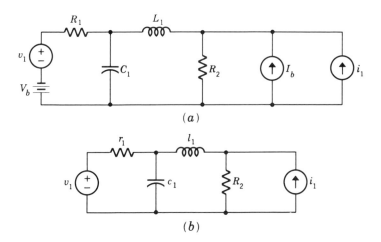

Fig. 3-32   (a) A network containing the nonlinear elements R_1, L_1, and C_1; (b) a linear network which can be used to calculate the time-varying components of current if v_1 and i_1 are small enough.

be used to calculate only the currents or voltages that result from small changes in the voltages and/or currents.

How small must the signal generator's voltages or currents be for the linear model to be valid? That is, how accurate is the approximation that yields the incremental elements? A measure of this can be obtained by studying a relation such as Eq. (1-74). For instance, in the case of capacitance, we can write the expression for the charge transferred from plate to plate versus voltage across the capacitor in a Taylor series about the operating point [see the equation preceding Eq. (1-74)]. This yields

$$q = Q_0 + \frac{dq}{dv}\bigg|_{v=V_0} v_1 + \frac{1}{2!}\frac{d^2q}{dv^2}\bigg|_{v=V_0} v_1{}^2 + \cdots \tag{3-58}$$

where V_0 is the operating-point voltage of the capacitor and v_1 is the change in voltage about V_0; that is, the total voltage across the capacitor is

$$v = V_0 + v_1 \tag{3-59}$$

Then, if v_1 is small enough, we can approximate Eq. (3-58) by

$$q = Q_0 + \frac{dq}{dv}\bigg|_{v=V_0} v_1 \tag{3-60}$$

Since $i = dq/dt$, we can write

$$i = \frac{dq}{dt} = \frac{dq}{dv}\bigg|_{v=V_0} \frac{dv_1}{dt} \tag{3-61}$$

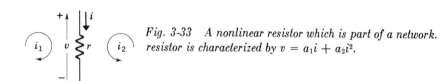

Fig. 3-33   *A nonlinear resistor which is part of a network.   The resistor is characterized by $v = a_1 i + a_2 i^2$.*

Thus for the signal components we need only use the incremental capacitance

$$C = \frac{dq}{dv}\Big|_{v=V_0} \tag{3-62}$$

The accuracy of this manipulation depends upon the accuracy of Eq. (3-60); that is, a measure of the accuracy is obtained by comparing the difference between Eqs. (3-58) and (3-60).   This involves studying the relative magnitudes of the derivatives of the charge-vs.-voltage curve at $v = V_0$ and the powers of the signal components of the voltages.

The second class of nonlinear problems occurs when we cannot approximate the circuit with a linear one.   In this event we must deal with nonlinear elements.   If we are to use loop, nodal, or cut-set analysis, we should work with the branch currents or voltages, which may be expressed in terms of loop currents or nodal or cut-set voltages.   A simple example will illustrate this procedure (in Chap. 7 we shall present another procedure which is much more suited to the analysis of nonlinear circuits).   Consider the nonlinear resistor illustrated in Fig. 3-33.   Assume that it is part of a network, and that there are two loop currents in it.   Let us assume that the voltage across the resistor is specified as a function of the current in it by the relation

$$v = a_1 i + a_2 i^2 \tag{3-63}$$

where a_1 and a_2 are known constants.   The current i can be expressed in terms of the loop currents as

$$i = i_1 + i_2 \tag{3-64}$$

Substituting Eq. (3-64) into Eq. (3-63), we obtain the voltage drop in terms of the loop current.   This yields

$$v = a_1(i_1 + i_2) + a_2(i_1 + i_2)^2 \tag{3-65}$$

Note that it is *not* valid to consider that each loop current acts by itself where v is computed—that is, we may *not* write $v = (a_1 i_1 + a_2 i_1{}^2) + (a_1 i_2 + a_2 i_2{}^2)$.

In loop analysis we express the voltage drops across the elements in terms of the currents through them.   However, if the elements are nonlinear, this may not always be possible.   For instance, consider the nonlinear resistance whose voltage-current characteristic is given in Fig. 3-34a.   The voltage is a single-valued function of the current.   Thus, if the current is known, the voltage can always be obtained.   However, if the voltage is specified, and it lies between V_1 and V_2, then the current cannot be uniquely specified; it can have any one of three values. We call this a *current-controlled nonlinear resistance,* since the current uniquely determines the voltage. A loop analysis can be set up on a network containing such a resistance, but an ordinary nodal analysis cannot (without difficulty), since the current cannot, in general, be expressed as a simple function of the voltage. The nonlinear resistance characterized by Fig. 3-34*b* is one in which the current can always be expressed in terms of the voltage. This is called a *voltage-controlled nonlinear resistance.* Note that the voltage cannot be expressed as a single-valued function of the current in this case. This type of resistance can be studied more easily in terms of nodal or cut-set analysis than in terms of loop analysis.

As an illustration of the loop analysis of a circuit containing nonlinear elements, consider Fig. 3-35. We shall assume that the nonlinear resistance is current controlled, with the voltage drop across the resistor r a function of the current in it, given by

$$v = f_R(i) \tag{3-66}$$

where $f_R(i)$ is some single-valued function of current. The voltage drop across the inductance as a function of the current through it is given by Eq. (1-111). We can also express the voltage drop across the inductance as a function of the current through it in a different fashion. The flux linkages of the coil (see Sec. 1-10) are a function of the current through it, related by $\phi = Li$ [see Eq. (1-92)]. If the inductance is linear, then L is independent of current. In the nonlinear case we can state

$$\phi = f_L(i) \tag{3-67}$$

That is, the flux linkages are some function of current. The voltage drop across the coil is $d\phi/dt$. Hence

$$v = \frac{df_L(i)}{dt} \tag{3-68}$$

Fig. 3-34   *Voltage-current characteristics of nonlinear resistances: (a) current controlled; (b) voltage controlled.*

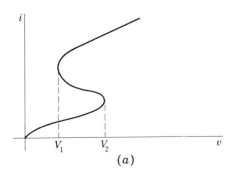
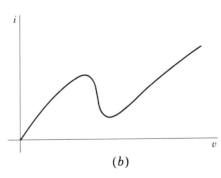

(a)   (b)

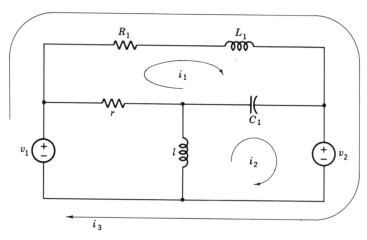

Fig. 3-35   *A network containing nonlinear elements.   r and l are nonlinear and R_1, C_1, and L_1 are linear.*

Since $f_L(i)$ is a function of i alone, we can write

$$v = \frac{df_L(i)}{di}\bigg|_i \frac{di}{dt} \tag{3-69}$$

Note that $df_L(i)/di$ is evaluated at the instantaneous value of i.   If we compare Eq. (3-69) with Eq. (1-111), we obtain

$$\left(l + i\frac{dl}{di}\right)_i = \frac{df_L(i)}{di}\bigg|_i \tag{3-70}$$

where l is defined as the ratio of the flux linkages to the current through the coil.   Note that in the nonlinear case l is a function of i.

A nonlinear capacitor is not included in the circuit of Fig. 3-35 because in practice nonlinear capacitors are voltage-controlled devices and thus do not lend themselves to simple loop analysis.

Now let us perform a loop analysis of Fig. 3-35.   The voltage drops across the nonlinear elements are given by Eqs. (3-66) and (3-69).   For convenience, the loop currents have been chosen such that there is only one current in each nonlinear element.   Then, writing loop currents, we have

$$0 = f_R(i_1) + \frac{1}{C_1}\int (i_1 - i_2)\,dt + R_1(i_1 + i_3) + L_1\frac{d(i_1 + i_3)}{dt} \tag{3-71a}$$

$$0 = \frac{df_L(i_2)}{di_2}\bigg|_{i_2} \frac{di_2}{dt} + \frac{1}{C_1}\int (i_2 - i_1)\,dt - v_2 \tag{3-71b}$$

$$0 = -v_1 + R_1(i_3 + i_1) + L_1\frac{d(i_1 + i_3)}{dt} + v_2 \tag{3-71c}$$

These can be rearranged in a form that is more suitable for solution. If the loop currents are not chosen such that each nonlinear element has only one loop current, the equations can become so cumbersome that it may at times be desirable to use the branch-current method instead. There are other procedures (see Chap. 7) that can be used to characterize nonlinear circuits. However, in this chapter we shall discuss only methods related to loop, nodal, or cut-set analysis.

In simple nodal or cut-set analysis we must express the currents through the nonlinear elements in terms of the voltages across them. Thus we consider networks with voltage-controlled nonlinear resistances and nonlinear capacitors (in general, nonlinear inductors are current controlled). The voltage-current relation for a nonlinear capacitor is given by Eq. (1-67). Alternatively, we can state that the charge transferred from one plate of the capacitor to another is given by

$$q = f_c(v) \tag{3-72}$$

That is, the charge transferred is some function of the voltage across the capacitor. Since $i = dq/dt$, we have for the current through the capacitor

$$i = \frac{df_c(v)}{dt} = \frac{df_c(v)}{dv}\bigg|_v \frac{dv}{dt} \tag{3-73}$$

The actual details of the nodal or cut-set analysis are very similar to those for a linear network, and are left to the reader.

3-9   Resistive networks and solution of simultaneous equations by means of determinants

The network-analysis procedures that we have discussed result in sets of simultaneous integral-differential equations. In this section we shall consider techniques for the solution of these equations when the network elements are all linear time-invariant resistances. Then, instead of integral-differential equations, we obtain a set of linear simultaneous equations with constant coefficients. In subsequent chapters we shall apply the methods developed in this section to procedures for the solution of simultaneous integral-differential equations.

If we have a network that contains only generators and resistors, then a mesh, nodal, or cut-set analysis of it will yield equations of the form

$$
\begin{aligned}
y_1 &= a_{11}x_1 + a_{12}x_2 + \cdots + a_{1n}x_n \\
y_2 &= a_{21}x_1 + a_{22}x_2 + \cdots + a_{2n}x_n \\
&\;\cdot\;\cdot\;\cdot\;\cdot\;\cdot\;\cdot\;\cdot\;\cdot\;\cdot\;\cdot\;\cdot\;\cdot\;\cdot\;\cdot\;\cdot\;\cdot \\
y_n &= a_{n1}x_1 + a_{n2}x_2 + \cdots + a_{nn}x_n
\end{aligned} \tag{3-74}
$$

where $x_1, x_2, \ldots, x_n$ represent unknown currents in a mesh analysis and

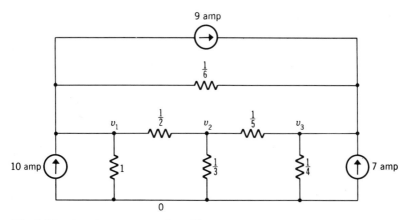

Fig. 3-36   A resistance network.   All resistance values are in ohms.

unknown voltages in a nodal or cut-set analysis.   The a_{ij} ($i = 1,2, \ldots, n$ and $j = 1,2, \ldots, n$) terms are constant coefficients.   The y_i ($i = 1,2, \ldots, n$) terms represent known quantities.   For instance, a nodal analysis of the network of Fig. 3-36 yields

$$1 = 9v_1 - 2v_2 - 6v_3 \tag{3-75a}$$

$$0 = -2v_1 + 10v_2 - 5v_3 \tag{3-75b}$$

$$16 = -6v_1 - 5v_2 + 15v_3 \tag{3-75c}$$

These simultaneous equations can be solved in a straightforward way.   For instance, we can solve Eq. (3-75c) for v_3 and substitute it in Eqs. (3-75a) and (3-75b).   Two equations with two unknowns result.   One of these can be solved for v_2, and then, when this is substituted in the remaining equation, we can solve for v_1.   In general, we can solve any number of simultaneous equations by substitutions of this type.   However, we shall now discuss another procedure which often proves very convenient in solving simultaneous equations.

Let us first introduce the concept of a *determinant*, which is an array of numbers.   The determinant has a *numerical value*.   After considering this array and the techniques for evaluating it, we shall apply determinants to the solution of simultaneous equations.   A determinant contains as many rows as columns.   It is denoted by enclosing the numbers within two vertical bars. A typical determinant is

$$\Delta = \begin{vmatrix} a_{11} & a_{12} & \cdots & a_{1n} \\ a_{21} & a_{22} & \cdots & a_{2n} \\ \cdots & \cdots & \cdots & \cdots \\ a_{n1} & a_{n2} & \cdots & a_{nn} \end{vmatrix} \tag{3-76}$$

Note that Δ represents not only the array, but a number. We shall now consider how to evaluate it. The rules for this evaluation are in fact chosen to make the determinant a useful tool in the solution of simultaneous equations. For the time being, however, consider these rules as arbitrary. The *order* of a determinant is a number which is equal to the number of its rows (or columns). The simplest determinant we need consider is of second order; that is, it consists of two rows and two columns. A typical second-order determinant is

$$\Delta = \begin{vmatrix} a_{11} & a_{12} \\ a_{21} & a_{22} \end{vmatrix} \tag{3-77}$$

where the numerical value of Δ is defined as

$$\Delta = a_{11}a_{22} - a_{12}a_{21} \tag{3-78}$$

For instance,

$$\begin{vmatrix} 1 & -2 \\ -2 & 6 \end{vmatrix} = 1(6) - (-2)(-2) = 2$$

We evaluate determinants of higher order in terms of second-order ones. To do this, we introduce the concepts of a *minor* and a *cofactor*. A minor of a determinant is a new determinant formed by striking out one row and one column of the original determinant. The minor will be written as M_{ij}, where i is the removed row and j is the removed column. For instance, for a determinant such as

$$\Delta = \begin{vmatrix} a_{11} & a_{12} & a_{13} & a_{14} \\ a_{21} & a_{22} & a_{23} & a_{24} \\ a_{31} & a_{32} & a_{33} & a_{34} \\ a_{41} & a_{42} & a_{43} & a_{44} \end{vmatrix} \tag{3-79}$$

some typical minors are

$$M_{11} = \begin{vmatrix} a_{22} & a_{23} & a_{24} \\ a_{32} & a_{33} & a_{34} \\ a_{42} & a_{43} & a_{44} \end{vmatrix} \tag{3-80a}$$

$$M_{23} = \begin{vmatrix} a_{11} & a_{12} & a_{14} \\ a_{31} & a_{32} & a_{34} \\ a_{41} & a_{42} & a_{44} \end{vmatrix} \tag{3-80b}$$

A somewhat more useful definition is that of the cofactor, written as Δ_{ij}. This consists of a minor M_{ij} multiplied by $+1$ or -1 in accordance with the definition

$$\Delta_{ij} = (-1)^{i+j} M_{ij} \tag{3-81}$$

That is, if $i + j$ is an even number, the cofactor and its corresponding minor are equal. If $i + j$ is an odd number, the cofactor is the negative of its minor.

For example, for the determinant of Eq. (3-79), two cofactors are

$$\Delta_{11} = \begin{vmatrix} a_{22} & a_{23} & a_{24} \\ a_{32} & a_{33} & a_{34} \\ a_{42} & a_{43} & a_{44} \end{vmatrix} \tag{3-82a}$$

$$\Delta_{23} = (-1) \begin{vmatrix} a_{11} & a_{12} & a_{14} \\ a_{31} & a_{32} & a_{34} \\ a_{41} & a_{42} & a_{44} \end{vmatrix} \tag{3-82b}$$

As a further illustration, consider a numerical example.   Let

$$\Delta = \begin{vmatrix} 1 & 2 & 3 \\ 3 & 4 & 4 \\ 7 & 6 & 3 \end{vmatrix} \tag{3-83}$$

Then

$$\Delta_{33} = \begin{vmatrix} 1 & 2 \\ 3 & 4 \end{vmatrix} = 4 - 6 = -2 \tag{3-84a}$$

$$\Delta_{12} = (-1) \begin{vmatrix} 3 & 4 \\ 7 & 3 \end{vmatrix} = -1(9 - 28) = 19 \tag{3-84b}$$

Now we can state a rule that will enable us to evaluate any determinant by expanding it along *one* of its rows *or* by expanding it along *one* of its columns. To obtain the numerical value of a determinant we multiply each of the elements of any one row (or any one column) by their respective cofactors (for example, we multiply a_{13} by Δ_{13}) and then take the sum of all these terms. Thus for the general determinant of Eq. (3-76) we can write

$$\Delta = a_{k1}\Delta_{k1} + a_{k2}\Delta_{k2} + \cdots + a_{kn}\Delta_{kn} \qquad k = 1, 2, \ldots, n \tag{3-85a}$$

or

$$\Delta = a_{1j}\Delta_{1j} + a_{2j}\Delta_{2j} + \cdots + a_{nj}\Delta_{nj} \qquad j = 1, 2, \ldots, n \tag{3-85b}$$

In Eq. (3-85a) we have written the determinant in terms of the coefficients of the kth row and their cofactors.   In Eq. (3-85b) we have done this in terms of the jth column.   Note that Eqs. (3-85) represent $2n$ equations.   Any one of these can be used.

Let us illustrate this evaluation with the determinant of Eq. (3-83). Expansion along the first column yields

$$\Delta = 1\Delta_{11} + 3\Delta_{21} + 7\Delta_{31}$$

Substituting, we obtain

$$\Delta = 1(1) \begin{vmatrix} 4 & 4 \\ 6 & 3 \end{vmatrix} + 3(-1) \begin{vmatrix} 2 & 3 \\ 6 & 3 \end{vmatrix} + 7(1) \begin{vmatrix} 2 & 3 \\ 4 & 4 \end{vmatrix} = -4 \tag{3-86a}$$

We can also expand along the second row to obtain

$$\Delta = 3\Delta_{21} + 4\Delta_{22} + 4\Delta_{32}$$

$$= 3(-1)\begin{vmatrix} 2 & 3 \\ 6 & 3 \end{vmatrix} + 4(1)\begin{vmatrix} 1 & 3 \\ 7 & 3 \end{vmatrix} + 4(-1)\begin{vmatrix} 1 & 2 \\ 7 & 6 \end{vmatrix} = -4 \quad (3\text{-}86b)$$

We can evaluate the determinant of Eq. (3-83) by expanding along any one of its row or columns, and we shall always obtain the answer -4.

As a final example, consider the evaluation of the determinant of Eq. (3-79). If we expand along the second column, we obtain

$$\Delta = a_{12}(-1)\begin{vmatrix} a_{21} & a_{23} & a_{24} \\ a_{31} & a_{33} & a_{34} \\ a_{41} & a_{43} & a_{44} \end{vmatrix} + a_{22}\begin{vmatrix} a_{11} & a_{13} & a_{14} \\ a_{31} & a_{33} & a_{34} \\ a_{41} & a_{43} & a_{44} \end{vmatrix}$$

$$+ a_{32}(-1)\begin{vmatrix} a_{11} & a_{13} & a_{14} \\ a_{21} & a_{23} & a_{24} \\ a_{41} & a_{43} & a_{44} \end{vmatrix} + a_{42}\begin{vmatrix} a_{11} & a_{13} & a_{14} \\ a_{21} & a_{23} & a_{24} \\ a_{31} & a_{33} & a_{34} \end{vmatrix} \quad (3\text{-}87)$$

Each of the third-order determinants can be evaluated as in the preceding example.

In evaluating a third-order determinant three second-order determinants must be calculated. If a fourth-order determinant is to be evaluated, then four determinants of third order must be evaluated. This requires the evaluation of 12 second-order determinants. In general, the amount of work required to evaluate a determinant varies as the factorial of its order.

Expansion of a determinant along any one of its rows or columns will always yield the same numerical answer. This can be proved in a straightfoward but tedious way, for a determinant of specific order, by expanding the determinants in all possible ways, using letters for each of the elements; all $2n$ equations [see Eqs. (3-85)] will yield the same result. The arithmetic is tedious; the details are left to the reader.

Let us now use determinants to evaluate a general set of simultaneous equations. For instance, consider Eqs. (3-74), which we shall repeat here:

$$y_1 = a_{11}x_1 + a_{12}x_2 + \cdots + a_{1n}x_n$$

$$y_2 = a_{21}x_1 + a_{22}x_2 + \cdots + a_{2n}x_n$$

$$\cdots \cdots \cdots \cdots \cdots \cdots \cdots \cdots \quad (3\text{-}88)$$

$$y_n = a_{n1}x_1 + a_{n2}x_2 + \cdots + a_{nn}x_n$$

The procedure that we shall use is called *Cramer's rule*. The first step is to write the equation in the form of Eq. (3-88); that is, we write all the knowns on the left-hand side. The unknowns must all be written in the same order in each equation (x_1 first, x_2 second, and so on). We then form a determinant called the *system determinant*, or *characteristic determinant*, which consists of the array of the coefficients of the unknowns.   Each coefficient appears in the same relative position as it does in the simultaneous equations.   Hence

$$\Delta = \begin{vmatrix} a_{11} & a_{12} & \cdots & a_{1n} \\ a_{21} & a_{22} & \cdots & a_{2n} \\ \cdots & \cdots & \cdots & \cdots \\ a_{n1} & a_{n2} & \cdots & a_{nn} \end{vmatrix} \tag{3-89}$$

Then any of the unknowns can be obtained with the relation

$$x_k = \frac{y_1\Delta_{1k} + y_2\Delta_{2k} + \cdots + y_n\Delta_{nk}}{\Delta} \qquad k = 1, 2, \ldots, n \tag{3-90}$$

For instance,

$$x_3 = \frac{y_1\Delta_{13} + y_2\Delta_{23} + \cdots + y_n\Delta_{n3}}{\Delta} \tag{3-91}$$

Hence we can evaluate all the unknowns.

Consider the numerator of Eq. (3-90).   It can be obtained by expanding a determinant which is the same as Δ, except that the kth column has been replaced by a column which consists of the known terms.   To illustrate this procedure, let us solve Eqs. (3-75) for v_3.   The characteristic determinant is

$$\Delta = \begin{vmatrix} 9 & -2 & -6 \\ -2 & 10 & -5 \\ -6 & -5 & 15 \end{vmatrix} = 585 \tag{3-92}$$

Then

$$x_3 = \frac{1\Delta_{13} + 0\Delta_{23} + 16\Delta_{33}}{585} = \frac{1{,}446}{585} = 2.47 \tag{3-93}$$

Note that we can express the numerator of x_3 as a determinant by replacing the third column of Δ by a column consisting of the knowns; that is,

$$x_3 = \frac{\begin{vmatrix} 9 & -2 & 1 \\ -2 & 10 & 0 \\ -6 & -5 & 16 \end{vmatrix}}{\Delta} \tag{3-94}$$

A straightfoward but tedious proof of Cramer's rule consists in comparing, in a general sense, the solution obtained by the expansion of the determinants with the one determined by simply substituting unknowns.

Since the work required to evaluate a determinant varies in accordance with the factorial of the order of the determinant, the work required to solve a set of simultaneous equations varies with the factorial of the number of unknowns. This is why the choice between mesh and nodal (or cut-set) analysis is usually based on which procedure yields the fewest unknowns.

3-10 Matrices and matrix representation of equations

We have briefly discussed matrices [see Eqs. (3-15) and (3-30)]. In this section we shall introduce them formally and demonstrate how they can be used as a very convenient representation for a set of simultaneous equations. First let us define matrices and some of their mathematical operations. These operations are defined in such a way as to make matrices useful when working with simultaneous equations.

A matrix is just an array of numbers, symbolically denoted by square brackets. Thus a matrix $[A]$ is

$$[A] = \begin{bmatrix} a_{11} & a_{12} & \cdots & a_{1m} \\ a_{21} & a_{22} & \cdots & a_{2m} \\ \cdots & \cdots & \cdots & \cdots \\ a_{n1} & a_{n2} & \cdots & a_{nm} \end{bmatrix} \tag{3-95}$$

The terms a_{ij} are called the *elements of the matrix*. The subscripts indicate their position within the matrix. The first subscript indicates the row and the second the column. Note that the number of rows and columns of a matrix need not be equal. The elements a_{ij} can be numbers or mathematical expressions [for example, see Eqs. (3-15) and (3-30)]. If a matrix has only one column, it is called a *column matrix*. Similarly, a matrix with only one row is called a *row matrix*. A matrix with an equal number of rows and columns is called a *square matrix*.

Equality of matrices

If two matrices are equal, then every element of one matrix is equal to the corresponding element of the other. *This requires that the two matrices have the same number of rows, and also that they have the same number of columns.* For instance, if

$$\begin{bmatrix} a_{11} & a_{12} & a_{13} \\ a_{21} & a_{22} & a_{23} \end{bmatrix} = \begin{bmatrix} 1 & 2 & 3 \\ 4 & 5 & 6 \end{bmatrix} \tag{3-96}$$

then

$$a_{11} = 1 \tag{3-97a}$$

$$a_{12} = 2 \tag{3-97b}$$

$$a_{13} = 3 \tag{3-97c}$$

$$a_{21} = 4 \tag{3-97d}$$

$$a_{22} = 5 \tag{3-97e}$$

$$a_{23} = 6 \tag{3-97f}$$

Addition and subtraction of matrices

If two matrices are added or subtracted, then their corresponding elements are added or subtracted.   Not all matrices can be added or subtracted.   *If two matrices are to be added or subtracted, they must have the same number of rows. They must also have the same number of columns.*   For instance,

$$\begin{bmatrix} a_{11} & a_{12} & a_{13} \\ a_{21} & a_{22} & a_{23} \end{bmatrix} + \begin{bmatrix} b_{11} & b_{12} & b_{13} \\ b_{21} & b_{22} & b_{23} \end{bmatrix} = \begin{bmatrix} a_{11} + b_{11} & a_{12} + b_{12} & a_{13} + b_{13} \\ a_{21} + b_{21} & a_{22} + b_{22} & a_{23} + b_{23} \end{bmatrix}$$

$$(3\text{-}98)$$

Multiplication of matrices

Two matrices are multiplied according to the following rules:

$$\begin{bmatrix} a_{11} & a_{12} & \cdots & a_{1m} \\ a_{21} & a_{22} & \cdots & a_{2m} \\ \cdots & \cdots & \cdots & \cdots \\ a_{n1} & a_{n2} & \cdots & a_{nm} \end{bmatrix} \begin{bmatrix} b_{11} & b_{12} & \cdots & b_{1j} \\ b_{21} & b_{22} & \cdots & b_{2j} \\ \cdots & \cdots & \cdots & \cdots \\ b_{m1} & b_{m2} & \cdots & b_{mj} \end{bmatrix} = \begin{bmatrix} c_{11} & c_{12} & \cdots & c_{1j} \\ c_{21} & c_{22} & \cdots & c_{2j} \\ \cdots & \cdots & \cdots & \cdots \\ c_{n1} & c_{n2} & \cdots & c_{nj} \end{bmatrix}$$

$$(3\text{-}99)$$

where

$$c_{kq} = a_{k1}b_{1q} + a_{k2}b_{2q} + \cdots + a_{km}b_{mq} \tag{3-100}$$

To obtain c_{kq}, elements of the kth row of the first matrix are associated with elements of the qth column of the second matrix in accordance with Eq. (3-100).   There must be an equal number of terms in the rows of the first matrix and in the columns of the second.   Thus, when two matrices are multiplied, *the number of columns in the first matrix must equal the number of rows in the second.*   If this is not true, then the matrices cannot be multiplied. Matrices which can be multiplied are said to be *conformable*.   Note also that a matrix product $[A][B]$ is *not necessarily equal to* $[B][A]$.   In fact, the second product may not even exist, although the first does (the number of columns of the second matrix does not have to be equal to the number of rows of the first, even though the converse is true).   For these reasons we must distinguish between *premultiplying* and *postmultiplying* a matrix.

When two matrices are multiplied, the resulting product has as many rows as the first matrix and as many columns as the second one.   As an example consider

$$\begin{bmatrix} 1 & 2 & 5 \\ 3 & 4 & 6 \end{bmatrix} \begin{bmatrix} 1 & 1 & 1 \\ 2 & 1 & 2 \\ 3 & 1 & 1 \end{bmatrix} = \begin{bmatrix} 20 & 8 & 10 \\ 29 & 13 & 17 \end{bmatrix} \tag{3-101}$$

Scalar multiplication

If each element in a matrix is multiplied by the same term, then we can factor this from the matrix. That is, the single term is written preceding the matrix. For example,

$$\begin{bmatrix} aa_{11} & aa_{12} \\ aa_{21} & aa_{22} \end{bmatrix} = a \begin{bmatrix} a_{11} & a_{12} \\ a_{21} & a_{22} \end{bmatrix}$$

The unit matrix

In the square matrix

$$[A] = \begin{bmatrix} a_{11} & a_{12} & \cdots & a_{1n} \\ a_{21} & a_{22} & \cdots & a_{2n} \\ \cdots\cdots\cdots\cdots\cdots \\ a_{n1} & a_{n2} & \cdots & a_{nn} \end{bmatrix} \tag{3-102}$$

the terms a_{11}, a_{22}, . . . , a_{nn} constitute the *principal diagonal* of the square matrix. If all the elements of a square matrix except those on the principal diagonal are zero, then the matrix is called a *diagonal matrix*. For instance, a diagonal matrix is

$$[A] = \begin{bmatrix} a_{11} & 0 & \cdots & 0 \\ 0 & a_{22} & \cdots & 0 \\ \cdots\cdots\cdots\cdots\cdots \\ 0 & 0 & \cdots & a_{nn} \end{bmatrix} \tag{3-103}$$

If all the elements on the principal diagonal of a diagonal matrix are equal to one, then the matrix is called a *unit matrix* and is designated by [U]:

$$[U] = \begin{bmatrix} 1 & 0 & \cdots & 0 \\ 0 & 1 & \cdots & 0 \\ \cdots\cdots\cdots\cdots \\ 0 & 0 & \cdots & 1 \end{bmatrix} \tag{3-104}$$

At times the unit matrix is written as $[U_b]$, indicating that it has b rows and columns.

If a unit matrix of n rows and n columns premultiplies a matrix $[A]$ of n rows or postmultiplies a matrix $[A]$ of n columns, the resultant matrix is equal to $[A]$. To demonstrate this we need only carry out the rules of matrix multiplication:

$$\begin{bmatrix} 1 & 0 & \cdots & 0 \\ 0 & 1 & \cdots & 0 \\ \cdots\cdots\cdots\cdots \\ 0 & 0 & \cdots & 1 \end{bmatrix} \begin{bmatrix} a_{11} & a_{12} & \cdots & a_{1q} \\ a_{21} & a_{22} & \cdots & a_{2q} \\ \cdots\cdots\cdots\cdots\cdots \\ a_{n1} & a_{n2} & \cdots & a_{nq} \end{bmatrix} = \begin{bmatrix} a_{11} & a_{12} & \cdots & a_{1q} \\ a_{21} & a_{22} & \cdots & a_{2q} \\ \cdots\cdots\cdots\cdots\cdots \\ a_{n1} & a_{n2} & \cdots & a_{nq} \end{bmatrix} \tag{3-105}$$

Matrix representation of a set of simultaneous equations

Let us examine a general set of simultaneous equations and see how matrix representation can be used as a convenient representation of them. Consider the equations

$$
\begin{aligned}
y_1 &= a_{11}x_1 + a_{12}x_2 + \cdots + a_{1n}x_n \\
y_2 &= a_{21}x_1 + a_{22}x_2 + \cdots + a_{2n}x_n \\
&\cdots\cdots\cdots\cdots\cdots\cdots\cdots\cdots\cdots \\
y_n &= a_{n1}x_1 + a_{n2}x_2 + \cdots + a_{nn}x_n
\end{aligned}
\tag{3-106}
$$

We can write these in matrix form as

$$
\begin{bmatrix} y_1 \\ y_2 \\ \cdot \\ \cdot \\ \cdot \\ y_n \end{bmatrix}
=
\begin{bmatrix}
a_{11} & a_{12} & \cdots & a_{1n} \\
a_{21} & a_{22} & \cdots & a_{2n} \\
& \cdots\cdots\cdots\cdots & & \\
a_{n1} & a_{n2} & \cdots & a_{nn}
\end{bmatrix}
\begin{bmatrix} x_1 \\ x_2 \\ \cdot \\ \cdot \\ x_n \end{bmatrix}
\tag{3-107}
$$

The multiplication on the right-hand side of Eq. (3-107) results in a matrix of n rows and one column. When each of these elements is equated to the corresponding elements on the left-hand side of Eq. (3-107), the result is Eqs. (3-106).

We can represent Eqs. (3-106) or (3-107) in a very compact form. Let

$$
[y] = \begin{bmatrix} y_1 \\ y_2 \\ \cdot \\ \cdot \\ \cdot \\ y_n \end{bmatrix}
\tag{3-108a}
$$

$$
[x] = \begin{bmatrix} x_1 \\ x_2 \\ \cdot \\ \cdot \\ x_n \end{bmatrix}
\tag{3-108b}
$$

$$
[A] = \begin{bmatrix}
a_{11} & a_{12} & \cdots & a_{1n} \\
a_{21} & a_{22} & \cdots & a_{2n} \\
& \cdots\cdots\cdots\cdots & & \\
a_{n1} & a_{n2} & \cdots & a_{nn}
\end{bmatrix}
\tag{3-108c}
$$

Then Eqs. (3-106) can be written as

$$[y] = [A][x] \tag{3-109}$$

The matrix $[A]$ is called the *coefficient matrix* of the set of simultaneous equations.

Inverse matrices

Consider that we have a square matrix of order n.   The *order* of a square matrix is equal to the number of its rows (or columns).   Let us assume that we can find another square matrix of order n, which we designate as $[A]^{-1}$, such that

$$[A]^{-1}[A] = [U] \tag{3-110}$$

The matrix $[A]^{-1}$ is called the *inverse* of $[A]$.   If $[A]$ is the coefficient matrix of a set of simultaneous equations, then a knowledge of $[A]^{-1}$ will yield a solution to these equations.   For instance, suppose we have a set of simultaneous equations given by [see Eqs. (3-106) to (3-109)]

$$[y] = [A][x] \tag{3-111}$$

Assume that $[A]^{-1}$ exists and is known.   Then, if we premultiply both sides of Eq. (3-111) by $[A]^{-1}$, we have

$$[A]^{-1}[y] = [A]^{-1}[A][x] = [U][x] = [x] \tag{3-112}$$

We let

$$[A]^{-1} = \begin{bmatrix} b_{11} & b_{12} & \cdots & b_{1n} \\ b_{21} & b_{22} & \cdots & b_{2n} \\ \cdots & \cdots & \cdots & \cdots \\ b_{n1} & b_{n2} & \cdots & b_{nn} \end{bmatrix} \tag{3-113}$$

and, substituting Eqs. (3-108a), (3-108b), and (3-113) into Eq. (3-112), we obtain

$$\begin{aligned} b_{11}y_1 + b_{12}y_2 + \cdots + b_{1n}y_n &= x_1 \\ b_{21}y_1 + b_{22}y_2 + \cdots + b_{2n}y_n &= x_2 \\ \cdots \cdots \cdots \cdots \cdots \cdots \cdots \cdots \\ b_{n1}y_1 + b_{n2}y_2 + \cdots + b_{nn}y_n &= x_n \end{aligned} \tag{3-114}$$

Thus we have obtained the unknowns in terms of known quantities, and hence the equations are solved.

Let us see how the inverse matrix can be obtained from the coefficient matrix of a set of simultaneous equations.   Compare Eqs. (3-114) with Eqs. (3-90), which are used to solve a set of simultaneous equations identical with Eqs. (3-106) [in Eqs. (3-90) write out n equations for $k = 1, 2, \ldots, n$ to make this comparison].   We have

$$b_{ij} = \frac{\Delta_{ji}}{\Delta} \tag{3-115}$$

where Δ is the determinant of the coefficients in the coefficient matrix of the set of simultaneous equations.   Each element of this determinant occupies a position corresponding to its position in the coefficient matrix.   For example, for $[A]$ given by Eq. (3-108c) Δ is given by Eq. (3-89).   Then Δ_{ji} is the jith cofactor of Δ.   Note that we obtain b_{ij} by using the jith cofactor.   Thus, if $[A]$ is given by Eq. (3-108c), we can write

$$[A]^{-1} = \begin{bmatrix} \dfrac{\Delta_{11}}{\Delta} & \dfrac{\Delta_{21}}{\Delta} & \cdots & \dfrac{\Delta_{n1}}{\Delta} \\ \dfrac{\Delta_{12}}{\Delta} & \dfrac{\Delta_{22}}{\Delta} & \cdots & \dfrac{\Delta_{n2}}{\Delta} \\ \cdots & \cdots & \cdots & \cdots \\ \dfrac{\Delta_{1n}}{\Delta} & \dfrac{\Delta_{2n}}{\Delta} & \cdots & \dfrac{\Delta_{nn}}{\Delta} \end{bmatrix} = \frac{1}{\Delta} \begin{bmatrix} \Delta_{11} & \Delta_{21} & \cdots & \Delta_{n1} \\ \Delta_{12} & \Delta_{22} & \cdots & \Delta_{n2} \\ \cdots & \cdots & \cdots & \cdots \\ \Delta_{1n} & \Delta_{2n} & \cdots & \Delta_{nn} \end{bmatrix} \tag{3-116}$$

The matrix

$$[A]_a = \begin{bmatrix} \Delta_{11} & \Delta_{21} & \cdots & \Delta_{n1} \\ \Delta_{12} & \Delta_{22} & \cdots & \Delta_{n2} \\ \cdots & \cdots & \cdots & \cdots \\ \Delta_{1n} & \Delta_{2n} & \cdots & \Delta_{nn} \end{bmatrix} \tag{3-117}$$

is called the *adjoint* of $[A]$.   Thus the inverse of a matrix is equal to its adjoint divided by the characteristic determinant.

It is possible that $\Delta = 0$.   In this case $[A]^{-1}$ does not exist.   This means that the set of simultaneous equations are *not* linearly independent and hence do not possess a solution.

As an example let us solve the simultaneous equations given by

$$\begin{bmatrix} 10 \\ 20 \end{bmatrix} = \begin{bmatrix} 1 & 2 \\ 3 & 4 \end{bmatrix} \begin{bmatrix} x_1 \\ x_2 \end{bmatrix} \tag{3-118}$$

We have

$$\Delta = \begin{bmatrix} 1 & 2 \\ 3 & 4 \end{bmatrix} = -2$$

Hence

$$[A]^{-1} = \frac{1}{-2} \begin{bmatrix} 4 & -2 \\ -3 & 1 \end{bmatrix}$$

$$\begin{bmatrix} x_1 \\ x_2 \end{bmatrix} = [A]^{-1} \begin{bmatrix} 10 \\ 20 \end{bmatrix} = -\frac{1}{2} \begin{bmatrix} 4 & -2 \\ -3 & 1 \end{bmatrix} \begin{bmatrix} 10 \\ 20 \end{bmatrix} = -\frac{1}{2} \begin{bmatrix} 0 \\ -10 \end{bmatrix}$$

Thus

$$x_1 = 0$$
$$x_2 = 5$$

In general, when two matrices are multiplied, their order *cannot* be commuted. That is, in general, $[A][B] \neq [B][A]$. However, when inverse matrices are used, the order can be commuted. For instance, if we premultiply both sides of Eq. (3-112) by $[A]$, we have

$$[A][A]^{-1}[y] = [A][x]$$

Comparison with Eq. (3-111) shows that

$$[y] = [A][A]^{-1}[y]$$

It can be shown that any matrix that does not change the matrix it multiplies is a unit matrix. Hence

$$[A][A]^{-1} = [U]$$

Comparing this with Eq. (3-110), we obtain

$$[A]^{-1}[A] = [A][A]^{-1} = [U] \tag{3-119}$$

BIBLIOGRAPHY

Balabanian, N.: "Fundamentals of Circuit Theory," chap. 2, Allyn and Bacon, Inc., Boston, 1961.

Brenner, E., and M. Javid: "Analysis of Electric Circuits," chap. 16, McGraw-Hill Book Company, New York, 1959.

Clement, P. R., and W. C. Johnson: "Electrical Engineering Science," chap. 9, McGraw-Hill Book Company, New York, 1960.

Freidland, B., O. Wing, and R. Ash: "Principals of Linear Networks," chaps. 4 and 5, McGraw-Hill Book Company, New York, 1961.

Guillemin, E. A.: "Introductory Circuit Theory," chaps. 1 and 2 and pp. 112–120, John Wiley & Sons, Inc., New York, 1953.

Close, C. M.: "The Analysis of Linear Circuits," chap. 2, Harcourt, Brace & World, Inc., New York, 1966.

Van Valkenburg, M. E.: "Network Analysis," 2d ed., chap. 3, Prentice-Hall, Inc., Englewood Cliffs, N.J., 1964.

PROBLEMS

3-1. Find a tree for each of the networks of Fig. 3-37.

3-2. Find a tree of the nonplanar network of Fig. 3-38.

3-3. Specify the chords for each of the networks of Figs. 3-37 and 3-38.   Use the trees determined in Probs. 3-1 and 3-2.

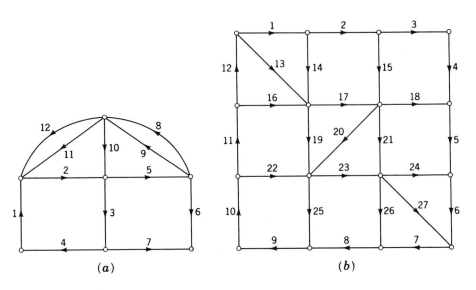

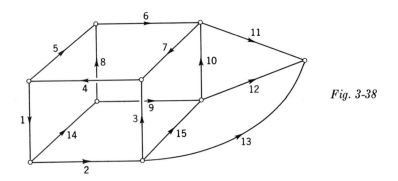

(a)   (b)

Fig. 3-37

Fig. 3-38

3-4. Verify Eqs. (3-1) and (3-2) for the networks of Figs. 3-37 and 3-38.

3-5. For each of the networks of Figs. 3-37 and 3-38 specify a tree.   Then specify all the chord-branch voltages in terms of the tree-branch voltages.

3-6. For each of the networks and trees of Prob. 3-5 specify the tree-branch currents in terms of the chord currents.

3-7. For each of the networks of Fig. 3-37 choose a tree.   Then draw a set of basic meshes and express all the branch currents in terms of the loop currents.

3-8. Repeat Prob. 3-7 for the network of Fig. 3-38.

3-9. Perform a loop analysis on the network of Fig. 3-39.   Use basic meshes.

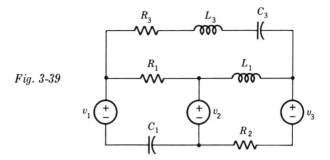

Fig. 3-39

3-10. Perform a loop analysis on the network of Fig. 3-40*a*. Use basic meshes. Note that this network is topologically equivalent to that of Fig. 3-37*a*.

Fig. 3-40

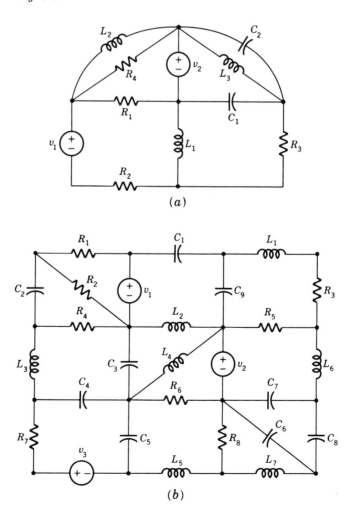

(a)

(b)

3-11. Repeat Prob. 3-10 for the network of Fig. 3-40*b*. Note that this network is topologically equivalent to that of Fig. 3-37*b*.

3-12. Repeat Prob. 1-30 for the network of Fig. 3-41. Note that this network is topologically equivalent to that of Fig. 3-38.

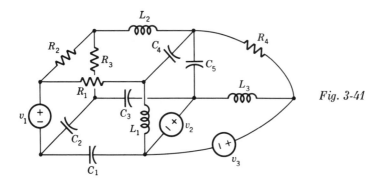

Fig. 3-41

3-13. Perform a loop analysis on the network of Fig. 3-39. Use the procedure illustrated in Fig. 3-10 to obtain the loop currents.

3-14. Repeat Prob. 3-13 for the network of Fig. 3-40*a*.

3-15. Repeat Prob. 3-13 for the network of Fig. 3-40*b*.

3-16. Repeat Prob. 3-13 for the network of Fig. 3-41.

3-17. Perform a loop analysis on the network of Fig. 3-42. Convert the current generators to voltage generators. Which branch currents can be determined in the converted network? Which must be determined from the original network?

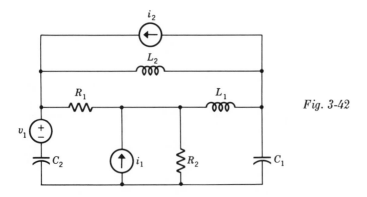

Fig. 3-42

3-18. Rewrite the equations of Probs. 3-15 and 3-16, using the operator notation of Eqs. (3-12) and (3-13).

3-19. Perform a mesh analysis on the network of Fig. 3-43.

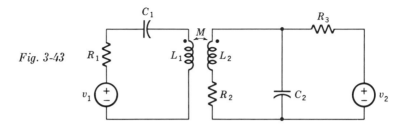

Fig. 3-43

3-20. Perform a nodal analysis on the network of Fig. 3-44.

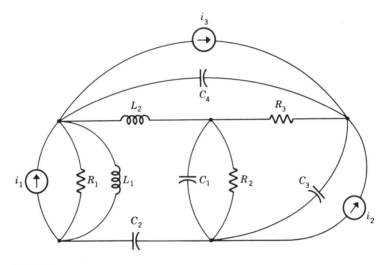

Fig. 3-44

3-21. Repeat Prob. 3-20 for the network of Fig. 3-45.

Fig. 3-45

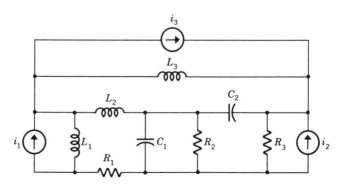

3-22. Repeat Prob. 3-20 for the network of Fig. 3-46.

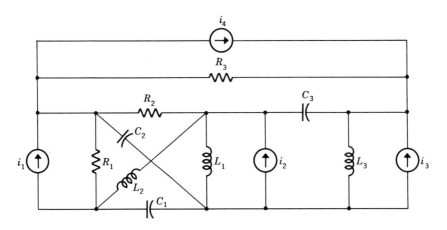

Fig. 3-46

3-23. Perform a nodal analysis on the network of Fig. 3-42. Convert the voltage generator to a current generator. Which branch voltages can be determined in the converted network? Which must be determined from the original network?

3-24. Repeat Prob. 3-23 for the network of Fig. 3-41.

3-25. Repeat Prob. 3-23 for the network of Fig. 3-43.

3-26. For each of the networks of Fig. 3-37 choose a tree and obtain a set of basic cut sets.

3-27. Repeat Prob. 3-26 for the network of Fig. 3-38.

3-28. For the cut sets of Prob. 3-26 write all the branch voltages in terms of the cut-set voltages.

3-29. Repeat Prob. 3-28 for the network of Fig. 3-38.

3-30. Perform a cut-set analysis on the network of Fig. 3-44. Use a set of basic cut sets which do not result in nodal analysis.

3-31. Repeat Prob. 3-30 for the network of Fig. 3-45.

3-32. Repeat Prob. 3-30 for the network of Fig. 3-46.

3-33. Repeat Prob. 3-30, but now generate a set of cut sets by the procedure illustrated in Fig. 3-27.

3-34. Repeat Prob. 3-33 for the network of Fig. 3-45.

3-35. Repeat Prob. 3-33 for the network of Fig. 3-46.

3-36. Perform a cut-set analysis on the network of Fig. 3-43. Convert the voltage generators to current generators. Answer the questions of Prob. 3-23.

3-37. Perform a loop analysis on the circuit of Fig. 3-47. The equations should be in a form that is suitable for solution.

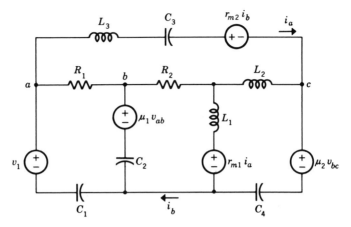

Fig. 3-47

3-38. Perform a loop analysis on the circuit of Fig. 3-48. Convert the current generators to voltage generators. Take care to express i_b properly. *Hint:* $i_b = v_{ab}/R_3$. Write this in terms of loop currents. Why must i_b be determined from the original network?

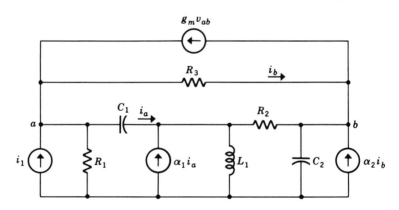

Fig. 3-48

3-39. Perform a nodal analysis of the network of Fig. 3-48.

3-40. Perform a nodal analysis on the network of Fig. 3-47. Convert the voltage generators to current generators. Be careful to express the dependent-generator values in terms of values in the original network and then to express these in terms of nodal voltages. Why must this be done?

3-41. Repeat Prob. 3-39, using cut-set analysis.

3-42. Repeat Prob. 3-40, using cut-set analysis.

3-43. Perform a loop analysis on the network of Fig. 3-39.   Assume that R_1, C_1, and L_1 are time varying in accordance with the relations

$$R_1 = R_1(1 + a \sin t)$$

$$C_1 = C_1(1 + b \cos t^2)$$

$$L_1 = L_1(1 + d \sin 2t)$$

3-44. Repeat Prob. 3-43 for the circuit of Fig. 3-40a.

3-45. Perform a nodal analysis of the circuit of Fig. 3-45, with R_1, C_1, and L_1 time varying as defined in Prob. 3-43.

3-46. Repeat Prob. 3-45 for the circuit of Fig. 3-46.

3-47. Perform a loop analysis of the network of Fig. 3-39, but now assume that R_1 and L_1 are nonlinear and the voltage drop across R_1 in terms of the current through it is $v_{R_1} = i + a_2 i^2$.   The flux linkages for L_1 in terms of its current are given by $\phi_{L_1} = b_1 i + b_2 i^2$.

3-48. Repeat Prob. 3-47 for the circuit of Fig. 3-40a.

3-49. Perform a nodal analysis of the circuit of Fig. 3-45, but now assume that R_1 and C_1 are nonlinear and that the current through R_1 in terms of the voltage across it is $i = a_1 v_1 + a_2 v_1^2$.   The charge transferred from one plate of C_1 to the other in terms of the voltage across it is $q = b_1 v + b_3 v^3$.

3-50. Repeat Prob. 3-49 for the circuit of Fig. 3-46.

3-51. Evaluate the determinant

$$\begin{vmatrix} 20 & 1 \\ 1 & 5 \end{vmatrix}$$

3-52. Evaluate the determinant

$$\begin{vmatrix} 1 & 2 & 3 \\ 4 & 5 & 6 \\ 7 & 8 & 9 \end{vmatrix}$$

3-53. Evaluate the determinant

$$\begin{vmatrix} 1 & 1 & 3 & 4 & 5 \\ 6 & 7 & 8 & 9 & 10 \\ 11 & 12 & 13 & 14 & 15 \\ 16 & 17 & 18 & 19 & 20 \\ 21 & 22 & 23 & 24 & 25 \end{vmatrix}$$

3-54. Prove the relation

$$\begin{vmatrix} a_{11} & a_{12} & a_{13} \\ a_{21} & a_{22} & a_{23} \\ a_{31} & a_{32} & a_{33} \end{vmatrix} = \begin{vmatrix} a_{11} + k a_{31} & a_{12} + k a_{32} & a_{13} + k a_{33} \\ a_{21} & a_{22} & a_{23} \\ a_{31} & a_{32} & a_{33} \end{vmatrix}$$

This is a special case of a general result that any row (or column) of a determinant can be multiplied by a constant and added to another row (or column) without changing the value of the determinant.

3-55. Use the statement of Prob. 3-35 to prove that a determinant is equal to zero if two rows (or two columns) are the same.   Verify the proof by using Eq.

(3-85) to evaluate

$$\begin{bmatrix} a_{11} & a_{12} & a_{13} \\ a_{11} & a_{12} & a_{13} \\ a_{31} & a_{32} & a_{33} \end{bmatrix}$$

3-56. Solve the following simultaneous equations for x_1, x_2, and x_3 by means of determinants:

$$10 = 5x_1 + 10x_2 + 15x_3$$
$$15 = 10x_1 + 20x_2 + 35x_3$$
$$4 = 5x_1 - 6x_2 + 7x_3$$

3-57. Obtain the current in the 3-ohm resistance of Fig. 3-49.

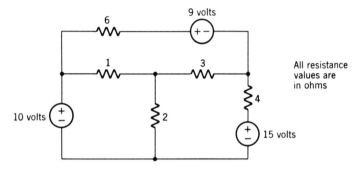

Fig. 3-49

3-58. Obtain the voltage across the ½-ohm resistance of Fig. 3-50.

Fig. 3-50

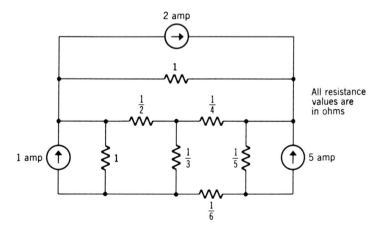

3-59. Perform the matrix operation

$$\begin{bmatrix} 1 & 2 & 4 & 4 & 7 \\ 5 & 6 & 7 & 8 & 9 \end{bmatrix} - \begin{bmatrix} 9 & -10 & 2 & 1 & 3 \\ 4 & 6 & 7 & -5 & 8 \end{bmatrix}$$

3-60. Multiply the matrices

$$\begin{bmatrix} 1 & 2 & 3 & -1 & -1 \\ -4 & -2 & 1 & 6 & -2 \\ 4 & -5 & -2 & 1 & 6 \\ 7 & -8 & 15 & -9 & 6 \end{bmatrix} \begin{bmatrix} 1 & 4 & 2 \\ 2 & 6 & 1 \\ -1 & -5 & 7 \\ 1 & -2 & -8 \\ 4 & 1 & 5 \end{bmatrix}$$

3-61. Write the equations of Prob. 3-56 in matrix form.

3-62. Find the value of x_1 in the matrix equation

$$\begin{bmatrix} 1 \\ 2 \\ 5 \end{bmatrix} = \begin{bmatrix} 1 & 2 & 3 \\ 4 & 1 & 2 \\ 1 & 1 & 1 \end{bmatrix} \begin{bmatrix} x_1 \\ x_2 \\ x_3 \end{bmatrix}$$

3-63. Find $[A]^{-1}$ for the matrix given below. Verify that $[A][A]^{-1} = [A]^{-1}[A] = [U]$.

$$[A] = \begin{bmatrix} 1 & 2 & 1 \\ 1 & 1 & 1 \\ 2 & 2 & 3 \end{bmatrix}$$

3-64. Repeat Prob. 3-63 for the matrix

$$[A] = \begin{bmatrix} 1 & 1 & 2 & 1 & 2 \\ 1 & 1 & 1 & 1 & 1 \\ 2 & 2 & 2 & 2 & 4 \\ 1 & 3 & 1 & 1 & 2 \\ 1 & 4 & 3 & 2 & 2 \end{bmatrix}$$

Initial Conditions and Classical Solution of Differential Equations

4

In this chapter we shall consider classical procedures for the solution of the integral-differential equations obtained from mesh, nodal, or cut-set analysis. In the next chapter we shall obtain additional procedures for the solution of these equations which are in many cases much less tedious to apply. However, a knowledge of the classical method is essential to a thorough understanding of the techniques for solving these equations and is in itself useful in certain analysis procedures.

Integral-differential equations do not have unique solutions. The solutions contain constants that are independent of the equations and are usually established from the initial conditions of the network.   Therefore before we consider procedures for solving the equations, let us discuss these initial conditions in some detail.

4-1   Initial conditions

The integral-differential equations that result from the mesh, nodal, or cut-set analyses discussed in the last chapter do not uniquely determine the currents and voltages of a network.   Constants appear in the solution which are arbitrary as far as the equations are concerned.   Let us illustrate this with a very simple example.

Consider the circuit of Fig. 4-1.   At some arbitrary time, which we shall call $t = 0$, the switch sw is closed, and it remains closed thereafter.   Thus for $t > 0$ we can perform a loop analysis on this circuit which yields

$$V = L \frac{di}{dt} \tag{4-1}$$

Since V is a constant, we can solve this equation very simply.   Rearranging, we obtain

$$V \, dt = L \, di \tag{4-2a}$$

and integration yields

$$\int L \, di = \int V \, dt \tag{4-2b}$$

Hence

$$Li = Vt + K_1$$

where K_1 is a constant of integration.   Then we can write

$$i(t) = \frac{V}{L} t + K \tag{4-3}$$

where the constant K is given by $K = K_1/L$.   Note that if Eq. (4-3) is substituted into Eq. (4-1), an equality is obtained for any value of K.   This verifies our results.

In order to determine $i(t)$ completely, we must establish the value of K. Since Eq. (4-1) is satisfied for any constant K, it cannot be used here.   If

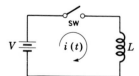

V $i(t)$ L *Fig. 4-1   A very simple circuit.*

sw

we knew the value of $i(t)$ for *any* time $(t > 0)$, then we could substitute it into Eq. (4-3) to determine K. For instance, if at $i = 1$ sec $i(t) = i_1$, where (in some way) i_1 is known, then substitution in Eq. (4-3) would yield

$$i_1 = \frac{V}{L} + K$$

or

$$K = i_1 - \frac{V}{L} \qquad (4\text{-}4)$$

and $i(t)$ would be completely determined.

Figure 4-1 does not supply sufficient information for us to determine the current at any specific time $t > 0$. For $t < 0$ the switch is open, and we know that $i = 0$, but, this tells us nothing about the current for $t > 0$. Actually, we will be concerned with the times an instant before zero and an instant after zero. These are called *zero minus* $(0-)$ and *zero plus* $(0+)$, respectively. We know that

$$i(0-) = 0 \qquad (4\text{-}5)$$

The question is, what is $i(0+)$? If it is also zero, then substitution in Eq. (4-3) yields

$$K = 0 \qquad (4\text{-}6)$$

In general, we shall know conditions in a network just before it is switched on (at $t = 0-$). If we can determine the conditions at $t = 0+$, then we shall be able to determine the constants that appear in the solution of the integral-differential equations. Let us now see if we can relate conditions at $0-$ to those at $0+$ for the various circuit elements.

Inductance

The voltage drop across an inductance in terms of the current in it is given by

$$v = L \frac{di}{dt} \qquad (4\text{-}7)$$

Let us now consider whether i can change discontinuously. A discontinuous change in i is illustrated in Fig. 4-2. That is, at $t = t_0$, $i(t)$ changes by a non-zero amount in zero time. If the current has such a discontinuity, then its derivative will be infinite at $t = t_0$. Thus [see Eq. (4.7)], if the current through an inductor changes discontinuously, then the voltage drop across it becomes infinite. Kirchhoff's voltage law must be satisfied in this network, so an infinite voltage will have to exist across at least one other circuit element. If this is not possible, then the voltage drop across the inductance cannot be infinite. For instance, in Fig. 4-1, the voltage drop across the inductance must always be v, which is given as a finite value. Hence the voltage across the

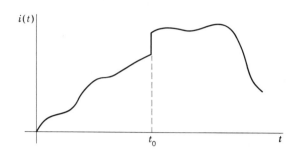

Fig. 4-2. A curve illustrating a discontinuous change at $t = t_0$.

inductor cannot be infinite, and thus [see Eq. (4-7)] the current cannot change instantaneously.

As another example, consider Fig. 4-3.   For $t > 0$ we have

$$v = Ri + L\frac{di}{dt} \qquad\qquad (4\text{-}8)$$

If v is finite, then a discontinuous finite change in i produces an infinite voltage drop across the inductor.   This requires that there be an infinite voltage drop across R.   This is impossible, since i is finite.   [It can be shown that an infinite discontinuous change in i would require that di/dt be what is called a "higher-order-of-magnitude infinity."   Then Eq. (4-8) still would not be satisfied.]   One way of producing an infinite voltage drop across an inductor is to have generators in the circuit which produce infinite voltages.   Usually these do not exist (there are some exceptions to this which will be discussed subsequently).   *In general, the current in an inductance cannot change instantaneously if the voltage drop across it cannot be infinite.*   Thus in practical circuits, if the current in an inductor at $t = 0-$ is $i(0-)$, then the current through it at $t = 0+$ will be given by

$$i(0+) = i(0-) \qquad\qquad (4\text{-}9)$$

In any circuit that can actually be built the voltages will be restricted to finite values, and Eq. (4-9) will be valid for the inductors.

At times it is desirable to approximate actual circuits with ideal ones.   This must be done with care.   For instance, consider Fig. 4-4, where an ideal current generator is connected to an inductor.   If $i(t)$ is such that it has a discon-

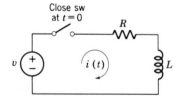

Fig. 4-3   A simple resistor-inductor circuit.

Fig. 4-4 An ideal current generator connected to an inductor.

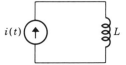

tinuous change, then, if necessary, the ideal generator will produce infinite voltage to maintain its current at $i(t)$. In this case, theoretically, the current through the inductor can change instantaneously. Although such ideal generators cannot be built, they often serve as convenient approximations to actual circuits. For instance, a practical current generator might produce a very large voltage and change the current in the inductance very rapidly; the approximation of such a circuit by the idealization of Fig. 4-4 could produce a network that can be analyzed more easily and, for most times, yield very accurate results. Usually, however, we shall not consider such ideal circuits, and Eq. (4-9) can be used.

Another condition to consider can be illustrated by the circuit of Fig. 4-3. We can open the switch when the current through the inductor is not zero, and if the current instantaneously becomes zero, then the voltage across the inductor and the switch will become infinite. In an actual circuit the switch will arc, and the current will fall to zero in a nonzero time.

Mutual inductance

In circuits containing mutual inductance the results are similar (except for one exception which we shall discuss subsequently). For instance, consider the coupled coils of Fig. 4-5. The voltage drops across the coils are given by

$$v_1(t) = L_1 \frac{di_1}{dt} - M \frac{di_2}{dt} \tag{4-10a}$$

$$v_2(t) = -M \frac{di_1}{dt} + L_2 \frac{di_2}{dt} \tag{4-10b}$$

Any discontinuous change in i_1 or i_2 will make $v_1(t)$ or $v_2(t)$ infinite. The discussion concerning the inductor also applies here. We can then state that *the current through the coupled coils cannot change instantaneously if the voltages across them are restricted to finite values.*

Fig. 4-5 A pair of coupled coils.

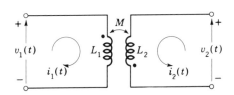

There is one exception to the preceding discussion.   If

$$L_1 L_2 - M^2 = 0 \tag{4-11}$$

and i_1 and i_2 are such that

$$L_1 \frac{di_1}{dt} = M \frac{di_2}{dt} \tag{4-12}$$

then $v_1(t)$ and $v_2(t)$ will *both* be zero.   In this case the infinite derivatives will cancel each other, and a discontinuous change in current will be allowed.   Coils which satisfy Eq. (4-11) are called unity-coupled coils [see Eq. (1-134)].   Equation (4-11) represents the largest value of mutual inductance that can theoretically be obtained.   In practical circuits this value can only be approached. Thus the currents in a pair of coupled coils can change discontinuously only in an ideal circuit [and even then, only if Eq. (4-12) is satisfied].   As with inductors, ideal circuits at times represent convenient approximations.   Also as with inductors, if we have (ideal) circuits where infinite voltages are allowed, then the current through coupled coils can change instantaneously.

Capacitors

The current "through" a capacitor in terms of the voltage across it is

$$i = C \frac{dv}{dt} \tag{4-13}$$

Thus an instantaneous change in voltage must be accompanied by an infinite current (on an instantaneous basis).   In practical circuits infinite currents would generally produce infinite voltage drops in some elements.   Since this would usually lead to a violation of Kirchhoff's voltage law, such infinite currents cannot exist (see the discussion of this situation as related to inductance). As an example, consider the circuit of Fig. 4-6.   If the voltage across the capacitor changed instantaneously by a finite amount, then $i(t)$ would become infinite.   This would produce an infinite voltage drop across R, and Kirchhoff's voltage law would then require that the generator voltage also be infinite. However, it is finite.   Thus the voltage across the capacitor in Fig. 4-5 *cannot* change instantaneously.   In general, *the voltage across a capacitor cannot change instantaneously if the current through it is restricted to finite values.*

This will be the case in all practical circuits, but not necessarily in all ideal

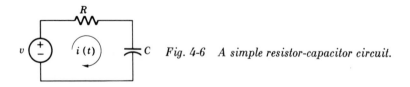

Fig. 4-6   A simple resistor-capacitor circuit.

circuits. For instance, in Fig. 4-6 let $R = 0$. In this case an infinite current will not produce an infinite voltage drop. In fact, if v varies instantaneously, then so will the voltage across the capacitor. Such an ideal circuit cannot be built, since any generator will have some resistance associated with it. However, as we have discussed, there are times when it is convenient to approximate actual circuits by ideal ones.

Resistances

The voltage across a resistance in terms of the current through it is given by

$$v = iR \tag{4-14}$$

There are no derivatives here, and the voltage and current can change instantaneously if the circuit conditions warrant it.

4-2 Initial derivatives

If we know the currents through the inductors and the voltages across the capacitors at $t = 0+$, we can often determine the values of the derivatives of the voltages and currents of the network at $t = 0+$. Note that we are not actually solving the circuit, since these derivatives are obtained only for $t = 0+$, and not for all values of time. Usually all we need do to establish these values is apply Kirchhoff's laws. Let us illustrate this with some simple examples.

Consider the circuit of Fig. 4-3. For $t > 0$

$$v = Ri + L\frac{di}{dt} \tag{4-15}$$

Assume that $i(0-) = 0$. Hence $i(0+) = 0$. Thus at $t = 0+$ we can substitute into Eq. (4-15) to obtain

$$v(0+) = L\frac{di}{dt}\Big|_{t=0+} \tag{4-16}$$

where $v(t)$, and hence $v(0+)$, is known. It must be emphasized that Eq. (4-16) is valid only at $t = 0+$, and at no other times. To obtain higher-order derivatives evaluated at $t = 0+$, we differentiate Eq. (4-15). This yields

$$\frac{dv}{dt} = R\frac{di}{dt} + L\frac{d^2i}{di^2} \tag{4-17}$$

At $t = 0+$ all the quantities except the second derivative are known [$(di/dt)_{t=0+}$ was found in Eq. (4-16)]. Thus we have

$$\frac{d^2i}{dt^2}\Big|_{t=0+} = \frac{1}{L}\frac{dv}{dt}\Big|_{t=0+} - \frac{R}{L}\frac{di}{dt}\Big|_{t=0+}$$

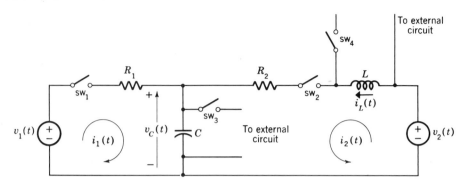

Fig. 4-7   A two-loop circuit.   For $t < 0$, sw$_1$ and sw$_2$ are open and sw$_3$ and sw$_4$ are closed.   The external circuits establish $v_C(0-) = V_0$ and $i_L(0-) = I_0$.   At $t = 0-$, sw$_1$ and sw$_2$ are closed, and then sw$_3$ and sw$_4$ are opened.

Note that we must differentiate Eq. (4-15), and *not* Eq. (4-16).   Equation (4-16) cannot be differentiated because it is valid only at one instant of time. If higher-order derivatives are required, then Eq. (4-17) can be differentiated successively.

This procedure can be used with more complex networks.   For instance, consider Fig. 4-7.   Assume that through some external circuitry, which is removed at $t = 0-$, the initial voltage across the capacitor at $t = 0-$ is made to be V_0 and the initial current through the inductor at $t = 0-$ is established at I_0.   Let us now determine the initial values of $i_1(t)$ and $i_2(t)$ as well as their derivatives.   We write loop equations for the circuit, keeping the terms that represent individual branch-voltage drops together (we do not write the equations in a form suitable for solution).   Thus for $t > 0$ we have

$$v_1(t) = R_1 i_1 + \frac{1}{C} \int (i_1 + i_2)\, dt \qquad (4\text{-}18a)$$

$$v_2(t) = \frac{1}{C} \int (i_1 + i_2)\, dt + R_2 i_2 + L \frac{di_2}{dt} \qquad (4\text{-}18b)$$

The current through the inductance and the voltage across the capacitor cannot change instantaneously, so

$$i_L(0+) = i_2(0+) = I_0 \qquad (4\text{-}19a)$$

$$v_C(0+) = \frac{1}{C} \int (i_1 + i_2)\, dt \bigg|_{t=0+} = V_0 \qquad (4\text{-}19b)$$

Substituting into Eqs. (4-18), we have

$$v_1(0+) = R i_1(0+) + V_0 \qquad (4\text{-}20a)$$

$$v_2(0+) = V_0 + R_2 I_0 + L \frac{di_2}{dt} \bigg|_{t=0+} \qquad (4\text{-}20b)$$

Thus

$$i_1(0+) = \frac{v_1(0+) - V_0}{R} \tag{4-21a}$$

$$i_2(0+) = I_0 \tag{4-21b}$$

$$\left.\frac{di_2}{dt}\right|_{t=0+} = \frac{v_2(0+) - V_0 - R_2 I_0}{L} \tag{4-21c}$$

(Note that $v_1(t)$ and $v_2(t)$ are known.)

To obtain higher-order derivatives we must return to Eqs. (4-18) and differentiate [note that Eqs. (4-20) cannot be differentiated, since they are valid at only one instant of time]. This differentiation yields

$$\frac{dv_1}{dt} = R \frac{di_1}{dt} + \frac{1}{C} (i_1 + i_2) \tag{4-22a}$$

$$\frac{dv_2}{dt} = \frac{1}{C} (i_1 + i_2) + R_2 \frac{di_2}{dt} + L \frac{d^2 i_2}{dt^2} \tag{4-22b}$$

Then at $t = 0+$ we have

$$\left.\frac{dv_1}{dt}\right|_{t=0+} = R \left.\frac{di_1}{dt}\right|_{t=0+} + \frac{1}{C} i_1(0+) + \frac{I_0}{C} \tag{4-23a}$$

$$\left.\frac{dv_2}{dt}\right|_{t=0+} = \frac{1}{C} i_1(0+) + \frac{I_0}{C} + R \left.\frac{di_2}{dt}\right|_{t=0+} + L \left.\frac{d^2 i}{dt^2}\right|_{t=0+} \tag{4-23b}$$

All the quantities in these equations are known or have been determined except $(di_1/dt)_{t=0+}$ and $(d^2 i_2/dt^2)_{t=0+}$. These can be obtained by solving Eqs. (4-23). If higher-order derivatives are desired, then Eqs. (4-22) can be differentiated successively.

In the foregoing example we assumed only one loop current in the inductor. If there are more, then the initial condition I_0 specifies the algebraic sum of all these loop currents.

It is interesting to note that we usually can evaluate all the derivatives of the currents at $t = 0+$. These can be used in a Taylor series expansion of the unknown currents. Thus, we have developed a procedure which can, at times, be used to solve the circuit integral-differential equations. However, later in the chapter we shall obtain far more useful techniques, which yield the solution in a closed form.

The procedures described above can be applied to nodal or cut-set analysis as well as to loop analysis. For example, assume that Fig. 4-8 represents the network for $t > 0$. For $t < 0$ assume that other circuitry, which is removed at $t = 0-$, has established the initial current through the inductor, $i_L(0-) = I_0$, and the initial voltage across the capacitor, $v_2(0-) = V_0$. Since the voltage across the capacitor and the current through the inductor cannot change

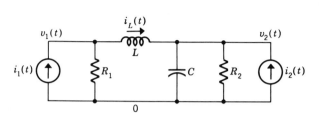

*Fig. 4-8   A two-node cir-
cuit that represents a network for $t > 0$. Assume
that external circuitry, which
has been removed at $t = 0-$,
has established the initial
current through the inductor
as $i_L(0-) = I_0$ and the
initial voltage across the
capacitor as $v_2(0-) = V_0$.*

instantaneously in this circuit, we have

$$i_L(0+) = i_L(0-) = I_0 \tag{4-24a}$$

$$v_2(0+) = v_2(0-) = V_0 \tag{4-24b}$$

Now we perform a nodal analysis of the circuit of Fig. 4-8, keeping the terms that represent individual branch currents grouped together (that is, we do not put the equations in a form suitable for solution).   Thus we have

$$i_1 = G_1 v_1 + \frac{1}{L} \int (v_1 - v_2)\, dt \tag{4-25a}$$

$$i_2 = G_2 v_2 + C \frac{dv_2}{dt} + \frac{1}{L} \int (v_2 - v_1)\, dt \tag{4-25b}$$

The initial current through the inductor is

$$I_0 = \frac{1}{L} \int (v_1 - v_2)\, dt \Big|_{t=0+} \tag{4-26}$$

Then, substituting initial conditions into Eqs. (4-25), we obtain

$$i_1(0+) = G_1 v_1(0+) + I_0 \tag{4-27a}$$

$$i_2(0+) = G_2 V_0 + C \frac{dv_2}{dt} \Big|_{t=0+} - I_0 \tag{4-27b}$$

Hence

$$v_1(0+) = \frac{i_1(0+) - I_0}{G_1} \tag{4-28a}$$

$$\frac{dv_2}{dt} \Big|_{t=0+} = \frac{i_2(0+) + I_0 - G_2 V_0}{C} \tag{4-28b}$$

Higher-order derivatives can be obtained by successive differentiation of Eqs. (4-25).

4-3   Linear differential equations with constant coefficients

Loop, nodal, or cut-set analyses of linear time-invariant networks lead to a set of simultaneous integral-differential equations whose coefficients are constants. If necessary, we can differentiate each of these equations with respect to time. The integrations will be eliminated, and a set of simultaneous differential equations will result.   We shall see later that the solution of this set of simultaneous equations leads to a set of higher-order differential equations, each of which has only one unknown.   At present, however, let us concern ourselves with the solution of one such equation.

The equation will have the form

$$a_n \frac{d^n x}{dt^n} + a_{n-1} \frac{d^{n-1} x}{dt^{n-1}} + \cdots + a_2 \frac{d^2 x}{dt^2} + a_1 \frac{dx}{dt} + a_0 x = y(t) \qquad (4\text{-}29)$$

where $x(t)$ is the unknown function of time, $a_0, a_1, \ldots, a_n$ are known constants, and $y(t)$ is a known function of time.   The constants $a_0, a_1, \ldots, a_n$ are functions of the circuit elements, and $y(t)$ is a function of the known generators.   By extending the operator notation of Eq. (3-12),

$$p^k f(t) = \frac{d^k f(t)}{dt^k} \qquad (4\text{-}30)$$

we can write Eq. (4-29) in more compact form as

$$a_n p^n x + a_{n-1} p^{n-1} x + \cdots + a_1 p x + a_0 x = y(t) \qquad (4\text{-}31)$$

or

$$(a_n p^n + a_{n-1} p^{n-1} + \cdots + a_1 p + a_0) x = y(t) \qquad (4\text{-}32)$$

Let us consider some aspects of $x(t)$, which is the solution of Eq. (4-29), (4-31), or (4-32).   Assume that in some way we have obtained an $x(t)$ which we think is a solution of Eq. (4-29).   To verify it, we substitute it into Eq. (4-29). If the evaluation of the left-hand side of this equation yields $y(t)$, then this $x(t)$ actually is a solution.   If $y(t)$ is not obtained by evaluating the right-hand side of Eq. (4-29), then $x(t)$ is not a solution.   Let us assume that we have found such a solution, which we shall call $x_P(t)$.

Now consider another equation, which is very similar to Eq. (4-29), except that $y(t) = 0$:

$$a_n \frac{d^n x}{dt^n} + a_{n-1} \frac{d^{n-1} x}{dt^{n-1}} + \cdots + a_1 \frac{dx}{dt} + a_0 x = 0 \qquad (4\text{-}33)$$

This equation is called the *homogeneous differential equation*.   Assume that we have in some way found a solution to this homogeneous equation, which we call $x_C(t)$; that is, when $x_C(t)$ is substituted into Eq. (4-33), we obtain zero for the left-hand side.   Then, if $x_P(t)$ is a solution to Eq. (4-29),

$$x(t) = x_P(t) + x_C(t) \qquad (4\text{-}34)$$

will also be a solution to it.   This can be demonstrated if we substitute Eq. (4-34) into Eq. (4-29).   We have

$$a_n \frac{d_n[x_P(t) + x_C(t)]}{dt^n} + \cdots + a_1 \frac{d[x_P(t) + x_C(t)]}{dt}$$
$$+ a_0[x_P(t) + x_C(t)] = y(t) \quad (4\text{-}35)$$

and, rearranging these equations, we obtain

$$a_n \frac{d^n x_P(t)}{dt^n} + \cdots + a_1 \frac{dx_P(t)}{dt} + a_0 x_P(t) + a_n \frac{d^n x_C(t)}{dt^n}$$
$$+ \cdots + a_1 \frac{dx_C(t)}{dt} + a_0 x_C(t) = y(t) \quad (4\text{-}36)$$

However, $x_C(t)$ satisfies Eq. (4-33), and if we substitute this value of zero into Eq. (4-36), we obtain

$$a_n \frac{d^n x_P(t)}{dt^n} + \cdots + a_1 \frac{dx_P(t)}{dt} + a_0 x_P(t) = y(t) \quad (4\text{-}37)$$

This is the same as Eq. (4-29), and $x_P(t)$ is a solution to it.   Hence $x(t)$ as given by Eq. (4-34) will also be a solution to the differential equation.

The solution $x_C(t)$ to the homogeneous equation is called the *complementary solution*. $x_P(t)$ is called the *particular solution*.   In general, the solution to these differential equations is given by the sum of the complementary and the particular solutions.   The complementary solution is the solution to the homogeneous equation which does not contain $y(t)$.   Thus the complementary solution depends only upon the elements of the network, and not upon the generators.   (We shall see later, however, that the complementary solution contains arbitrary constants which are functions of the generators, the initial conditions, and the element values.)   The particular solution includes the effects of the generators.

Let us now consider techniques for evaluating the complementary and particular solutions.   We shall discuss the complementary solution first.   Let us guess at a solution.   Substitution in Eq. (4-33) will substantiate this guess if it is correct.   As a trial solution, let us consider

$$x(t) = Ke^{bt} \quad (4\text{-}38)$$

where K is a constant.   Substitution in Eq. (4-33) yields

$$Ke^{bt}(a_n b^n + a_{n-1} b^{n-1} + \cdots + a_1 b + a_0) = 0 \quad (4\text{-}39)$$

If Eq. (4-38) is a valid solution, then the left-hand side of Eq. (4-39) must be zero.   If we set $Ke^{bt} = 0$, a solution will result, but it is trivial, since this is equivalent to setting $x(t) = 0$.   Thus if Eq. (4-38) is to be a nontrivial solution of the homogeneous equation, we must set

$$a_n b^n + a_{n-1} b^{n-1} + \cdots + a_1 b + a_0 = 0 \quad (4\text{-}40)$$

This is called the *characteristic equation*. It is simply an algebraic equation in the variable b. This equation has n roots, which are the only values of b that will cause the left-hand side of Eq. (4-39) to be zero. Hence we can state that Eq. (4-38) is a solution to Eq. (4-33) if, and only if, b is one of the roots of Eq. (4-40). Note that the constant K is arbitrary. We can write Eq. (4-40) in factored form as

$$a_n(b - b_1)(b - b_2) \cdots (b - b_n) = 0 \qquad (4\text{-}41)$$

Then the roots of this equation, and thus the allowable values of b, are b_1, b_2, . . . , b_n.

With the operator notation of Eq. (4-30) Eq. (4-33) becomes

$$a_n p^n + a_{n-1} p^{n-1} + \cdots + a_1 p + a_0 = 0 \qquad (4\text{-}42)$$

If we consider the p terms as just algebraic quantities, then Eqs. (4-42) and (4-40) have the same form, and the roots of Eq. (4-42) yield the allowable values of b.

Equation (4-41) indicates that if the highest derivative of the homogeneous equation is of degree n, there will be n possible values of b that can be used in Eq. (4-38) as a solution. If we assume for the time being that all the b_1, b_2, . . . , b_n are different, we shall demonstrate that a possible solution of the homogeneous equation is

$$x(t) = K_1 e^{b_1 t} + K_2 e^{b_2 t} + \cdots + K_n e^{b_n t} = \sum_{i=1}^{n} K_i e^{b_i t} \qquad (4\text{-}43)$$

where K_1, K_2, . . . , K_n are arbitrary constants. Equation (4-43) states that if n different terms of the form $K_1 e^{b_1 t}$, $K_2 e^{b_2 t}$, . . . are each solutions to the homogeneous equation, then the sum of all these terms will also be a solution. This can be verified by substituting Eq. (4-43) into Eq. (4-33) to obtain

$$a_n \frac{d^n}{dt^n}(K_1 e^{b_1 t} + \cdots + K_n e^{b_n t}) + \cdots + a_1 \frac{d}{dt}(K_1 e^{b_1 t} + \cdots + K_n e^{b_n t})$$
$$+ a_0(K_1 e^{b_1 t} + \cdots + K_n e^{b_n t}) = 0 \quad (4\text{-}44a)$$

This can be rewritten as

$$\left(a_n \frac{d^n K_1 e^{b_1 t}}{dt^n} + \cdots + a_1 \frac{d}{dt} K_1 e^{b_1 t} + a_0 K_1 e^{b_1 t} \right) + \cdots + \left(a_n \frac{d^n}{dt^n} K_n e^{b_n t} \right.$$
$$\left. + \cdots + a_1 \frac{d}{dt} K_n e^{b_n t} + a_0 K_n e^{b_n t} \right) = 0 \quad (4\text{-}44b)$$

Since each of the terms of Eq. (4-43) is a solution to Eq. (4-33), then each of the terms in parentheses in Eq. (4-44b) will be zero, and an equality is obtained. Thus Eq. (4-43) is substantiated as a solution to the homogeneous equation.

Must we use all the terms of Eq. (4-43) in the solution? Why not simplify the equation by setting some of the K_1, K_2, . . . equal to zero? Actually, we require a solution with as many arbitrary constants as are given in Eq. (4-43). Since there are n independent arbitrary constants, we can specify n independent initial conditions.   If we use fewer than n terms in the solution, then our solution will not be complete.   It can be shown that an nth-order differential equation will result from a network that has n arbitrary initial conditions.   We must be able to incorporate *all* these initial conditions into our solution, so all the terms of Eq. (4-43) must be used.   For example, in Fig. 4-7 there are two independent initial conditions, $i_L(0-)$ and $v_C(0-)$, and the solution for either $i_1(t)$ or $i_2(t)$ must contain sufficient freedom that they can be specified.   Therefore there must be two arbitrary constants in each solution.

For a completely rigorous proof we should ascertain that Eq. (4-43) is the most general form of the solution of the homogeneous equation.   That is, we should show that there are no solutions in addition to those given in Eq. (4-43).   A mathematical analysis will indicate this, but such an analysis is beyond the scope of this chapter.

Now suppose that two or more of the roots of Eq. (4-40) are equal.   In this case the solution must be modified somewhat.   Note that if $K_1e^{b_1t} + K_2e^{b_2t}$ is a solution and $b_1 = b_2$, then we can write this as $(K_1 + K_2)e^{b_1t}$.   However, $K_1 + K_2$ can be written simply as a new constant K_1'.   Thus it appears that one arbitrary constant is eliminated if two of the roots of the characteristic equation are equal.   Actually, this is not true, since we can include additional solutions in this case.

Let us assume that $b_1 = b_2$ in Eq. (4-41).   If we let

$$x(t) = K_1e^{bt} \tag{4-45}$$

and substitute in Eq. (4-33), we obtain

$$a_n \frac{d^n}{dt^n} K_1e^{bt} + \cdots + a_1 \frac{d}{dt} K_1e^{bt} + a_0 K_1e^{bt}$$

$$= K_1e^{bt}(b - b_1)^2(b - b_3) \cdots (b - b_n) \tag{4-46}$$

Now we partially differentiate both sides of this equation with respect to b and interchange the order of total differentiation and partial differentiation on the left-hand side.   We shall assume that the solution is such that this can be done. Thus we have

$$a_n \frac{d^n}{dt^n} \frac{\partial}{\partial b} (K_1e^{bt}) + \cdots + a_1 \frac{d}{dt} \frac{\partial}{\partial b} (K_1e^{bt}) + a_0 \frac{\partial}{\partial b} K_1e^{bt}$$

$$= t(b - b_1)^2(b - b_3) \cdots (b - b_n)K_1e^{bt}$$

$$+ K_1e^{bt}[2(b - b_1)(b - b_3) \cdots (b - b_n)]$$

$$+ (b - b_1)^2 \frac{\partial}{\partial b} [(b - b_3) \cdots (b - b_n)] \tag{4-47}$$

If we let $b = b_1$, the right-hand side of Eq. (4-47) becomes zero.   Hence, after substituting

$$\frac{\partial}{\partial b} K_1 e^{bt} \Big|_{b=b_1} = K_1 t e^{b_1 t}$$

in Eq. (4-47), we obtain

$$a_n \frac{d^n}{dt^n} (K_1 t e^{b_1 t}) + \cdots + a_1 \frac{d}{dt} (K_1 t e^{b_1 t}) + a_0 (K_1 t e^{b_1 t}) = 0 \qquad (4\text{-}48)$$

This is the equation that would have resulted if we had assumed that

$$x(t) = K_1 t e^{b_1 t} \qquad (4\text{-}49)$$

was a solution to the homogeneous equation and substituted it into Eq. (4-33). Equation (4-48) verifies that it is in fact a solution. Note that the right-hand side of Eq. (4-47) becomes zero only when $b = b_1$ *if* b_1 is a multiple root of the characteristic equation.

The value of the constant K_1 can be changed without voiding our results. If the roots of the characteristic equation are $b_1, b_1, b_3, \ldots, b_n$, the solution has the form

$$x(t) = K_1 e^{b_1 t} + K_2 t e^{b_1 t} + K_3 e^{b_3 t} + \cdots + K_n e^{b_n t} \qquad (4\text{-}50)$$

Now let us assume that there are r identical roots of the characteristic equation, $b_1, b_1, \ldots, b_1, b_{r+1}, \ldots, b_n$. The solution will be of the form

$$x(t) = K_1 e^{b_1 t} + K_2 t e^{b_1 t} + \cdots + K_r t^{r-1} e^{b_1 t} + K_{r+1} e^{b_{r+1} t} + \cdots + K_n e^{b_n t} \qquad (4\text{-}51)$$

This can be established by considering an equation that is similar to Eq. (4-46), except that the right-hand side is

$$K_1 e^{b_1 t} (b - b_1)^r (b - b_{r+1}) \cdots (b - b_n)$$

This equivalent equation is then partially differentiated r times with respect to b. The details follow those of Eqs. (4-46) to (4-49) and are left to the reader. If there is more than one set of multiple roots, then each such set leads to solutions of the type discussed. Thus, if the characteristic equation is of degree n, then there will always be n independent constants.

If the roots of the characteristic equation are real numbers, then the solution to the homogeneous equation consists of a sum of exponential terms. However, the roots may not be real; they may be complex numbers. For instance, we could have

$$b_1 = \sigma + j\omega \qquad (4\text{-}52)$$

where σ and ω are real numbers and

$$j = \sqrt{-1} \qquad (4\text{-}53)$$

The solution will still be given by Eq. (4-43).

We must now determine the significance of $e^{(\sigma+j\omega)t}$. This can be written as

$$e^{(\sigma+j\omega)t} = e^{\sigma t}e^{j\omega t} \tag{4-54}$$

The first factor is simply an exponential term.   Let us consider the second one.
We shall make use of the Taylor series for the exponential

$$e^x = 1 + x + \frac{x^2}{2!} + \frac{x^3}{3!} + \frac{x^4}{4!} + \cdots \tag{4-55}$$

Then if

$$x = j\omega t$$

substitution in Eq. (4-55) yields

$$e^{j\omega t} = 1 - \frac{(\omega t)^2}{2!} + \frac{(\omega t)^4}{4!} - \cdots + j\left[\omega t - \frac{(\omega t)^3}{3!} + \cdots\right] \tag{4-56}$$

The Taylor series expansion for the sine and cosine are

$$\sin \omega t = \omega t - \frac{(\omega t)^3}{3!} + \frac{(\omega t)^5}{5!} - \cdots \tag{4-57a}$$

$$\cos \omega t = 1 - \frac{(\omega t)^2}{2!} + \frac{(\omega t)^4}{4!} - \cdots \tag{4-57b}$$

Comparing Eqs. (4-57) with Eq. (4-56), we obtain

$$e^{j\omega t} = \cos \omega t + j \sin \omega t \tag{4-58}$$

This equation is known as *Euler's relation*.   Thus a root of the characteristic
equation of the form of Eq. (4-52) leads to a term of solution of the form

$$K_1 e^{\sigma t}(\cos \omega t + j \sin \omega t) \tag{4-59}$$

In general, the solution of the integral-differential equations of networks
will be for actual currents or voltages.   These must be real functions of time,
and the appearance of the imaginary term (the one containing $j = \sqrt{-1}$) may
be startling.   However, there are two facts that will lead to solutions which
contain only real terms even if the values of b are not real.   First, the coefficients of the characteristic equation, Eq. (4-40), will be real numbers, so the
complex roots will occur in conjugate pairs.   That is, if b_1 is given by Eq.
(4-52), then there will be another root (call it b_2) such that

$$b_2 = \sigma - j\omega \tag{4-60}$$

Thus there will be a term in the solution

$$K_2 e^{\sigma t}(\cos \omega t - j \sin \omega t) \tag{4-61}$$

Second, the constants K_1 and K_2 will turn out to be conjugates.   That is, if

$$K_1 = A_1 + jB_1 \tag{4-62a}$$

then

$$K_2 = A_1 - jB_1 \tag{4-62b}$$

If we substitute Eqs. (4-62) into relations (4-59) and (4-61), we obtain for the sum of these two terms (note that the solution of the differential equation contains their sum)

$$K_1 e^{\sigma t}(\cos \omega t + j \sin \omega t) + K_2 e^{\sigma t}(\cos \omega t - j \sin \omega t)$$
$$= 2e^{\sigma t}(A_1 \cos \omega t - B_1 \sin \omega t) \tag{4-63}$$

Thus, even if the characteristic equation has complex roots, the solution of the differential equation can be real. In general, the constants will always be such that this is so.

At times hyperbolic functions, rather than exponential ones, are used to express the solution of the homogeneous equation. The hyperbolic sine and hyperbolic cosine can be considered to be *defined* by

$$\cosh bt = \frac{e^{bt} + e^{-bt}}{2} \tag{4-64a}$$

$$\sinh bt = \frac{e^{bt} - e^{-bt}}{2} \tag{4-64b}$$

Alternatively, we can write

$$e^{bt} = \cosh bt + \sinh bt \tag{4-65}$$

As an example of the solution of a homogeneous differential equation, consider

$$\frac{d^2x}{dx^2} + 5\frac{dx}{dt} + 6x = 0 \tag{4-66}$$

If we assume a solution in the form of Eq. (4-38) and substitute it, we obtain

$$Ke^{bt}(b^2 + 5b + 6) = 0$$

Factoring the characteristic equation, we have

$$(b + 2)(b + 3) = 0$$

Thus the solution is

$$x(t) = K_1 e^{-2t} + K_2 e^{-3t} \tag{4-67}$$

Now let us discuss the solution of the particular differential equation [see Eq. (4-29)]. If we assume that the complete solution of the differential equation is given by the sum of the complementary and particular solutions, then the particular solution need contain no arbitrary constants. The required degrees of freedom necessary to establish the initial conditions are supplied by the complementary solution, and any solution that satisfies Eq. (4-29) will yield the desired particular solution. As a solution procedure we shall consider the *method of undetermined coefficients.* This is not a completely general technique in that it will not yield solutions for all possible $y(t)$ of Eq. (4-29). However, for most networks and generators encountered, the $y(t)$ obtained will be such that the method of undetermined coefficients will work. In this method the solution is assumed to be a sum of terms with constant multipliers. The form of the terms is determined from a knowledge of $y(t)$, and the remainder of the differential equation is used just to establish the values of the constant multipliers. The forms of the terms of the solution have been established by using more general methods to solve the differential equations. Here we shall merely state the results of these general methods.

Let us illustrate this procedure with an example. If $y(t)$ is a constant, then the form of $x_P(t)$ will also be a constant. In this case we write

$$x_P(t) = A_1 \tag{4-68}$$

where A_1 is a constant. This constant is different from those we have encountered in the complementary solution; it will be determined directly from the differential equation. For example, let us solve

$$\frac{d^2x}{dt^2} + 5\frac{dx}{dt} + 6x = 12 \tag{4-69}$$

The complementary solution has been obtained by solving the homogeneous equation given in Eq. (4-66). To obtain the particular solution we substitute Eq. (4-68) into Eq. (4-69), and noting that the derivative of a constant is zero, we obtain

$$6A_1 = 12$$

or

$$A_1 = 2 \tag{4-70}$$

If a constant value of A_1 could not have been found, then Eq. (4-68) would not have been a particular solution, and another method would have to be used to obtain it. Now, combining the particular solution with the complementary solution, we obtain the complete solution of Eq. (4-68) as

$$x(t) = 2 + K_1e^{-2t} + K_2e^{-3t} \tag{4-71}$$

The constants K_1 and K_2 are determined from initial conditions. For instance, if

$$x(0+) = 0 \tag{4-72a}$$

$$\frac{dx}{dt}\bigg|_{t=0+} = 1 \tag{4-72b}$$

then substitution of Eq. (4-72a) into (4-71) yields

$$0 = 2 + K_1 + K_2 \tag{4-73}$$

We differentiate Eq. (4-71) with respect to time,

$$\frac{dx(t)}{dt} = 0 - 2K_1 e^{-2t} - 3K_2 e^{-3t} \tag{4-74}$$

and substitute Eq. (4-72b) to obtain

$$1 = -2K_1 - 3K_2 \tag{4-75}$$

Equations (4-73) and (4-75) constitute two simultaneous equations which can be solved for K_1 and K_2. This solution yields

$$K_1 = -5 \tag{4-76a}$$

$$K_2 = 3 \tag{4-76b}$$

and substitution of these values into Eq. (4-71) gives the complete solution for $x(t)$,

$$x(t) = 2 - 5e^{-2t} + 3e^{-t} \tag{4-77}$$

Note that part of this solution $(-5e^{-2t} + 3e^{-t})$ falls off as time increases and approaches zero asymptotically. This is the part of the solution that is due to the complementary solution; it is called the *transient solution*. This solution which decays to zero is typical of the complementary solutions of the differential equations of many networks. If the particular solution does not contain terms which become arbitrarily small for large time, then any terms in the complete solution that do become arbitrarily small are called the transient solution.

We have considered obtaining the particular solution when $y(t)$ is a constant. Table 4-1 indicates trial solutions[1] for other types of $y(t)$. The A terms in the table are constants which are evaluated by substitution in the differential equation. If $y(t)$ consists of more than one of the terms in the left-hand column of the table, then the particular solution will contain a sum

Table 4-1   Trial solutions for the method of undetermined coefficients

$y(t)$	Terms in particular solution
Y_0 (const)	A_1
t	$A_1 t + A_0$
t^n	$A_n t^n + A_{n-1} t^{n-1} + \cdots + A_1 + A_0$
$\sin \omega t$	$A_1 \sin \omega t + A_2 \cos \omega t$
$\cos \omega t$	$A_1 \sin \omega t + A_2 \cos \omega t$
e^{bt}	$A_1 e^{bt}$
$e^{bt} \sin \omega t$	$A_1 e^{bt} \sin \omega t + A_2 e^{bt} \cos \omega t$
$e^{bt} \cos \omega t$	$A_1 e^{bt} \sin \omega t + A_2 e^{bt} \cos \omega t$

of the corresponding terms in the right-hand column.   For instance, if

$$y(t) = 3 + 4t + 2 \sin 3t \qquad (4\text{-}78)$$

then the particular solution will be

$$x_P(t) = A_0 + A_1 t + A_2 + A_3 \sin 3t + A_4 \cos 4t \qquad (4\text{-}79a)$$

The constants A_0 and A_2 can be combined, so that we have

$$x_P(t) = A_1 t + A_2 + A_3 \sin 3t + A_4 \cos 4t \qquad (4\text{-}79b)$$

The constants are evaluated by substitution in the differential equation.

Note that the constant multipliers of the terms of $y(t)$ do not affect the form of $x_P(t)$.   They will, of course, affect the constant multipliers of the terms of $x_P(t)$.

If $y(t)$ leads to a term in Table 4-1 that is also part of the complementary solution, then the form of the particular solution must be modified.   If the characteristic equation [see Eq. (4-40)] has a simple root which leads to the complementary solution, and $y(t)$ leads to the same term in Table 4-1 for the particular solution, then we multiply the term in the particular solution by t. If the characteristic equation has a multiple root of order m, and this term leads to a solution of the complementary solution which is the same as a term in Table 4-1 for the particular solution, then we multiply that term in the particular solution by t^m.

To illustrate all these ideas with some examples let us solve

$$\frac{d^2x}{dt^2} + 5\frac{dx}{dt} + 6x = e^{-4t} \qquad (4\text{-}80)$$

The complementary solution for this equation is given by Eq. (4-67).   From Table 4-1 we obtain the particular solution as

$$x_P(t) = A_1 e^{-4t} \qquad (4\text{-}81)$$

Note that the particular solution is not the same as any part of the complementary solution, since the exponents are different.   Substitution of Eq. (4-81) into Eq. (4-80) yields

$$16A_1 e^{-4t} - 20A_1 e^{-4t} + 6A_1 e^{-4t} = e^{-4t}$$

or, equivalently,

$$(2A_1 - 1)e^{-4t} = 0 \qquad (4\text{-}82)$$

If this is to be valid for all time, then

$$A_1 = \tfrac{1}{2} \qquad (4\text{-}83)$$

Thus the complete solution is given by

$$x(t) = \tfrac{1}{2}e^{-4t} + K_1 e^{-2t} + K_2 e^{-3t} \qquad (4\text{-}84)$$

Let us now consider the solution of a similar equation,

$$\frac{d^2x}{dx^2} + 5\frac{dx}{dt} + 6x = 3e^{-2t} \tag{4-85}$$

In this case the form of the particular solution is identical with a term of the complementary solution [Eq. (4-67)]. Hence we modify this term from Table 4-1 by multiplying it by t,

$$x_P(t) = A_1te^{-2t} \tag{4-86}$$

Substitution in Eq. (4-85) yields

$$A_1e^{-2t} = 3e^{-2t}$$

or

$$A_1 = 3 \tag{4-87}$$

Thus the complete solution of the differential equation is

$$x(t) = 3te^{-2t} + K_1e^{-2t} + K_2e^{-3t} \tag{4-88}$$

As a final example let us obtain the solution of

$$\frac{d^2x}{dt^2} + 5\frac{dx}{dt} + 6x = e^{-4t} + 3e^{-2t} \tag{4-89}$$

The particular solution consists of a sum of the individual particular solutions, which are given in Eqs. (4-81) and (4-86). Thus

$$x_P(t) = A_1e^{-4t} + A_2te^{-2t} \tag{4-90}$$

Substituting Eq. (4-90) into Eq. (4-89) and manipulating, we have

$$(2A_1 - 1)e^{-4t} + (A_2 - 3)e^{-2t} = 0 \tag{4-91}$$

If this is to be true for all values of time, then the coefficients of e^{-4t} and e^{-2t} must both be zero, because e^{-4t} and e^{-2t} are independent functions of time. Hence

$$A_1 = \frac{1}{2}$$
$$A_2 = 3$$

and the complete solution is

$$x(t) = \frac{1}{2}e^{-4t} + 3te^{-2t} + K_1e^{-2t} + K_2e^{-3t} \tag{4-92}$$

If $y(t)$ contains terms such as sin ωt or cos ωt, then care should be taken. For instance, in this case, if the complementary solution has a term of the form $e^{j\omega t}$, then [see Eq. (4-58)] the complementary solution and $y(t)$ contain identical terms, and the particular solution must contain terms of the form t sin ωt and t cos ωt. Note that $e^{\sigma t}$ sin ωt is *not* the same form as sin ωt.

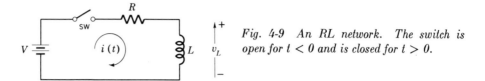

Fig. 4-9   An RL network.   The switch is open for $t < 0$ and is closed for $t > 0$.

4-4   The response of RL, RC, and RLC networks

We shall now define some widely used terms and apply the results of the last section to some simple networks.   These examples will illustrate the procedures we have discussed; however, even more important, they will provide some insight into the ways in which voltages and currents can vary in electric networks.

RL networks

Let us obtain an expression for the current in the network of Fig. 4-9.   For $t > 0$ this network is characterized by the equation

$$V = Ri + L\frac{di}{dt} \tag{4-93}$$

The homogeneous differential equation is

$$Ri + L\frac{di}{dt} = 0 \tag{4-94}$$

The complementary solution will be in the form

$$i_C(t) = Ke^{bt} \tag{4-95}$$

Substitution gives us

$$(R + Lb)Ke^{bt} = 0 \tag{4-96}$$

Thus

$$b = -\frac{R}{L} \tag{4-97}$$

and the complementary solution is

$$i_C(t) = Ke^{-(R/L)t} \tag{4-98}$$

From Table 4-1 we see that the form of the particular solution is

$$i_P(t) = A \tag{4-99}$$

Substituting in Eq. (4-93) and solving, we obtain

$$i_P(t) = A = \frac{V}{R} \tag{4-100}$$

Thus the equation for the current $i(t)$ is

$$i(t) = \frac{V}{R} + Ke^{-(R/L)t} \tag{4-101}$$

To evaluate K we make use of initial conditions. Since the switch was open at $t = 0-$, we state $i(0-) = 0$. The current in this inductance cannot change instantaneously with time, so

$$i(0+) = i(0-) = 0 \tag{4-102}$$

Substituting in Eq. (4-101), we have

$$K = -\frac{V}{R} \tag{4-103}$$

and the complete expression for the current is

$$i(t) = \frac{V}{R}(1 - e^{-(R/L)t}) \tag{4-104}$$

Let us study this equation. A typical response is shown in Fig. 4-10. Note that the current starts at a value of zero and then builds up exponentially to the value V/R. The physical explanation of this result is that the presence of the inductance does not allow the current to change instantaneously, so the initial value of the current is zero. As the current builds up, the voltage drop across the resistance increases. Thus the voltage drop across the inductance, and therefore the rate of change of current, decreases. As the current approaches a constant, the voltage drop across the inductance approaches zero,

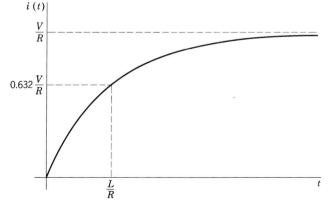

Fig. 4-10   A plot of the current in the circuit of Fig. 4-9.

and the entire generator voltage is across the resistance.   The final value of current is V/R, which is the value it would be if there were no inductance.

Let us see how the exponent of Eq. (4-104) affects the curve.   Consider a particular value of time, which we shall call T, where the exponent is equal to unity:

$$T = \frac{L}{R} \qquad\qquad\qquad (4\text{-}105)$$

This value of T is called the *time constant* of the circuit.   The value of e^{-1} is 0.368, and $1 - e^{-1} = 0.632$.   Thus in one time-constant time the current has risen to 63.2 percent of its final value.   Table 4-2 is useful in determining the response at times which are multiples of one time constant.   In a time equal to one time constant $e^{-t/T}$ falls off from 1 to 0.368.   This result is somewhat more general than it appears.   Consider $e^{-t_0/T}$, where t_0 is an arbitrary time.   If we increase the time to $t_0 + T$, the exponential becomes

$$e^{-(t_0+T)/T} = e^{-1}e^{-t_0}$$

Thus at the end of *any* interval of time whose length is equal to one time constant $e^{-t/T}$ will be 0.368 times its value at the start of the interval.

Another interpretation can be placed on the time constant.   Consider

$$\frac{de^{-t/T}}{dt} = -\frac{1}{T}e^{-t/T}$$

At $t = 0$ this derivative is given by

$$\frac{de^{-t/T}}{dt}\bigg|_{t=0} = -\frac{1}{T}$$

If the function $e^{-t/T}$ did not fall off exponentially, but fell instead as a straight line of slope $-1/T$ (its initial slope), from its starting point of unity it would reach zero, in a time equal to the time constant T.   Of course, this does not actually occur.   We see from Table 4-2 that in a time equal to five time constants the current has reached 99.3 percent of its final value.

The time constant determines the "speed" of response of the circuit.

Table 4-2   Exponential values

x	e^{-x}	$1 - e^{-x}$
0	1	0
1	0.368	0.632
2	0.135	0.865
3	0.050	0.950
4	0.018	0.982
5	0.007	0.993

Actually, the current never reaches its final value; it just approaches it asymptotically. Let us say that for all practical purposes the current has reached the final value of V/R after a time equal to five times the time constant. Now let us consider a circuit where $L/R = 1$. In this case it will take 5 sec for the current to "reach" the final value. However, if we reduce the L/R ratio to 10^{-3}, then the current will reach its final value after 5 msec. Thus the *ratio* of the inductance to the resistance is important in establishing the rate at which this circuit responds.

Often we are interested in the relative shape of the response curve of Fig. 4-10. For this type of study it is more convenient not to plot the vertical axis in terms of the actual current, but instead to adjust its scale so that the final value is unity. In this way we can determine the current at any instant as a fraction of the final value. Such a process is called *normalization*.

As an illustration, in Eq. (4-104) the final value of the current is

$$I_f = \frac{V}{R} \tag{4-106}$$

Now we divide both sides of Eq. (4-104) by I_f. This procedure, called *normalization with respect to I_f*, yields

$$\frac{i(t)}{I_f} = 1 - e^{-(R/L)t} \tag{4-107}$$

We can plot this curve. However, before we do so, let us carry the normalization one step further. If we substitute Eq. (4-105) for R/L, we obtain

$$\frac{i(t)}{I_f} = 1 - e^{-t/T} \tag{4-108}$$

The time has now been normalized in terms of the time-constant time. This curve is plotted in Fig. 4-11. It is useful because it can be applied immediately to any network of the form of Fig. 4-9 by simply calculating I_f and T.

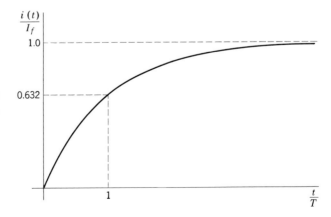

Fig. 4-11   A plot of the normalized current given by Eq. (4-108).

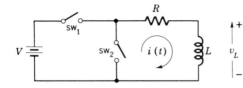

Fig. 4-12   An RL circuit that illustrates a decaying transient.   Assume that sw₁ is closed at t = − ∞ and is opened at t = 0+ and that sw₂ is closed at t = 0−.

Now let us study the circuit of Fig. 4-12.   Switch sw₁ is closed for a very long time.   We indicate this by saying that it is closed at $t = -\infty$.   Actually, it need be closed only long enough that the current through the inductance is essentially V/R.   Then, at some time we shall call $t = 0$, we close sw₂ and open sw₁, in that order.   The differential equation of this circuit is then, for $t > 0$,

$$0 = Ri + L\frac{di}{dt} \tag{4-109}$$

This is just a homogeneous equation.   Its solution is

$$i(t) = Ke^{-(R/L)t} \tag{4-110}$$

To evaluate the constant K we make use of the initial condition

$$i(0-) = i(0+) = \frac{V}{R} \tag{4-111}$$

Then $K = V/R$.   Substituting in Eq. (4-110), we obtain

$$i(t) = \frac{V}{R}\,e^{-(R/L)t} \tag{4-112}$$

Before we plot this curve, let us normalize it.   At $t = 0$, the value of current is V/R.   Thus we shall call this the initial value of current

$$I_0 = \frac{V}{R} \tag{4-113}$$

The exponent of Eq. (4-112) is the same as it is in Eq. (4-103).   Hence we shall define the time constant by Eq. (4-105).   Then, substituting Eqs. (4-105) and (4-113) into Eq. (4-112), we obtain

$$i(t) = I_0 e^{-t/T} \tag{4-114}$$

This function, with the curve normalized with respect to the initial value, is plotted in Fig. 4-13. The current starts at the initial value of $I_0 = V/R$, because the inductance does not permit it to change instantaneously.   However, there is no generator in the circuit, so the current must fall off because the resistance dissipates power in the form of heat.   The initial energy stored in the magnetic field of the inductance leaves the circuit in the form of this heat.

Since the stored energy is finite, and no energy is added, the current cannot be constant. It decays exponentially, and in one time-constant time becomes 36.8 percent of its initial value. From Table 4-2 we see that in a time equal to five times the time constant the current falls off to 0.7 percent of its final value. Thus the factor which affects the speed of response of this circuit is the same as that for Fig. 4-9; that is, the *ratio* of L to R.

Let us now obtain the voltage drop across the inductance in the circuit of Figs. 4-9 and 4-12. Differentiating Eq. (4-104) and multiplying by L, we obtain

$$v_L(t) = Ve^{-(R/L)t}$$

The *shape* of this curve is given by Fig. 4-13 [the labeling of the vertical axis should be changed to $v_L(t)/V$]. The voltage drop across the inductance is largest at $t = 0$, when it is equal to V. Thus there is zero voltage drop across R (see Fig. 4-9), and the initial value of the current is zero. As the current approaches a final, constant value, the voltage drop across the inductance becomes zero.

To obtain the voltage drop across the inductance of Fig. 4-12 we differentiate Eq. (4-112) with respect to time and multiply by L. This yields

$$v_L(t) = -Ve^{-(R/L)t} \tag{4-115}$$

The form of this curve is the negative of that given in Fig. 4-13 [the labeling of the vertical axis must be changed to $-v_L(t)/V$]. The initial value of voltage across the inductance is $-V$. The voltage drop appears across the resistance (see Fig. 4-12), maintaining the current at the initial value of V/R. The polarity of the voltage is such that the current is in the correct direction. As time increases, the current falls off and approaches the constant value of zero. The magnitude of the voltage across the inductance also approaches zero.

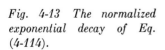

Fig. 4-13 The normalized exponential decay of Eq. (4-114).

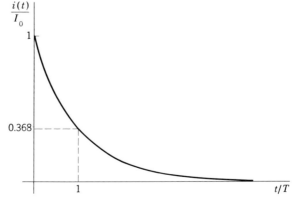

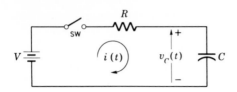

Fig. 4-14 A simple resistor-capacitor circuit. The switch is closed at $t = 0$.

RC networks

Let us obtain the current and voltage in the simple resistor-capacitor network of Fig. 4-14. For $t > 0$, when the switch is closed, we have

$$V = Ri + \frac{1}{C}\int i\,dt \tag{4-116}$$

If we differentiate both sides of this equation with respect to time, noting that the derivative of a constant is zero, we obtain

$$0 = R\frac{di}{dt} + \frac{1}{C}i \tag{4-117}$$

The solution to this homogeneous equation is

$$i(t) = Ke^{-t/RC} \tag{4-118}$$

Let us assume that at $t = 0-$, just before the switch was closed, the voltage across the capacitor was zero. Then, since the voltage across this capacitor cannot change instantaneously,

$$v_c(0+) = v_c(0-) = 0 \tag{4-119}$$

Thus the full generator voltage appears initially across the resistance, and therefore the initial voltage across the resistance is equal to V. Then, applying Ohm's law, we obtain

$$i(0+) = \frac{V}{R} \tag{4-120}$$

and, substituting in Eq. (4-118), we have

$$K = \frac{V}{R} \tag{4-121}$$

Thus

$$i(t) = \frac{V}{R}e^{-t/RC} \tag{4-122}$$

This curve is of exactly the same form as Fig. 4-13 if we normalize as follows:

$$i(t) = I_0 e^{-t/T} \tag{4-123}$$

At $t = 0$, $i(0) = V/R$. Hence

$$I_0 = \frac{V}{R} \tag{4-124}$$

The exponent of the exponential of Eq. (4-122) is equal to 1 when $t = T$, where

$$T = RC \tag{4-125}$$

This is the time constant for this circuit. That is, in one time-constant time the current will fall off to 36.8 percent of its initial value. The remaining falloff is characterized by Table 4-2 and Fig. 4-13. Thus the speed of response of this circuit is determined by the *product RC*.

Before we consider the physical reasons for the shape of this curve, let us determine the voltage across the capacitor. This is given by $(1/C)\int i\,dt$. Hence

$$v_C(t) = -Ve^{-t/RC} + K_1 \tag{4-126}$$

From the initial conditions we have determined that at $t = 0+$, $v_C(0+) = 0$. Hence $K = V_1$, and

$$v_C(t) = V(1 - e^{-t/RC}) \tag{4-127}$$

This curve is plotted in Fig. 4-11 if we now label the vertical axis $v_c(t)/V$. The time constant for this circuit is given by Eq. (4-125). Thus in one time-constant time the voltage will build up to 63.2 percent of its final value.

The shape of the voltage-current curves is determined by the following physical factors. Initially the voltage across the capacitor is zero. It then acts as a *short circuit;* that is, it acts for an instant as though it were an ideal conductor. Thus the initial current is V/R. As charge flows into the capacitor (from one plate to the other), the voltage across it builds up, and hence the voltage drop across the resistance must decrease. The current through the resistance is always equal to the voltage across it divided by R, so the current decreases. Finally, the voltage across the capacitor becomes equal to the battery voltage, and the current becomes zero.

Now let us analyze the circuit of Fig. 4-15. Switch sw_1 is closed for a very long time, that is, for a long enough time that the voltage across the capacitor has essentially reached its final value of V. At $t = 0-$, sw_1 is opened, and at $t = 0+$, sw_2 is closed. For $t > 0$ a loop analysis of this circuit yields

$$0 = Ri + \frac{1}{C}\int i\,dt \tag{4-128}$$

Fig. 4-15 An RC circuit. Assume that sw_1 *has been closed from* $t = -\infty$ *to* $t = 0-$ *and is opened at* $t = 0-$, *and that* sw_2 *is then closed at* $t = 0+$.

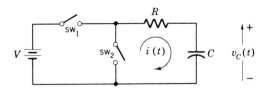

Differentiating this equation, we obtain

$$0 = R\frac{di}{dt} + \frac{1}{C}i \qquad (4\text{-}129)$$

This is the same as Eq. (4-117). Thus the solution is

$$i(t) = Ke^{-t/RC}$$

The initial voltage across the capacitor is given by

$$v_C(0+) = v_C(0-) = V \qquad (4\text{-}130)$$

This voltage appears across the resistor. However, its polarity is such that it causes the current to be opposite to the direction indicated by the arrow. Hence

$$i(0+) = K = -\frac{V}{R} \qquad (4\text{-}131)$$

Thus the current is

$$i(t) = -\frac{V}{R}e^{-t/RC} \qquad (4\text{-}132)$$

To obtain the voltage across the capacitor we use the relation $v_C = (1/C)\int i\, dt$. Hence

$$v_C(t) = Ve^{-t/RC} + K_2 \qquad (4\text{-}133)$$

Then, from Eq. (4-130), which gives the initial value of the voltage, $K_2 = 0$ and

$$v_C(t) = Ve^{-t/RC} \qquad (4\text{-}134)$$

The curves for the voltage and the current are given by Fig. 4-13, with the vertical axis properly labeled. In the case of $i(t)$ the actual curve is the negative of that of Fig. 4-13.

Let us discuss the physical basis for these results. When sw_1 is closed, charge flows from one plate of the capacitor to the other until the voltage across it is equal to V. When sw_1 is opened and sw_2 is closed, the capacitor begins to *discharge*. That is, the excess charge stored on one of its plates flows to the other plate through the resistance. This causes the magnitude of the voltage $V_C(t)$ to decrease. This charge flow constitutes the current. When the capacitor discharges, the direction of charge flow (and current) is opposite to the direction of original charge flow. Initially the voltage across the capacitor is large, and so is the magnitude of the current. However, as the discharge process continues, the voltage across the capacitor and the current decrease. Finally, the voltage across the capacitor and the current become zero. This phenomenon can also be discussed on an energy basis. Initially, there is energy stored in the electrostatic field of the capacitor. The

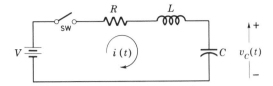

Fig. 4-16   A simple RLC circuit.

current through the resistance dissipates power in the form of heat. Since there is only a finite amount of energy stored initially, and none is added, the current must fall to zero.

RLC networks

Now let us analyze the circuit of Fig. 4-16, which contains resistance, inductance, and capacitance.   Assume that the switch is closed at $t = 0$.   Then loop analysis yields

$$V = Ri + L\frac{di}{dt} + \frac{1}{C} \int i \, dt \tag{4-135}$$

Differentiating, we obtain

$$0 = L\frac{d^2i}{dt^2} + R\frac{di}{dt} + \frac{1}{C} \tag{4-136}$$

Thus the characteristic equation is

$$Lb^2 + Rb + \frac{1}{C} = 0$$

or, equivalently,

$$L\left(b^2 + \frac{R}{L}b + \frac{1}{LC}\right) = 0 \tag{4-137}$$

The roots of this quadratic occur at

$$b = -\frac{R}{2L} \pm \sqrt{\left(\frac{R}{2L}\right)^2 - \frac{1}{LC}} \tag{4-138}$$

Let us call these roots b_1 and b_2.   They can be complex numbers.

We shall make some substitutions which will simplify this relation and give us further insight into the character of the roots.   If the expression $(R/2L)^2 - 1/LC$ is negative, then the square root will be imaginary and the roots will be complex.   If $(R/2L)^2 - 1/LC$ is positive, then both roots of Eq. (4-138) will be real and negative.   The borderline case occurs when

$$\left(\frac{R}{2L}\right)^2 = \frac{1}{LC} \tag{4-139}$$

Let us call the value of resistance which satisfies this equation R_{crit}.   Substituting in Eq. (4-139), we obtain

$$R_{\text{crit}} = 2\sqrt{\frac{L}{C}} \tag{4-140}$$

Let us also call

$$\omega_0 = \frac{1}{\sqrt{LC}} \tag{4-141}$$

Then we can write Eq. (4-138) as

$$b_1, b_2 = -\frac{R_{\text{crit}}}{2L}\frac{R}{R_{\text{crit}}} \pm \sqrt{\left(\frac{R_{\text{crit}}}{2L}\right)^2 \frac{R^2}{R_{\text{crit}}^2} - \frac{1}{LC}} \tag{4-142}$$

Substituting Eqs. (4-140) and (4-141) into Eq. (4-142), we obtain

$$b_1, b_2 = -\omega_0 \frac{R}{R_{\text{crit}}} \pm \omega_0 \sqrt{\left(\frac{R}{R_{\text{crit}}}\right)^2 - 1} \tag{4-143}$$

To reduce the size of Eq. (4-143) further let us define an expression which we shall call the *damping factor d*:

$$d = \frac{R}{R_{\text{crit}}} \tag{4-144}$$

Thus Eq. (4-143) becomes

$$b_1, b_2 = -\omega_0 d \pm \omega_0 \sqrt{d^2 - 1} \tag{4-145}$$

If $d > 1$ ($R > R_{\text{crit}}$), then b_1 and b_2 will be two real roots. If $d < 1$ ($R < R_{\text{crit}}$), then two complex roots will result. If $d = 1$ ($R = R_{\text{crit}}$), then there will be a double real root to the characteristic equation.

Now let us consider the solution to Eq. (4-136). The particular solution is of the form

$$i_P(t) = A \tag{4-146}$$

This is because the $y(t)$ function (see Table 4-1) is a constant (zero). Substituting into Eq. (4-136), we obtain

$$i_P(t) = 0 \tag{4-147}$$

Thus the complete solution just consists of the solution of the homogeneous equation. Note, for example, that Eq. (4-136) is the same as the homogeneous equation.

Now let us consider the three cases.

Case 1: $d > 1$ ($R > R_{\text{crit}}$)

The roots of the characteristic equation, b_1 and b_2, will both be real. Thus the form of the solution will be

$$i(t) = K_1 e^{b_1 t} + K_2 e^{b_2 t} \tag{4-148}$$

where, from Eq. (4-145),

$$b_1, b_2 = -\omega_0 d \left(1 \mp \sqrt{1 - \frac{1}{d^2}} \right) \qquad (4\text{-}149)$$

Since d is greater than unity, $\sqrt{1 - 1/d^2}$ will be less than 1. Thus both b_1 and b_2 are negative real numbers. To evaluate the constants we must know the initial conditions. Let us assume that the current is zero at $t = 0-$. In addition, we shall assume that the initial voltage across the capacitor $v_C(0-)$ is also zero. Hence

$$i(0+) - i(0-) = 0 \qquad (4\text{-}150a)$$

$$v_C(0+) = v_C(0-) = 0 \qquad (4\text{-}150b)$$

The effect of the initial condition of Eq. (4-150a) can be incorporated in the solution by substituting it in Eq. (4-148). To incorporate the effect of Eq. (4-150b) we could integrate Eq. (4-148) to obtain the voltage across the capacitor. Instead, let us obtain $(di/dt)_{t=0+}$. Substituting the initial conditions into Eq. (4-135), and noting that $(1/C)\int i \, dt = v_C(t)$, we obtain, at $t = 0+$,

$$V = L \frac{di}{dt} \Big|_{t=0+}$$

Hence

$$\frac{di}{dt} \Big|_{t=0+} = \frac{V}{L} \qquad (4\text{-}151)$$

Then, substituting Eq. (4-150a) into Eq. (4-148) and Eq. (4-151) into the derivative of Eq. (4-148) (that is, $b_1 K_1 e^{b_1 t} + b_2 K_2 e^{b_2 t}$), all evaluated at $t = 0$, we obtain

$$0 = K_1 + K_2 \qquad (4\text{-}152a)$$

$$\frac{V}{L} = K_1 b_1 + K_2 b_2 \qquad (4\text{-}152b)$$

Solving these, we have

$$K_1 = -K_2 = \frac{V}{L(b_1 - b_2)} \qquad (4\text{-}153)$$

We substitute this and Eq. (4-149) into Eq. (4-148) and obtain the solution for $i(t)$,

$$i(t) = \frac{V}{2L\omega_0 \sqrt{d^2 - 1}} \left\{ \exp\left[-\omega_0 d \left(1 - \sqrt{1 - \frac{1}{d^2}} \right) t \right] \right.$$
$$\left. - \exp\left[-\omega_0 d \left(1 + \sqrt{1 - \frac{1}{d^2}} \right) t \right] \right\} \qquad (4\text{-}154)$$

Before discussing the shape of the response, let us consider cases 2 and 3. We shall then discuss all the values simultaneously.

Case 2: $d = 1$ ($R = R_{crit}$)

The characteristic equation has two real roots; however [see Eq. (4-145)], they are both equal and are given by

$$b_1 = b_2 = -\omega_0 d = -\omega_0 \tag{4-155}$$

The form of the solution must be modified, since these roots are equal [see Eqs. (4-45) to (4-49)]. Thus

$$i(t) = K_1 e^{b_1 t} + K_2 t e^{b_1 t} \tag{4-156}$$

To evaluate the constants we shall also require di/dt; this is given by

$$\frac{di(t)}{dt} = (b_1 K_1 + K_2) e^{b_1 t} + K_2 t b_1 e^{b_1 t} \tag{4-157}$$

Then, substituting the initial conditions of Eqs. (4-150a) and (4-151) into Eqs. (4-156) and (4-157), respectively, we obtain

$$0 = K_1 \tag{4-158a}$$

$$\frac{V}{L} = b_1 K_1 + K_2 \tag{4-158b}$$

Solving for K_2, we obtain

$$K_2 = \frac{V}{L} \tag{4-159}$$

Thus, substituting Eqs. (4-158a) and (4-159) into Eq. (4-156), we have

$$i(t) = \frac{V}{L} t e^{-\omega_0 t} \tag{4-160}$$

Case 3: $d < 1$ ($R < R_{crit}$)

The form of the solution is the same in this case as in case 1. In fact, we can use Eq. (4-154) here. However, now b_1 and b_2 will be complex numbers, and complex numbers will appear in Eq. (4-154). To manipulate Eq. (4-154) into a form that is more readily understood we write

$$\sqrt{d^2 - 1} = \sqrt{-(1 - d^2)} = j\sqrt{1 - d^2}$$

so that Eq. (4-154) becomes

$$i(t) = \frac{V e^{-\omega_0 dt}}{2jL\omega_0 \sqrt{1 - d^2}} [\exp(j\omega_0 t \sqrt{1 - d^2}) - \exp(-j\omega_0 t \sqrt{1 - d^2})] \tag{4-161}$$

Then, substituting Euler's relations [Eq. (4-58)], we obtain

$$i(t) = \frac{V e^{-\omega_0 dt}}{L\omega_0 \sqrt{1 - d^2}} \sin(\omega_0 t \sqrt{1 - d^2}) \tag{4-162}$$

Let us now plot the results of cases 1, 2, and 3 and compare the curves.

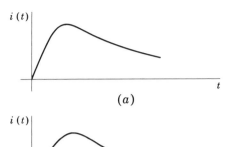

$Fig.$ *4-17   The current in the RLC circuit*
of Fig. 4-16: (a) case 1 overdamped; (b) case
2 critically damped; (c) case 3 underdamped.

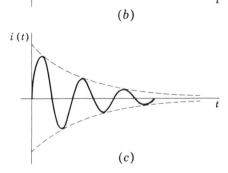

The curve for case 1 is shown in Fig. 4-17a.   From Eq. (4-154) we see that the initial response is zero because of the subtraction of the two exponentials. The second term has a larger exponent than the first one, and hence it decays faster with time.   Thus $i(t)$ rises and then falls off as both exponentials decay toward zero.

The curve for case 2 is plotted in Fig. 4-17b; its equation is Eq. (4-160). This is initially zero because of the factor of t.   As t departs from zero, the expression becomes positive and $i(t)$ increases.   For large values of time the exponential decreases at a rate which is faster than the increase in t, and the response falls off as shown (in general, for any positive a, $t^n e^{-at}$ approaches zero as t approaches infinity).

The curve for case 3 is drawn in Fig. 4-17c; this is taken from Eq. (4-162). Note that the character of the curve changes completely.   The response is in the form of a sine curve multiplied by a decayed exponential.   That is, the amplitude of the sine wave falls off with time.   As the size of the resistance is increased (that is, as d increases), the rate of falloff of the sinusoid increases (note that the exponent of the exponential is $\omega_0 dt$).   This is why d is called the damping factor.   Case 3 is called the *underdamped case*.   If d, the damping, is increased sufficiently, case 1 results.   This is called the *overdamped case.* Case 2, the transition between case 1 and case 3, is called the *critically damped* case.

Let us consider that R is varied so that the results change from case 1, to case 2, and finally to case 3. In case 1 or 2 (see Figs. 4-17a and b) the current approaches zero for large time in essentially an exponential falloff. If we decreases R below R_{crit}, then the curve falls to zero in a finite time but it "overshoots its mark" and actually becomes negative. This overshooting persists, and the current oscillates about its final value for an indefinite time.

Let us consider the physical basis for this. The voltage across an inductance is proportional to the rate of change of the current through it. The polarity of this voltage will be such that it tends to resist the change. At the instant the current reaches its first zero in Fig. 4-17c it is changing at a maximum rate. This produces a voltage drop across the inductance, which causes the current to become negative. In addition, charge flows from one plate of the capacitor to another, producing a voltage across the capacitor. At a maximum or minimum of current this voltage plus the voltage drop across the resistance become equal to V. Thus the current cannot increase further. In fact, in all three cases, after very long (indefinite) times the current approaches zero, and the voltage across the capacitor is equal to V at that time. In cases 1 and 2 the voltage drop across the resistor is large enough to offset the oscillatory effect of the inductor and capacitor. Hence the sinusoidal oscillation does not result.

Lossless networks

If $R = 0$, then $d = 0$ [see Eq. (4-144)]. In this case there are no elements which dissipate power in the form of heat, and the network is termed *lossless*. The energy supplied by the generator is stored in the magnetic field of the inductor and the electrostatic field of the capacitor [note that Eq. (4-136) is the same as the result that would obtain if there were no generator]. The sinusoid of case 3 becomes damped because this energy is dissipated in the resistor in the form of heat. If $d = 0$ there is no resistance, and the energy is alternately stored in the electrostatic field and in the electromagnetic field. The current does not fall exponentially to zero, and Eq. (4-162) becomes

$$i(t) = \frac{V}{L\omega_0} \sin \omega_0 t \tag{4-163}$$

The response is then just a nondecaying sinusoid, as illustrated in Fig. 4-18.

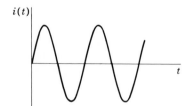

$i(t)$

t

Fig. 4-18   The current in the circuit of Fig. 4-16 when $R = 0$.

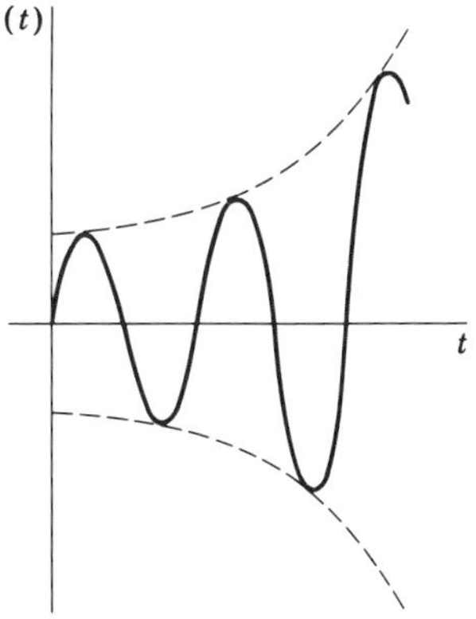

$i(t)$

Fig. 4-19   The current in the circuit of Fig. 4-16 when R is negative. Note that the values of the maxima increase exponentially with time.

Negative resistances

We have worked with circuits where R is a positive or a zero number.   Indeed, a negative R would result in a violation of the law of conservation of energy, since power is supplied *to* the circuit when current is in the resistance.   We cannot build circuits that violate the law of conservation of energy, but electronic devices often incorporate a power supply (the battery in a portable radio or the 60-Hz power line).   In such cases it is possible for a circuit element to supply power to the remainder of the circuit.   This power has been taken from the power supply.   It often becomes convenient to represent part of this circuit by a negative resistance.

Let us consider that such a negative resistance $-R$ is incorporated into the circuit of Fig. 4-16.   Equation (4-162) will still characterize the current in the circuit, except that d [see Eq. (4-144)] will now be a negative quantity.   We can write Eq. (4-162) in this case as

$$i(t) = \frac{V e^{\omega|d|/t}}{L\omega_0 \sqrt{1 - d^2}} \sin \omega_0 t \sqrt{1 - d^2} \tag{4-164}$$

The response of this circuit is an exponentially increasing sinusoid.   A typical response is shown in Fig. 4-19.   In this case the resistance supplies power to the circuit (from a power supply), and so an increasing, rather than a decreasing, sinusoid results.

The magnitude of the current will at times become arbitrarily large for sufficiently large values of time.   In practical circuits the amplitude of the current is always limited.   This is because all circuits become nonlinear when the magnitudes of their currents or voltages are large enough.   These nonlinearities limit the magnitude of the current.   This will be discussed in Sec. 7-7.

4-5 Behavior of inductors and capacitors in circuits where the currents and voltages have become constants

If the generators in an electric network produce voltages and currents that do not change with time, then all the voltages and/or currents of the circuits often become constant at sufficiently large values of time.   For instance, consider Figs. 4-11, 4-13, and 4-17, which illustrate voltages and currents for the networks of Sec. 4-4.   For sufficiently large times each of these curves approaches a constant.   This is not always the case (see Figs. 4-18 and 4-19), but in most networks with constant generators it will be so.

Let us now consider the behavior of inductors and capacitors at the time when the voltages and currents become constants.   This will enable us to determine the final values of the response without solving differential equations. The voltage across an inductor is given by

$$v = L \frac{di}{dt} \tag{4-165}$$

If i is constant, then $v = 0$, independently of the constant value of i.   A circuit element whose voltage is zero, independently of the current through it, behaves as an ideal conductor.   Circuits are equivalent if they have the same voltage-current characteristics (see Sec. 2-4).   Thus, if the circuit currents become constant, we can replace all inductors by short circuits (ideal conductors) *to obtain the final response.*

The current through a capacitor is given by

$$i = C \frac{dv}{dt} \tag{4-166}$$

Thus, if the circuit voltages are constant, there will be no current through the capacitor.   An element that contains no current independently of the voltage across it behaves as an open circuit.   Thus at those times when the circuit voltages are constant we can replace the capacitors by open circuits to analyze the circuit.

To illustrate these ideas let us obtain the final value of the currents in Fig. 4-20.   An investigation of this circuit will show that its final responses approach constant values.   To obtain the final response we can replace the inductor by a short circuit and the capacitor by an open circuit, as shown in Fig. 4-20b.   From this we calculate the final values of i_1 and i_2 as

$$i_{1,f} = \frac{V_1}{R_1} \tag{4-167a}$$

$$i_{2,f} = 0 \tag{4-167b}$$

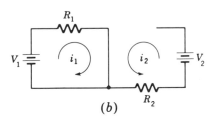

Fig. 4-20 (a) A circuit whose currents and voltages approach constant values; (b) a modification of this circuit that can be used to calculate the final values.

4-6 Simultaneous linear integral-differential equations with constant coefficients

In Sec. 4-3 we discussed the solution of differential equations that contained only one unknown. Mesh, nodal, or cut-set analyses of networks usually lead to a set of simultaneous integral-differential equations. Thus each equation has many unknowns. In this section we shall see how to reduce such a set of simultaneous equations to a set of differential equations each of which has only *one* unknown. We shall use the operator notation of Eqs. (3-12), (3-13), and (4-30) here.

From Chap. 3 we know that a typical set of integral-differential equations [such as Eqs. (3-11) and (3-29)] will be of the form

$$y_1(t) = \left(\alpha_{11}p + \beta_{11} + \frac{\gamma_{11}}{p}\right)x_1(t) + \left(\alpha_{12}p + \beta_{12} + \frac{\gamma_{12}}{p}\right)x_2(t)$$

$$+ \cdots + \left(\alpha_{1n}p + \beta_{1n} + \frac{\gamma_{1n}}{p}\right)x_n(t)$$

$$y_2(t) = \left(\alpha_{21}p + \beta_{21} + \frac{\gamma_{21}}{p}\right)x_1(t) + \left(\alpha_{22}p + \beta_{22} + \frac{\gamma_{22}}{p}\right)x_2(t)$$

$$+ \cdots + \left(\alpha_{2n}p + \beta_{2n} + \frac{\gamma_{2n}}{p}\right)x_n(t) \qquad (4\text{-}168)$$

$$\cdots \cdots \cdots \cdots \cdots \cdots \cdots \cdots \cdots \cdots \cdots \cdots$$

$$y_n(t) = \left(\alpha_{n1}p + \beta_{n1} + \frac{\gamma_{n1}}{p}\right)x_1(t) + \left(\alpha_{n2}p + \beta_{n2} + \frac{\gamma_{n2}}{p}\right)x_2(t)$$

$$+ \cdots + \left(\alpha_{nn}p + \beta_{nn} + \frac{\gamma_{nn}}{p}\right)x_n(t)$$

The $x_k(t)$ $(k = 1,2, \ldots ,n)$ represent unknown currents in loop analysis and unknown voltages in nodal or cut-set analysis. The $y_k(t)$ $(k = 1,2, \ldots ,n)$ represent the known generator terms, and the α_{ik}, β_{ik}, and λ_{ik} are functions of the linear time-invariant circuit elements.

It is often more convenient to work only with differential equations than with integral-differential equations. If we differentiate both sides of Eqs. (4-168) with respect to time, we can eliminate the integrals. Let us do this. Note that differentiation can be represented symbolically by multiplying by p. Thus Eqs. (4-168) become

$$py_1(t) = (\alpha_{11}p^2 + \beta_{11}p + \gamma_{11})x_1(t) + (\alpha_{12}p^2 + \beta_{12}p + \gamma_{12})x_2(t)$$
$$+ \cdots + (\alpha_{1n}p^2 + \beta_{1n}p + \gamma_{1n})x_n(t)$$

$$py_2(t) = (\alpha_{21}p^2 + \beta_{21}p + \gamma_{21})x_1(t) + (\alpha_{22}p^2 + \beta_{22}p + \gamma_{22})x_2(t)$$
$$+ \cdots + (\alpha_{2n}p^2 + \beta_{2n}p + \gamma_{2n})x_n(t) \quad (4\text{-}169)$$

$$\cdots \cdots \cdots \cdots \cdots \cdots \cdots \cdots \cdots \cdots$$

$$py_n(t) = (\alpha_{n1}p^2 + \beta_{n1}p + \gamma_{n1})x_1(t) + (\alpha_{n2}p^2 + \beta_{n2}p + \gamma_{n2})x_2(t)$$
$$+ \cdots + (\alpha_{nn}p^2 + \beta_{nn}p + \gamma_{nn})x_n(t)$$

Note that the $y_k(t)$ are known functions; thus their derivatives $py_k(t)$ are also known.

Now we shall consider the solution of this set of simultaneous equations. Let us adopt the notation

$$a_{ik} = \alpha_{ik}p^2 + \beta_{ik}p + \gamma_{ik} \quad (4\text{-}170)$$

If we make this substitution, then Eqs. (4-169) have the same form as Eqs. (3-88), except that the known terms have been replaced by their derivatives. We evaluated ordinary simultaneous equations by using Cramer's rule (see Sec. 3-9). Now we shall apply this rule to the solution of simultaneous differential equations.

Let us first state the procedure for solving these equations. Subsequently we shall discuss its justification. For the time being let's treat the differential operator p as an algebraic quantity and form the determinant

$$\Delta = \begin{vmatrix} \alpha_{11}p^2 + \beta_{11}p + \gamma_{11} & \alpha_{12}p^2 + \beta_{12}p + \gamma_{12} & \cdots & \alpha_{1n}p^2 + \beta_{1n}p + \gamma_{1n} \\ \alpha_{21}p^2 + \beta_{21}p + \gamma_{21} & \alpha_{22}p^2 + \beta_{22}p + \gamma_{22} & \cdots & \alpha_{2n}p^2 + \beta_{2n}p + \gamma_{2n} \\ \cdots \cdots \cdots \cdots \cdots \cdots \cdots \cdots \cdots \cdots \\ \alpha_{n1}p^2 + \beta_{n1}p + \gamma_{n1} & \alpha_{n2}p^2 + \beta_{n2}p + \gamma_{n2} & \cdots & \alpha_{nn}p^2 + \beta_{nn}p + \gamma_{nn} \end{vmatrix}$$
$$(4\text{-}171)$$

This determinant and its cofactor are evaluated in accordance with the rules given in Sec. 3-9. Thus they lead to polynomials with the variable p. Cramer's rule for ordinary simultaneous equations is expressed in Eq. (3-90). The form of this equation is meaningless, however, when p is a differential operator. If p is to have meaning, it must operate on a function of time. That is, it must be written so that it appears to multiply that function of time.

If we rearrange Eq. (3-90) so that each differential operator operates on a function of time, we can remove this objection. We then have

$$\Delta x_k(t) = \Delta_{1k}py_1(t) + \Delta_{2k}py_2(t) + \cdots + \Delta_{nk}py_n(t) \qquad k = 1, 2, \ldots, n$$

$$(4\text{-}172)$$

[note that the right-hand sides of Eqs. (4-169) are $py_k(t)$, and not $y_k(t)$]. This represents a set of equations (one for each value of k) each of which has one unknown. When the determinant and its cofactor are expanded, we shall obtain a polynomial in p, $b_np^n + b_{n-1}p^{n-1} + \cdots + b_1p + b_0$. Since all the $y_k(t)$ are known and can be differentiated, the right-hand side of Eq. (4-172) will consist of a known function of time, which is a sum of known quantities and their derivatives of various orders. Thus each of these equations will have only one unknown and will be of the form studied in Sec. 4-3. Hence *the equations can be solved by the methods presented there.*

Let us discuss the validity of the solution of these simultaneous equations. It can be demonstrated that by appropriate operations on the equations we can successively eliminate variables from Eqs. (4-169). For instance, if we operate on the first equation by differentiating both sides twice and multiplying by α_{2n}, and then again operate on the first equation by differentiating both sides once and multiplying by β_{2n}, and then sum these two equations and the original equation multiplied by γ_{2n}, we obtain a new equation. In operator form this can be obtained by multiplying both sides of the first of Eqs. (4-169) by $\alpha_{2n}p^2 + \beta_{2n}p + \gamma_{2n}$. In similar fashion, we can operate on the second of Eqs. (4-169) in a way that is equivalent to multiplying both sides of it by $\alpha_{1n}p^2 + \beta_{1n}p + \gamma_{1n}$ (we must assume that these operations are cumulative, that is, that the order in which they are performed does not matter). Then, if we subtract the two equations that result, we obtain a new equation which does not contain $x_n(t)$.

By successive repetition of this procedure we can eventually obtain an equation which contains only one unknown. The equation formed in this way will be the same as the one obtained by Cramer's rule [Eq. (4-172)]. Thus one way that Cramer's rule can be justified is by comparing the solution obtained by Cramer's rule with one obtained by mathematical manipulation. There are stronger and more elegant mathematical procedures that can be used to justify Cramer's rule, but these are beyond the scope of this chapter.

As an example of the procedure discussed above, let us solve the network of Fig. 4-21 for the loop currents. For $t > 0$ mesh analysis of this circuit yields

$$1 = (1 + p)i_1 + i_2 \qquad\qquad (4\text{-}173a)$$

$$1 + e^{-t} = i_1 + \left(1 + \frac{2}{p}\right)i_2 \qquad\qquad (4\text{-}173b)$$

To eliminate the $1/p$ term, we differentiate the second equation (note that it

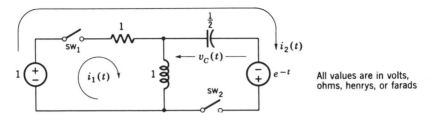

Fig. 4-21   A simple network.   At t = 0 switches sw₁ and sw₂ are closed.   The initial conditions are $i_1(0-) = 0$ and $v_C(0-) = 0$.

is not necessary to differentiate the first one as well).   Thus we obtain

$$1 = (1 + p)i_1 + i_2 \tag{4-174a}$$

$$-e^{-t} = pi_1 + (2 + p)i_2 \tag{4-174b}$$

Then we form the determinant

$$\Delta = \begin{vmatrix} 1 + p & 1 \\ p & 2 + p \end{vmatrix} = p^2 + 2p + 2 \tag{4-175}$$

Substitution in Eq. (4-172) using the values $k = 1$ and $k = 2$ in turn, yields

$$(p^2 + 2p + 2)i_1 = (2 + p)1 + e^{-t} \tag{4-176a}$$

$$(p^2 + 2p + 2)i_2 = -p1 - (1 + p)e^{-t} \tag{4-176b}$$

We perform the mathematical operations indicated on the right-hand side of these equations, noting that the derivative of a constant is zero, to obtain

$$(p^2 + 2p + 2)i_1 = 2 + e^{-t} \tag{4-177a}$$

$$(p^2 + 2p + 2)i_2 = 0 \tag{4-177b}$$

The characteristic equation for both of these equations is

$$b^2 + 2b + 2 = 0 \tag{4-178}$$

with roots

$$b_1, b_2 = -1 \pm j \tag{4-179}$$

Thus the complementary solutions are

$$i_{1C}(t) = K_1 e^{(-1+j)t} + K_2 e^{(-1-j)t} \tag{4-180a}$$

$$i_{2C}(t) = K_3 e^{(-1+j)t} + K_4 e^{(-1-j)t} \tag{4-180b}$$

Note that both complementary solutions have the same form.   In general, all the complementary solutions of a set of simultaneous equations will be the same, since they will all have the same homogeneous equations [see Eq. (4-172)].

Now let us evaluate the particular solutions. From Table 4-1 we have

$$i_{1P}(t) = A_0 + A_1 e^{-t} \tag{4-181}$$

Substituting in Eq. (4-177a), we obtain

$$2A_0 + A_1 e^{-t} = 2 + e^{-t} \tag{4-182}$$

This must be true for all values at positive time. Hence

$$A_0 = 1 \tag{4-183a}$$

$$A_1 = 1 \tag{4-183b}$$

Thus the complete solution for $i_1(t)$ is

$$i_1(t) = 1 + e^{-t} + K_1 e^{(-1+j)t} + K_2 e^{(-1-j)t} \tag{4-184}$$

Equation (4-177b) is in the form of a homogeneous equation, so the particular solution for $i_2(t)$ will be zero. Thus the complete solution for $i_2(t)$ is just the complementary solution

$$i_2(t) = K_3 e^{(-1+j)t} + K_4 e^{(-1-j)t} \tag{4-185}$$

There are four unknown constants that must be determined. There are four initial conditions that can be specified. From the data given in Fig. 4-21 we have

$$i_1(0+) = i_1(0-) = 0 \tag{4-186}$$

To obtain additional initial conditions let us rewrite Eqs. (4-173), using R, L, and C to represent the values of resistance, inductance, and capacitance, respectively. We shall also group the terms representing a single voltage drop together. Hence

$$1 = R(i_1 + i_2) + L \frac{di_1}{dt} \tag{4-187a}$$

$$1 + e^{-t} = R(i_1 + i_2) + \frac{1}{C} \int i_2 \, dt \tag{4-187b}$$

The initial voltage across the capacitor is given by

$$v_C(0+) = v_C(0-) = 0 \tag{4-188}$$

Substituting Eqs. (4-188) and (4-186) into Eq. (4-187b), evaluated at $t = 0+$, we obtain

$$2 = Ri_2(0+)$$

Since $R = 1$ ohm, we have

$$i_2(0+) = 2 \tag{4-189}$$

Substituting Eqs. (4-186) and (4-189) into Eq. (4-187a), evaluated at $t = 0+$, we have

$$1 = 2R + L\frac{di_1}{dt}\bigg|_{t=0+}$$

$L = 1$ henry and $R = 1$ ohm, so we have

$$\frac{di_1}{dt}\bigg|_{t=0+} = -1 \tag{4-190}$$

Differentiation of Eq. (4-187b) with respect to time then yields

$$-e^{-t} = R\frac{di_1}{dt} + R\frac{di_2}{dt} + \frac{i_2}{C} \tag{4-191}$$

We evaluate this at $t = 0+$ and substitute Eqs. (4-186), (4-189), (4-190), and the value $R = 1$ to give

$$-1 = -1 + \frac{di_2}{dt}\bigg|_{t=0+} + 4$$

or

$$\frac{di_2}{dt}\bigg|_{t=0+} = -4 \tag{4-192}$$

Now we are in a position to evaluate the constants. Substituting Eq. (4-186) into (4-184), evaluated at $t = 0$, we obtain

$$0 = 2 + K_1 + K_2 \tag{4-193a}$$

Differentiating Eq. (4-184) with respect to time, evaluating it at $t = 0$, and substituting Eq. (4-190) yields

$$-1 = -1 + (-1 + j)K_1 + (-1 - j)K_2 \tag{4-193b}$$

Solving Eqs. (4-193a) and (4-193b), we obtain

$$K_1 = -1 + j \tag{4-194a}$$
$$K_2 = -1 - j \tag{4-194b}$$

Substituting in Eq. (4-184), we have

$$i_1(t) = 1 + e^{-t} + e^{-t}[(-1 + j)e^{jt} + (-1 - j)e^{-jt}] \tag{4-195}$$

and substitution of Eq. (4-158) gives us

$$i_1(t) = 1 + e^{-t}(1 - 2\cos t - 2\sin t) \tag{4-196}$$

To obtain $i_2(t)$ we substitute Eqs. (4-189) and (4-192) into Eq. (4-185) and its derivative, both evaluated at $t = 0+$. This yields

$$2 = K_3 + K_4 \tag{4-197a}$$
$$-4 = (-1 + j)K_3 + (-1 - j)K_4 \tag{4-197b}$$

and solution of these equations yields

$$K_3 = 1 + j \tag{4-198a}$$

$$K_4 = 1 - j \tag{4-198b}$$

After substituting these values into Eq. (4-185) and manipulating, we obtain

$$i_2(t) = 2e^{-t}(\cos t - \sin t) \tag{4-199}$$

Thus we have solved for the loop currents of the network.

In addition to illustrating the procedure for solving simultaneous integral-differential equations, this example illustrates a further fact. The procedure for evaluating the constants of the particular solution is often as tedious as, or even *more tedious* than, the procedure for evaluating the differential equations. To obtain the differential equations we had to solve a set of second-order simultaneous equations. To solve for the constants we had to evaluate *two* sets of second-order simultaneous equations. In more complex networks the process of evaluating the simultaneous equations can become extremely tedious. In the next chapter we shall discuss a procedure whereby much of the tedious work connected with evaluating the constants is eliminated.

4-7 Nonlinear and time-varying equations

In this chapter we have discussed the solutions of linear differential equations with constant coefficients. Classical procedures do exist for the solution of some nonlinear differential equations and/or differential equations with non-constant coefficients. However, a procedure employing state variables, which we shall develop in Chap. 7, is often far better, especially when computer solutions are contemplated. In many instances this procedure has replaced the classical ones. We shall therefore defer discussion of the solution of these equations until Chap. 7.

REFERENCE

[1] Hildebrand, F. B.: "Advanced Calculus for Engineers," p. 12, Prentice-Hall Inc., Engelwood Cliffs, N.J., 1949.

BIBLIOGRAPHY

Clement, P. R., and W. C. Johnson: "Electrical Engineering Science," chap. 7, McGraw-Hill Book Company, New York, 1960.

Close, C. M.: "The Analysis of Linear Circuits," chap. 4, Harcourt, Brace & World, Inc., New York, 1966.

Guillemin, E. A.: "Introductory Circuit Theory," chap. 5, John Wiley & Sons, Inc., New York, 1953.

Hildebrand, F. B.: "Advanced Calculus for Engineers," chap. 1, Prentice-Hall, Inc., Englewood Cliffs, N.J., 1949.

Morris, M., and O. E. Brown: "Differential Equations," rev. ed., chap. 4, Prentice-Hall, Inc., Englewood Cliffs, N.J., 1942.

Pearson, S. I., and G. J. Maler: "Introductory Circuit Analysis," pp. 87–102, John Wiley & Sons, Inc., New York, 1965.

Skilling, H. H.: "Electrical Engineering Circuits," 2d ed., pp. 30–48, John Wiley & Sons, Inc., New York, 1965.

Van Valkenburg, M. E.: "Network Analysis," 2d ed., chaps. 4, 5, and 6, Prentice-Hall, Inc., Englewood Cliffs, N.J., 1964.

PROBLEMS

4-1. Discuss the statement that in most electric circuits the voltage across a capacitance and the current through an inductance cannot change instantaneously.   State when this is applicable and when it is not.

4-2. For the network of Fig. 4-22 find the value of the loop currents, their first derivatives, and their second derivatives, all evaluated at $t = 0+$.

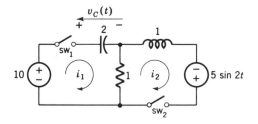

$v_C(0-) = 1$ volt $i_2(0-) = 0$ amp
At $t = 0$ close sw_1 and sw_2
All values are in volts, ohms, henrys, or farads

Fig. 4-22

4-3. Repeat Prob. 4-2 for the circuit of Fig. 4-23.

Fig. 4-23

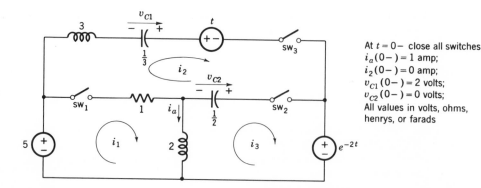

At $t = 0-$ close all switches
$i_a(0-) = 1$ amp;
$i_2(0-) = 0$ amp;
$v_{C1}(0-) = 2$ volts;
$v_{C2}(0-) = 0$ volts;
All values in volts, ohms, henrys, or farads

4-4. For the network of Fig. 4-24 find the values of the nodal voltages and their first and second derivatives, all evaluated at $t = 0+$.

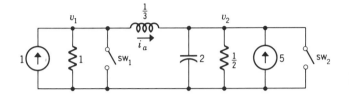

For $t < 0$ all switches are closed; at $t = 0$ open them
$i_a(0-) = 1$ amp
$v_2(0-) = 0$ volts
All values in amperes, ohms, henrys, or farads

Fig. 4-24

4-5. Repeat Prob. 4-4 for a set of cut-set voltages.
4-6. Repeat Prob. 4-4 for the network of Fig. 4-25.

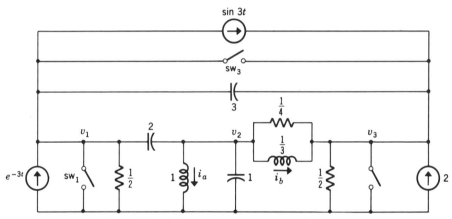

For $t < 0$ all switches are closed; at $t = 0$ open them
$i_a(0-) = 1$ amp; $i_b(0-) = 2$ amp
$v_1(0-) - v_2(0-) = 3$ volts; $v_1(0-) - v_3(0-) = 2$ volts; $v_2(0-) = 1$ volt
All values are in amperes, ohms, henrys, or farads

Fig. 4-25

4-7. Repeat Prob. 4-5 for the network of Fig. 4-25.
4-8. Obtain the complementary solution of the differential equation

$$\frac{d^3x}{dt^3} + 6\frac{d^2x}{dt^2} + 11\frac{dx}{dt} + 6x = 4e^{-t/2}$$

(a root of the characteristic equation is -1).

4-9. Obtain the complementary solution of the differential equation

$$\frac{d^2x}{dt^2} + \frac{dx}{dt} + 3x = -3$$

The answer should be in terms of sines and cosines.

4-10. Obtain the complete solution of the differential equation of Prob. 4-8. Assume that

$$x(0+) = 1 \qquad \frac{dx}{dt}\bigg|_{t=0+} = 1 \qquad \frac{d^2x}{dt^2}\bigg|_{t=0+} = 2$$

4-11. Repeat Prob. 4-10, but now assume that the initial conditions are

$$x(0+) = 1 \qquad \frac{d^2x}{dt^2}\bigg|_{t=0+} = 2 \qquad \frac{d^3x}{dt^3}\bigg|_{t=0+} = 1$$

4-12. Obtain the complete solution of the differential equation of Prob. 4-9. Assume that

$$x(0+) = 0 \qquad \frac{dx}{dt}\bigg|_{t=0+} = 1$$

4-13. Repeat Prob. 4-12, but now assume that

$$x(0+) = -1 \qquad \frac{dx}{dt}\bigg|_{t=0+} = 0$$

4-14. Repeat Prob. 4-12, but now assume that

$$x(0+) = \tfrac{1}{2} \qquad \frac{dx}{dt}\bigg|_{t=0+} = \tfrac{1}{2}$$

4-15. Solve the differential equation

$$\frac{d^2x}{dt^2} + 2\frac{dx}{dt} + x = 3$$

Assume that

$$x(0+) = 1 \qquad \frac{dx}{dt}\bigg|_{t=0+} = 0$$

4-16. Repeat Prob. 4-15 for the differential equation

$$\frac{d^2x}{dt^2} + 2\frac{dx}{dt} + x = e^{-t}$$

4-17. Solve the differential equation

$$\frac{d^2x}{dt^2} + x = e^{-t}$$

Assume that

$$x(0+) = 0 \qquad \frac{dx}{dt}\bigg|_{t=0+} = 1$$

4-18. Repeat Prob. 4-17 for the differential equation

$$\frac{d^2x}{dt^2} + x = \sin t$$

4-19. For the circuit of Fig. 4-9 $V = 10$ volts, $R = 1$ ohm, and $L = 2$ henrys. Plot curves of $i(t)$ and $v_C(t)$.

4-20. Repeat Prob. 4-19, but now assume that $L = 2 \times 10^{-6}$ henrys. Compare this result with that of Prob. 4-19.

4-21. For the circuit of Fig. 4-12 $V = 10$ volts, $R = 1$ ohm, and $L = 2$ henrys. Plot curves of $i(t)$ and $v_L(t)$.

4-22. For the circuit of Prob. 4-21 calculate the energy dissipated in the resistance (for all time $0 \le t \le \infty$) as heat. Show that this is equal to the initial energy stored in the magnetic field of the inductance (at $t = 0+$).

4-23. For the circuit of Fig. 4-14 $V = 10$ volts, $R = 1$ ohm, $C = 1$ farad, and $v_C(0-) = 2$ volts. Plot curves of $i(t)$ and $v_C(t)$.

4-24. Repeat Prob. 4-23, but now assume that $V_C(0-) = -2$ volts.

4-25. For the circuit of Fig. 4-15 $V = 10$ volts, $R = 1$ ohm, and $C = 1$ μf (10^{-6} farad). Plot curves of $i(t)$ and $v_C(t)$.

4-26. For the circuit of Prob. 4-25 calculate the total energy (for all $0 \le t \le \infty$) dissipated in the resistance. Show that it is equal to the initial energy (at $t = 0-$) stored in the capacitor.

4-27. For the circuit of Fig. 4-16 $V = 10$ volts, $R = 3$ ohms, $L = 1$ henry, and $C = 1$ farad. $i(0-) = 0$ and $v_C(0-) = 0$. Plot curves of $i(t)$, the voltage across the inductance, and $v_C(t)$.

4-28. Repeat Prob. 4-27, but now assume that $v_C(0-) = 10$ volts.

4-29. Repeat Prob. 4-27, but now assume that $R = 2$ ohms.

4-30. Repeat Prob. 4-27, but now assume that $R = 1$ ohm.

4-31. Repeat Prob. 4-27, but now assume that $R = 0$ ohms.

4-32. Repeat Prob. 4-27, but now assume that $R = 0$ ohms, $L = 10^{-3}$ henry, and $C = 1$ μf. Compare the results with those of Prob. 4-31.

4-33. Repeat Prob. 4-27, but now assume that $R = -1$ ohm.

4-34. Find the final value of the nodal voltages of the network of Fig. 4-24.

4-35. Solve the simultaneous differential equations

$$(p + 1)x_1 + \left(p + \frac{1}{p}\right) x_2 = e^{-t}$$

$$px_1 + \left(p + \frac{2}{p}\right) x_2 = 0$$

Assume that

$$x_1(0+) = x_2(0+) = 0 \qquad \left.\frac{dx_1}{dt}\right|_{t=0+} = 1 \qquad \left.\frac{dx_2}{dt}\right|_{t=0+} = 1$$

4-36. Obtain all the loop currents as functions of time for the network of Fig. 4-22.

4-37. Repeat Prob. 4-36 for the network of Fig. 4-23.

4-38. Obtain all the nodal voltages as functions of time for the network of Fig. 4-24.

4-39. Repeat Prob. 4-38, but now use cut-set voltages which are not nodal voltages.

4-40. Repeat Prob. 4-38 for the network of Fig. 4-25.

4-41. Repeat Prob. 4-39 for the network of Fig. 4-25.

4-42. Use loop analysis to find the current in the 1-henry coil of Fig. 4-26.

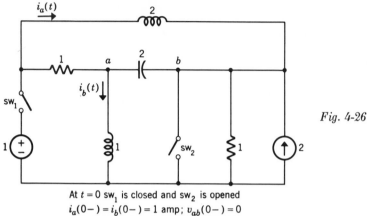

Fig. 4-26

At $t = 0$ sw$_1$ is closed and sw$_2$ is opened

$i_a(0-) = i_b(0-) = 1$ amp; $v_{ab}(0-) = 0$

All values are in volts, amperes, ohms, henrys, or farads

4-43. Repeat Prob. 4-42, but now use nodal analysis.

4-44. Use loop analysis to find $i_b(t)$ in Fig. 4-27.

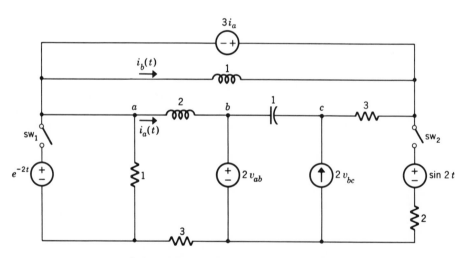

At $t = 0$ close sw$_1$ and sw$_2$

$i_a(0-) = 0$; $v_{bc}(0-) = 0$; $i_b(0-) = 1$ amp

All values are in volts, amperes, ohms, henrys, and farads

Fig. 4-27

4-45. Repeat Prob. 4-44, but now use nodal analysis.

4-46. Repeat Prob. 4-44, but now use cut-set analysis. Choose a set of cut sets that do not lead to nodal analysis.

The Laplace Transform

5

In this chapter we shall discuss the *Laplace transform,* a powerful mathematical technique for solving differential equations. We shall find that application of the Laplace transform to the solution of linear differential equations with constant coefficients results in a procedure that is much less tedious than the classical method. We can obtain the complementary and particular solutions in a single operation. Even more important is the fact that the initial conditions are incorporated into the network equations at the start, and we do not have to solve additional sets of simultaneous equations to evaluate unknown constants. In addition, the Laplace transform will provide us with additional insight into network response and the effect of initial conditions.

The connection between the Laplace transform and the solution of differential equations may not be evident at the start. However, after the Laplace transform has been introduced we shall develop procedures for the solution of linear differential equations with constant coefficients.

5-1   The Laplace transform

Let us begin by defining the Laplace transform and some of its basic properties. Although the primary use of the Laplace transform is in the solution of differential equations, we shall not discuss these solutions here.   In the next section we shall introduce topics that are directly applicable to the solution of the integral-differential equations of lumped linear time-invariant networks.   The discussions of this section lay the necessary groundwork.

A general transformation is one which transforms a function of one variable into a function of another variable.   The Laplace transform is called an *integral transform*, since it involves an integral.   It is defined by

$$\mathbf{F}(s) \ = \ \int_0^\infty f(t)e^{-st} \, dt \tag{5-1}$$

That is, we multiply $f(t)$ by the exponential e^{-st} and then integrate it from zero to infinity.   The resultant function is a function of s but not of t.   We use a capital letter to indicate this, since $\mathbf{F}(s)$ is not time varying.

In general, s is a complex number which we can write as

$$s = \sigma + j\omega \tag{5-2}$$

The $\mathbf{F}$ in $\mathbf{F}(s)$ is designated by boldface type because it is a complex number; s also is a complex number, but it is conventional not to indicate it in boldface.

The lower limit of integration is zero, because *it is assumed that we are dealing with functions of time that are zero for $t < 0$.*   In general, this is representative of the functions with which we shall be working.   That is, we shall usually seek the response of a network to generators which are applied at some time which we call $t = 0$.

We consider that s is a variable and that it can take on any value.   However, we shall see that Re s (the real part of $s = \sigma$) will be somewhat restricted. Let us consider an actual function of time to see how this restriction comes about.   For instance, consider that $f(t) = 1$ for $t > 0$.   Then

$$\mathbf{F}(s) \ = \ \int_0^\infty e^{-st} \, dt = \int_0^\infty e^{-\sigma t}e^{-j\omega t} \, dt \tag{5-3}$$

If σ is negative, then the integrand (the term inside the integral) becomes arbitrarily large as t becomes large.   The integrand approaches infinity as t approaches infinity.   In this case the integrand is such that the integral will not exist.   Note that the integrand is given by

$$e^{-st} = e^{-\sigma t}(\cos \omega t + j \sin \omega t) \tag{5-4}$$

If t approaches infinity and σ is negative, then the value of this function is not *defined* in an ordinary sense (sin ωt does not approach a given value as t approaches infinity).   This is another reason that the integral does not exist in an ordinary sense.

Now consider that $\sigma = 0$. In this case Eq. (5-4) becomes

$$e^{-st} = \cos \omega t + j \sin \omega t \tag{5-5}$$

Again, in an ordinary sense the integral of Eq. (5-3) will not exist, since $\cos \omega t$ and $\sin \omega t$ are not defined as t approaches infinity.

However, if σ is positive, the e^{-st} falls off exponentially and approaches zero as t approaches infinity. Equation (5-4) falls off in the same way, and the integral of Eq. (5-3) will exist. Thus, if Eq. (5-3) is to be complete, we should add the restriction that Re $s = \sigma > 0$.

For any function $f(t)$ we can perform the following test to determine allowable values of σ. If

$$\int_0^\infty |f(t)| e^{-\sigma t} \tag{5-6}$$

exists for $\sigma > \sigma_0$, where σ_0 is a constant, then the Laplace transform will also exist for $\sigma > \sigma_0$ (by taking the absolute value of the functions we make it more difficult for the integral to converge to finite values). In general, we use a value of σ large enough that the integrand falls off to zero; then the integral will exist. Functions that can be restricted in such a way are said to be of *exponential order*. For instance,

$$\lim_{t \to \infty} t^n e^{-\sigma t} = 0 \qquad \text{for any } n \text{ as long as } \sigma > 0 \tag{5-7a}$$

$$\lim_{t \to \infty} e^{5t} e^{-\sigma t} = 0 \qquad \text{for } \sigma > 5 \tag{5-7b}$$

A function that is not of exponential order is e^{t^2}. However, all functions that are ordinarily encountered in practical networks will be of exponential order.

To be complete Eq. (5-1) should include the restriction on Re s. That is, we should write it as

$$\mathbf{F}(s) = \int_0^\infty f(t) e^{-st} \, dt \qquad \text{Re } s = \sigma > \sigma_0 \tag{5-8}$$

where σ_0 is determined from $f(t)$. We shall see that in many applications we can neglect this restriction on Re s as long as the Laplace transform exists for some s. However, in advanced studies, where $f(t)$ is obtained from $\mathbf{F}(s)$ by complex-variable procedures, the restriction on Re s becomes very important.

Let us illustrate this by obtaining the Laplace transforms of some functions of time. The first of these is the *unit step function*, which is defined as

$$f(t) > \left\{ \begin{array}{ll} & t < 0 \\ & t > 0 \end{array} \right. \tag{5-9}$$

and is illustrated in Fig. 5-1. This function, a very useful one in electric circuit analysis, can be generated simply with a switch in series with a battery. In fact, the unit step function is often used as the mathematical representation

Fig. 5-1   The unit-step function u(t).

of a switch.   The Laplace transform is given by

$$\mathbf{F}(s) = \int_0^\infty 1 e^{-st}\, dt \qquad \text{Re } s = \sigma > 0 \tag{5-10}$$

Integrating, we obtain

$$\mathbf{F}(s) = \left[-\frac{1}{s}\, e^{-st} \right]_0^\infty$$

After substitution, noting that $\lim\limits_{t \to \infty} e^{-st} = 0$, we have

$$\mathbf{F}(s) = \frac{1}{s} \qquad \text{Re } s = \sigma > 0 \tag{5-11}$$

Let us now obtain the Laplace transform of $u(t) \sin \omega_0 t$; note that by multiplying a function by $u(t)$ we obtain the same function for $t > 0$, but the resulting function is zero for $t < 0$.   We have

$$\mathbf{F}(s) = \int_0^\infty \sin \omega_0 t\, e^{-st}\, dt \qquad \text{Re } s = \sigma > 0 \tag{5-12a}$$

Integration yields

$$\mathbf{F}(s) = \left. \frac{e^{-st}(s \sin \omega_0 t - \omega_0 \cos \omega_0 t)}{s^2 + \omega_0^2} \right|_0^\infty$$

and, after substitution, we have

$$\mathbf{F}(s) = \frac{\omega_0}{s^2 + \omega_0^2} \qquad \text{Re } s = \sigma > 0 \tag{5-12b}$$

As another example we shall obtain the Laplace transform of $u(t)e^{-at} \sin \omega_0 t$. We start with

$$\mathbf{F}(s) = \int_0^\infty e^{-at} \sin \omega_0 t\, e^{-st}\, dt \qquad \text{Re } s > -a \tag{5-13a}$$

Integrating, we obtain

$$\mathbf{F}(s) = \frac{\omega_0}{(s + a)^2 + \omega_0^2} \qquad \text{Re } s > -a \tag{5-13b}$$

From Eqs. (5-11), (5-12b), or (5-13b) we see that we have functions in which s can take on almost any values (not only those restricted by Re $s > \sigma_0$) and the function will remain well behaved.   For instance, in Eq. (5-11), if we let $s = -3$, then $\mathbf{F}(s) = -\frac{1}{3}$.   In many instances, therefore, we shall not consider the restriction on Re s. There is a process called *analytic continuation* whereby these functions can be extended to values of Re s other than those given by Re $s > \sigma_0$.

Actually, the Laplace transform represented by Eq. (5-8) is just half of a set of equations called the *Laplace transform pair*. These are given by

$$\mathbf{F}(s) = \int_0^\infty f(t)e^{-st}\,dt \qquad \text{Re } s > \sigma_0 \tag{5-14a}$$

$$f(t) = \frac{1}{2\pi j}\int_{C-j\infty}^{C+j\infty} \mathbf{F}(s)e^{st}\,ds \qquad C > \sigma_0 \tag{5-14b}$$

where $j = \sqrt{-1}$. That is, Eq. (5-14a) is used to obtain the Laplace transform from a function of time. Equation (5-14b), called the *inverse Laplace transform*, is used to obtain the function of time from a Laplace transform. It can be demonstrated that Eqs. (5-14a) and (5-14b) are compatible; that is, if we use a given $f(t)$ to obtain $\mathbf{F}(s)$ from Eq. (5-14a), substitution of the resulting $\mathbf{F}(s)$ in Eq. (5-14b) will yield the given $f(t)$. Such a demonstration is beyond the scope of this chapter, as is evaluation of the details of Eq. (5-14b). However, we shall discuss some of the general aspects of this evaluation here.

Equation (5-14b) is a line integral similar to that of Eq. (1-8). In this case the path of integration lies in a region called the *s plane* which is shown in Fig. 5-2. The variable $s = \sigma + j\omega$ can take on a doubly infinite set of values for $-\infty \leq \sigma \leq \infty$ and for $-\infty \leq \omega \leq \infty$. We can represent a single value of s as a point in space by the s plane of Fig. 5-2. The real value of s is given by the horizontal axis, while the vertical axis gives the imaginary value of s. The path of integration of Eq. (5-14b) is parallel to the $j\omega$ (imaginary) axis. The value of C gives the location of the path. In evaluating the inverse-transform integral it is important that the path lie to the right of σ_0. We shall not be directly concerned with the inverse-transform integral; hence the value of σ_0 will not always be considered.

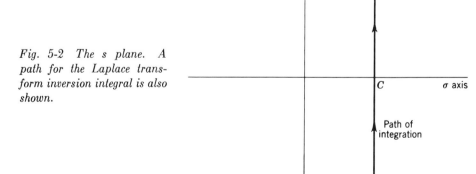

Fig. 5-2   The s plane.   A path for the Laplace transform inversion integral is also shown.

Let us introduce some notation which will aid us in our discussions. $\mathcal{L}[f(t)]$ will be used to indicate the Laplace transform of $f(t)$. Hence

$$\mathbf{F}(s) = \mathcal{L}[f(t)] \qquad (5\text{-}15)$$

We shall designate the inverse Laplace transform as $\mathcal{L}^{-1}$, where

$$\mathcal{L}^{-1}[\mathbf{F}(s)] = f(t) \qquad (5\text{-}16)$$

We shall find it necessary to obtain the inverse Laplace transforms of many functions. The direct Laplace transform of Eq. 5-14a is a matter of simple integration. By performing these integrations for many different functions we can build up a table of Laplace transforms. It would be very helpful if we could use such a table to obtain the inverse Laplace transform. As a matter of fact, if

$$\mathcal{L}[u(t)] = \frac{1}{s} \qquad (5\text{-}17)$$

[see Eqs. (5-10) and (5-11)] we can state that $\mathcal{L}^{-1}[1/s] = u(t)$ provided that the Laplace transform is *unique*—that is, unless there is another function of time which also has $1/s$ as its Laplace transform.

It can be proved that the Laplace transform is essentially unique; that is, if

$$\mathcal{L}[f_1(t)] = \mathcal{L}[f_2(t)] \qquad (5\text{-}18a)$$

then

$$f_1(t) = f_2(t) \qquad (5\text{-}18b)$$

except possibly at a finite number of points. Figure 5-3, for example, illustrates a function that is equal to the unit step function except at three points. The Laplace transform of Fig. 5-3 is also $1/s$. In practical situations we shall not deal with functions with such single-point discontinuities. Thus for all cases of interest we can state that the Laplace transform is unique. From

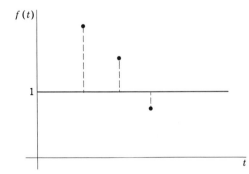

Fig. 5-3   *A function that is almost equal to the unit step function.*

Table 5-1   Laplace transforms

$f(t)$	$\mathbf{F}(s)$
$u(t)$	$1/s$
$u(t)e^{-at}$	$1/(s + a)$
$u(t) \sin \omega_0 t$	$\omega_0/(s^2 + \omega_0{}^2)$
$u(t) \cos \omega_0 t$	$s/(s^2 + \omega_0{}^2)$
$u(t)e^{-at} \sin \omega_0 t$	$\omega_0/[(s + a)^2 + \omega_0{}^2]$
$u(t)e^{-at} \cos \omega_0 t$	$(s + a)/[(s + a)^2 + \omega_0{}^2]$
$u(t)t$	$1/s^2$
$u(t)te^{-at}$	$1/(s + a)^2$
$u(t)t^n$	$n!/s^{n+1}$
$u(t)t^n e^{-at}$	$n!/(s + a)^{n+1}$

Eqs. (5-11), (5-12), and (5-13), then, we have

$$\mathcal{L}^{-1}\left[\frac{1}{s}\right] = u(t) \tag{5-19a}$$

$$\mathcal{L}^{-1}\left[\frac{\omega_0}{s^2 + \omega_0{}^2}\right] = u(t) \sin \omega_0 t \tag{5-19b}$$

$$\mathcal{L}^{-1}\left[\frac{\omega_0}{(s + a)^2 + \omega_0{}^2}\right] = u(t)e^{-at} \sin \omega_0 t \tag{5-19c}$$

Thus, by taking the Laplace transform of many functions we can build up a table that can be used both for taking Laplace transforms and also for taking inverse Laplace transforms.   Such a table is given here as Table 5-1. This table can be used in the solution of most circuit analysis problems.   We shall obtain additional transforms when they are needed.

One additional property of the Laplace transform is the property of *linearity*.   Let us assume that we have two functions of time, $f_1(t)$ and $f_2(t)$, such that

$$\mathcal{L}[f_1(t)] = \mathbf{F}_1(s) = \int_0^\infty f_1(t)e^{-st}\, dt \tag{5-20a}$$

$$\mathcal{L}[f_2(t)] = \mathbf{F}_2(s) = \int_0^\infty f_2(t)e^{-st}\, dt \tag{5-20b}$$

We now wish to determine $\mathcal{L}[a_1 f_1(t) + a_2 f_2(t)]$, where a_1 and a_2 are constants. Substituting in Eq. (5-1), we obtain

$$\mathcal{L}[a_1 f_1(t) + a_2 f_2(t)] = \int_0^\infty [a_1 f_1(t) + a_2 f_2(t)]e^{-st}\, dt \tag{5-21a}$$

Manipulation gives us

$$\mathcal{L}[a_1 f_1(t) + a_2 f_2(t)] = a_1 \int_0^\infty f_1(t)e^{-st}\, dt + a_2 \int_0^\infty f_2(t)e^{-st}\, dt \tag{5-21b}$$

Comparison with Eqs. (5-20) shows that

$$\mathcal{L}[a_1 f_1(t) + a_2 f_2(t)] = a_1 \mathbf{F}_1(s) + a_2 \mathbf{F}_2(s) \tag{5-22}$$

We have demonstrated two important facts: (1) The Laplace transform of a constant times a function is equal to the constant times the Laplace transform of the function, and (2) the Laplace transform of the sum of two functions is equal to the sum of the Laplace transforms of the individual functions.

5-2   The Laplace transform of the derivative and the integral: elementary differential equations

In this section we shall obtain the Laplace transforms of the derivative and integral of a function in terms of the Laplace transform of the function itself. There relations will allow us to solve linear integral-differential equations with constant coefficients in a simple and straightforward manner.

Let us obtain the Laplace transform of the derivative. Suppose we have a function $f(t)$ whose Laplace transform is $\mathbf{F}(s)$. Let us obtain $\mathcal{L}[(d/dt)f(t)]$ in terms of $\mathbf{F}(s)$. If we substitute in Eq. (5-1), we have

$$\mathcal{L}\left[\frac{df(t)}{dt}\right] = \int_0^\infty \frac{df(t)}{dt} e^{-st}\, dt \tag{5-23}$$

Now we integrate by parts. In general, we can write

$$\int_0^\infty u\, dv = uv \Big|_0^\infty - \int_0^\infty v\, du \tag{5-24}$$

In Eq. (5-23) we let

$$u = e^{-st} \tag{5-25a}$$

$$dv = \frac{df(t)}{dt}\, dt = df(t) \tag{5-25b}$$

Thus

$$du = -se^{-st}\, dt \tag{5-26a}$$

$$v = f(t) \tag{5-26b}$$

Then, substituting in Eq. (5-24), we obtain

$$\mathcal{L}\left[\frac{df(t)}{dt}\right] = [f(t)e^{-st}]_0^\infty + \int_0^\infty sf(t)e^{-st}\, dt \tag{5-27}$$

We assume that Re s is large enough so that $\lim_{t\to\infty} f(t)e^{-st} = 0$. Then

$$[f(t)e^{-st}]_0^\infty = -f(0) \tag{5-28}$$

(we shall discuss this in greater detail subsequently). In addition, s is a constant as far as the integration is concerned. Hence

$$\int_0^\infty sf(t)e^{-st}\, dt = s\int_0^\infty f(t)e^{-st}\, dt = s\mathbf{F}(s) \tag{5-29}$$

That is, the integral is just s times $\mathcal{L}[f(t)]$. Therefore

$$\mathcal{L}\left[\frac{df(t)}{dt}\right] = s\mathbf{F}(s) - f(0) \tag{5-30}$$

This result states that the Laplace transform of the derivative of a function is s times the Laplace transform of the function minus the initial value of the function.

The initial value needs much further clarification. In the last chapter we saw that initial conditions were considered at $t = 0+$ (after the switches were closed), and that these initial conditions were obtained from known initial conditions at $t = 0-$. Thus the initial condition of Eq. (5-30) should be in terms of either $f(0+)$ or $f(0-)$. We *must define* the lower limits of integration in the Laplace transform as either $0+$ or $0-$ to establish which initial condition is to be used. At this point such a discussion may appear academic, since we have established that in practical circuits $f(0-) = f(0+)$. However, we also saw (see Sec. 4-1) that in certain *ideal* circuits $f(0+)$ is *not* equal to $f(0-)$. In these cases $f(0-)$, and not $f(0+)$, will be known. These ideal circuits are often used to simplify approximate analyses of circuits. Moreover, the ideal analysis of a circuit is often used to rate the circuit (in Secs. 5-14 and 5-15, we shall discuss such analyses). Thus it is important to specify very carefully whether the lower limit of Eq. (5-1) is $0-$ or $0+$. That is, we can consider that there are two Laplace transforms, defined by

$$\mathbf{F}_{0-}(s) = \int_{0-}^\infty f(t)e^{-st}\, dt \tag{5-31}$$

$$\mathbf{F}_{0+}(s) = \int_{0+}^\infty f(t)e^{-st}\, dt \tag{5-32}$$

and *we must pick one of them.* If we use Eq. (5-31) as the definition of the Laplace transform, $f(0)$ is replaced by $f(0-)$ in Eq. (5-30). If Eq. (5-32) is used as the fundamental definition, then $f(0)$ is replaced by $f(0+)$ in Eq. (5-30). Since $f(0-)$, and not $f(0+)$, will always be known, it is often much more convenient to use the definition of Eq. (5-31), and *we shall do so.*

There are certain problems introduced by using $f(0-)$ that we must consider and resolve. We have been working with circuits such as that of Fig. 5-4a, where switches are closed at $t = 0$. This network does not exist at $t = 0-$, so we cannot write equations for it. We must be able to write them if we are to work with Eq. (5-31). To eliminate this problem, we replace the network of Fig. 5-4a with that of Fig. 5-4b. That is, we replace the generators in series with switches by generators of equal voltages multiplied by $u(t)$. This achieves the same effect (the generator is turned on at $t = 0$), and, the circuit of Fig. 5-4b is in existence at $t = 0-$.

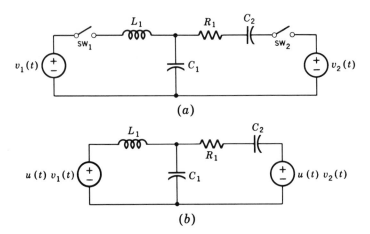

Fig. 5-4   (a) *A network with switches* sw$_1$ *and* sw$_2$ *closed at* $t = 0$*;* (b) *an equivalent network valid for* $t \geq 0$ *that is in existance at* $t = 0-$.

In general, we shall use unit step functions in conjunction with generators to produce the effect of switches.   This does not limit our procedures at all, since for $t > 0$ (when we are interested in the response) both networks are identical.   In addition, we can specify arbitrary initial conditions.   For instance, in either circuit of Fig. 5-4 we can assume that there is external circuitry which is removed just prior to $t = 0-$; this external circuitry establishes an initial current in the inductor and initial voltages across the capacitors.   The same procedure was used with classical analysis and is completely general.   We shall assume, then, that Eq. (5-31) is the fundamental definition of the Laplace transform.   Usually we shall write the lower limit of integration as 0, with the understanding that this means $0-$.   Thus the expression that we shall use for the transform of the derivative is

$$\mathcal{L}\left[\frac{df(t)}{dt}\right] = s\mathbf{F}(s) - f(0-) \tag{5-33}$$

As an example of this let us obtain the Laplace transform of $(d/dt)u(t) \sin \omega_0 t$.   From Table 5-1,

$$\mathcal{L}[u(t) \sin \omega_0 t] = \frac{\omega_0}{s^2 + \omega_0^2} \tag{5-34}$$

Then

$$\mathcal{L}\left[\frac{d}{dt} u(t) \sin \omega_0 t\right] = \mathcal{L}[u(t)\omega_0 \cos \omega_0 t] = \frac{\omega_0 s}{s^2 + \omega_0^2} - 0 \tag{5-35}$$

We see that here $\mathcal{L}[u(t)\omega_0 \cos \omega_0 t]$ is as given in Table 5-1.

We must be careful in taking derivatives of functions multiplied by the unit step, such as $f(t)u(t)$. For instance,

$$\frac{d}{dt}[u(t) \cos t] \neq -u(t) \sin t \tag{5-36a}$$

even though

$$\frac{d}{dt} \cos t = -\sin t \tag{5-36b}$$

This is because $u(t) \cos t$ is 0 for $t = 0-$ and is 1 at $t = 0+$. Thus $u(t) \cos t$ is discontinuous at $t = 0$, and its derivative is infinite there. However, $\cos t$ is continuous there.

For example, consider [see Table 5-1 and Eq. (5-33)]

$$\mathcal{L}\left[\frac{d}{dt} u(t) \cos t\right] = s \frac{s}{s^2 + 1} - 0 = \frac{s^2}{s^2 + 1} \tag{5-37}$$

Note that $u(0-) = 0$. In addition,

$$\mathcal{L}[-u(t) \sin t] = \frac{-1}{s^2 + 1} \tag{5-38}$$

Equations (5-37) and (5-38) are both valid, even though they are not equal. They represent the transform of different functions. In Sec. 5-14 we shall discuss this further and examine a limit process that will enable us to work with the derivatives of functions which become discontinuous at a limit.

Let us illustrate the use of the transform of a derivative by solving the very simple circuit of Fig. 5-5. The differential equation of this circuit is

$$Vu(t) = Ri(t) + L\left[\frac{di(t)}{dt}\right] \tag{5-39}$$

Now, $i(t)$ is unknown. Thus its Laplace transform $\mathbf{I}(s)$ is also unknown. The Laplace transform of both sides of Eq. (3-39) yields

$$\int_0^\infty Vu(t)e^{-st}\, dt = \int_0^\infty Ri(t)e^{-st}\, dt + \int_0^\infty L\left[\frac{di(t)}{dt}\right]e^{-st}\, dt \tag{5-40}$$

Fig. 5-5 (a) A simple RL network; assume that at $t = 0$ the switch is closed and assume that an external circuit, which is removed at $t = 0$, has established $i(0-) = I_0$; (b) an equivalent network that exists at $t = 0-$.

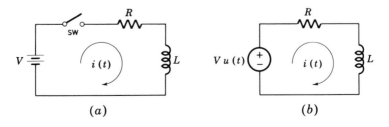

(a)   *(b)*

The integral on the left-hand side is V times $\mathcal{L}[u(t)]$, which is given in Table 5-1 as $V(1/s)$. The first integral on the right-hand side is $R\mathbf{I}(s)$. The second integral is obtained from Eq. (5-33). Thus we have

$$\frac{V}{s} = R\mathbf{I}(s) + L[s\mathbf{I}(s) - i(0-)] \tag{5-41a}$$

Manipulating and substituting $i(0-) = I_0$, we obtain

$$\frac{V}{s} + LI_0 = (R + Ls)\mathbf{I}(s) \tag{5-41b}$$

The differential equation has become an algebraic equation in the variable s. This will be the general case and is an important consequence of the Laplace transform.   That is, *the Laplace transform transforms ordinary differential equations into algebraic equations.*

Solving Eq. (5-41b) for the unknown $\mathbf{I}(s)$ gives us

$$\mathbf{I}(s) = \frac{(V/s) + LI_0}{R + Ls} \tag{5-42a}$$

We now have determined $\mathcal{L}[i(t)] = \mathbf{I}(s)$.   To obtain $i(t)$ we must take the inverse Laplace transform of $\mathbf{I}(s)$.   This expression does not appear in Table 5-1.   However, we can manipulate Eq. (5-42a) and write it as

$$\mathbf{I}(s) = \frac{V}{R}\frac{1}{s} - \frac{V - I_0 R}{R}\frac{1}{s + (R/L)} \tag{5-42b}$$

(a systematic procedure for performing manipulations of this type will be discussed in the next section).   Both $1/s$ and $1/(s + R/L)$ are given in Table 5-1.   Hence we can now obtain the inverse Laplace transform.   This is

$$i(t) = \frac{V}{R}u(t) - \frac{V - I_0 R}{R}e^{-(R/L)t}u(t) \tag{5-43a}$$

or

$$i(t) = \frac{V}{R} - \frac{V - I_0 R}{R}e^{-(R/L)t} \qquad \text{for } t > 0 \tag{5-43b}$$

Comparison shows this result to be the same as that of Eq. (4-104) [note that Eq. (4-104) was derived with the assumption that $I_0 = 0$].   The differential equation has been solved in a straightforward way.   Note especially that the initial conditions have been incorporated without the need to solve for unknown constants.

We can extend Eq. (5-33) to obtain the Laplace transforms of higher-order derivatives.   We have

$$\frac{d^2 f(t)}{dt^2} = \frac{d}{dt}\frac{df(t)}{dt} \tag{5-44}$$

From Eq. (5-33), noting that the function which is differentiated is $df(t)/dt$, we obtain

$$\mathcal{L}\left[\frac{d^2f(t)}{dt^2}\right] = s\mathcal{L}\left[\frac{df(t)}{dt}\right] - \frac{df(t)}{dt}\bigg|_{t=0-} \tag{5-45}$$

Substitution of Eq. (5-33) for $\mathcal{L}[df(t)/dt]$ yields

$$\mathcal{L}\left[\frac{d^2f(t)}{dt^2}\right] = s^2\mathbf{F}(s) - sf(0-) - \frac{df(t)}{dt}\bigg|_{t=0-} \tag{5-46}$$

where $\mathbf{F}(s) = \mathcal{L}[f(t)]$. By successive applications of this procedure we can obtain the Laplace transform of higher-order derivatives. This yields

$$\mathcal{L}\left[\frac{d^nf(t)}{dt^n}\right] = s^n\mathbf{F}(s) - s^{n-1}f(0-) - s^{n-2}\frac{df(t)}{dt}\bigg|_{t=0-}$$
$$- \cdots - \frac{d^{n-1}f(t)}{dt^{n-1}}\bigg|_{t=0-} \tag{5-47}$$

Let us now obtain the Laplace transform of the integral of a function in terms of the Laplace transform of the function itself. Once we have done this, we shall be able to obtain directly the Laplace transforms of the integral-differential equations obtained from loop, nodal, or cut-set analysis. We shall consider that $\mathcal{L}[f(t)] = \mathbf{F}(s)$ and determine $\mathcal{L}[\int f(t)\, dt]$. To avoid confusion we shall write the variable of integration as τ. Then we can write the integral as

$$f^{(-1)}(t) = \int f(\tau)\, d\tau \tag{5-48}$$

where the symbol $f^{(-1)}(t)$ represents the indefinite integral. The indefinite integral is actually [see Eq. (1-52)]

$$f^{(-1)}(t) = \int_{-\infty}^{t} f(\tau)\, d\tau \tag{5-49}$$

Thus we can write

$$\frac{df^{(-1)}(t)}{dt} = f(t) \tag{5-50}$$

Now we take the Laplace transform of both sides of Eq. (5-50). This yields

$$\mathcal{L}\left[\frac{df^{(-1)}(t)}{dt}\right] = \mathbf{F}(s) \tag{5-51}$$

Application of Eq. (5-33), the Laplace transform of the derivative, to the left-hand side of this equation gives us

$$\mathcal{L}[f^{(-1)}(t)] - f^{(-1)}(0-) = \mathbf{F}(s) \tag{5-52}$$

and, after solving for $\mathcal{L}[f^{(-1)}(t)]$, we obtain

$$\mathcal{L}[f^{(-1)}(t)] = \mathcal{L}\left[\int f(t)\, dt\right] = \frac{\mathbf{F}(s)}{s} + \frac{f^{(-1)}(0-)}{s} \tag{5-53}$$

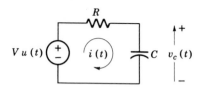

Fig. 5-6   *A simple RC circuit.   Assume that an external circuit, which is removed at t = 0, has established $v_C(0-) = V_0$.*

Let us clarify the meaning of $f^{(-1)}(0-)$.   If we substitute $0-$ for t in Eq. (5-49), we obtain

$$f^{(-1)}(0-) = \int_{-\infty}^{0-} f(t)\, dt \tag{5-54}$$

We can illustrate this with a more definite result.   The voltage drop across a capacitor in terms of the current into it is given by

$$v(t) = \frac{1}{C} \int i(t)\, dt = \frac{1}{C} \int_{-\infty}^{0-} i(t)\, dt + \int_{0-}^{t} i(\tau)\, d\tau \tag{5-55}$$

Then $\int_{-\infty}^{0-} i(t)\, dt$ is charge stored on one plate of the capacitor at $t = 0-$ and $(1/C)\int_{-\infty}^{0-} i(t)\, dt$ is $v(0-)$, the initial voltage across the capacitor.   Now, using Eq. (5-53) to take the Laplace transform of $v(t)$, we have

$$\mathbf{V}(s) = \frac{\mathbf{I}(s)}{Cs} + \frac{(1/C)\int_{-\infty}^{0-} i(t)\, dt}{s} = \frac{\mathbf{I}(s)}{Cs} + \frac{v(0-)}{s} \tag{5-56}$$

Thus the initial voltage across the capacitor is incorporated in our relations.

Let us illustrate the use of this relation for the Laplace transform of the integral in the solution of a simple network.   Consider Fig. 5-6, where the unit step function represents a switch.   The loop equation of this circuit is

$$Vu(t) = Ri + \frac{1}{C} \int i\, dt \tag{5-57}$$

The Laplace transform of both sides of this equation yields

$$\frac{V}{s} = R\mathbf{I}(s) + \frac{\mathbf{I}(s)}{Cs} + \frac{V_0}{s} \tag{5-58}$$

Thus the integral equation has been replaced by an algebraic one, where the unknown $\mathbf{I}(s)$ is $\mathcal{L}[i(t)]$, and we have used Eq. (5-53) to obtain the Laplace transform of the integral.   Then, solving for $\mathbf{I}(s)$, we have

$$\mathbf{I}(s) = \frac{V - V_0}{R(s + 1/RC)} \tag{5-59}$$

We have now found $\mathcal{L}[i(t)]$.   Using Table 5-1 to evaluate the inverse Laplace transform, we obtain

$$i(t) = \frac{V - V_0}{R} e^{-t/RC} \tag{5-60}$$

Again we have incorporated the effect of initial conditions without having had to evaluate constants. We have also reduced the solution of the differential equation to the procedure of solving an algebraic one and obtaining the inverse transform.

The two simple examples above illustrate some of the advantages of the Laplace transform over the classical procedure discussed in the last chapter. When we consider more elaborate examples, the advantages of the Laplace transform will be still more apparent.

5-3 Partial-fraction expansions

In general, application of the Laplace transform will convert integral-differential equations of mesh, nodal, or cut-set analysis algebraic equations. Equations (5-33), (5-47), and (5-53) illustrate that the Laplace transforms of the derivatives or integrals of a function are just the Laplace transform of the function multiplied by s^n, plus some terms involving initial conditions which may be multiplied by s^n. In addition, the generators, which are functions of time, usually become algebraic functions of s when the Laplace transform is taken. Thus the transformed form of integral-differential equations will be algebraic equations.

The solution to a set of algebraic simultaneous equations is in general the ratio of two polynomials in s [see, for example, Eq. (5-42)]. We shall see additional examples of this in the next sections. For the time being, however, assume that we wish to obtain a function $x(t)$, and that we have obtained its Laplace transform $\mathbf{X}(s)$, expressed as

$$\mathbf{X}(s) = \frac{a_m s^m + a_{m-1}s^{m-1} + \cdots + a_1 s + a_0}{b_n s^n + b_{n-1}s^{n-1} + \cdots + b_1 s + b_0} \tag{5-61}$$

We must obtain the inverse Laplace transform of $\mathbf{X}(s)$ to obtain $x(t) = \mathcal{L}^{-1}[\mathbf{X}(s)]$. A function of the form of Eq. (5-61) is not given in Table 5-1. An infinite table would be required to list the inverse transforms of Eq. (5-61) for all possible m and n. Instead of compiling an unduly large table, let us explore a procedure that will enable us to break up Eq. (5-61) into a sum of terms each of which can be tabulated. We shall then be able to use Table 5-1 to obtain the inverse Laplace transform as a sum of functions of time.

The technique that we shall use is called *partial-fraction expansion*. In order to use it, Eq. (5-61) must be a proper fraction. That is, the highest power of the denominator must be greater than the highest power of the numerator. If it is not, we can always use long division to make this so. That is, if $m > n$, we can write

$$\mathbf{X}(s) = d_{m-n}s^{m-n} + d_{m-n-1}s^{m-n-1} + \cdots + d_1 s + d_0$$
$$+ \frac{\alpha_{n-1}s^{n-1} + \alpha_{n-2}s^{n-2} + \cdots + \alpha_1 s + \alpha_0}{b_n s^n + b_{n-1}s^{n-1} + \cdots + b_1 s + b_0} \tag{5-62}$$

Let us illustrate this with an example. Suppose that

$$X(s) = \frac{s^4 + 4s^3 + 2s^2 + 3s + 1}{s^2 + 2s + 1} \tag{5-63}$$

Then we can set up the long division as

$$
\begin{array}{r}
s^2 + 2s - 3 \\
s^2 + 2s + 1 \overline{\smash{\big)}\, s^4 + 4s^3 + 2s^2 + 3s + 1} \\
\underline{s^4 + 2s^3 + s^2} \\
2s^3 + s^2 + 3s + 1 \\
\underline{2s^3 + 4s^2 + 2s} \\
-3s^2 + s + 1 \\
\underline{-3s^2 - 6s - 3} \\
7s + 4
\end{array}
$$

The remainder is $7s + 4$, so we write

$$X(s) = s^2 + 2s - 3 + \frac{7s + 4}{s^2 + 2s + 1} \tag{5-64}$$

Thus we have obtained a proper fraction plus terms involving powers of s (that is, s^2, $2s$, -3).

The inverse Laplace transforms of terms such as K_0, $K_1 s$, $K_2 s^2$, or, in general, $K_n s^n$, where the K are constants, have not as yet been considered. We shall discuss such functions in Sec. 5-14. Ordinarily we shall not encounter such functions, and for the present let us consider that we are dealing with an $X(s)$ of the form

$$X(s) = \frac{\alpha_{n-1} s^{n-1} + \alpha_{n-2} s^{n-2} + \cdots + \alpha_1 s + \alpha_0}{b_n s^n + b_{n-1} s^{n-1} + \cdots + b_1 s + b_0} \tag{5-65}$$

where α_k and b_k are known constants. If we factor the denominator; we have

$$X(s) = \frac{\alpha_{n-1} s^{n-1} + \alpha_{n-2} s^{n-2} + \cdots + \alpha_1 s + \alpha_0}{b_n(s - s_1)(s - s_2) \cdots (s - s_n)} \tag{5-66}$$

For the time being let us assume that the roots $s_1, s_2, \ldots, s_n$ are all different. We shall demonstrate that we can write Eq. (5-66) as

$$X(s) = \frac{K_1}{s - s_1} + \frac{K_2}{s - s_2} + \cdots + \frac{K_n}{s - s_n} \tag{5-67}$$

To prove this, suppose we combine all the terms of Eq. (5-67). This yields

$$X(s) = \frac{(K_1 + K_2 + \cdots + K_n)s^{n-1} + \cdots + K_1 s_2 s_3 \cdots s_n}{+ K_2 s_1 s_3 \cdots s_n + \cdots + K_n s_1 s_2 \cdots s_{n-1}}{(s - s_1)(s - s_2) \cdots (s - s_n)} \tag{5-68}$$

The denominator of Eq. (5-68) is the same as that of Eq. (5-66) (assume that b_n divides all the coefficients of the numerator). We must be able to set the coefficients of the numerator of Eq. (5-68) equal to the corresponding ones of Eq. (5-66). There are n coefficients, α_{n-1}, α_{n-2}, . . . , α_1, α_0. Since there are also n constants, K_1, K_2, . . . , K_n, we have sufficient freedom to set the coefficients of the numerator of Eq. (5-68) equal to those of the numerator of Eq. (5-66). The simultaneous equations are

$$K_1 + K_2 + \cdots + K_n = \frac{\alpha_{n-1}}{b_n}$$

$$\cdots \cdots \cdots \cdots \cdots \cdots \cdots \cdots \cdots \cdots \cdots \tag{5-69}$$

$$K_1 s_2 s_3 \cdots s_n + K_2 s_1 s_3 \cdots s_n + \cdots + K_n s_1 s_2 \cdots s_{n-1} = \frac{\alpha_0}{b_n}$$

The previous discussion proves the validity of the partial-fraction expansion. However, it would be very tedious to use Eqs. (5-69) to evaluate the unknown constants of Eq. (5-67). There is another procedure that is far easier to use. Since the unknowns are constants, they are not functions of s. Hence we can evaluate them using any value of s. We shall see that certain values of s will reduce the amount of work required. As an example, let us determine K_1 in Eq. (5-67). We multiply both sides of this equation by $s - s_1$. This yields

$$(s - s_1)X(s) = K_1 + (s - s_1)\left(\frac{K_2}{s - s_2} + \frac{K_3}{s - s_3} + \cdots + \frac{K_n}{s - s_n}\right) \tag{5-70}$$

Now let $s = s_1$. All the terms on the right-hand side of Eq. (5-70) except K_1 become zero because of the factor $(s - s_1)$. The left-hand side becomes the constant $[(s - s_1)X(s)]_{s=s_1}$. Note that this factor is not zero, because $X(s)$ has a factor of $s - s_1$ in its denominator which cancels the $s - s_1$ multiplying term. This cancellation should be performed *before* $s = s_1$ is substituted. Thus the particular value $s = s_1$ allows us to determine K_1 without solving simultaneous equations. To solve for K_2 we use essentially the same procedure, except that we multiply both sides of Eq. (5-67) by $s - s_2$, and then we let $s = s_2$. In general, then, we can state that

$$K_i = [(s - s_i)X(s)]_{s=s_i} \tag{5-71}$$

Let us illustrate this procedure with some simple examples. We obtain the inverse Laplace transform of

$$X(s) = \frac{s^2 + 8s + 6}{s^3 + 3s^2 + 2s} = \frac{s^2 + 8s + 6}{s(s + 1)(s + 2)} \tag{5-72}$$

Then

$$X(s) = \frac{K_1}{s} + \frac{K_2}{s + 1} + \frac{K_3}{s + 2} \tag{5-73}$$

To evaluate K_1 we multiply both sides of Eq. (5-73) by s and substitute

Eq. (5-72).   This yields

$$\mathbf{K}_1 + s\left(\frac{\mathbf{K}_2}{s+1} + \frac{\mathbf{K}_3}{s+2}\right) = \frac{s(s^2 + 8s + 6)}{s(s+1)(s+2)} \tag{5-74}$$

We cancel the common factor of s from the numerator and denominator of the right-hand side of Eq. (5-74), and *then* we let $s = 0$.   This yields

$$\mathbf{K}_1 = 3 \tag{5-75a}$$

Proceeding in a similar manner, we obtain

$$\mathbf{K}_2 = [(s+1)\mathbf{X}(s)]_{s=-1} = \frac{s^2 + 8s + 6}{s(s+2)}\bigg|_{s=-1} = 1 \tag{5-75b}$$

$$\mathbf{K}_3 = [(s+2)\mathbf{X}(s)]_{s=-2} = \frac{s^2 + 8s + 6}{s(s+1)}\bigg|_{s=-2} = -3 \tag{5-75c}$$

Then substitution of Eqs. (5-75) into Eq. (5-73) yields

$$\mathbf{X}(s) = \frac{3}{s} + \frac{1}{s+1} - \frac{3}{s+2} \tag{5-76}$$

From Table 5-1, for the inverse Laplace transform we obtain

$$x(t) = u(t)(3 + e^{-t} - 3e^{-2t}) \tag{5-77}$$

The constants in the partial-fraction expansion can be complex numbers. Consider another example.   Suppose we have

$$\mathbf{X}(s) = \frac{s+2}{s^2 + 2s + 2} = \frac{s+2}{(s+1+j)(s+1-j)} \tag{5-78}$$

Any complex roots will occur in conjugate pairs, since the coefficients of $\mathbf{X}(s)$ are real.   The fact that the roots of the denominator of $\mathbf{X}(s)$ are complex numbers does not change any of the previous results.   We write

$$\mathbf{X}(s) = \frac{\mathbf{K}_1}{s+1+j} + \frac{\mathbf{K}_2}{s+1-j} \tag{5-79}$$

where

$$\mathbf{K}_1 = [(s+1+j)\mathbf{X}(s)]_{s=-1-j} = \frac{s+2}{s+1-j}\bigg|_{s=-1-j} = \frac{1-j}{-2j} = \frac{1}{2}(1+j) \tag{5-80a}$$

$$\mathbf{K}_2 = [(s+1-j)\mathbf{X}(s)]_{s=-1+j} = \frac{s+2}{s+1+j}\bigg|_{s=-1+j} = \frac{1+j}{2j} = \frac{1}{2}(1-j) \tag{5-80b}$$

Substituting Eqs. (5-80) into Eq. (5-79), we obtain

$$\mathbf{X}(s) = \frac{\frac{1}{2}(1+j)}{s+1+j} + \frac{\frac{1}{2}(1-j)}{s+1-j}$$

and from Table 5-1 we see that

$$\mathcal{L}^{-1}\left[\frac{1}{s+a}\right] = u(t)e^{-at}$$

This expression is valid even if a is not a real number.

Then, taking the inverse Laplace transform of $\mathbf{X}(s)$, we obtain

$$x(t) = \tfrac{1}{2}(1+j)e^{-(1+j)t} + \tfrac{1}{2}(1-j)e^{-(1-j)t}$$

Now substitution of Euler's relation [Eq. (4-58)] yields

$$x(t) = \tfrac{1}{2}(1+j)e^{-t}(\cos t - j \sin t) + \tfrac{1}{2}(1-j)e^{-t}(\cos t + j \sin t)$$

and, combining terms, we have

$$x(t) = e^{-t}(\cos t + \sin t)u(t)$$

There is a convenient alternative procedure that can be used to calculate the constants in the partial-fraction expansion. Let us assume that the function $\mathbf{X}(s)$ of Eq. (5-65) is the ratio of two polynomials in s such that

$$\mathbf{X}(s) = \frac{\mathbf{P}(s)}{\mathbf{Q}(s)} \tag{5-81}$$

where $\mathbf{P}(s)$ and $\mathbf{Q}(s)$ are the numerator and denominator polynomials. If $\mathbf{Q}(s)$ has a simple root at $s = s_i$, the constant corresponding to it in the partial-fraction expansion is given by Eq. (5-71) as

$$\mathbf{K}_i = \frac{(s-s_i)\mathbf{P}(s)}{\mathbf{Q}(s)}\bigg|_{s=s_i}$$

Now we write

$$\mathbf{Q}(s) = (s-s_i)\mathbf{M}(s) \tag{5-82}$$

where $\mathbf{M}(s)$ does not have a root at $s = s_i$. Thus

$$\mathbf{K}_i = \frac{\mathbf{P}(s_i)}{\mathbf{M}(s_i)} \tag{5-83a}$$

We evaluate the derivative of Eq. (5-82) at $s = s_i$,

$$\frac{d\mathbf{Q}(s)}{ds}\bigg|_{s=s_i} = \left[(s-s_i)\frac{d\mathbf{M}(s)}{ds} + \mathbf{M}(s)\right]_{s=s_i}$$

and substitute $s = s_i$ to obtain

$$\frac{d\mathbf{Q}(s)}{ds}\bigg|_{s=s_i} = \mathbf{M}(s_i)$$

Thus we can write Eq. (5-83a) as

$$\mathbf{K}_i = \frac{\mathbf{P}(s_i)}{\mathbf{Q}'(s_i)} \tag{5-83b}$$

where we have used the somewhat improper notation

$$\frac{d\mathbf{Q}(s)}{ds}\bigg|_{s=s_i} = \mathbf{Q}'(s_i)$$

That is, the constant in the partial-fraction expansion is evaluated by substituting $s = s_i$ into the ratio of the numerator to the derivative of the denominator of the given expression.

As an example consider Eq. (5-72) again.   We have

$$\mathbf{X}(s) = \frac{s^2 + 8s + 6}{s^3 + 3s^2 + 2s} = \frac{s^2 + 8s + 6}{s(s + 1)(s + 2)} = \frac{\mathbf{K}_1}{s} + \frac{\mathbf{K}_2}{s + 1} + \frac{\mathbf{K}_3}{s + 2}$$

Differentiation of the denominator gives us

$$\frac{\mathbf{P}(s)}{\mathbf{Q}'(s)} = \frac{s^2 + 8s + 6}{3s^2 + 6s + 2}$$

Then

$$\mathbf{K}_1 = \frac{\mathbf{P}(s)}{\mathbf{Q}'(s)}\bigg|_{s=0} = 3$$

$$\mathbf{K}_2 = \frac{\mathbf{P}(s)}{\mathbf{Q}'(s)}\bigg|_{s=-1} = 1$$

$$\mathbf{K}_3 = \frac{\mathbf{P}(s)}{\mathbf{Q}'(s)}\bigg|_{s=-2} = -3$$

We have thus far assumed that all the roots of the denominator of Eq. (5-66) were all different.   If there are multiple roots, then this development must be modified somewhat.   Let us assume that $\mathbf{X}(s)$ is written in the form

$$\mathbf{X}(s) = \frac{\alpha_{n-1}s^{n-1} + \alpha_{n-2}s^{n-2} + \cdots + \alpha_1 s + \alpha_0}{(s - s_1)^r(s - s_2) \cdots (s - s_{n-r+1})} \tag{5-84}$$

We still must have n arbitrary constants in the partial-fraction expansion. To obtain these we write the expansion in the form

$$\mathbf{X}(s) = \frac{\mathbf{K}_{11}}{(s - s_1)^r} + \frac{\mathbf{K}_{12}}{(s - s_1)^{r-1}} + \cdots + \frac{\mathbf{K}_{1r}}{s - s_1} + \frac{\mathbf{K}_2}{s - s_2}$$

$$+ \cdots + \frac{\mathbf{K}_{n-r+1}}{s - s_{n-r+1}} \tag{5-85}$$

Note that there is not only a term whose denominator is $(s - s_1)^r$, but there are also terms whose denominators are $(s - s_1)^{r-1}$, $(s - s_1)^{r-2}$, . . . , $(s - s_1)$. The validity of this expression can be demonstrated by combining all the terms over a common denominator [which is the denominator of Eq. (5-84)]. The resulting numerator of Eq. (5-85) can then be equated to the numerator of Eq. (5-84) by adjusting the constants $\mathbf{K}_{11}$, $\mathbf{K}_{12}$, . . . , $\mathbf{K}_{1r}$, $\mathbf{K}_2$, . . . , $\mathbf{K}_{n-r+1}$. This development is similar to that of Eqs. (5-66) to (5-69), and the details are left to the reader.

We now must develop a relatively simple way to determine the constants of Eq. (5-85). If we multiply both sides of this equation by $(s - s_1)^r$, we have

$$(s - s_1)^r \mathbf{X}(s) = \mathbf{K}_{11} + (s - s_1)\mathbf{K}_{12} + (s - s_1)^2 \mathbf{K}_{13} + \cdots$$
$$+ (s - s_1)^{r-1} \mathbf{K}_{1r} + (s - s_1)^r \left(\frac{\mathbf{K}_2}{s - s_2} + \cdots + \frac{\mathbf{K}_{n-r+1}}{s - s_{n-r+1}} \right) \quad (5\text{-}86)$$

Now let $s = s_1$. All the terms on the right-hand side except first one become zero. Thus

$$\mathbf{K}_{11} = [(s - s_1)^r \mathbf{X}(s)]_{s=s_1} \quad (5\text{-}87)$$

Note that the factor $(s - s_1)^r$ is cancelled by the same factor in the denominator of $\mathbf{X}(s)$.

Now let us determine $\mathbf{K}_{12}$. Differentiation of both sides of Eq. (5-86) with respect to s yields

$$\frac{d}{ds}[(s - s_1)^r \mathbf{X}(s)] = \mathbf{K}_{12} + 2(s - s_1)\mathbf{K}_{13} + \cdots + r - 1(s - s_1)^{r-2}\mathbf{K}_{1r}$$
$$+ (s - s_1)^{r-1} \text{ [other terms]} \quad (5\text{-}88)$$

Then, setting $s = s_1$, we obtain

$$\mathbf{K}_{12} = \frac{d}{ds}[(s - s_1)^r \mathbf{X}(s)]_{s=s_1} \quad (5\text{-}89)$$

To evaluate Eq. (5-89) properly we must multiply $(s - s_1)^r$ by $\mathbf{X}(s)$ *before* we differentiate. To obtain $\mathbf{K}_{13}$ we differentiate Eq. (5-88) with respect to s and then let $s = s_1$. Repeating this procedure, we obtain, in general,

$$\mathbf{K}_{1i} = \frac{1}{(i - 1)!} \frac{d^{i-1}}{ds^{i-1}}[(s - s_1)^r \mathbf{X}(s)]_{s=s_1} \quad (5\text{-}90)$$

Note that the product $(s - s_1)^r \mathbf{X}(s)$ should be taken *before* the differentiation is performed. The constants $\mathbf{K}_2$, $\mathbf{K}_3$, $\ldots$, $\mathbf{K}_{n-r+1}$ in Eq. (5-85) are determined from Eq. (5-71).

If there is more than one set of multiple roots, then each set is treated as in Eqs. (5-84) to (5-90). For instance, if we have

$$\mathbf{X}(s) = \frac{\alpha_5 s^5 + \alpha_4 s^4 + \alpha_3 s^3 + \alpha_2 s^2 + \alpha_1 s + \alpha_0}{(s - s_1)^3 (s - s_2)^2 (s - s_3)} \quad (5\text{-}91)$$

then the partial-fraction expansion will be of the form

$$\mathbf{X}(s) = \frac{\mathbf{K}_{11}}{(s - s_1)^3} + \frac{\mathbf{K}_{12}}{(s - s_1)^2} + \frac{\mathbf{K}_{13}}{s - s_1} + \frac{\mathbf{K}_{21}}{(s - s_2)^2} + \frac{\mathbf{K}_{22}}{s - s_2} + \frac{\mathbf{K}_3}{s - s_3}$$
$$(5\text{-}92)$$

The constants corresponding to the multiple roots are evaluated by means of Eq. (5-90). We can change the notation here to indicate that there is more than one set of multiple roots.   For example, we can write

$$\mathbf{K}_{ni} = \frac{1}{(i-1)!} \frac{d^{i-1}}{ds^{i-1}} [(s-s_n)^{r_n}\mathbf{X}(s)]_{s=s_n} \tag{5-93}$$

where r_n is the multiplicity of the root numbered n.   For instance, in Eq. (5-92), when $n = 1$,

$$s_1 = s_1$$
$$r_1 = 3$$
$$i = 1, 2, 3$$

and when $n = 2$,

$$s_2 = s_2$$
$$r_2 = 2$$
$$i = 1, 2$$

The constants which correspond to simple roots of the denominator of $\mathbf{X}(s)$ are evaluated by means of Eq. (5-71).

Let us now consider an example.   Given

$$\mathbf{X}(s) = \frac{s+2}{(s+1+j)^2(s+1-j)^2} \tag{5-94}$$

the partial-fraction expansion has the form

$$\mathbf{X}(s) = \frac{\mathbf{K}_{11}}{(s+1+j)^2} + \frac{\mathbf{K}_{12}}{s+1+j} + \frac{\mathbf{K}_{21}}{(s+1-j)^2} + \frac{\mathbf{K}_{22}}{s+1-j} \tag{5-95}$$

and multiplying both sides of Eq. (5-95) by $(s+1+j)^2$ gives us

$$\begin{aligned}(s+1+j)^2\mathbf{X}(s) &= \frac{s+2}{(s+1-j)^2} \\ &= \mathbf{K}_{11} + \mathbf{K}_{12}(s+1+j) \\ &\quad + (s+1+j)^2 \left[\frac{\mathbf{K}_{21}}{(s+1-j)^2} + \frac{\mathbf{K}_{22}}{s+1-j} \right] \end{aligned} \tag{5-96}$$

Then

$$\mathbf{K}_{11} = [(s+1+j)^2\mathbf{X}(s)]_{s=-1-j} = \frac{1-j}{-4} = -\tfrac{1}{4} + j\tfrac{1}{4} \tag{5-97}$$

We differentiate Eq. (5-96) and then set $s = -1 - j$.   This yields

$$\frac{(s+1-j)^2 - 2(s+2)(s+1-j)}{(s+1-j)^4}\bigg|_{s=-1-j} = \mathbf{K}_{12} \tag{5-98}$$

Hence

$$\mathbf{K}_{12} = \tfrac{1}{4}j$$

Proceeding in a similar way, we obtain

$$\mathbf{K}_{21} = -\tfrac{1}{4} - j\tfrac{1}{4}$$

$$\mathbf{K}_{22} = -\tfrac{1}{4}j$$

Substitution in Eq. (5-95) yields

$$\mathbf{X}(s) = \frac{-\tfrac{1}{4} + j\tfrac{1}{4}}{(s + 1 + j)^2} + \frac{\tfrac{1}{4}j}{s + 1 + j} + \frac{-\tfrac{1}{4} - j\tfrac{1}{4}}{(s + 1 - j)^2} + \frac{-\tfrac{1}{4}j}{s + 1 - j} \tag{5-99}$$

and from Table 5-1 we obtain

$$\mathcal{L}^{-1}\left[\frac{1}{(s + a)^2}\right] = u(t)te^{-at} \tag{5-100}$$

This is valid even if a is not a real number.

Thus from Eqs. (5-100) and (5-82) we have

$$x(t) = (-\tfrac{1}{4} + j\tfrac{1}{4})te^{(-1-j)t} + (-\tfrac{1}{4} - j\tfrac{1}{4})te^{(-1+j)t} + j\tfrac{1}{4}e^{(-1-j)t}$$
$$- j\tfrac{1}{4}e^{(-1+j)t} \tag{5-101}$$

and substitution of Eq. (4-58) gives us

$$x(t) = (-\tfrac{1}{4} + j\tfrac{1}{4})te^{-t}(\cos t - j \sin t) + (-\tfrac{1}{4} - j\tfrac{1}{4})te^{-t}(\cos t + j \sin t)$$
$$+ j\tfrac{1}{4}e^{-t}(\cos t - j \sin t) - j\tfrac{1}{4}e^{-t}(\cos t + j \sin t) \tag{5-102}$$

Then, combining terms, we obtain

$$x(t) = e^{-t}[\tfrac{1}{2}t(-\cos t + \sin t) + \tfrac{1}{2}\sin t] \tag{5-103}$$

Note that the solution will be real for any network, since the current and voltage are physical quantities. Thus when we have complex expressions, the imaginary terms will cancel, and we need not evaluate them. Until one has sufficient experience in doing this, however, it is advisable to write equations of the form of Eq. (5-102) before discarding the imaginary terms.

There are some relations among the constants in the partial-fraction expansion that can easily be obtained. This is often a help in evaluating some constants or in checking to see that all the constants have been properly evaluated. If all the roots of the denominator of Eq. (5-65) are simple, we have [see Eq. (5-67)]

$$\mathbf{X}(s) = \frac{\mathbf{K}_1}{s - s_1} + \frac{\mathbf{K}_2}{s - s_2} + \cdots + \frac{\mathbf{K}_n}{s - s_n}$$

Now we let s approach zero:

$$\mathbf{X}(0) = -\frac{\mathbf{K}_1}{s_1} - \frac{\mathbf{K}_2}{s_2} - \cdots - \frac{\mathbf{K}_n}{s_n}$$

This is one simple form that can be used. Let us obtain some alternative ones. Substitution of $s = 0$ in Eq. (5-65) yields

$$-\frac{\mathbf{K}_1}{s_1} - \frac{\mathbf{K}_2}{s_2} - \cdots - \frac{\mathbf{K}_n}{s_n} = \frac{a_0}{b_0}$$

From Eq. (5-69) we can write

$$\mathbf{K}_1 + \mathbf{K}_2 + \cdots + \mathbf{K}_n = \frac{a_{n-1}}{b_n}$$

Another form of this result can be obtained by multiplying both sides of Eq. (5-67) by s and then letting s approach infinity:

$$\mathbf{K}_1 + \mathbf{K}_2 + \cdots + \mathbf{K}_n = \lim_{s \to \infty} s\mathbf{X}(s)$$

If there are multiple roots in the denominator of $\mathbf{X}(s)$, a similar set of results can be obtained. For instance, consider that $\mathbf{X}(s)$ is expressed in a partial-fraction expansion of the form of Eq. (5-85). Then at $s = 0$ we have

$$\mathbf{X}(0) = \frac{\mathbf{K}_{11}}{-s_1{}^r} + \frac{\mathbf{K}_{12}}{-s_1{}^{r-1}} + \cdots + \frac{\mathbf{K}_{1r}}{-s_1} + \frac{\mathbf{K}_2}{-s_2} + \cdots + \frac{\mathbf{K}_{n-r+1}}{s_{n-r+1}}$$

Another relation can be obtained by multiplying both sides of Eq. (5-85) by s and letting s approach infinity. This yields

$$\mathbf{K}_{1r} + \mathbf{K}_2 + \cdots + \mathbf{K}_{n-r+1} = \lim_{s \to \infty} s\mathbf{X}(s)$$

In general, $\lim_{s \to \infty} s\mathbf{X}(s)$ will be the sum of the constant terms in the partial-fraction expansion whose denominators contain only the *first* power of s. This is true whether or not the denominator of $\mathbf{X}(s)$ has multiple roots.

5-4 The RLC network

As a simple example of the previous procedure let us analyze the RLC network of Fig. 5-7. This circuit was analyzed in Sec. 4-4 by classical methods. We shall now analyze it in terms of the Laplace transform. Because of the ease with which initial conditions can be handled with the Laplace transform, we shall generalize the analysis somewhat by using arbitrary initial conditions.

Loop analysis of the circuit of Fig. 5-7 yields

$$Vu(t) = Ri + L\frac{di}{dt} + \frac{1}{C}\int i\,dt \tag{5-104}$$

Taking the Laplace transform of both sides of the equation, we obtain

$$\frac{V}{s} = R\mathbf{I}(s) + L[s\mathbf{I}(s) - i(0-)] + \frac{1}{Cs}\mathbf{I}(s) + \frac{v_C(0-)}{s} \tag{5-105}$$

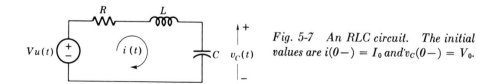

Fig. 5-7 An RLC circuit. The initial values are $i(0-) = I_0$ and $v_C(0-) = V_0$.

Substituting the initial conditions given in Fig. 5-7 and rearranging, we have

$$\frac{V - V_0}{s} + LI_0 = \left(R + Ls + \frac{1}{Cs}\right) \mathbf{I}(s) \tag{5-106a}$$

Manipulation gives us

$$\mathbf{I}(s) = \frac{V - V_0 + LI_0 s}{L[s^2 + (R/L)s + (1/LC)]} \tag{5-106b}$$

which in factored form becomes

$$\mathbf{I}(s) = \frac{V - V_0 + LI_0 s}{L(s - b_1)(s - b_2)} \tag{5-106c}$$

The roots, b_1 and b_2, are given by

$$b_1, b_2 = -\frac{R}{2L} \pm \sqrt{\left(\frac{R}{2L}\right)^2 - \frac{1}{LC}} \tag{5-107}$$

Note that this is the same as Eq. (4-138), which gives the roots of the characteristic equation. Thus we can have two real negative roots, two equal real negative roots, or two complex roots. These correspond to the cases 1, 2, and 3, which we considered in Sec. 4-4. If the roots are to be real, then $R > R_{\text{crit}}$, where [see Eq. (4-140)]

$$R_{\text{crit}} = 2\sqrt{\frac{L}{C}} \tag{5-108}$$

If we substitute the damping factor $d = R/R_{\text{crit}}$ and $\omega_0 = 1/\sqrt{LC}$, we obtain [see Eq. (4-145)]

$$b_1, b_2 = -\omega_0 d \pm \omega_0 \sqrt{d^2 - 1} \tag{5-109}$$

Then, expanding Eq. (5-106c) in partial fractions, we have

$$\mathbf{I}(s) = \frac{K_1}{s - b_1} + \frac{K_2}{s - b_2} \tag{5-110}$$

where

$$K_1 = [(s - b_1)\mathbf{I}(s)]_{s=b_1} = \frac{V - V_0 + LI_0 b_1}{L(b_1 - b_2)} \tag{5-111a}$$

Substitution of Eq. (5-109) and $\omega_0 = 1/\sqrt{LC}$ gives us

$$K_1 = \frac{V - V_0 + LI_0 b_1}{2L\omega_0 \sqrt{d^2 - 1}} \tag{5-111b}$$

Similarly,

$$K_2 = [(s - b_2)\mathbf{I}(s)]_{s=b_2} = \frac{V - V_0 + LI_0 b_2}{L(b_2 - b_1)} = \frac{V - V_0 + LI_0 b_2}{-2L\omega_0 \sqrt{d^2 - 1}} \tag{5-112}$$

Now let us consider case 1 ($d > 1$), where b_1 and b_2 are real and negative.

We use Table 5-1 to take the inverse Laplace transform of $\mathbf{I}(s)$ and substitute for K_1 and K_2.   This yields

$$i(t) = \frac{V - V_0}{2L\omega_0 \sqrt{d^2 - 1}} \exp\left(-\omega_0\, dt\right)[\exp\left(\omega_0 t \sqrt{d^2 - 1}\right)$$

$$- \exp\left(-\omega_0 t \sqrt{d^2 - 1}\right)] + \frac{I_0 \exp\left(-\omega_0\, dt\right)}{2\omega_0 \sqrt{d^2 - 1}}$$

$$\times \left[b_1 \exp\left(\omega_0 t \sqrt{d^2 - 1}\right) - b_2 \exp\left(-\omega_0 t \sqrt{d^2 - 1}\right)\right] \quad (5\text{-}113)$$

Comparison with Eq. (4-154) shows that the results are the same [note that Eq. (4-154) is derived on the assumption that V_0 and I_0 are zero].

In case 3 $(d < 1)$ Eq. (5-113) still applies, but now each square root is complex.   Thus substitution and application of Euler's relation [Eq. (4-58)] gives us

$$i(t) = \frac{V - V_0}{j2L\omega_0 \sqrt{1 - d^2}} e^{-\omega_0\, dt} 2j \sin \omega_0 t \sqrt{1 - d^2} + \frac{I_0 e^{-\omega_0\, dt}}{j2\omega_0 \sqrt{1 - d^2}}$$

$$\times \left[(-\omega_0 d + j\omega_0 \sqrt{1 - d^2})\,(\cos \omega_0 t \sqrt{1 - d^2} + j \sin \omega_0 t \sqrt{1 - d^2})\right.$$

$$\left. - (-\omega_0 d - j\omega_0 \sqrt{1 - d^2})\,(\cos \omega_0 t \sqrt{1 - d^2} - j \sin \omega_0 t \sqrt{1 - d^2})\right]$$

After manipulating, we have

$$i(t) = \frac{V - V_0}{L\omega_0 \sqrt{1 - d^2}} e^{-\omega_0\, dt} \sin \omega_0 t \sqrt{1 - d^2}$$

$$+ \frac{I_0 e^{-\omega_0\, dt}}{\omega_0 \sqrt{1 - d^2}}\left(-\omega_0 d \sin \omega_0 t \sqrt{1 - d^2} + \omega_0 \sqrt{1 - d^2} \cos \omega_0 t \sqrt{1 - d^2}\right)$$

$$(5\text{-}114)$$

Now let us consider case 2.   In this case $d = 1$, and the two roots are equal. We have [see Eq. (5-109)]

$$d_1 = d_2 = -\omega_0 \qquad\qquad\qquad\qquad\qquad\qquad (5\text{-}115)$$

and Eq. (5-106c) becomes

$$\mathbf{I}(s) = \frac{V - V_0 + LI_0 s}{L(s + \omega_0)^2} \qquad\qquad\qquad\qquad\qquad (5\text{-}116)$$

This is the multiple-root case.   Expanding in partial fractions, we obtain

$$\mathbf{I}(s) = \frac{K_1}{(s + \omega_0)^2} + \frac{K_2}{s + \omega_0} \qquad\qquad\qquad\qquad (5\text{-}117)$$

Then

$$\mathbf{K}_1 = [(s - \omega_0)^2 \mathbf{I}(s)]_{s=-\omega_0} = \frac{V - V_0 + LI_0 s}{L}\bigg|_{s=-\omega_0} = \frac{V - V_0 - I_0 R/2}{L}$$

$$(5\text{-}118)$$

Note that $\omega_0 = 1/\sqrt{LC}$ and that in this case $R = R_{\text{crit}} = 2\sqrt{L/C}$ [see Eq.

(5-108)]. To obtain K_2 we use the relation

$$K_2 = \frac{d}{ds}\,[(s - \omega_0)^2 \mathbf{I}(s)]_{s=-\omega_0} = I_0 \tag{5-119}$$

Thus

$$\mathbf{I}(s) = \frac{V - V_0 - I_0 R/2}{L}\,\frac{1}{(s + \omega_0)^2} + \frac{I_0}{s + \omega_0} \tag{5-120}$$

The inverse Laplace transform is, from Table 5-1,

$$i(t) = \frac{V - V_0 - I_0 R}{L}\,te^{-\omega_0 t} + I_0 e^{-\omega_0 t} \tag{5-121}$$

Typical examples of the responses of cases 1, 2, and 3 are given in Sec. 4-4.

Note that these solutions are far less tedious to obtain than those in Sec. 4-4. Moreover, a more general case is considered here, where the Laplace transform allows us to include arbitrary initial conditions.

5-5   Transformed networks and initial-condition generators

We have thus far applied the Laplace transform to the analysis of simple networks. Before we consider general loop, nodal, or cut-set analyses, let us discuss some further simplifying procedures.

Consider the voltage drop across single inductance, which is part of a network. Such an inductance is shown in Fig. 5-8a. The voltage drop across it is given by

$$v_L(t) = L\,\frac{di}{dt} \tag{5-122}$$

In any loop analysis it is the $v_L(t)$ term that appears in the equations. As discussed in Sec. 2-4, any circuit that produces the same $v_L(t)$ in response to the same current and initial conditions is equivalent to the inductance. Furthermore, two functions that have the same Laplace transforms are essentially equal. Thus a circuit which has the same Laplace transform of the voltage in response to the current as does the actual network can be considered equivalent to the actual network. The Laplace transform of Eq. (5-122) yields

$$\mathbf{V}_L(s) = Ls\mathbf{I}(s) - Li(0-) \tag{5-123}$$

where

$$\mathcal{L}[v_L(t)] = \mathbf{V}_L(s)$$
$$\mathcal{L}[i(t)] = \mathbf{I}(s)$$

Now consider the circuit of Fig. 5-8b. This is called the *transformed form* of the circuit of Fig. 5-8a, since we have taken the Laplace transform of the

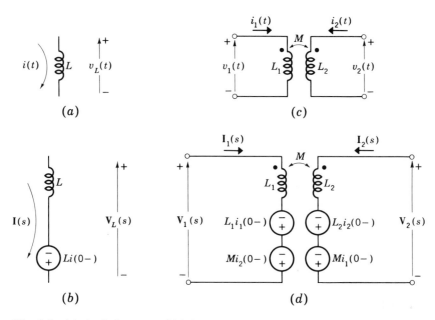

Fig. 5-8 (a) *An inductance which is part of a network;* (b) *a transformed form of this inductance;* (c) *a pair of coupled coils that are part of a network;* (d) *a transformed form of this network.*

voltage and current of Fig. 5-8a. A voltage generator $Li(0-)$, corresponding to the initial current term of Eq. (5-123), has been added to this network. We wish the network of Fig. 5-8b to produce the transformed equation, Eq. (5-123), directly. This is possible if we adopt the convention that *the Laplace transform of the voltage drop across an inductance, with zero initial current, is given by the product of the Laplace transform of the current and Ls.* The inductance in the transformed network is assumed to have zero initial current. If the actual inductance has an initial current, as it does in this case, then we add a voltage generator $Li(0-)$ in series with the inductance. This produces the proper transformed equation.

In other words, to obtain a network that relates the Laplace transforms of the voltage across an inductance and the current through it, we draw a network consisting of the series interconnection of the inductor and a voltage generator of voltage $Li(0-)$. The voltage drop across the "inductance part" of the transformed network is given by $Ls\mathbf{I}(s)$. Then the voltage drop across the entire equivalent transformed inductance is given by Eq. (5-123).

The circuit of Fig. 5-8a and Eq. (5-122) are said to be in the *time domain*, since they relate a voltage and a current as functions of time. On the other hand, the circuit of Fig. 5-8b and Eq. (5-123) are said to be in the *Laplace transform domain* (or simply, the *transform domain*), since they relate the

Laplace transform of a voltage and a current.   The network in the transform domain is called a *transformed network*.

In the transformed network we have produced the effect of an initial condition by means of a voltage generator.   This is called an *initial-condition generator*.   Once this convenient device has been included, we do not have to consider initial conditions any further.   *They will automatically be taken care of by the initial-condition generator.*   This procedure is especially helpful in loop analysis when there is more than one loop current in the inductance.

We can also use initial-condition generators when there are mutual inductances in the circuit.   For instance, consider Fig. 5-8c.   In the time domain

$$v_1(t) = L_1 \frac{di_1}{dt} + M \frac{di_2}{dt}$$

$$v_2(t) = M \frac{di_1}{dt} + L_2 \frac{di_2}{dt}$$

The Laplace transform of these equations yields

$$\mathbf{V}_1(s) = Ls\mathbf{I}_1(s) - Li_1(0-) + Ms\mathbf{I}_2(s) - Mi_2(0-) \qquad (5\text{-}124a)$$

$$\mathbf{V}_2(s) = Ms\mathbf{I}_1(s) - Mi_1(0-) + L_2s\mathbf{I}_2(s) - L_2i_2(0-) \qquad (5\text{-}124b)$$

Now consider the circuit of Fig. 5-8d, which is the transformed form of the circuit of Fig. 5-8c.   Initial-condition generators for each of the inductors (see Fig. 5-8b) have been included.   In addition, initial-condition generators corresponding to $Mi_1(0-)$ and $Mi_2(0-)$ have been included.   The network of Fig. 5-8d will produce the transformed equations of Eqs. (5-124) directly if we use the convention we have established for the Laplace transform of the voltage across the inductance, and also add the convention that *the Laplace transform of the mutual-inductance term in each coil of a pair of coupled coils, with zero initial conditions, is given by Ms times the Laplace transform of the current in the other coil.*   As before, initial conditions are accounted for by the initial-condition generators.   If the position of one of the dots is changed, then we replace M by $-M$ in the above equations and in Fig. 5-8d.   If more than two coils are coupled together, these results can be extended by considering one pair of coupled coils at a time.

Now let us consider the capacitor of Fig. 5-9a and obtain its transformed

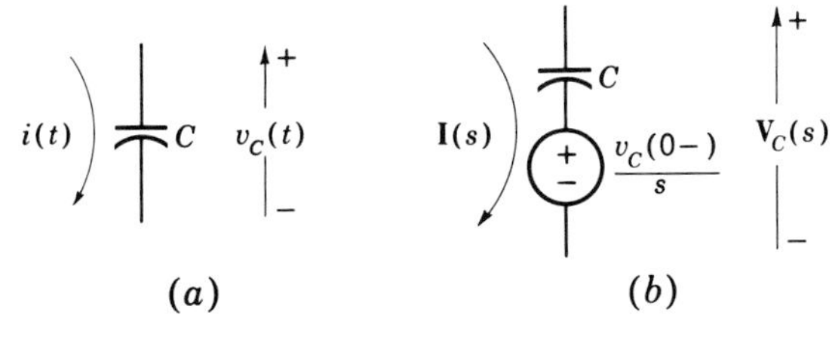

Fig. 5-9   (a) A capacitance that is part of a network; (b) a transformed form of this capacitance.

(a) (b)

network.   The voltage drop across the capacitance is given by

$$v_c(t) = \frac{1}{C} \int i \, dt \tag{5-125}$$

We take the Laplace transform of this equation,

$$\mathbf{V}_c(s) = \frac{\mathbf{I}(s)}{Cs} + \frac{v_c(0-)}{s} \tag{5-126}$$

where, as usual, the boldface capital letters represent the Laplace transforms of the corresponding quantities represented by lowercase letters.

Now consider the transformed network of Fig. 5-9b, which we shall use to obtain Eq. (5-126).   The initial-voltage term of Eq. (5-126) is accounted for by the voltage generator $v(0-)/s$.   This is the initial-condition generator for the capacitor.   To obtain the correct expression for $\mathbf{V}_C(s)$ we adopt the convention that *the Laplace transform of the voltage drop across a capacitor, with zero initial voltage, is given by the product of the Laplace transform of the current through it and $1/Cs$.*   The capacitor in the transformed network is assumed to have zero initial voltage.   If the actual capacitor has an initial voltage across it, then its effect is taken into account by the initial-condition generator.

Let us apply these transformed networks to the simple RLC network of Fig. 5-7.   We shall replace the inductor and capacitor of this network by their transformed forms.   In addition, let us replace the voltage generator by one whose voltage is the Laplace transform of the given voltage generator.   Such a network is shown in Fig. 5-10.   We write the loop equation for this network, using the rules that we have discussed in this section, and obtain

$$\frac{V}{s} = R\mathbf{I}(s) + Ls\mathbf{I}(s) - Li(0-) + \frac{1}{Cs}\mathbf{I}(s) + \frac{v_C(0-)}{s} \tag{5-127}$$

We see that this is identical with Eq. (5-105).

In general, to form a complete transformed network we replace inductors and capacitors with the circuits of Figs. 5-8b and 5-9b, respectively.   Any independent generators are replaced by their Laplace transforms.   The variables in any dependent generators are also replaced by their Laplace

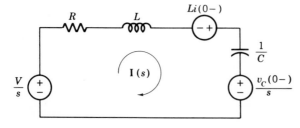

Fig.   5-10   The   transformed form of Fig. 5-7.

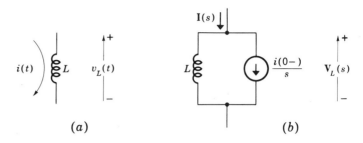

Fig. 5-11   *(a) An inductor that is part of a network; (b) a transformed form of this inductance.*

transforms. This is because in taking the Laplace transforms of the integral-differential equations of network analysis the generator terms are just replaced by their Laplace transforms. We shall discuss these concepts further in the next section.

The transformed form of the network in Figs. 5-8*b* and 5-9*b* is *completely general* and can be used in any loop, nodal, or cut-set analysis. However, in nodal or cut-set analysis it is more convenient to express the initial-condition generators as current generators. Let us now do this. Consider the circuit of Fig. 5-11*a*. The current through the inductor in terms of the voltage drop across it is

$$i(t) = \frac{1}{L} \int v_L \, dt \tag{5-128}$$

The Laplace transform of this equation yields

$$\mathbf{I}(s) = \frac{\mathbf{V}_L(s)}{Ls} + \frac{i(0-)}{s} \tag{5-129}$$

Note that

$$i(t) = \frac{1}{L} \int_{-\infty}^{t} v_L \, dt \tag{5-130}$$

and at $t = 0-$ the initial value of the integral is $\int_{-\infty}^{0-} v_L(t) \, dt$. Dividing this by L, we obtain $i(0-)$, which is the value substituted in Eq. (5-129).

Now consider the network of Fig. 5-11*b*, which includes an initial-condition current generator. Note that $\mathbf{I}(s)$ is the sum of the current generator $i(0-)/s$ and $\mathbf{V}_L(s)/Ls$. To obtain the correct current through the inductance we need only use the convention for the transform of the voltage drop across an inductance, which can also be stated in the following way: *the Laplace transform of the current through an inductance, with zero initial current, is given by the product of the Laplace transform of the voltage across it and $1/Ls$.* The transformed

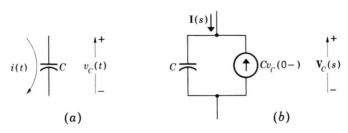

Fig. 5-12   (a) A capacitor that is part of a network; (b) a transformed form of this capacitor.

inductance does not have any initial conditions; they are accounted for by
using an initial-condition generator.   Application of this convention to Fig.
5-11b then gives us Eq. (5-129).   Thus we have a valid representation of the
transformed network.

It should be emphasized that Figs. 5-8b and 5-11b are completely compatible
and general.   However, Fig. 5-8b is more convenient to use with loop analysis
and Fig. 5-11b is more convenient to use with nodal or cut-set analysis.

If nodal analysis is to be applied to circuits with coupled coils, then we set
up the equations as discussed in Sec. 3-4 and take their transforms.   The
equivalent circuit of Fig. 3-22b can be used if there are zero initial conditions.

Now let us obtain a transformed network for the capacitor whose initial-
condition generator is a current generator.   Consider Fig. 5-12a.   The current
in terms of the voltage drop is

$$i(t) = C \frac{dv_c}{dt} \tag{5-131}$$

Taking the Laplace transform of this equation, we obtain

$$\mathbf{I}(s) = Cs\mathbf{V}_c(s) - Cv_c(0-) \tag{5-132}$$

The network of Fig. 5-12b includes an initial-current generator.   The current
$\mathbf{I}(s)$ is the sum of the current through the capacitor and the generator current,
$-Cv_c(0-)$.   To obtain the correct current through the capacitor we need only
restate the convention for the voltage drop across the capacitor as follows:
*the Laplace transform of the current through a capacitance, with zero initial voltage,
is given by the product of the Laplace transform of the voltage across it and Cs.*
As before, the transformed capacitor has zero initial voltage across it, and the
initial conditions are accounted for by an initial-condition generator.   Applying these comments to Fig. 5-12b, we obtain Eq. (5-132).   Hence we have a
valid representation of the transformed network.

Figures 5-9b and 5-12b are both general.   It is more convenient to use
Fig. 5-9b with loop analysis and Fig. 5-12b with nodal or cut-set analysis.

5-6 Use of the Laplace transform in mesh, nodal, and cut-set analysis

In applying Laplace transform techniques to mesh, nodal, or cut-set analysis we can replace the given network by its transformed form. Then we use the rules of the last section to write the Laplace transform of the circuit equations directly. We shall illustrate this with several examples.

Consider the mesh analysis of the circuit of Fig. 5-13*a*. The transformed form of this network is given in Fig. 5-13*b*, with each inductor and capacitor replaced by the circuits of Figs. 5-8*b* and 5-9*b*, respectively. The generator voltages and the loop currents are replaced by their Laplace transforms. These are known quantities in the case of the generator voltages and unknowns in the case of the currents. We now apply the rules of loop analysis developed in Chap. 3 to this network. The voltage drop across the resistors, inductors,

Fig. 5-13   (a) *A three-loop network, with initial conditions given by* $i_a(0-)$, $i_b(0-)$, $v_{ab}(0-)$, *and* $v_{cd}(0-)$; (b) *the transformed form of this network.*

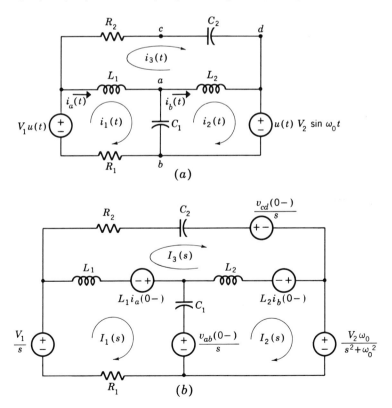

and capacitors in the transform domain are given by $R\mathbf{I}(s)$, $Ls\mathbf{I}(s)$ and $(1/Cs)\mathbf{I}(s)$, respectively (see Sec. 5-5). The voltage drop across a resistor is $Ri(t)$, and its Laplace transform is $R\mathbf{I}(s)$. The initial-condition generators are treated just as though they were independent generators. Thus we obtain

$$\frac{V_1}{s} + L_1 i_a(0-) - \frac{v_{ab}(0-)}{s} = \left(R_1 + L_1 + \frac{1}{C_1 s}\right)\mathbf{I}_1(s)$$

$$- \frac{1}{C_1 s}\mathbf{I}_2(s) - L_1 s \mathbf{I}_3(s) \quad (5\text{-}133a)$$

$$\frac{v_{ab}(0-)}{s} + L_2 i_b(0-) - \frac{V_2 \omega_0}{s^2 + \omega_0{}^2} = -\frac{1}{C_1 s}\mathbf{I}_1(s)$$

$$+ \left(L_2 S + \frac{1}{C_1 s}\right)\mathbf{I}_2(s) - L_2 s \mathbf{I}_3(s) \quad (5\text{-}133b)$$

$$- L_1 i_a(0-) - \frac{v_{cd}(0-)}{s} - L_2 i_b(0-) = -L_1 s \mathbf{I}_1(s) - L_2 s \mathbf{I}_2(s)$$

$$+ \left(R_2 + L_1 s + L_2 s + \frac{1}{C_2 s}\right)\mathbf{I}_3(s) \quad (5\text{-}133c)$$

Hence with the transformed network the simultaneous equations can be written directly in Laplace transform form. We shall consider the actual solution of these equations in the next section.

The use of the transformed network eliminates some tedious operations. For example, consider the integral-differential equations for the network of Fig. 5-12a:

$$u(t)V_1 = \left(R_1 + L_1 p + \frac{1}{C_1 p}\right)i_1 - \frac{1}{C_1 p} i_2 - L_1 p i_3 \quad (5\text{-}134a)$$

$$-u(t)V_2 \sin \omega_0 t = -\frac{1}{C_1 p} i_1 + \left(L_2 p + \frac{1}{C_1 p}\right)i_2 - L_2 p i_3 \quad (5\text{-}134b)$$

$$0 = -L_1 p i_1 - L_2 p i_2 + \left(R_2 + L_1 p + L_2 p + \frac{1}{C_2 p}\right)i_3 \quad (5\text{-}134c)$$

Taking the Laplace transform of these equations, we obtain

$$\frac{V_1}{s} = \left(R_1 + L_1 s + \frac{1}{C_1 s}\right)\mathbf{I}_1(s) - L_1 i_1(0-) + \frac{1}{C_1 s}\int_{-\infty}^{0-} i_1 \, dt$$

$$- \frac{1}{C_1 s}\mathbf{I}_2(s) - \frac{1}{C_1 s}\int_{-\infty}^{0-} i_2 \, dt - L_1 s \mathbf{I}_3(s) + L_1 i_3(0-) \quad (5\text{-}135a)$$

$$-\frac{V_2 \omega_0}{s^2 + \omega_0{}^2} = -\frac{1}{C_1 s}\mathbf{I}_1(s) - \frac{1}{C_1 s}\int_{-\infty}^{0-} i_1 \, dt + \left(L_2 s + \frac{1}{C_1 s}\right)\mathbf{I}_2(s)$$

$$- L_2 i_2(0-) + \frac{1}{C_1 s}\int_{-\infty}^{0-} i_2 \, dt - L_2 s \mathbf{I}_3(s) + L_2 i_3(0-) \quad (5\text{-}135b)$$

$$0 = -L_1 s \mathbf{I}_1(s) + L_1 i_1(0-) - L_2 s \mathbf{I}_2(s) + L_2 i_2(0-)$$

$$+ \left(R_2 + L_1 s + L_2 s + \frac{1}{C_2 s}\right)\mathbf{I}_3(s) - L_1 i_3(0-) - L_2 i_3(0-)$$

$$+ \frac{1}{C_2 s}\int_{-\infty}^{0-} i_3 \, dt \quad (5\text{-}135c)$$

The initial conditions are not in the form of the given initial conditions. Let us make some substitutions to rectify this:

$$i_a(t) = i_1(t) - i_3(t) \tag{5-136a}$$

$$i_b(t) = i_2(t) - i_3(t) \tag{5-136b}$$

$$v_{ab}(t) = \frac{1}{C_1} \int_{-\infty}^{t} [i_1(t) - i_2(t)] \, dt \tag{5-136c}$$

$$v_{cd}(t) = \frac{1}{C_2} \int_{-\infty}^{t} i_3(t) \, dt \tag{5-136d}$$

When Eqs. (5-136), with $t = 0-$, are substituted into Eqs. (5-135) and are manipulated, Eqs. (5-134) result. Note that use of the transformed networks eliminates the unnecessary tedium entailed in the use of Eqs. (5-135) and (5-136).

Compare Eqs. (5-134) with Eqs. (5-133). The differential equations written in operator form are similar to those in Laplace transform form. Note that in Eqs. (5-133) the Laplace transform variable s has replaced p, the differential operator. In addition, the initial-condition terms are added, and the transforms of the generator voltages are taken in the Laplace transform case.

As an example of nodal analysis, consider the circuit of Fig. 5-14a. The transformed form of this circuit is given in Fig. 5-14b, with current generators as the initial-condition generators. These are obtained from Figs. 5-11b and 5-12b. The Laplace transforms of the currents through a resistance, inductance, and capacitance in terms of the Laplace transform voltage across them are given by $G_1 V(s)$, $(1/Ls) V(s)$, and $Cs V(s)$, respectively. With this transformation we can write the nodal equations in transformed form as

$$\frac{I_1}{s} - \frac{i_a(0-)}{s} - \frac{i_b(0-)}{s} - \frac{1}{s+a} = \left(G_1 + \frac{1}{L_1 s} + \frac{1}{L_2 s} \right) V_1(s)$$
$$- \frac{1}{L_1 s} V_2(s) - \frac{1}{L_2 s} V_3(s) \tag{5-137a}$$

$$\frac{i_a(0-)}{s} + C_1 v_2(0-) = -\frac{1}{L_1 s} V_1(s) + \left(\frac{1}{L_1 s} + C_1 s + G_2 \right) V_2(s) - G_2 V_3(s)$$
$$\tag{5-137b}$$

$$\frac{I_2 s}{s^2 + \omega_0{}^2} + \frac{i_b(0-)}{s} + \frac{1}{s+a} + C_2 v_3(0-) = -\frac{1}{L_2 s} V_1(s) - G_2 V_2(s)$$
$$+ \left(G_2 + C_2 s + \frac{1}{L_2 s} \right) V_3(s) \tag{5-137c}$$

We shall consider the solution of these equations in the next section.

Now let us apply cut-set analysis to the network of Fig. 5-14. We shall work with the transformed network of Fig. 5-15, where a valid set of cut sets is indicated. As an aid in visualizing the cut sets the network of Fig. 5-14b is redrawn with the nodes clearly indicated (the reader should practice obtaining valid sets of cut sets from Fig. 5-14b without looking at Fig. 5-15). Writing

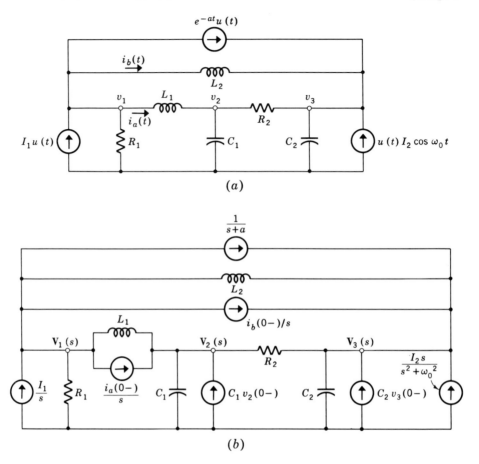

Fig. 5-14 (a) *A three-node network, with initial conditions given by* $i_a(0-)$, $i_b(0-)$, $v_2(0-)$, *and* $v_3(0-)$; (b) *the transformed form of this network.*

cut-set equations for the network of Fig. 5-15, we obtain

$$\frac{I_1}{s} - \frac{1}{s+a} - \frac{i_b(0-)}{s} - \frac{i_a(0-)}{s} = \left(G_1 + \frac{1}{L_1 s} + \frac{1}{L_2 s}\right) \mathbf{V}_{c1}(s)$$

$$+ \left(\frac{1}{L_2 s} + G_1\right) \mathbf{V}_{c2}(s) - \frac{1}{L_2 s} \mathbf{V}_{c3}(s) \quad (5\text{-}138a)$$

$$\frac{I_1}{s} - \frac{1}{s+a} - \frac{i_b(0-)}{s} + C_1 v_2(0-) = \left(\frac{1}{L_2 s} + G_1\right) \mathbf{V}_{c1}(s)$$

$$+ \left(\frac{1}{L_2 s} + G_1 + G_2 + C_1 s\right) \mathbf{V}_{c2}(s) - \left(\frac{1}{L_2 s} + G_2\right) \mathbf{V}_{c3}(s) \quad (5\text{-}138b)$$

$$\frac{i_b(0-)}{s} + \frac{1}{s+a} + \frac{I_2 s}{s^2 + \omega_0^2} + C_2 v_3(0-) = -\frac{1}{L_2 s} \mathbf{V}_{c1}(s)$$

$$- \left(\frac{1}{L_2 s} + G_2\right) \mathbf{V}_{c2}(s) + \left(\frac{1}{L_2 s} + G_2 + C_2 s\right) \mathbf{V}_{c3}(s) \quad (5\text{-}138c)$$

In general, as we have observed for loop analysis, the equations written in operator notation are similar to the Laplace transform forms.   They can be obtained from the Laplace transform forms by substituting the operator p for s and removing the initial-condition terms.   This can be obtained from the relations for the transforms of the derivative and the integral [see Eqs. (5-33) and (5-53)].   Differentiation results in multiplication by s, and integration results in division by s.   Similarly, differentiation is *indicated* by multiplying by p, and integration is *indicated* by division by p.   The generator terms are replaced by their transforms in the Laplace transform case.

As a final example let us analyze Fig. 5-16a, which includes a dependent generator.   The transformed network is shown in Fig. 5-16b.   Note that we have taken the Laplace transforms of all generator quantities, including the dependent generator.   Loop analysis then yields

$$\frac{1}{s+1} + Li_a(0-) = (R_1 + L_1 s)\mathbf{I}_1(s) - L_1 s \mathbf{I}_2(s) - R_1 \mathbf{I}_3(s) \qquad (5\text{-}139a)$$

$$-Li_a(0-) - \frac{v_{ac}(0-)}{s} - \mu \mathbf{V}_{ab}(s) = -L_1 s \mathbf{I}_1(s)$$
$$+ \left(L_1 s + \frac{1}{C_1 s} \right) \mathbf{I}_2(s) - \frac{1}{C_1 s} \mathbf{I}_3(s) \quad (5\text{-}139b)$$

$$\frac{v_{ac}(0-)}{s} = -R_1 \mathbf{I}_1(s) - \frac{1}{C_1 s} \mathbf{I}_2(s) + \left(R_1 + R_2 + \frac{1}{C_1 s} \right) \mathbf{I}_3(s) \qquad (5\text{-}139c)$$

Fig. 5-15   The network of Fig. 5-14b redrawn.   A set of basic cut sets are marked.   The tree chosen consists of branches L_1, R_2, and C_2.

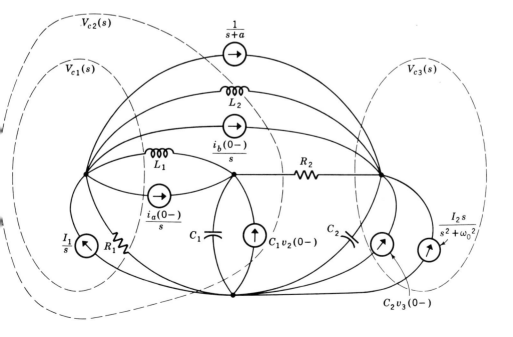

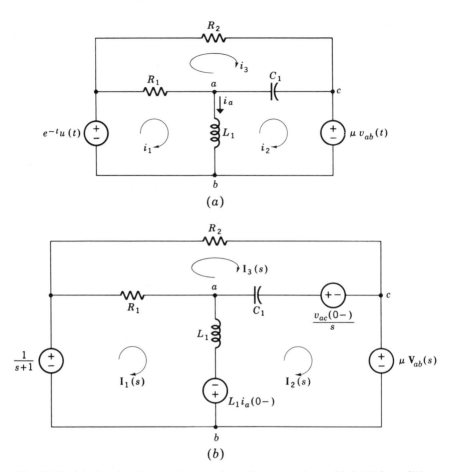

Fig. 5-16   (a) A network containing a dependent generator, with initial conditions $i_a(0-)$ and $v_{ac}(0-)$; (b) the transformed form of this network.

Now we must evaluate $\mathbf{V}_{ab}(s)$ in terms of known quantities or unknown currents.   From Fig. 5-16b we have

$$\mathbf{V}_{ab}(s) = L_1 s[\mathbf{I}_1(s) - \mathbf{I}_2(s)] - L_1 i_a(0-) \tag{5-140}$$

and substitution into Eqs. (5-139) yields

$$\frac{1}{s+1} + L i_a(0-) = (R_1 + L_1 s)\mathbf{I}_1(s) - L_1 s \mathbf{I}_2(s) - R_1 \mathbf{I}_3(s) \tag{5-141a}$$

$$-L i_a(0-)(1-\mu) - \frac{v_{ac}(0-)}{s} = -L_1 s(1-\mu)\mathbf{I}_1(s)$$

$$+ \left[L_1(1-\mu)s + \frac{1}{C_1 s} \right] \mathbf{I}_2(s) - \frac{1}{C_1 s} \mathbf{I}_3(s) \tag{5-141b}$$

$$\frac{v_{ac}(0-)}{s} = -R_1 \mathbf{I}_1(s) - \frac{1}{C_1 s} \mathbf{I}_2(s) + \left(R_1 + R_2 + \frac{1}{C_1 s} \right) \mathbf{I}_3(s) \tag{5-141c}$$

These equations are now in a form that is suitable for solution.

5-7   Solution of simultaneous equations in Laplace transform form

The simultaneous equations of loop, nodal, or cut-set analysis in Laplace transform form are simultaneous algebraic equations; thus the analysis of Sec. 3-9 is applicable. That is, we can solve these equations for any one unknown transformed quantity by Cramer's rule. As an illustration, consider a typical set of simultaneous equations of the form

$$\mathbf{Y}_1(s) = \left(\alpha_{11}s + \beta_{11} + \frac{\gamma_{11}}{s}\right)\mathbf{X}_1(s) + \left(\alpha_{12}s + \beta_{12} + \frac{\gamma_{12}}{s}\right)\mathbf{X}_2(s)$$
$$+ \cdots + \left(\alpha_{1n}s + \beta_{1n} + \frac{\gamma_{1n}}{s}\right)\mathbf{X}_n(s)$$

$$\mathbf{Y}_2(s) = \left(\alpha_{21}s + \beta_{21} + \frac{\gamma_{21}}{s}\right)\mathbf{X}_1(s) + \left(\alpha_{22}s + \beta_{22} + \frac{\gamma_{22}}{s}\right)\mathbf{X}_2(s)$$
$$+ \cdots + \left(\alpha_{2n}s + \beta_{2n} + \frac{\gamma_{2n}}{s}\right)\mathbf{X}_n(s) \qquad (5\text{-}142)$$

$$\cdots \cdots \cdots \cdots \cdots$$

$$\mathbf{Y}_n(s) = \left(\alpha_{n1}s + \beta_{n1} + \frac{\gamma_{n1}}{s}\right)\mathbf{X}_1(s) + \left(\alpha_{n2}s + \beta_{n2} + \frac{\gamma_{n2}}{s}\right)\mathbf{X}_2(s)$$
$$+ \cdots + \left(\alpha_{nn}s + \beta_{nn} + \frac{\gamma_{nn}}{s}\right)\mathbf{X}_n(s)$$

The terms $\mathbf{Y}_1(s)$, $\mathbf{Y}_2(s)$, . . . , $\mathbf{Y}_n(s)$ represent the sums of the Laplace transforms of known generator quantities. These generators are either actual generators or initial-condition generators. The terms $\mathbf{X}_1(s)$, $\mathbf{X}_2(s)$, . . . , $\mathbf{X}_n(s)$ are the Laplace transforms of the unknowns (unknown currents in the case of loop analysis and unknown voltages in the case of nodal or cut-set analysis). The α, β, and γ terms are functions of the elements of the network [see Eqs. (5-133), (5-137), and (5-138)].

Now let us consider the solution of Eqs. (5-142). We first set up the characteristic determinant

$$\Delta = \begin{vmatrix} \alpha_{11}s + \beta_{11} + \dfrac{\gamma_{11}}{s} & \alpha_{12}s + \beta_{12} + \dfrac{\gamma_{12}}{s} & \cdots & \alpha_{1n}s + \beta_{1n} + \dfrac{\gamma_{1n}}{s} \\ \alpha_{21}s + \beta_{21} + \dfrac{\gamma_{21}}{s} & \alpha_{22}s + \beta_{22} + \dfrac{\gamma_{22}}{s} & \cdots & \alpha_{2n}s + \beta_{2n} + \dfrac{\gamma_{2n}}{s} \\ \cdots \cdots \cdots & & & \cdots \cdots \\ \alpha_{n1}s + \beta_{n1} + \dfrac{\gamma_{n1}}{s} & \alpha_{n2}s + \beta_{n2} + \dfrac{\gamma_{n2}}{s} & \cdots & \alpha_{nn}s + \beta_{nn} + \dfrac{\gamma_{nn}}{s} \end{vmatrix}$$

$$(5\text{-}143)$$

This determinant and its cofactors are evaluated in accordance with the rules presented in Sec. 3-9.

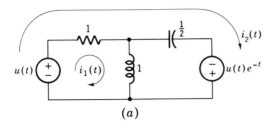

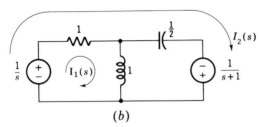

Fig. 5-17 (a) A two-loop network, with the initial current in the inductor and the initial voltage across the capacitor both zero; (b) the transformed form of this network.

We can evaluate the unknowns by means of Cramer's rule [see Eq. (3-90)]. Then, rewriting this, we have

$$\mathbf{X}_k(s) = \frac{\Delta_{1k}\mathbf{Y}_1(s) + \Delta_{2k}\mathbf{Y}_2(s) + \cdots + \Delta_{nk}\mathbf{Y}_n(s)}{\Delta} \qquad k = 1, 2, \ldots, n$$

$$(5\text{-}144)$$

The determinant and its cofactor are made up of products and sums of terms of the form $\alpha s + \beta + \gamma/s$. Each $\mathbf{Y}_k(s)$ is also the ratio of polynomials in s. Thus, by multiplying the numerator and denominator by the appropriate polynomial factors, we can express $\mathbf{X}_k(s)$ as the ratio of two polynomials in s; that is,

$$\mathbf{X}_k(s) = \frac{a_m s^m + a_{m-1} s^{m-1} + \cdots + a_1 s + a_0}{b_n s^n + b_{n-1} s^{n-1} + \cdots + b_1 s + b_0} \qquad (5\text{-}145)$$

Then $\mathbf{X}_k(t)$ can be evaluated by taking the inverse Laplace transform according to the partial-fraction-expansion techniques of Sec. 5-3.

As an example of this procedure let us obtain the currents in the network of Fig. 5-17. This is the same network that was analyzed in Sec. 4-6 and will illustrate the advantages of the Laplace transform over the classical method. We start with loop-analysis equations for Fig. 5-17b,

$$\frac{1}{s} = (1 + s)\mathbf{I}_1(s) + \mathbf{I}_2(s) \qquad (5\text{-}146a)$$

$$\frac{1}{s} + \frac{1}{s+1} = \mathbf{I}_1(s) + \left(1 + \frac{2}{s}\right)\mathbf{I}_2(s) \qquad (5\text{-}146b)$$

The determinant is

$$\Delta = \begin{vmatrix} 1+s & 1 \\ 1 & 1+\dfrac{2}{s} \end{vmatrix} = s + 2 + \frac{2}{s} = \frac{s^2 + 2s + 2}{s} \tag{5-147}$$

Then

$$\mathbf{I}_1(s) = \frac{1/s + 2/s^2 - 1/s - 1/(s+1)}{\Delta} \tag{5-148a}$$

Manipulating and clearing fractions, we obtain

$$\mathbf{I}_1(s) = \frac{-s^2 + 2s + 2}{s(s+1)(s^2 + 2s + 2)} = \frac{-s^2 + 2s + 2}{s(s+1)(s+1+j)(s+1-j)} \tag{5-148b}$$

Partial-fraction expansion then yields

$$\mathbf{I}_1(s) = \frac{1}{s} + \frac{1}{s+1} + \frac{-1-j}{s+1+j} + \frac{-1+j}{s+1-j} \tag{5-148c}$$

We use Table 5-1 to take the inverse Laplace transform,

$$i_1(t) = u(t)[1 + e^{-t} + (-1-j)e^{-t}e^{-jt} + (-1+j)e^{-t}e^{jt}] \tag{5-149}$$

and, after applying Euler's relation and combining terms, we have

$$i_1(t) = u(t)[1 + e^{-t}(1 - 2\cos t - 2\sin t)] \tag{5-150}$$

To obtain $i_2(t)$ we again apply Cramer's rule to Eqs. (5-146). This yields

$$\mathbf{I}_2(s) = \frac{-1/s + (1+s)[1/s + 1/(s+1)]}{\Delta} \tag{5-151a}$$

Substituting Eq. (5-147) and manipulating, we obtain

$$\mathbf{I}_2(s) = \frac{2s}{s^2 + 2s + 2} = \frac{2s}{(s+1+j)(s+1-j)} \tag{5-151b}$$

and partial-fraction expansion gives us

$$\mathbf{I}_2(s) = \frac{1-j}{s+1+j} + \frac{1+j}{s+1-j} \tag{5-151c}$$

From Table 5-1 we obtain

$$i_2(t) = (1-j)e^{-t}e^{-jt} + (1+j)e^{-t}e^{jt} \tag{5-152a}$$

and, after applying Euler's relation and manipulating, we finally have

$$i_2(t) = 2e^{-t}(\cos t - \sin t)u(t) \tag{5-152b}$$

Compare this example with that of Sec. 4-6 and note the great reduction in work when the Laplace transform is used instead of classical procedures.

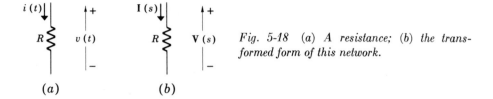

Fig. 5-18   (*a*) *A resistance;* (*b*) *the trans-formed form of this network.*

5-8   Impedance and admittance

The voltage across a resistance and the current through it have the same waveform.   Hence we can define the resistance as the ratio of the voltage to the current (see Sec. 1-4).   For instance, in Fig. 5-18*a*

$$R = \frac{v(t)}{i(t)} \qquad\qquad (5\text{-}153)$$

Again, note that this ratio is constant; *it is not a function of time, even though v and i may be functions of time.*   It is also important to note that this ratio is *independent* of both the voltage and the current.   In the transformed domain we can write

$$R = \frac{\mathbf{V}(s)}{\mathbf{I}(s)} \qquad\qquad (5\text{-}154)$$

The concept of a parameter that relates the voltage across an element to the current through it by a ratio which is not a function either of time or of the voltage and current is a useful one.   (In the next sections we shall see some of these uses.)   However, we cannot obtain such a ratio for inductance or capacitance, since the ratio of the voltage across them to the current through them does vary with time.   For instance, in an inductance

$$v = L\frac{di}{dt} \qquad\qquad (5\text{-}155)$$

For example if $i = t$, then $v = L$, and then this ratio is not constant.   Note that the ratio of v to i must be independent of time for *all possible* values of v and i.   For instance, if we use $i = e^{-at}$, then $v = -aLe^{-at}$, and $v/i = -aL$ is independent of time.   However, this would *not* be called an impedance, since it is independent of time only for a particular waveform of the applied voltages and/or currents.

   In transformed form the voltages and currents are no longer functions of time.   Consider the inductor of Fig. 5-19*a*, which is represented in transformed form with the assumption that there are zero initial conditions.   The relation between $\mathbf{V}(s)$ and $\mathbf{I}(s)$ is $\mathbf{V}(s) = Ls\mathbf{I}(s)$.   Thus we can write

$$\frac{\mathbf{V}(s)}{\mathbf{I}(s)} = Ls \qquad\qquad (5\text{-}156)$$

Similarly, for the capacitance of Fig. 5-19b we can write

$$\frac{\mathbf{V}(s)}{\mathbf{I}(s)} = \frac{1}{Cs} \tag{5-157}$$

These ratios are independent of time, voltage, and current. The ratio of $\mathbf{V}(s)$ to $\mathbf{I}(s)$ is given in dimensions of volts per ampere or ohms, as is resistance. However, it is undesirable to call this ratio "resistance," since resistors are not the only kind of circuit element involved. Thus a new name is used— *impedance*. Impedance is usually designated by the symbol $\mathbf{Z}(s)$. For instance, in Eqs. (5-156) and (5-157) we have, for the impedance of the inductor and capacitor, respectively,

$$\mathbf{Z}_L(s) = Ls \tag{5-158}$$

$$\mathbf{Z}_C(s) = \frac{1}{Cs} \tag{5-159}$$

For the resistor of Eq. (5-154), we have

$$\mathbf{Z}_R(s) = R \tag{5-160}$$

Thus resistance is a special case of impedance. An impedance relates the transform of the current through an element to the transform of the voltage across it, independently of time, voltage, and current.

In defining impedance we must assume zero initial conditions (zero initial current in an inductor and zero initial voltage across a capacitor). If there is an independent generator (such as an initial-condition generator) in the circuit, then the voltage across the element can no longer be expressed as impedance times the current. For instance, consider Eq. (5-123), which gives the transform of the voltage across an inductor with nonzero initial conditions. Here

$$\frac{\mathbf{V}_L(s)}{\mathbf{I}(s)} = Ls - \frac{Li(0-)}{\mathbf{I}(s)} \tag{5-161}$$

We do not have a ratio that is independent of the current, and we cannot manipulate it in any way to obtain such a ratio. Hence, when we define impedance, it is with the assumption that all the initial conditions are zero.

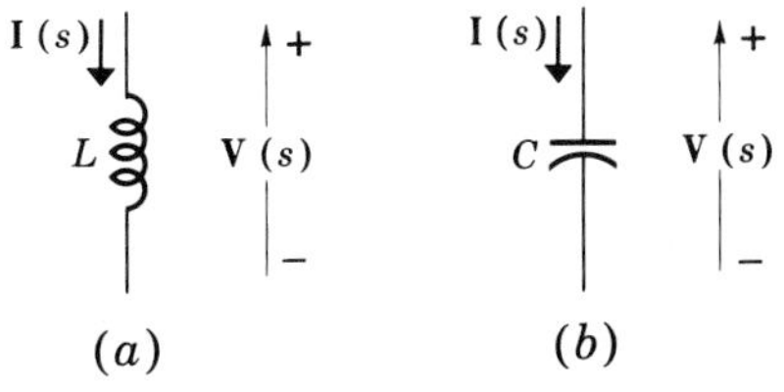

Fig. 5-19 Transformed networks with zero initial conditions: (a) an inductance; (b) a capacitance.

(a)　　　　　　　　(b)

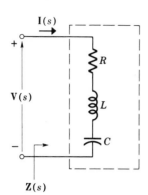

Fig. 5-20   *A more general impedance.*

We can generalize the preceding results somewhat. Consider that we have some circuit elements enclosed in a "black box" (see Sec. 2-4) with two terminals. The ratio of the voltage across the black box to the current that produces it is defined as the impedance of the black box. For instance, consider Fig. 5-20, which consists of a resistor, an inductor, and a capacitor in series (within the black box). We assume zero initial conditions. Then, applying simple loop analysis, we have

$$\mathbf{V}(s) = \left(R + Ls + \frac{1}{Cs} \right) \mathbf{I}(s) \tag{5-162}$$

The impedance is defined as the ratio of the terminal voltage to the terminal current. Hence

$$\mathbf{Z}(s) = R + Ls + \frac{1}{Cs} \tag{5-163}$$

This satisfies the conditions for an impedance. The ratio of $\mathbf{V}(s)/\mathbf{I}(s)$ is independent of time, voltage, and current.

We have discussed the fact that we cannot express an impedance if there are initial-condition generators in the circuit. Actually, if the black box of Fig. 5-20 contained *any* independent generators, we could not express the ratio of voltage to current as a function independent of voltage or current. Hence, in speaking of an impedance we assume that the circuit has no independent generators, initial-condition or otherwise.

Often it is convenient to work with the reciprocal of impedance, that is, the ratio of current to voltage. This is termed the *admittance* and is designated as $\mathbf{Y}(s)$,

$$\mathbf{Y}(s) = \frac{1}{\mathbf{Z}(s)} \tag{5-164}$$

For instance, from Eqs. (5-158), (5-159), and (5-160) we have, for the inductor, capacitor, and resistor, respectively,

$$\mathbf{Y}_L(s) = \frac{1}{Ls} \tag{5-165}$$

$$\mathbf{Y}_C(s) = Cs \tag{5-166}$$

$$\mathbf{Y}_R(s) = \frac{1}{R} = G \tag{5-167}$$

Thus the admittance of the resistance is the conductance.

At times we wish to speak of *either* an impedance or an admittance. A word that denotes either term is *immittance*.

5-9   Interconnection of impedances

When several impedances are interconnected, the resulting network can at times be represented by a single equivalent impedance as far as external conditions are concerned; that is, the behavior of any external circuitry is unchanged if the original network is replaced by the equivalent one.   For instance, the three impedances of Fig. 5-20 can be represented by the single impedance of Eq. (5-163).   In general, if we have an interconnection of circuit elements with no independent generators (initial-condition or otherwise), and these are enclosed in a "black box" which has only two terminals, then we can determine an equivalent impedance for this network.   That is, if the black box of Fig. 5-21 contains only circuit elements with zero initial conditions, then we can determine an equivalent impedance $\mathbf{Z}(s)$ for it which will relate $\mathbf{E}(s)$ and $\mathbf{I}(s)$ as

$$\mathbf{Z}(s) = \frac{\mathbf{V}(s)}{\mathbf{I}(s)} \tag{5-168}$$

From the conditions outside the black box it will be impossible to tell the equivalent impedance from the actual network.   Thus, once the impedance is determined, the current in response to any voltage (or vice versa) can easily be determined.

It is often far easier to analyze a network if a group of impedances can be combined into a single one.   The network of Fig. 5-21 is called a *oneport*

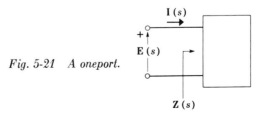

Fig. 5-21   A oneport.

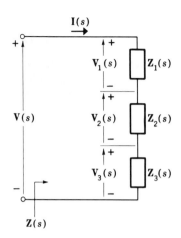

Fig. 5-22 *Impedances in series.*

network or a *oneport*, since it has only one pair of terminals that can serve as a "port of entry." It is also called a *one-terminal pair*. Let us assume that the oneport contains a known network and determine $\mathbf{Z}(s)$. The equivalent impedance is often called the *driving-point impedance* or the *input impedance* of the network. Again (see Sec. 2-4) it should be stressed that this equivalent impedance is equivalent only for external conditions. Let us consider some specific configurations.

Impedances in series

Let us determine the equivalent impedance of the series connection of impedances shown in Fig. 5-22. The small boxes represent single elements. For instance, each box could contain a resistor, or an inductor, or a capacitor. However, we assume that there are no independent or initial-condition generators. The ratio of the terminal voltage of each box to its terminal current is given by its impedance. For instance,

$$\frac{\mathbf{V}_1(s)}{\mathbf{I}(s)} = \mathbf{Z}_1(s) \tag{5-169}$$

Then, writing a loop equation for this network, we have

$$\mathbf{V}(s) = \mathbf{V}_1(s) + \mathbf{V}_2(s) + \mathbf{V}_3(s) \tag{5-170}$$

Hence

$$\mathbf{V}(s) = \mathbf{I}(s)[\mathbf{Z}_1(s) + \mathbf{Z}_2(s) + \mathbf{Z}_3(s)] \tag{5-171}$$

We can write the equation in this form because the terminal currents of each of the impedances are the same. This is the definition of a series circuit (see Sec. 2-4). The equivalent impedance of this network is given by Eq.

(5-168).   Hence

$$\mathbf{Z}(s) = \mathbf{Z}_1(s) + \mathbf{Z}_2(s) + \mathbf{Z}_3(s) \qquad (5\text{-}172)$$

Thus the equivalent impedance is just the sum of the individual impedances. In general, *if we have any number of impedances connected in series, the equivalent impedance is the sum of the individual impedances.*   An example of this is the determination of $\mathbf{Z}(s)$ for Fig. 5-20 in Eq. (5-163).

At times the admittances rather than the impedances are expressed [for example, $\mathbf{Y}(s) = 1/\mathbf{Z}(s)$, $\mathbf{Y}_1(s) = 1/\mathbf{Z}_1(s)$, and so on].   Substituting in Eq. (5-172), we have

$$\frac{1}{\mathbf{Y}(s)} = \frac{1}{\mathbf{Y}_1(s)} + \frac{1}{\mathbf{Y}_2(s)} + \frac{1}{\mathbf{Y}_3(s)} \qquad (5\text{-}173)$$

Thus *the equivalent admittance of a series connection of admittances is the reciprocal of the sum of the admittances.*   In this case, however, it is more convenient to work with impedances.

Impedances in parallel

Now let us consider a parallel interconnection of impedances such as that shown in Fig. 5-23.   A parallel interconnection of networks is characterized by the fact that each network has the same voltage across it.   Then

$$\mathbf{I}(s) = \mathbf{I}_1(s) + \mathbf{I}_2(s) + \mathbf{I}_3(s) = \mathbf{V}(s)\left[\frac{1}{\mathbf{Z}_1(s)} + \frac{1}{\mathbf{Z}_2(s)} + \frac{1}{\mathbf{Z}_3(s)}\right] \qquad (5\text{-}174)$$

The equivalent impedance of this network is given by [see Eq. (5-168)]

$$\frac{1}{\mathbf{Z}(s)} = \frac{1}{\mathbf{Z}_1(s)} + \frac{1}{\mathbf{Z}_2(s)} + \frac{1}{\mathbf{Z}_3(s)} \qquad (5\text{-}175)$$

In general, *if any number of impedances are connected in parallel, the equivalent impedance is given by the reciprocal of the sum of the reciprocals of the individual impedances.*

If we work with admittances [for example, $\mathbf{Y}(s) = 1/\mathbf{Z}(s)$], then Eq. (5-175)

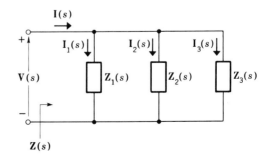

Fig. 5-23   Impedances in parallel.

becomes

$$\mathbf{Y}(s) = \mathbf{Y}_1(s) + \mathbf{Y}_2(s) + \mathbf{Y}_3(s) \tag{5-176}$$

In general, *when admittances are connected in parallel, the equivalent admittance is given by the sum of the individual admittances.* It is often more convenient to work with admittance when impedances are connected in parallel. As an example let us obtain the equivalent impedance or admittance of the oneport of Fig. 5-24. For convenience we shall work here with admittance. The individual admittances are given in Eqs. (5-165) to (5-167). The equivalent admittance of this network is

$$\mathbf{Y}(s) = \frac{1}{Ls} + G_1 + C_1 s + C_2 s = \frac{L(C_1 + C_2)s^2 + G_1 Ls + 1}{Ls} \tag{5-177}$$

The equivalent impedance of this network is just the reciprocal of the admittance.

General interconnection of impedances

We can obtain an equivalent input impedance for a oneport even if the individual impedances are not simply connected in series or in parallel. At times, to simplify the network, we can combine subnetworks of the given network as impedances in series or in parallel. By repeating this procedure we may be able to obtain the equivalent impedance. As an example of this technique let us find the input impedance of the network of Fig. 5-25a. As a first step, $\mathbf{Z}_3(s)$ and $\mathbf{Z}_4(s)$ can be combined in series as the single impedance $\mathbf{Z}_3(s) + \mathbf{Z}_4(s)$. The resulting network is illustrated in Fig. 5-25b. Now we obtain a single impedance to replace the combination of $\mathbf{Z}_2(s)$ in parallel with $\mathbf{Z}_3(s) + \mathbf{Z}_4(s)$,

$$\frac{1}{1/\mathbf{Z}_2(s) + 1/[\mathbf{Z}_3(s) + \mathbf{Z}_4(s)]} = \frac{\mathbf{Z}_2[\mathbf{Z}_3(s) + \mathbf{Z}_4(s)]}{\mathbf{Z}_2(s) + \mathbf{Z}_3(s) + \mathbf{Z}_4(s)} \tag{5-178}$$

The resulting network, shown in Fig. 5-25c, consists of two impedances in series. Thus the input impedance of the network is given by the sum of these two impedances. Hence

$$\mathbf{Z}(s) = \mathbf{Z}_1(s) + \frac{\mathbf{Z}_2(s)[\mathbf{Z}_3(s) + \mathbf{Z}_4(s)]}{\mathbf{Z}_2(s) + \mathbf{Z}_3(s) + \mathbf{Z}_4(s)} \tag{5-179}$$

At each stage in the reduction of the network of Fig. 5-25 we have replaced a subnetwork consisting of several impedances by a single equivalent imped-

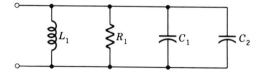

Fig. 5-24   A oneport consisting of elements in parallel.

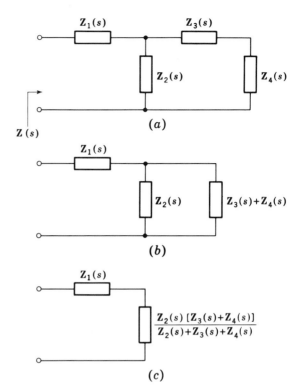

Fig. 5-25   (a) A network; (b) the network with $\mathbf{Z}_3(s)$ and $\mathbf{Z}_4(s)$ combined in series; (c) the network with $[\mathbf{Z}_3(s) + \mathbf{Z}_4(s)]$ combined in parallel with $\mathbf{Z}_2(s)$.

ance.   As we discussed in Sec. 2-4, if two networks have the same terminal-voltage–current relation, then they are equivalent *as far as external conditions are concerned*.   For instance, the single impedance $\mathbf{Z}_3(s) + \mathbf{Z}_4(s)$ of Fig. 5-25*b* is equivalent to the series interconnection of $\mathbf{Z}_3(s)$ and $\mathbf{Z}_4(s)$ in Fig. 5-25*a* as long as we are external to $\mathbf{Z}_3(s)$ and $\mathbf{Z}_4(s)$.   Thus Fig. 5-25*a* and *c* are equivalent as far as external conditions are concerned.

The procedure of combining impedances to obtain an equivalent impedance is convenient.   However, it is not always applicable, since the impedances of the network cannot always be combined.   For instance, consider Fig. 5-26*a*. There is no way that we can combine impedances to simplify this network. To determine the input impedance $\mathbf{Z}(s)$ of this network we rely on the fundamental definition given by Eq. (5-168).   That is, $\mathbf{Z}(s)$ is the ratio of the one-port's terminal voltage to its terminal current in transformed form.   To determine this ratio we can assume that a voltage generator $\mathbf{V}_1(s)$ is applied to the terminals, as shown in Fig. 5-26*b*, and perform an analysis to determine the terminal current $\mathbf{I}_1(s)$.   The impedance is then given by the ratio $\mathbf{V}_1(s)/\mathbf{I}_1(s)$. We can also proceed in the fashion shown in Fig. 5-26*c* to apply a current generator $\mathbf{I}_1(s)$ to the terminals of the network, and obtain the resulting terminal voltage.   Again, the impedance is given by $\mathbf{V}_1(s)/\mathbf{I}_1(s)$.   The generators $\mathbf{V}_1(s)$

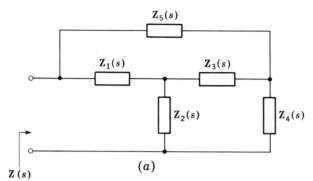

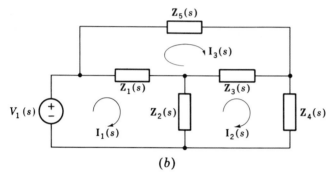

Fig. 5-26 (a) A network whose input impedance cannot be obtained by combining impedances; (b) a circuit using loop analysis which can be used to determine the input impedance; (c) a circuit using nodal analysis which can be used to determine the input impedance.

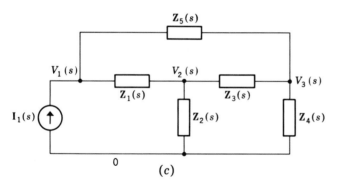

and $\mathbf{I}_1(s)$ need not be specified, since the impedance is independent of the generator.

To illustrate these procedures let us perform a loop analysis on the network of Fig. 5-26b.   This yields

$$\mathbf{V}_1(s) = [\mathbf{Z}_1(s) + \mathbf{Z}_2(s)]\mathbf{I}_1(s) - \mathbf{Z}_2(s)\mathbf{I}_2(s) - \mathbf{Z}_1(s)\mathbf{I}_3(s) \qquad (5\text{-}180a)$$

$$0 = -\mathbf{Z}_2(s)\mathbf{I}_1(s) + [\mathbf{Z}_2(s) + \mathbf{Z}_3(s) + \mathbf{Z}_4(s)]\mathbf{I}_2(s) - \mathbf{Z}_3(s)\mathbf{I}_3(s) \qquad (5\text{-}180b)$$

$$0 = -\mathbf{Z}_1(s)\mathbf{I}_1(s) - \mathbf{Z}_3(s)\mathbf{I}_2(s) + [\mathbf{Z}_1(s) + \mathbf{Z}_3(s) + \mathbf{Z}_5(s)]\mathbf{I}_3(s) \qquad (5\text{-}180c)$$

We set up the characteristic determinant

$$\mathbf{\Delta} = \begin{vmatrix} \mathbf{Z}_1(s) + \mathbf{Z}_2(s) & -\mathbf{Z}_2(s) & -\mathbf{Z}_1(s) \\ -\mathbf{Z}_2(s) & \mathbf{Z}_2(s) + \mathbf{Z}_3(s) + \mathbf{Z}_4(s) & -\mathbf{Z}_3(s) \\ -\mathbf{Z}_1(s) & -\mathbf{Z}_3(s) & \mathbf{Z}_1(s) + \mathbf{Z}_3(s) + \mathbf{Z}_5(s) \end{vmatrix}$$

(5-181)

Then, applying Cramer's rule and solving for $\mathbf{I}_1(s)$, we obtain

$$\mathbf{I}_1(s) = \frac{\mathbf{V}_1(s)\mathbf{\Delta}_{11}}{\mathbf{\Delta}}$$

(5-182)

The input impedance is given by

$$\mathbf{Z}(s) = \frac{\mathbf{V}_1(s)}{\mathbf{I}_1(s)}$$

(5-183)

and, after substituting Eq. (5-182), we have

$$\mathbf{Z}(s) = \frac{\mathbf{\Delta}}{\mathbf{\Delta}_{11}}$$

(5-184)

Then we can obtain $\mathbf{Z}(s)$ by expanding the determinant of Eq. (5-181) and its cofactor.

Now let us use nodal analysis to obtain $\mathbf{Z}(s)$ for the circuit of Fig. 5-26c. This yields

$$\mathbf{I}_1(s) = [\mathbf{Y}_1(s) + \mathbf{Y}_5(s)]\mathbf{V}_1(s) - \mathbf{Y}_1(s)\mathbf{V}_2(s) - \mathbf{Y}_5(s)\mathbf{V}_3(s)$$

(5-185a)

$$0 = -\mathbf{Y}_1(s)\mathbf{V}_1(s) + [\mathbf{Y}_1(s) + \mathbf{Y}_2(s) + \mathbf{Y}_3(s)]\mathbf{V}_2(s) - \mathbf{Y}_3(s)\mathbf{V}_3(s)$$

(5-185b)

$$0 = -\mathbf{Y}_5(s)\mathbf{V}_1(s) - \mathbf{Y}_3(s)\mathbf{V}_2(s) + [\mathbf{Y}_3(s) + \mathbf{Y}_4(s) + \mathbf{Y}_5(s)]\mathbf{V}_3(s)$$

(5-185c)

where $\mathbf{Y}(s) = 1/\mathbf{Z}(s)$. We set up the characteristic determinant

$$\mathbf{\Delta} = \begin{vmatrix} \mathbf{Y}_1(s) + \mathbf{Y}_5(s) & -\mathbf{Y}_1(s) & -\mathbf{Y}_5(s) \\ -\mathbf{Y}_1(s) & \mathbf{Y}_1(s) + \mathbf{Y}_2(s) + \mathbf{Y}_3(s) & -\mathbf{Y}_3(s) \\ -\mathbf{Y}_5(s) & -\mathbf{Y}_3(s) & \mathbf{Y}_3(s) + \mathbf{Y}_4(s) + \mathbf{Y}_5(s) \end{vmatrix}$$

(5-186)

and solve for $\mathbf{V}_1(s)$ by Cramer's rule. This yields

$$\mathbf{V}_1(s) = \mathbf{I}_1(s)\frac{\mathbf{\Delta}_{11}}{\mathbf{\Delta}}$$

(5-187)

The impedance is given by

$$\mathbf{Z}(s) = \frac{\mathbf{\Delta}_{11}}{\mathbf{\Delta}}$$

(5-188)

Compare this equation with Eq. (5-184). They appear to be different. In Eq. (5-184) $\mathbf{\Delta}$ is written on the basis of the loop analysis, while in Eq. (5-188) it is written on the basis of the nodal analysis. These two determinants are different; hence the two relations for impedance appear different. However, the same value of impedance will be obtained from either one.

Let us now generalize these analyses. Consider the oneport represented by the black box of Fig. 5-27. We shall assume that the network within the black box is known and that in transformed form the oneport contains no independent generators (initial-condition or otherwise). However, it may contain any network that does not violate these restrictions. To determine the input impedance of the oneport let us first use loop analysis. We connect a voltage generator to the terminals of the network, as shown in Fig. 5-27*b*, and choose loop currents such that the *only* loop current through the generator is $\mathbf{I}_1(s)$ [see the discussion following Eq. (3-14)].

Now we perform a loop analysis on the network. Let us assume that this has been done, and that the characteristic determinant is $\overset{\text{L}}{\triangle}$ (we have placed an "L" within the delta to indicate that the determinant is written on a loop-analysis basis). Then Cramer's rule gives

$$\mathbf{I}_1(s) = \mathbf{V}_1(s) \frac{\overset{\text{L}}{\triangle}_{11}}{\overset{\text{L}}{\triangle}} \qquad\qquad (5\text{-}189)$$

Note that $\mathbf{V}_1(s)$ is the only generator of the network and that it lies only in the loop of $\mathbf{I}_1(s)$, so that only one term of Eq. (5-144) appears. The input impedance of the network is given by Eq. (5-168) as

$$\mathbf{Z}(s) = \frac{\overset{\text{L}}{\triangle}}{\overset{\text{L}}{\triangle}_{11}} \qquad\qquad (5\text{-}190)$$

We can also use nodal analysis to determine the input impedance of this network. In this case we "connect" a current generator to the input as shown in Fig. 5-27*c*. One terminal of the current generator should be chosen as the unknown nodal voltage $\mathbf{V}_1(s)$. The other terminal of the generator is then chosen as the reference node, as shown in Fig. 5-27*c*. Then we can perform a nodal analysis on the known network within the black box. Let us call the resulting characteristic determinant $\overset{\text{N}}{\triangle}$. Since $\mathbf{I}_1(s)$ is the only current

Fig. 5-27 (*a*) *A oneport that contains no independent generators and has no initial conditions;* (*b*) *a voltage generator connected to this network;* (*c*) *a current generator connected to this network.*

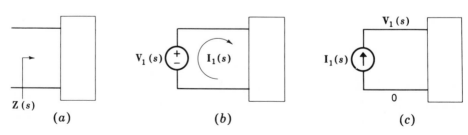

$\mathbf{Z}(s)$

(*a*)   (*b*)   (*c*)

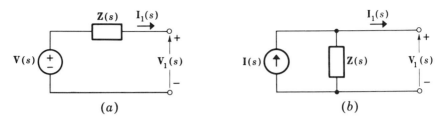

Fig. 5-28   (a) A voltage generator; (b) a current generator.   These are equivalent for external conditions if $\mathbf{I}(s) = \mathbf{E}(s)/\mathbf{Z}(s)$.

generator, we have

$$\mathbf{V}_1(s) = \mathbf{I}_1(s) \; \frac{\triangle N_{11}}{\triangle N} \tag{5-191}$$

Hence the input impedance is

$$\mathbf{Z}(s) = \frac{\triangle N_{11}}{\triangle N} \tag{5-192}$$

Either Eq. (5-190) or Eq. (5-192) can be used to determine the input impedance.   The choice depends upon whether loop or nodal analysis results in fewer unknowns (a determinant of lower order).   This is exactly analogous to the criteria used to determine whether mesh or nodal analysis should be used in an ordinary analysis procedure.

5-10   Equivalent voltage and current generators

In performing loop analyses it is convenient (especially in general proofs) to let all the generators be voltage generators, whereas for nodal or cut-set analysis it is convenient to let them be current generators.   In Sec. 2-4 we saw a procedure whereby a voltage generator in series with a resistance, an inductance, or a capacitance could be converted to a current generator, and a similar procedure whereby a current generator shunted by circuit elements could be converted to a voltage generator.   Now that we have developed the concept of an imped-ance, we can generalize these results somewhat.

Consider the voltage generator and the current generator of Fig. 5-28.   We shall now demonstrate that these can be made equivalent.   If Figs. 5-28a and b are equivalent as far as external conditions are concerned, then the relations between their terminal voltages and currents must be identical (see Sec. 2-4).

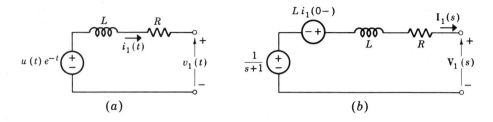

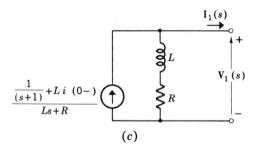

Fig. 5-29   (a) A voltage-generator circuit, with the initial condition given by $i_1(0-)$; (b) the transformed form of this network; (c) a current-generator circuit that is equivalent to (b) for external conditions.

Applying Kirchhoff's law to Fig. 5-28a, we obtain

$$\mathbf{V}_1(s) = \mathbf{V}(s) - \mathbf{I}_1(s)\mathbf{Z}(s) \tag{5-193}$$

Similarly, analysis of Fig. 5-28b gives us

$$\mathbf{V}_1(s) = \mathbf{I}(s)\mathbf{Z}(s) - \mathbf{I}_1(s)\mathbf{Z}(s) \tag{5-194}$$

Equations (5-193) and (5-194) are the relations between the terminal voltages and currents of the networks. They will be identical if the impedances are the same in each network and the generators are related by

$$\mathbf{V}(s) = \mathbf{I}(s)\mathbf{Z}(s) \tag{5-195}$$

(substitution of Eq. (5-195) into Eq. (5-194) demonstrates this). Thus, if the above conditions hold, external conditions for the two generators of Fig. 5-28 will be equivalent as far as external conditions are concerned.

As an example let us obtain a current generator that is externally equivalent (in transformed form) to the voltage generator of Fig. 5-29a. Note that there is an initial condition here. The transformed form of the network is shown in Fig. 5-29b. The two voltage generators can be considered to be a single one which produces a voltage

$$\mathbf{V}_g(s) = \frac{1}{s+1} + Li_1(0-) \tag{5-196}$$

In general, two or more voltage generators connected in series can be combined into a single one. The resultant network is then converted into a current generator by means of Fig. 5-28 and Eq. (5-195). This is shown in Fig. 5-29c. Manipulations of the type shown in Figs. 2-21 to 2-25 can also be performed in transformed form and are at times very useful.

As a final illustration of the use of some of these procedures we shall obtain a network with a voltage generator which is equivalent to the transformed form of Fig. 5-30a as far as external conditions are concerned. Figure 5-30b

Fig. 5-30 (a) A current-generator circuit, with the initial condition given by $i_a(0-)$; (b) the transformed form of the network; (c) an equivalent network obtained by using Figs. 2-23 and 2-24; (d) a voltage-generator circuit that is equivalent for external conditions; (e) a network equivalent to (d) with the voltage generators combined.

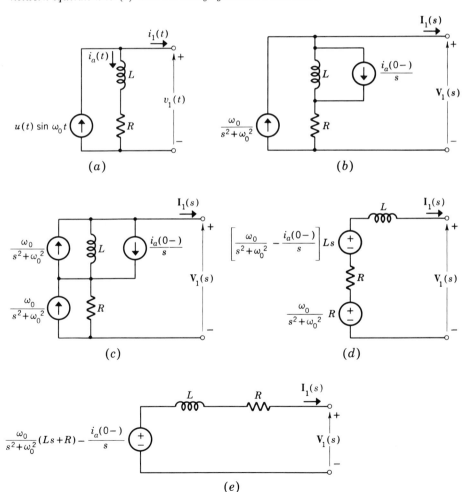

illustrates the transformed form of the network.   There are two current generators in this network.   To aid us in combining these elements we shall split
the original current generator into a series connection of two generators, each
of which is equal to the original one.   Then we can connect an ideal conductor
between their common point and the junction of the inductor and resistor
(this follows the procedure outlined in Fig. 2-24).   The resulting network is
shown in Fig. 5-30c.   The two current generators, which are connected in
parallel, can be combined into a single one whose current is

$$\frac{\omega_0}{s^2 + \omega_0{}^2} - \frac{i_a(0-)}{s}$$

The circuit now consists of two current generators, each shunted by an impedance.   Each of these can then be converted to a voltage generator by means of
Fig. 5-28 and Eq. (5-195), as shown in Fig. 5-30d.   Finally, the two voltage
generators in series are combined into a single one, as shown in Fig. 5-30e.
This network is equivalent to that of Fig. 5-30b as far as external conditions
are concerned.

It is interesting to note that the initial-condition generators of Figs. 5-11b
and 5-12b can be obtained from those of Figs. 5-8b and 5-9b, respectively, by
converting the voltage-generator forms into current-generator forms.   Conversely, the voltage generators of Fig. 5-8d can be converted into current
generators.

5-11   Transfer functions

In certain practical applications we deal with networks that have two pairs
of terminals.   One pair is termed the *input* and the other pair is termed the
output.   In general, we apply a generator to the input terminals, and we are
interested in the response at the output terminals (it is assumed that there are
no independent generators, either initial conditions or others, within the box).
The response consists of either a current in or the voltage across an impedance.
This impedance is usually termed the *load impedance*.   A high-fidelity phonograph amplifier is one example of this situation.   The input generator is the
voltage produced by the phonograph pickup, and the load impedance is the
loudspeaker.

A network that has two pairs of terminals is termed a *twoport network*,
or simply a *twoport*, since it has two "ports of entry."   It is sometimes called
a *two-terminal pair*.   Such a twoport, with a load impedance connected to
its output terminals, is shown in Figs. 5-31.   Usually we are interested in the
ratio of the output voltage or current to the input voltage or current in transformed form.   For instance,

$$\mathbf{K}_L(s) = \frac{\mathbf{V}_2(s)}{\mathbf{V}_1(s)} \tag{5-197}$$

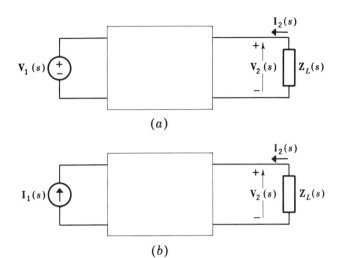

Fig. 5-31 Twoports: (a) with voltage-generator input; (b) with current-generator input.

is called the *transfer-voltage ratio*. The adjective "transfer" indicates that a response at one point in a network is related to a generator at a different point in the network. Once we know the transfer-voltage ratio of the network, we can find the output voltage in response to any input voltage, that is, we can find $\mathbf{V}_2(s) = \mathbf{K}_L(s)\mathbf{V}_1(s)$. We shall see an example of this subsequently.

We can also express a ratio which can be used to obtain the output current as a function of the input voltage. This is given by

$$\mathbf{Y}_T(s) = \frac{\mathbf{I}_2(s)}{\mathbf{V}_1(s)} \tag{5-198}$$

This quantity has the dimension of an admittance, amperes per volt. It is called a *transfer admittance*, since it relates a current at one part of the network to the voltage that produces it at another part of the network.

Consider the network of **Fig. 5-31b**, where the input is a current generator. Here we can define a *transfer-current ratio*

$$\mathbf{L}_T(s) = \frac{\mathbf{I}_2(s)}{\mathbf{I}_1(s)} \tag{5-199}$$

and a *transfer impedance*

$$\mathbf{Z}_T(s) = \frac{\mathbf{V}_2(s)}{\mathbf{I}_1(s)} \tag{5-200}$$

All these functions we have been considering are called *transfer functions*. In general, they relate an output voltage or current to the input voltage or current that causes it. The numerator of the transfer function is the response, and the denominator is the input (generator) quantity.

The impedances and admittances developed in Sec. 5-8 are called *driving-*

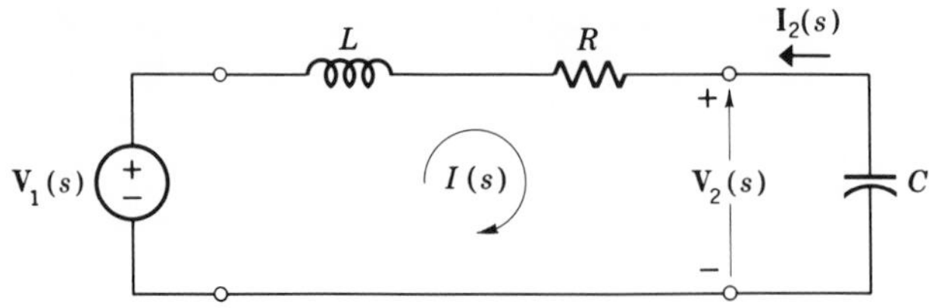

Fig. 5-32   A one-loop net-work.

point impedances or *driving-point admittances.*   These represent the ratio of a voltage to a current (or current to a voltage) at *only one* pair of terminals of the network.   Usually, where there is no possibility of confusion, these quantities are called simply impedances or admittances.

Let us now obtain the transfer-voltage ratio and the transfer admittance of the network of Fig. 5-32.   From a loop analysis we obtain

$$\mathbf{V}_1(s) = \mathbf{I}(s) \left(Ls + R + \frac{1}{Cs} \right) \tag{5-201}$$

The voltage across the capacitor is given by

$$\mathbf{V}_2(s) = \mathbf{I}(s) \frac{1}{Cs} \tag{5-202}$$

Then, solving for $\mathbf{I}(s)$ in Eq. (5-201), substituting in Eq. (5-202), and solving for $\mathbf{V}_2(s)/\mathbf{V}_1(s)$, we have

$$\mathbf{K}_L(s) = \frac{\mathbf{V}_2(s)}{\mathbf{V}_1(s)} = \frac{1/Cs}{Ls + R + 1/Cs} = \frac{1}{LC[s^2 + (R/L)s + 1/LC]} \tag{5-203}$$

Note that $\mathbf{K}_L(s)$ is independent of the input voltage $\mathbf{V}_1(s)$.   To obtain the transform of the output voltage in response to any input voltage we multiply $\mathbf{K}_L(s)$ by the transform of the input voltage.   That is,

$$\mathbf{V}_2(s) = \mathbf{K}_L(s)\mathbf{V}_1(s) = \frac{\mathbf{V}_1(s)}{LC[s^2 + (R/L)s + 1/LC]} \tag{5-204}$$

For instance, if $\mathbf{V}_1(s) = 1/s$, then

$$\mathbf{V}_2(s) = \frac{1}{sLC[s^2 + (R/L)s + 1/LC]} \tag{5-205}$$

The output current $\mathbf{I}_2(s)$ is the negative of $\mathbf{I}(s)$.   It is conventional to take the positive direction of the output current *into* the network.   Then

$$\mathbf{Y}_T(s) = \frac{\mathbf{I}_2(s)}{\mathbf{V}_1(s)} = -\frac{\mathbf{I}(s)}{\mathbf{V}_1(s)} = \frac{-1}{Ls + R + 1/Cs} = \frac{-s}{L[s^2 + (R/L)s + 1/LC]} \tag{5-206}$$

This transfer function will be independent of $\mathbf{V}_1(s)$.

In general, we shall use loop, nodal, or cut-set analysis to obtain the transfer function of the network.   These functions will have essentially the same form as the solution of the loop, nodal, or cut-set equations; *they will be expressible as the ratio of two polynomials in s.* Note also that they will be independent of the input generator; that is, their form will not depend upon the specific value of $\mathbf{V}_1(s)$ or $\mathbf{I}_1(s)$. Transfer functions are always a ratio of the output quantity to the input quantity, so the input quantities are "divided out" of the transfer function.

5-12   Poles and zeros

As we have seen, the solutions, in transformed form, of loop, nodal, or cut-set analyses, as well as impedances and transfer functions, will be in the form of the ratio of two polynomials in s. Let us study this form to understand it better. In general, we shall be dealing with a function of the form

$$\mathbf{W}(s) = \frac{a_m s^m + a_{m-1} s^{m-1} + \cdots + a_1 s + a_0}{b_n s^n + b_{n-1} s^{n-1} + \cdots + b_1 s + b_0} \tag{5-207}$$

where $\mathbf{W}(s)$ can represent a current, a voltage, an impedance, an admittance, or a transfer function in transformed form. The constants a_k $(k = 0,1, \ldots ,m)$ and b_k $(k = 0,1, \ldots ,n)$ are real numbers. Now let us assume that the numerator and denominator of $\mathbf{W}(s)$ are factored. Thus we can write Eq. (5-207) as

$$\mathbf{W}(s) = k \frac{(s - s_{01})(s - s_{02}) \cdots (s - s_{0m})}{(s - s_1)(s - s_2) \cdots (s - s_n)} \tag{5-208}$$

where

$$s_{01}, s_{02}, \ldots , s_{0m}$$

are the roots of the numerator of $\mathbf{W}(s)$ and

$$s_1, s_2, \ldots , s_n$$

are the roots of the denominator. k is a constant whose value is

$$k = \frac{a_m}{b_n} \tag{5-209}$$

Let us consider the value of $\mathbf{W}(s)$ for some specific values of s. In particular, we shall allow s to approach the values equal to the roots of the numerator and denominator of $\mathbf{W}(s)$. If we let $s = s_{01}$, then

$$\mathbf{W}(s_{01}) = 0 \tag{5-210}$$

This is because the numerator of $\mathbf{W}(s)$, and hence $\mathbf{W}(s)$, becomes zero when $s = s_{01}$. It is assumed that the numerator and denominator do not have roots in common [if they do, then these should be canceled before Eqs. (5-207) or (5-208) are written]. Since $\mathbf{W}(s) = 0$ when s is equal to any of the roots of the numerator, these roots are called the *zeros* of $\mathbf{W}(s)$. Thus the zeros of $\mathbf{W}(s)$ are $s_{01}, s_{02}, \ldots, s_{0m}$.

As s approaches one of the roots of the denominator of $\mathbf{W}(s)$, the value of the denominator approaches zero. Hence $\mathbf{W}(s)$ approaches infinity. The roots of the denominator of $\mathbf{W}(s)$ are called the *poles* of $\mathbf{W}(s)$. When s is equal to one of the poles, $\mathbf{W}(s)$ becomes infinite. The poles of Eq. (5-208) are $s_1, s_2, \ldots, s_n$.

We can be more rigorous in the definition of poles and zeros. If a function $\mathbf{W}(s)$ is such that we can find a term $(s - s_1)^n$, where

$$\lim_{s \to s_1} (s - s_1)^n \mathbf{W}(s) = \mathbf{K}$$

and $\mathbf{K}$ is a *nonzero finite constant*, then $\mathbf{W}(s)$ is said to have a pole of order n at $s = s_1$. Note that if $\mathbf{W}(s)$ has a pole at $s = s_1$, then $\lim\limits_{s \to s_1} \mathbf{W}(s)$ is infinite. The factor $(s - s_1)^n$ becomes zero at $s = s_1$ and "cancels" the infinite term. For instance,

$$\mathbf{W}(s) = \frac{1}{(s + 1)^3}$$

has a third-order pole at $s = -1$, since

$$\lim_{s \to -1} \frac{(s + 1)^3}{(s + 1)^3} = 1$$

Note that any exponent other than 3 will lead to *either* a zero or an infinite value of the limit. Thus the order of the pole is the order of the root of the denominator of $\mathbf{W}(s)$.

Similarly, if

$$\lim_{s \to s_1} \frac{\mathbf{W}(s)}{(s - s_1)^n} = \mathbf{K}$$

where $\mathbf{K}$ is a *nonzero finite* constant, then $\mathbf{W}(s)$ is said to have a zero of order n at $s = s_1$. For instance,

$$(s - s_1)^4$$

has a fourth-order zero at $s = 3$.

If we know the poles and zeros of a function, then we know the function except for a constant multiplier. For instance, if we know all the poles and zeros in Eq. (5-208), then we need only determine k to establish $\mathbf{W}(s)$ completely. In the time domain as well as in the transformed domain the value of k acts only as a constant multiplier. For instance, if $\mathbf{W}(s)$ represents the Laplace transform of a current and its inverse Laplace transform is $i(t)$, the inverse Laplace transform of $k\mathbf{W}(s)$ will be $ki(t)$. Very often we are concerned primarily with the shape of the response, and not with the multiplying factor. In this case a knowledge of the poles and zeros supplies us with all the pertinent

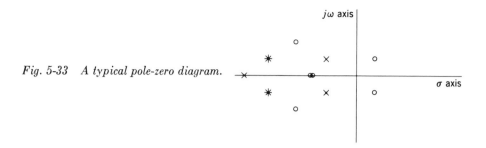

Fig. 5-33   A typical pole-zero diagram.

information.   A list could be used to specify the locations of the poles and zeros, but often a diagram called a *pole-zero diagram* is used instead.   Such a pole-zero diagram is illustrated in Fig. 5-33.   The *s* plane is drawn (see Fig. 5-2), and the poles and zeros are marked on it.   The poles are indicated by $\times$ and the zeros by $\bigcirc$.   The σ- and $j\omega$-axis coordinates give the real and imaginary value of the pole or zero in question.   If the pole or zero is not of first degree (that is, if the root of the denominator or numerator is not of first degree), then a multiple $\times$ or $\bigcirc$ can be placed on the diagram to indicate this. Since the roots of polynomials with real coefficients occur in complex-conjugate pairs, the poles and zeros will occur in such pairs.

Now let us consider that $\mathbf{W}(s)$ is the Laplace transform of some function of time $w(t)$.   To determine $w(t)$ we expand Eq. (5-208) in partial fractions. Each term in the partial-fraction expansion will correspond to one of the poles of $\mathbf{W}(s)$.   If the poles are simple (of first degree), then there will be a one-to-one correspondence between the poles and the terms in the partial-fraction expansion [see Eqs. (5-66) and (5-67)].   If there are multiple poles, then there will be additional terms in the partial-fraction expansion.   That is, if there is a third-order pole at s_1, then the partial-fraction expansion will have terms with third-, second-, and first-order poles of $s = s_1$ [see Eqs. (5-84) and (5-85)].   The poles (not the zeros) specify the type of terms present in the partial-fraction expansion.   *Both* the zeros and the poles, as well as the constant multiplier, determine the constants in the partial-fraction expansion.   *Thus the poles, and only the poles, of* $\mathbf{W}(s)$ *specify the type of time functions that are added to form* $w(t)$.   The poles, zeros, and constant multipliers determine the magnitudes of the various functions.

Since the pole locations play an extremely important part in the general character of a time function, let us study their effect further.   We shall use Table 5-1 to do this.   If the poles lie on the σ axis, then they will lead to terms in the partial-fraction expansion of the form $K/(s + a)$ or $K/(s + a)^n$.   This will lead to time functions of the form $e^{-at}u(t)$ or $t^{n-1}e^{-at}u(t)$ (multiplied by an appropriate constant).   If the pole does not lie on the σ axis, then the value of a will be a complex number.   This will lead to sinusoidal or cosinusoidal terms [see Eq. (4-58)].

The $j\omega$ axis is said to divide the s plane into a right part and a left part. These are called the *right half plane* and the *left half plane*. If poles lie in the left half plane, then they will lead to partial-fraction-expansion terms of the form $1/(s + a)^n$ ($n = 1,2,3, \ldots$), where the real part of a is positive. Let us consider that a is a real positive number. Then (see Table 5-1)

$$\mathcal{L}^{-1}\left[\frac{1}{(s + a)^n}\right] = \frac{t^{n-1}e^{-at}}{(n-1)!}\,u(t) \tag{5-211}$$

In general, if we apply L'Hospital's rule successively to obtain $\lim\limits_{t \to \infty} t^{n-1}e^{-at}$, we find that it is zero for any finite n as long as $a > 0$. The condition $a > 0$ is the same as the one that places the pole of $1/(s + a)$ in the left half plane. If a is complex and the root lies in the left half plane, then

$$a = \alpha + j\beta \tag{5-212}$$

where α is positive. Then

$$\mathcal{L}^{-1}\left[\frac{1}{(s + a + j\beta)^n}\right] = \frac{t^{n-1}e^{-\alpha t}e^{j\beta t}}{(n-1)!}\,u(t) \tag{5-213}$$

Each complex pole will have a corresponding conjugate one. Thus these poles will lead to terms of the form

$$\frac{t^{n-1}e^{-\alpha t}}{(n-1)!}\,\sin \beta t$$

$$\frac{t^{n-1}e^{-\alpha t}}{(n-1)!}\,\cos \beta t$$

which are multiplied by the appropriate constants. In either case, as t approaches infinity, $t^{n-1}e^{-\alpha t}$ approaches zero. Thus we can state that *poles in the left half plane lead to time functions that fall off to zero as t becomes large.*

The previous discussion also applies to poles in the right half plane, but now a and α in Eqs. (5-211) and (5-213) are negative. Thus the exponential terms *increase* with time, rather than decreasing. Hence *poles in the right half plane lead to time functions that become arbitrarily large as t becomes very large.*

Now let us consider poles that lie on the $j\omega$ axis. If these are simple, they will lead to partial-fraction-expansion terms of the form $1/s$ or $K/(s^2 + \omega_0^2)$. The latter has roots at $\pm j\omega_0$. These lead to time functions of the form $u(t)$ or $u(t)(K_1 \sin \omega_0 t + K_2 \cos \omega_0 t)$, respectively. Then *simple poles on the $j\omega$ axis lead to functions which become neither arbitrarily large nor small as t becomes very large.*

If the $j\omega$-axis roots are not simple, but are of multiplicity n, they lead to time functions of the type $t^{n-1}u(t)$ or $t^{n-1}u(t)(K_1 \sin \omega_0 t + K_2 \cos \omega_0 t)$. Then *multiple poles on the $j\omega$ axis lead to time functions that become arbitrarily large as t becomes very large.*

Now let us consider a typical solution of a loop, nodal, or cut-set analysis and see what determines the location of the poles of the transform of the loop current or nodal or cut-set voltages. From Eq. (5-144) we see that the solution of such an analysis is

$$\mathbf{X}_k(s) = \frac{\mathbf{\Delta}_{1k}\mathbf{Y}_1(s) + \mathbf{\Delta}_{2k}\mathbf{Y}_2(s) + \cdots + \mathbf{\Delta}_{nk}\mathbf{Y}_n(s)}{\mathbf{\Delta}} \qquad k = 1, 2, \ldots, n$$

(5-214)

where $\mathbf{X}_k(s)$ represents a current in loop analysis or a voltage in nodal or cut-set analyses. The $\mathbf{Y}_k(s)$ are generator terms, and $\mathbf{\Delta}$ is the characteristic determinant written on either a loop, nodal, or cut-set basis. When $\mathbf{\Delta}$ or its cofactors are expanded, the result is either a polynomial or a polynomial divided by s^n [the general form of $\mathbf{\Delta}$ is given by Eq. (5-143)]. We can always multiply numerator and denominator by s^n to obtain the ratio of two polynomials. A polynomial $a_n s^n + a_{n-1} s^{n-1} + \cdots + a_1 s + a_0$ can become infinite only at $s = \infty$. Then the poles of $\mathbf{X}_k(s)$ will occur at those values of s where $\mathbf{\Delta} = 0$ and at the poles of $\mathbf{Y}_1(s)$, $\mathbf{Y}_2(s)$, $\ldots$, $\mathbf{Y}_n(s)$. Note that $\mathbf{X}_k(s)$ becomes infinite at these points [at times there may be poles at $s = \infty$; these correspond to the power-series terms in Eq. (5-62)].

The zeros of $\mathbf{\Delta}$ are called *characteristic roots* of the network. The poles of $\mathbf{X}_k(s)$ will be the characteristic roots of the network plus the poles of the transforms of the generator voltages or currents. Thus the partial-fraction expansion of $\mathbf{X}_k(s)$ will contain terms corresponding to the characteristic roots plus terms with the same poles as the generators. Hence the time response can be grouped into two sets of terms. The type of terms in one set depends only upon the circuit elements, and not upon the generators. The *type* of terms in the other set depends upon the generators, and not upon the circuit elements. Note that if *both* sets have the same pole, then a multiple pole results, and *both* sets will interact. The terms due to the characteristic roots are equivalent to the complementary solution when classical methods are used. The terms due to the generator poles correspond to the particular solution in the classical method.

Usually the characteristic roots lead to poles in the left half plane. Thus these terms become very small as time increases, and the only terms that remain are those which correspond to the generators. These are called the *driven terms* or the *forced terms*. For example, consider Fig. 5-17. We shall find the solution for $i_1(t)$ given in Eqs. (5-146) to (5-150). The voltage generators are $u(t)$ and $e^{-t}u(t)$, with Laplace transforms $1/s$ and $1/(s + 1)$, respectively. From Eq. (5-147) we have $\mathbf{\Delta} = (s^2 + 2s + 2)/s$. Hence the characteristic roots occur at $s = -1 \pm j$. From Eq. (5-148c) we have

$$\mathbf{I}_1(s) = \frac{1}{s} + \frac{1}{s + 1} + \frac{-1 - j}{s + 1 + j} + \frac{-1 + j}{s + 1 - j}$$

The first two terms correspond to the generator poles, and the second two correspond to the characteristic roots. From Eq. (5-150) we have

$$i_1(t) = u(t) + u(t)e^{-t} - 2u(t)e^{-t}(\cos t + \sin t)$$

The first two terms are those that correspond to the generator poles; the last two correspond to the characteristic roots.   Note that the terms corresponding to the characteristic roots fall off as time becomes large (one of the generator terms also falls off because the generator itself falls off with time).

5-13   Stability

At times the transforms of the currents and voltages in a network contain components which have right-half-plane poles.   That is, in the time domain they build up without limit.   Actually, nonlinearities limit the amplitude of buildup, so that there is just a large component of these terms (see Sec. 4-4, where negative resistance is discussed; nonlinearities are discussed in detail in Chap. 7).   This type of operation, which is characterized by right-half-plane poles, is termed *oscillation*.   Often it is highly undesirable.   For instance, a public-address system may "howl" if the microphone is placed in front of the loudspeaker.   Such howling is oscillation.   Oscillation can cause complete malfunction in a control system (for example, the controlled rudder of a ship would swing up and back rapidly if the control system oscillated).   If a device oscillates, it is termed *unstable;* if it does not oscillate, it is called *stable*.

In general (see Sec. 5-12), the currents and voltages of a network will be composed of two sets of terms, one whose poles are the same as those of the independent generator(s) and another whose poles are roots of the characteristic determinant.   The stability or instability of a network is due to the latter set of poles.   That is, we assume that the independent generators are such that their voltages or currents do not increase without limit as time becomes large (note that these generators perform to desired specifications). In general, if a network produces a signal that increases without limit (neglecting nonlinearities) when the magnitudes of the voltages and/or currents of the independent generators are bounded, then it is unstable.   We usually want the network to respond to the independent generators.   There will generally be terms in the response that are not due to the generator poles, and if these increase without limit, they will obscure the desired signal, and the network is unsuitable.

The stability of the network depends upon the location of the poles of the characteristic determinant.   If they all lie in the left half plane, then the network will be stable.   However, if any one or more of them lies in the right half plane, or if there are multiple roots on the $j\omega$ axis, then the network will be unstable.   Note that a simple pole on the $j\omega$ axis is a borderline case of instability.

As an example consider the *RLC* network analyzed in Sec. 5-4.   The roots of the characteristic determinant are given by Eq. (5-107) as

$$s_1, s_2 = -\frac{R}{2L} \pm \sqrt{\left(\frac{R}{2L}\right)^2 - \frac{1}{LC}}$$

Let us consider that L and C are positive quantities but that R may take on negative values as well as positive ones. (The idea of a negative resistance is discussed toward the end of Sec. 4-4.) The response of the RLC circuit for the negative-resistance case is also discussed there, and it is shown that the response is exponentially damped if $R > 0$ and increases exponentially if $R < 0$. Thus the network is unstable if R is negative.

We shall explore this here by studying the poles of the characteristic response. Let us examine the roots and assume that

$$\left(\frac{R}{2L}\right)^2 < \frac{1}{LC}$$

Then Eq. (5-217) becomes

$$s_1, s_2 = -\frac{R}{2L} \pm j \sqrt{\frac{1}{LC} - \left(\frac{R}{2L}\right)^2}$$

Thus, if $R > 0$, the poles of the current $\mathbf{I}(s)$ [see Eq. (5-106c)] will lie in the left half plane, while if $R < 0$, the poles lie in the right half plane. Hence the network will be stable if R is positive and unstable if R is negative. These results are substantiated by Figs. 4-17 to 4-19, which illustrate the response of the RLC network for positive, zero, and negative resistance, respectively.

We have discussed this example in terms of a simple negative resistor. In general, however, the problem of instability in circuits is a complex one.

The stability of a network depends upon the location of the roots of its characteristic determinant. If all of these lie in the left half plane, the network will be stable. If any lie in the right half plane or are multiple and lie on the $j\omega$ axis, the network is unstable. We can factor the characteristic equation to determine the location of its roots. If the polynomial is more than second degree, however, this is very tedious. Let us now consider two procedures whereby we can ascertain whether the roots all lie in the left half plane *without* having to factor the polynomial. These procedures are called the *Hurwitz test* and the *Routh test*. In each of these we shall consider that we have a polynomial

$$\mathbf{D}(s) = d_n s^n + d_{n-1} s^{n-1} + \cdots + d_1 s + d_0 \tag{5-215}$$

and determine if all of its roots lie in the left half plane.

Before we consider the details of these tests, let us examine the polynomial itself. If it has only left-half-plane roots, then it will be composed of factors of the form

$$s + a_k$$

or

$$(s + a_k + jb_k)(s + a_k - jb_k) = (s + a_k)^2 + b_k{}^2 = s^2 + 2a_k s + a_k{}^2 + b_k{}^2$$

where all a_k and b_k are positive constants. If we multiply factors of this form together, all the coefficients of Eq. (5-215) will be positive, since all the a_k and b_k

are positive.   Note that the d_k $(k = 1, \ldots, n)$ are composed of the products and sums of the a's and b's so none of the d_k can be negative.   In addition, there can be no subtraction of terms, so that none of the coefficients of Eq. (5-215) can be zero.   Thus, if *any* of the $d_{n-1}, d_{n-2}, \ldots, d_1, d_0$ are zero or negative, $\mathbf{D}(s)$ cannot have all its roots in the left half plane.   Hence it must have some roots in the right half plane.   An exception to this is the case where $\mathbf{D}(s)$ is an *even polynomial* or an *odd polynomial* (that is, if it has only even powers or odd power of s, respectively).   In this case, even though some of the coefficients are zero, $\mathbf{D}(s)$ *may* have all its roots on the $j\omega$ axis; that is, it may be composed of factors of the form s or $(s + j\omega_0)(s - j\omega_0)$.   If these $j\omega$-axis roots are multiple, then the network will be unstable.   If they are simple, then the device is on the borderline of instability.

A polynomial that has all its roots in the left half plane is called a *Hurwitz polynomial*.   We wish to determine whether the polynomial $\mathbf{D}(s)$ is a Hurwitz polynomial.   If any of the coefficients $d_0, d_1, \ldots, d_{n-1}$ are negative or zero, then $\mathbf{D}(s)$ is not a Hurwitz polynomial.   However, even if all the $d_0, d_1, \ldots, d_{n-1}$ are positive, $\mathbf{D}(s)$ *can still have right-half-plane roots*.   Thus, if all the d's are positive, we must either factor $\mathbf{D}(s)$ or apply a test to determine whether it is a Hurwitz polynomial.

We shall now discuss these tests.   Note that we shall *not* derive the tests here, but shall simply state them, so that the reader can apply them in actual problems.

The Hurwitz test

The first step is to break up $\mathbf{D}(s)$ into the sum of two polynomials,

$$\mathbf{D}(s) = \mathbf{m}(s) + \mathbf{n}(s) \tag{5-216}$$

where $\mathbf{m}(s)$ is an even polynomial; that is, it contains all the even-powered terms, including the constant d_0, of $\mathbf{D}(s)$. $\mathbf{n}(s)$ is an odd polynomial.   Now we form the improper fraction

$$\phi(s) = \frac{\mathbf{m}(s)}{\mathbf{n}(s)} \tag{5-217a}$$

or

$$\phi(s) = \frac{\mathbf{n}(s)}{\mathbf{m}(s)} \tag{5-217b}$$

We shall use only one form of Eq. (5-217)—that in which the power of the numerator is greater than the power of the denominator [note that $\mathbf{m}(s)$ and $\mathbf{n}(s)$ cannot be of the same degree; since one is even and the other is odd, they will differ by one degree].   Let us, for the sake of discussion, use Eq. (5-217a) here.   Dividing $\mathbf{n}(s)$ into $\mathbf{m}(s)$ *once*, we obtain

$$\phi(s) = c_1 s + \frac{\mathbf{R}_1(s)}{\mathbf{n}(s)}$$

where $\mathbf{R}_1(s)$ is the remainder of the division [$\mathbf{R}_1(s)$ will be one degree less than $\mathbf{n}(s)$]. Now we form

$$\frac{\mathbf{n}(s)}{\mathbf{R}_1(s)} = c_2 s + \frac{\mathbf{R}_3(s)}{\mathbf{R}_2(s)}$$

and repeat the procedure successively [we form $\mathbf{R}_2(s)/\mathbf{R}_3(s)$, and so on]. The degrees of the remainder become smaller and smaller, and eventually the procedure terminates. If *any* of the constants $c_1, c_2, \ldots$ are not positive, then $\mathbf{D}(s)$ will have right-half-plane roots. If *all* the $c_1, c_2, \ldots$ are positive, then $\mathbf{D}(s)$ will be a Hurwitz polynomial (except for a special case which we shall discuss subsequently).

As an example consider

$$\mathbf{D}(s) = s^4 + 6s^3 + 9s^2 + 12s + 4$$

Then

$$\mathbf{m}(s) = s^4 + 9s^2 + 4$$

$$\mathbf{n}(s) = 6s^3 + 12s$$

We can set up the division in a compact form as

$$
\begin{array}{r}
\tfrac{1}{6}s \\
\hline
6s^3 + 12s\,\big|\,s^4 + 9s^2 + 4 \\
s^4 + 2s^2 \qquad\qquad \tfrac{6}{7}s \\
\hline
7s^2 + 4\,\big|\,6s^3 + 12s \\
6s^3 + 24\tfrac{4}{7}s \quad \tfrac{49}{60}s \\
\hline
60\tfrac{4}{7}s\,\big|\,7s^2 + 4 \\
7s^2 \qquad\qquad \tfrac{15}{7}s \\
\hline
4\,\big|\,60\tfrac{4}{7}s \\
60\tfrac{4}{7}s \\
\hline
\end{array}
$$

The c's then are $\tfrac{1}{6}$, $\tfrac{6}{7}$, $\tfrac{49}{60}$, and $\tfrac{15}{7}$. $\mathbf{D}(s)$ is a Hurwitz polynomial, since these are all positive.

If $\mathbf{D}(s)$ is such that $\mathbf{m}(s)$ and $\mathbf{n}(s)$ both have the *same* factor, then when the ratio is taken to form $\boldsymbol{\phi}(s)$, this factor will not affect the quotients $c_1, c_2, \ldots$. Thus no information about this factor will be supplied by the Hurwitz test. The only factor that $\mathbf{m}(s)$ and $\mathbf{n}(s)$ can *both* have in common is an even polynomial. This must also be a factor of $\mathbf{D}(s)$ [see Eq. (5-216)] and must be even, since the product of two even polynomials is an even polynomial and the product of an even polynomial and an odd polynomial is an odd polynomial.

Let us consider an even polynomial

$$\mathbf{E}(s) = s^{2k} + b_{k-1}s^{2k-2} + \cdots + b_1 s^2 + b_0$$

Substituting $-s$ for s and noting that $(-s)^2 = s^2$, we have

$$\mathbf{E}(s) = \mathbf{E}(-s)$$

Thus, if s_0 is a root of $\mathbf{E}(s)$, $-s_0$ will also be a root, and if $\mathbf{E}(s)$ has left-half-plane roots, it must also have right-half-plane roots. The only way that $\mathbf{E}(s)$ can have no right-half-plane roots is if *all* its roots lie on the $j\omega$ axis. Thus, if $\mathbf{D}(s)$ has an even-polynomial factor, it cannot be a Hurwitz polynomial.

In general, $\mathbf{D}(s)$ will not be in factored form (if it is, the test is unnecessary). Thus $\mathbf{E}(s)$ will not be easily recognized as a factor of $\mathbf{D}(s)$ or $\mathbf{m}(s)$ or $\mathbf{n}(s)$. However, the Hurwitz test will identify $\mathbf{E}(s)$. If the common factor is not canceled from $\mathbf{m}(s)$ and $\mathbf{n}(s)$, then it will be carried through the division and will *appear as the last divisor*. If the last divisor is not a constant, there is an even-polynomial factor.

As an example consider

$$\mathbf{D}(s) = (s^2 + 1)(s^2 + 2s + 2) = s^4 + 2s^3 + 3s^2 + 2s + 2$$

Then

$$\mathbf{m}(s) = s^4 + 3s^2 + 2 = (s^2 + 1)(s^2 + 2)$$

$$\mathbf{n}(s) = 2s^3 + 2s = (s^2 + 1)2s$$

In this case the polynomials are of low enough degree that we can identify the common factor (often this is not possible). Now we set up the long division

$$
\begin{array}{r}
\frac{1}{2}s \\ \hline
2s^3 + 2s\,\big)\,s^4 + 3s^2 + 2 \\
\underline{s^4 + s^2} \qquad s \\
2s^2 + 2\,\big)\,2s^3 + 2s \\
\underline{2s^3 + 2s} \\
0
\end{array}
$$

Note that the test terminated prematurely, since the last divisor was not a constant. In this case the last divisor is the even-polynomial factor

$$2s^2 + 2 = 2(s^2 + 1)$$

Thus the even factor can be identified from the last divisor. In general, if $\mathbf{D}(s)$ is to be a Hurwitz polynomial, then all the coefficients $c_1, c_2, \ldots$ in the Hurwitz test must be positive, and the test must not terminate prematurely.

There is one exception that must be considered. If the normal first coefficient of one of the remainders is zero and the rest of the remainder is not zero, then the test cannot proceed. In this case the remainder will not be one degree less than the divisor. To rectify this situation we change the coefficient of the second-highest-power term of $\mathbf{D}(s)$ from d_{n-1} to $d_{n-1} + \epsilon$ (for example, if $d_{n-1} = 6$, we replace it by $6 + \epsilon$). Then we perform the test, carrying the letter ϵ throughout. After the test is completed, we allow ϵ to became *very* small, and then we examine the c's. If any of them become negative when ϵ approaches zero, $\mathbf{D}(s)$ is not a Hurwitz polynomial.

The Routh test

Another procedure for determining whether the roots of a polynomial lie in the right half plane is the Routh test. It is very similar to the Hurwitz test, except that an array is used in place of the long division. We start by breaking up the polynomial $\mathbf{D}(s)$ into its even and odd parts [see Eq. (5-216)]. Then we can write

$$\mathbf{m}(s) = a_0 s^{2k} + a_1 s^{2k-2} + \cdots + a_k$$

$$\mathbf{n}(s) = b_0 s^{2k-1} + \cdots + b_{k-1} s$$

We have changed the notation of Eq. (5-215) here, but $\mathbf{D}(s)$ is still given by Eq. (5-216). We have assumed that $\mathbf{m}(s)$ is of higher degree than $\mathbf{n}(s)$. Now we form the following array [if the degree of $\mathbf{n}(s)$ is higher than that of $\mathbf{m}(s)$, then use the coefficients of $\mathbf{n}(s)$ to form the first row of the array]:

$$\begin{vmatrix} a_0 & a_1 & a_2 & \cdots & a_k \\ b_0 & b_1 & b_2 & \cdots & b_{k-1} \\ c_0 & c_1 & \cdots \cdots \cdots \cdots \\ d_0 & d_1 & \cdots \cdots \cdots \cdots \\ \cdots \cdots \cdots \cdots \cdots \cdots \end{vmatrix} \qquad (5\text{-}218)$$

The first two rows are obtained from the coefficients of $\mathbf{m}(s)$ and $\mathbf{n}(s)$, respectively. The third row is obtained from the equations

$$c_0 = \frac{b_0 a_1 - a_0 b_1}{b_0}$$

$$c_1 = \frac{b_0 a_2 - a_0 b_2}{b_0} \qquad (5\text{-}219)$$

$$c_2 = \frac{b_0 a_3 - a_0 b_3}{b_0}$$

$$\cdots \cdots \cdots \cdots$$

In a similar way, any row is generated from the two preceding it; for example, to obtain the d's we replace the a's by b's and the b's by c's in Eqs. (5-219). The operations of Eqs. (5-219) are essentially those of long division. In fact, the third row consists of the coefficients of the remainder of the first division of the Hurwitz test; the fourth row consists of the coefficients of the second remainder, and so on. In fact, the Routh and Hurwitz tests are essentially the same. When this procedure terminates, we examine the first column in the array. If any of its coefficients (a_0, b_0, c_0, . . .) are negative, then the polynomial $\mathbf{D}(s) = \mathbf{m}(s) + \mathbf{n}(s)$ will have right-half-plane roots. The number of right-half-plane roots is equal to the number of sign changes in the sequence a_0, b_0, c_0, d_0, ... Multiple roots are counted as the order of their multiplicity (for instance, a double root is counted twice).

Let us evaluate the same example we used for the Hurwitz test by using the Routh procedure. We start with

$$\mathbf{D}(s) = s^4 + 6s^3 + 9s^2 + 12s + 4$$

and then form the array

$$
\begin{vmatrix}
1 & 9 & 4 \\
6 & 12 & \\
7 & 4 & \\
60/7 & & \\
4 & & \\
0 & &
\end{vmatrix}
$$

All the coefficients of the first column are positive. Thus there are no roots in the right half plane. Compare this array and the long division of the first example. Note that the rows correspond to the remainders. Since we are interested in only the signs of the coefficients, we can multiply any row by a positive coefficient if it is convenient to do so.

If the Hurwitz test terminates prematurely, then so will the Routh test. The implications are the same in both cases. If the first term in one of the rows is zero, but the rest of the row is not zero, then the test cannot proceed. We use the same procedure here as in the Hurwitz case. That is, we replace the b_0 coefficient in the array by $b_0 + \epsilon$, set up the array, and *then* let ϵ become *very* small and examine the coefficients of the first column. If any of the coefficients become negative as ϵ approaches zero, then $\mathbf{D}(s)$ is not a Hurwitz polynomial.

5-14   The unit impulse

In this section we shall consider a special function of time called the *impulse function*. A network is often rated in terms of its response to this important function. In addition, the response of a network to an arbitrary time function can also be expressed in terms of its response to the unit impulse (this will be discussed in Sec. 5-20). Moreover, the Laplace transform of the unit impulse is simple and very convenient to work with. Finally, the impulse response of a network closely approximates the response to pulses of very short duration. However, it is much more convenient to work with the impulse.

The mathematical discussion of this section will be more heuristic than rigorous. A rigorous analysis requires distribution theory.[1] We shall use some elementary concepts of distribution theory here, but a complete discussion is beyond the scope of the chapter. We shall introduce the unit-impulse function on a limit basis. Consider the function of time $f_\delta(t)$ drawn in Fig. 5-34. This *flat-topped pulse* is zero for $t < 0$ and is also zero for $t > t_0$. For $0 < t \le$

Fig. 5-34 A pulse of duration t_0 sec and height $1/t_0$. In the limit, as t_0 approaches zero, this becomes the unit-impulse function $\delta(t)$.

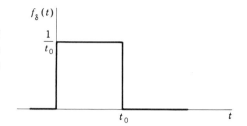

t_0 its value is constant at $1/t_0$. Thus the area under the curve of $f_\delta(t)$ is unity. This is independent of the value of t_0. Now let us consider that t_0 becomes smaller and smaller. The "width" of the pulse decreases, but its height increases, so that the area remains unity. One way of defining the impulse function is

$$\delta(t) = \lim_{t \to 0} f_\delta(t) \tag{5-220}$$

The letter delta denotes the impulse function, at times called the *delta function*. Nonmathematically speaking, the impulse function is a pulse of infinite height which is zero everywhere but at the origin. The area of the pulse is unity.

The integral of the impulse function

To obtain the Laplace transform of the impulse function we must integrate it. The impulse function is not an ordinary function, and in the usual sense, its integral does not exist. However, we shall *define* its integral based on a limit process. Let us consider

$$\int_{-\infty}^{\infty} f_\delta(t) \, dt = 1$$

The area under the $f_\delta(t)$ curve of Fig. 5-44 is always unity. Hence, in the limit, we shall *define*

$$\int_{-\infty}^{\infty} \delta(t) \, dt = 1 \tag{5-221}$$

Now let us consider the integral of the product of the impulse function and an ordinary function which is continuous at $t = 0$. We start with

$$\int_{-\infty}^{\infty} f_\delta(t) f(t) \, dt$$

where $f_\delta(t)$ is as defined in Fig. 5-34 and $f(t)$ is an ordinary function which is continuous at $t = 0$. Since $f_\delta(t) = 0$ for $t < 0$ and $t > t_0$ and $f(t) = 1/t_0$ for $0 \le t \le t_0$, we have

$$\int_{-\infty}^{\infty} f_\delta(t) \, \delta(t) \, dt = \int_0^{t_0} \frac{1}{t_0} f(t) \, dt = \frac{1}{t_0} \int_0^{t_0} f(t) \, dt \tag{5-222}$$

This equation is valid for any t_0.   As t_0 becomes very small, we integrate $f(t)$ over a very small range of t.   We assume that $f(t)$ is continuous in the neighborhood of the origin.   Thus, if t_0 is very close to zero, then $f(t) \approx f(0)$ in the range $0 \leq t \leq t_0$; that is, since $f(t)$ is continuous in the range $0 \leq t \leq t_0$ and t_0 is very small, $f(t)$ can change only very slightly in the range under consideration.   No matter how rapidly $f(t)$ changes, if it is continuous, we can always choose a t_0 small enough so that the change of $f(t)$ in the range is negligible.   Hence we can replace $f(t)$ in Eq. (5-222) by the constant $f(0)$.   This yields

$$\int_{-\infty}^{\infty} f_\delta(t) f(t) \, dt \approx \frac{1}{t_0} f(0) \int_0^{t_0} dt = f(0) \tag{5-223}$$

In the limit this approximate relation becomes exact.   Thus we shall *define*

$$\int_{-\infty}^{\infty} \delta(t) f(t) \, dt = f(0) \tag{5-224}$$

In distribution theory this equation is taken as the *fundamental definition of the impulse function.*

Since $\delta(t)$ is zero for $t < 0$ and also for $t > 0$, we can write

$$\int_a^b \delta(t) f(t) \, dt = f(0) \qquad a < 0, \, b > 0 \tag{5-225}$$

Also, we have

$$\int_{0-}^{0+} \delta(t) f(t) \, dt = f(0) \tag{5-226}$$

This is true because, in a heuristic sense, we assume that the entire impulse occurs in the differentially small interval between $0-$ and $0+$.   That is, we assume that the impulse starts *after* $t = 0-$ and ends *before* $0+$.   Similarly, we can write

$$\int_{0+}^{\infty} \delta(t) f(t) \, dt = 0 \tag{5-227}$$

The impulse is assumed to be "over" at $t = 0+$; thus this integral is zero.

The Laplace transform of the impulse function

Now let us obtain the Laplace transform of the unit-impulse function.   From the fundamental definition of the Laplace transform we have

$$\mathcal{L}[\delta(t)] = \int_{0-}^{\infty} \delta(t) e^{-st} \, dt \tag{5-228}$$

Then, from Eq. (5-225), where $a = 0-$ and $b = \infty$, and $f(t) = e^{st}$, we have

$$\mathcal{L}[\delta(t)] = 1 \tag{5-229}$$

Note that $e^{-st} \Big|_{s=0} = 1$.   Thus the impulse function has an extremely simple

Laplace transform.   We shall see in Sec. 5-16 that the Laplace transform of a pulse is much more complex than unity.   This is one reason that it is very desirable to work with impulse functions.

The use of 0− as a lower limit in the Laplace transform

In Sec. 5-2 we discussed the use of 0− and 0+ as the lower limit of integration in the Laplace transform and indicated that it was desirable to use 0−.   We now are in a position to demonstrate that this choice is a good one.   We shall use both forms of the Laplace transform to analyze a simple circuit with an impulse generator.   The generalization of this analysis will demonstrate the utility of 0− as the lower limit.

Consider the circuit of Fig. 5-35a, which contains an impulse generator. The transformed form of this network is shown in Fig. 5-35b.   The transformed form of the impulse generator is obtained simply by taking the Laplace transform of $V\delta(t)$.   Then, writing a loop equation for Fig. 5-35b, we obtain

$$V + Li(0-) = (R + Ls)\mathbf{I}(s) \qquad\qquad (5\text{-}230a)$$

Hence

$$\mathbf{I}(s) = \frac{V + Li(0-)}{L(s + R/L)} \qquad\qquad (5\text{-}230b)$$

Fig. 5-35   (a) *A simple RL circuit containing an impulsive voltage generator, with known initial condition* $i(0-)$; (b) *the transformed form of this network with* 0− *as the lower limit of integration;* (c) *the transformed form of this network with* 0+ *as the lower limit of integration; note that* $i(0+)$ *is unknown.*

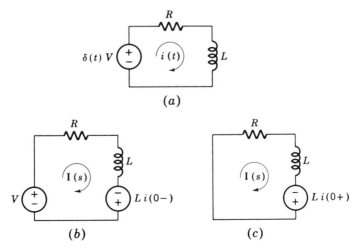

(a)

(b)   (c)

Then, from Table 5-1, we have

$$i(t) = \frac{V + Li(0-)}{L} e^{-(R/L)t} u(t) \tag{5-231}$$

If we let t approach zero, we obtain $i(0+)$. Consider that we start with a positive value of time and let t become smaller and smaller. This yields $i(0+)$. Thus

$$i(0+) = \frac{V}{L} + i(0-) \tag{5-232}$$

In this case the current through the inductance changed instantaneously. This should not be surprising, since the impulse generator generates an infinite voltage (see Sec. 4-1). Note that when $0-$ is used as the lower limit of integration in the Laplace transform, it is no more difficult to work with impulse functions than with ordinary generators. In fact, it is easier, since the Laplace transform of the impulse is so simple.

Now let us analyze Fig. 5-35a with the Laplace transform which has $0+$ as its lower limit of integration [see Eq. (5-32)]. We start by taking the Laplace transform of $\delta(t)$,

$$\mathcal{L}_{0+}[\delta(t)] = \int_{0+}^{\infty} \delta(t) e^{-st}\, dt = 0 \tag{5-233}$$

This is zero, since the impulse is "over" at $t = 0+$; thus the transformed form of Fig. 5-35a has the form shown in Fig. 5-35c (note that $0+$ replaces $0-$ in the initial conditions). Analyzing the circuit, we obtain

$$Li(0+) = (R + Ls)\mathbf{I}(s) \tag{5-234a}$$

or, equivalently,

$$\mathbf{I}(s) = \frac{i(0+)}{s + R/L} \tag{5-234b}$$

Taking the inverse transform, we obtain

$$i(t) = i(0+)e^{-(R/L)t} u(t) \tag{5-235}$$

This answer is correct. *However, $i(0+)$ is an unknown quantity.* That is, in general, we know the initial conditions prior to the application of the generator. If, as in this case, the generators cause the initial conditions to change instantaneously, then the initial conditions at $t = 0+$ are *unknown*. We can substitute Eq. (5-232) into Eq. (5-235) to obtain the answer in terms of known quantities. However, Eq. (5-232) was obtained with the $0-$ Laplace transform, which gave us the complete solution. There is no reason to solve the problem twice. Thus the use of the $0+$ Laplace transform results in unnecessary extra work. There are classical means of evaluating the $0+$ initial conditions when the $0-$ ones are known, but this method entails all the extra work encountered in the classical procedure in addition to the work of the $0+$ Laplace transform procedure. Thus the $0+$ Laplace transform entails much more work when the initial conditions change instantaneously. If the initial conditions do not change instantaneously, then both $0+$ and $0-$ Laplace transform procedures will result in the same amount of work.

For general network analysis, then, the $0-$ Laplace transform is by far the more desirable one to use. We have demonstrated this in terms of a simple example, but the discussion also applies to more complex networks. That is, the $0+$ Laplace transform entails the extra work of evaluating the $0+$ initial conditions. When impulse functions are present, this can be very tedious. The use of the $0-$ Laplace transform eliminates this tedium without complicating the analysis. Henceforth, when the Laplace transform is mentioned, unless otherwise stated, refer to the one with $0-$ as the lower limit of integration.

Differentiation of the impulse function

We have demonstrated that $\mathcal{L}[\delta(t)] = 1$. Hence we can state that

$$\mathcal{L}^{-1}[1] = \delta(t)$$

Let us now consider the inverse Laplace transform of s. From Eq. (5-33) we have

$$s\mathbf{F}(s) = \mathcal{L}\left[\frac{d}{dt}f(t)\right] + f(0-) \tag{5-236}$$

At $t = 0-$ we consider that the unit impulse is zero. That is, the infinite jump of the impulse is assumed to occur after $t = 0-$ and to end before $t = 0+$. Thus, substituting $\mathbf{F}(s) = 1$ into Eq. (5-236), we obtain

$$s = \mathcal{L}\left[\frac{d}{dt}\delta(t)\right] = \mathcal{L}[\delta'(t)] \tag{5-237}$$

The derivative of the unit impulse is called the *unit doublet*. A physical interpretation of this is shown in Fig. 5-36. As t_0 approaches zero, this curve becomes the unit doublet.

Fig. 5-36 A function of time which, as t_0 approaches zero, becomes the unit doublet.

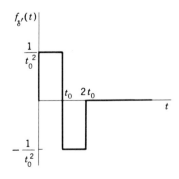

On a heuristic (but not a rigorous) basis, we can discuss the derivative of the unit impulse. Consider the pulse $f(t)$ of Fig. 5-34. There are two points at which its derivative becomes infinite—at $t = 0$ and at $t = t_0$. The first of these derivatives is positive, and the second is negative. Now consider Fig. 5-36. As t_0 approaches zero, this curve becomes a positive peak of "infinity squared," followed by a negative peak of "infinity squared." Since the impulse has an infinite discontinuity, it is reasonable to consider that its derivative has a higher-order discontinuity. Thus it appears reasonable that Fig. 5-36, in the limit, is the derivative of $\delta(t)$. It should be emphasized that this explanation is nonrigorous. On a rigorous basis, unless distribution theory is employed, these infinite functions do not exist. Thus this discussion here is intended merely to provide a "feel" for the doublet function.

We can differentiate $\delta(t)$ successively. This results in its transform being multiplied by s successively. Hence

$$\mathcal{L}^{-1}[s^n] = \frac{d^n \, \delta(t)}{dt^n} \tag{5-238}$$

Equation (5-238) can be used to obtain the inverse Laplace transform of the power-series terms of Eq. (5-62).

The derivative of discontinuous functions

We can use the impulse function to represent the derivative of an ordinary function which has a jump discontinuity. It must again be emphasized that on an ordinary basis such derivatives do not exist. A rigorous treatment in terms of distribution theory justifies the use of impulse functions in such applications, but here we shall discuss the results on purely a heuristic basis.

As an example of a discontinuous function consider the unit step $u(t)$ in Fig. 5-1. The discontinuity occurs at $t = 0$. We have demonstrated that [see Eq. (5-11)]

$$\mathcal{L}[u(t)] = \frac{1}{s}$$

We now use Eq. (5-33) to obtain the Laplace transform of its derivative. Since $u(0-) = 0$, we obtain

$$\mathcal{L}\left[\frac{d}{dt}\, u(t)\right] = 1 \tag{5-239}$$

However, this is the Laplace transform of the unit impulse. Thus

$$\frac{d}{dt}\, u(t) = \delta(t) \tag{5-240}$$

Note that $u(t)$ is constant except at $t = 0$, so its derivative is zero except at $t = 0$, where it is infinite. The impulse function has these properties.

Let us consider the derivative of another discontinuous function, $u(t) \cos t$. From Eq. (5-37) we have

$$\mathcal{L}\left[\frac{d}{dt} u(t) \cos t\right] = \frac{s^2}{s^2 + 1} \tag{5-241a}$$

Expanding this as in Eq. (5-62), we obtain

$$\mathcal{L}\left[\frac{d}{dt} u(t) \cos t\right] = 1 - \frac{1}{s^2 + 1} \tag{5-241b}$$

Then, taking the inverse Laplace transform of both sides of this equation, we have

$$\frac{d}{dt} u(t) \cos t = \delta(t) - \sin t \tag{5-242}$$

In general, the derivative of a function with finite discontinuities will contain impulses which occur at the discontinuities. If the discontinuity is b units, then the impulse function will be multiplied by b. In all our examples b was unity.

5-15   The unit-step response and the unit-impulse response

Often the function of a network is to *amplify* a signal applied at its input. For instance, consider the twoport of Fig. 5-31a. $\mathbf{V}_1(s)$ could represent the transform of an input signal whose magnitude is very small. We wish the output voltage $\mathbf{V}_2(s)$ to have the same form as $\mathbf{V}_1(s)$, but to be multiplied by a constant. In the time domain consider that the input signal is $v_1(t)$. Then the output signal $v_2(t)$ would ideally be

$$v_2(t) = k v_1(t) \tag{5-243}$$

That is, we desire a circuit which will produce an output voltage of the same waveform as the input, but k times as big as the input. Such a circuit is called an *amplifier*. In a high-fidelity phonograph amplifier, for example, the phonograph pickup produces the desired voltage. However, the signal is too small to operate the loudspeaker, so an amplifier is inserted between the phonograph pickup and the loudspeaker. Its purpose is to produce an output signal, equal to the input signal multiplied by a constant, which is large enough to operate the loudspeaker. The constant is termed the *amplification*.

Only an *ideal* amplifier has the relation of input to output voltages given in Eq. (5-243). Any practical amplifier will introduce *distortion;* that is, the output signal will *not* be a constant times the input signal. Thus the output waveform will be different from the input one. To test for distortion we could consider that an input signal is applied to the network, solve for (or experimentally measure) the output, and then compare the difference between the input

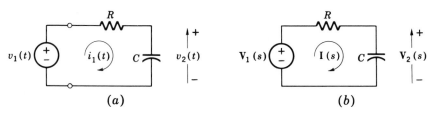

Fig. 5-37   (a) A simple network; (b) its transformed form.

and output signals.   If the input signal is irregular, however, it is difficult to
estimate the difference between it and the output signal.   Thus regular input
signals are usually used to test amplifiers.   The input signals most commonly
used are the unit step and the unit impulse.   The responses to these signals are
termed the *unit-step response* and the *unit-impulse response*, respectively.   In
the preceding discussion we assumed that the input and output signals were
both voltages.   Actually, either could be a voltage or a current.

Let us determine the unit-impulse and unit-step responses of the typical
network of Fig. 5-37a.   From Fig. 5-37b we obtain

$$\mathbf{I}(s) \; = \; \frac{\mathbf{V}_1(s)}{R + 1/Cs}$$

Then

$$\mathbf{V}_2(s) \; = \; \frac{1}{Cs}\,\mathbf{I}(s) \; = \; \frac{\mathbf{V}_1(s)}{RC(s + 1/RC)} \tag{5-244}$$

First let us find the unit-impulse response of the network.   In this case
$\mathbf{V}_1(s) = 1$, so

$$\mathbf{W}(s) \; = \; \frac{1}{RC(s + 1/RC)} \tag{5-245}$$

We shall use $w(t)$ as the symbolic representation of the unit-impulse response.
Its Laplace transform is $\mathbf{W}(s)$.   Then, from Table 5-1 we have

$$w(t) \; = \; u(t)\,\frac{1}{RC}\,e^{-(1/RC)t} \tag{5-246}$$

This curve, which is plotted in Fig. 5-38a, is just an exponential decay.   The
curve does not look at all like an impulse.   However, consider that the product
RC becomes very small; then $1/RC$ becomes very large, and thus the maximum
value of $w(t)$ becomes large.   Similarly, as RC becomes small—that is, as the
time constant (see Sec. 4-4) becomes small—the rate of decay of $i_0(t)$ becomes
rapid.   In the limit, as RC approaches zero, the curve becomes a unit impulse.
Thus to reduce the distortion of the circuit we make RC as small as possible.

Now let us obtain the unit-step response of this network.   In this case we let $\mathbf{V}_1(s) = 1/s$ in Eq. (5-244). Hence

$$\mathbf{A}(s) = \frac{1}{RCs(s + 1/RC)} = \frac{1}{s} - \frac{1}{s + 1/RC} \tag{5-247}$$

Taking the inverse Laplace transform, we have

$$a_2(t) = u(t)(1 - e^{-t/RC}) \tag{5-248}$$

where we have used $a(t)$ as the symbol for the unit-step response and $\mathbf{A}(s)$ as its Laplace transform. A plot of the curve is shown in Fig. 5-37b. This curve does not rise instantaneously to unity, as does the unit step. However, if RC is made small, then the rate of rise is increased. In the limit, as RC approaches zero, this curve does become the unit-step response. Thus to reduce the distortion we make RC as small as possible. This is the same conclusion we reached with the unit-impulse response. In general, either one can be used to rate the distortion and determine what should be done to reduce it.

Note that in this case the unit-impulse response is the derivative of the unit-step response. This result is general, since the unit-step response is obtained by multiplying $1/s$ times the transfer function of the network, and the

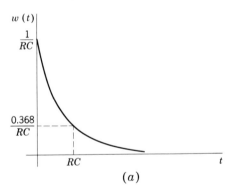

(a)

Fig. 5-38 (a) The unit-impulse response of the network of Fig. 5-37; (b) its unit-step response.

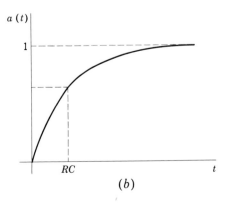

(b)

unit-impulse response is obtained by multiplying it by 1. Hence

$$\mathbf{W}(s) = s\mathbf{A}(s) \tag{5-249}$$

where $\mathbf{W}(s)$ and $\mathbf{A}(s)$ are the transforms of the unit-impulse response and the unit-step response, respectively. If we multiply a transform by s, we obtain the Laplace transform of the derivative with zero initial conditions. Thus $w(t) = (d/dt)a(t)$. It is also interesting to note that the unit-impulse response can be found simply by taking the inverse Laplace transform of the transfer function.

Often the unit-step responses of different networks are compared by means of some figures of merit. This entails the use of one or more numbers to compare *complete* curves. Thus we cannot obtain a complete description with such figures of merit. However, those that we shall use are convenient and often provide a satisfactory comparison of networks. One criterion that could be used to rate the unit-step response is the time it takes for $a(t)$ to reach its final value. However (see Fig. 5-38b), this time is often infinite. We might then use as a figure of merit the time it takes for the response to reach its final value "for all practical purposes." Often 90 percent of the final value is chosen as such a "practical final value." There is nothing special about the figure of 90 percent. In some applications 99 percent should be used, while in others 80 percent should be used. For our purpose here, however, let us use 90 percent as a typical value.

In order to discuss some other figures of merit that are used to rate the unit-step response of a network we must consider a more general form of response. A typical one is shown in Fig. 5-39. The unit-step response has been normal-

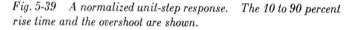

Fig. 5-39   A normalized unit-step response.   The 10 to 90 percent rise time and the overshoot are shown.

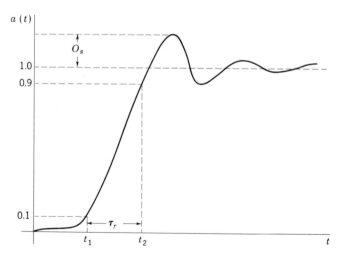

ized so that its final value is unity, and the response is drawn so that it stays small up to time t_1 and reaches 90 percent of its final value at t_2. Often a network introduces time delay without producing distortion. Again consider the high-fidelity amplifier. If its output is a faithful reproduction of the input but is delayed by $\frac{1}{10}$ sec, its performance would be considered perfect for almost all applications. Thus the delay time should not be added to the response time. For this reason we often do not consider that the response has started until it has reached 10 percent of its final value. This figure of 10 percent is also arbitrary; it is merely a typical value used to account for the time delay of the network. Thus to rate the response time we consider the time required for the response to rise from 10 percent of its final value to 90 percent of its final value. This is called the 10 *to* 90 *percent rise time* and is written τ_r.

There is one situation in which the delay time *should* be charged against the speed of response. In digital computers the networks process pulses in succession, and a pulse cannot be processed until it has reached a substantial fraction of its final value. Hence the delay time slows the time of response and should be "charged against" it. In such applications the 0 to 90 percent rise time is a figure of merit to be used.

There is one other figure of merit used to characterize the unit-step response. In Fig. 5-39 note that the unit-step response rises above its final value and then "swings" about it in a damped fashion. This can be considered to be a distortion of the response. To characterize it we introduce a parameter called *overshoot*. The overshoot is defined as

$$O_s = a(t)\Big|_{max} - 1 \tag{5-250}$$

where it is assumed that $a(t)$ has been normalized so that its final value is unity.

The 10 to 90 percent rise time and the overshoot are two parameters used to rate the unit-step response. Note that this is an attempt to characterize an entire curve in terms of only two figures. In working with responses which are all of the same general shape such a characterization is often successful. With an uncommon type of unit-step response, however, these simple characterizations cannot be used.

5-16   Time shift

At times we want to know the Laplace transform of a function of time which is the same as another function, except that it is delayed in time. To relate the Laplace transforms of these two time functions let us consider that

$$\mathcal{L}[u(t)f(t)] = \mathbf{F}(s) \tag{5-251}$$

and we wish to find $\mathcal{L}[u(t - t_1)f(t - t_1)]$. That is, the original function $f(t)$ is delayed by t_1 sec. From the fundamental definition of the Laplace transform

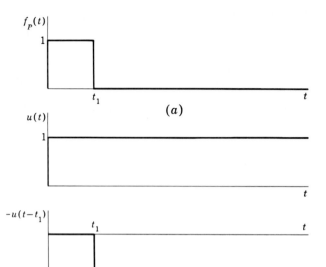

Fig. 5-40 (a) A flat-topped pulse; (b) two unit step functions whose sum yields the pulse of (a).

we have

$$\mathcal{L}[u(t - t_1)f(t - t_1)]$$
$$= \int_0^\infty u(t - t_1)f(t - t_1)e^{-st} \, dt = \int_{t_1}^\infty f(t - t_1)e^{-st} \, dt \quad (5\text{-}252)$$

Now we let

$$t - t_1 = \tau \tag{5-253}$$

Substituting in Eq. (5-252), we obtain

$$\mathcal{L}[u(t - t_1)f(t - t_1)] = \int_0^\infty f(\tau)e^{-s(\tau + t_1)} \, d\tau$$

However, e^{-st_1} is a constant as far as the integration is concerned, so

$$\mathcal{L}[u(t - t_1)f(t - t_1)] = e^{-st_1} \int_0^\infty f(\tau)e^{-s\tau} \, d\tau \tag{5-254}$$

The integral is just the definition of $\mathcal{L}[f(t)]$ (note that it does not matter if we call the variable of integration t or τ).   Hence

$$\mathcal{L}[u(t - t_1)f(t - t_1)] = e^{-st_1}\mathbf{F}(s) \tag{5-255}$$

Thus to obtain the Laplace transform of a function which has been delayed by t_1 sec we multiply the transform of the undelayed function by e^{-st_1}.

This relation is particularly useful in obtaining the Laplace transform of pulses.   As an example let us obtain the Laplace transform of the pulse $f_P(t)$ shown in Fig. 5-40a.   We can obtain $f_P(t)$ by taking the sum of the unit step and the negative unit step functions of Fig. 5-40b:

$$f_P(t) = u(t) - u(t - t_1) \tag{5-256}$$

Hence

$$F_P(s) = \mathcal{L}[u(t)] - \mathcal{L}[u(t - t_1)] \tag{5-257}$$

The Laplace transform of the unit step function is $1/s$. Then, applying Eq. (5-255), we obtain

$$\mathbf{F}(s) = \frac{1}{s}[1 - e^{-t_1 s}] \tag{5-258}$$

5-17   Semiperiodic functions

The semiperiodic signal is one that is often encountered.   It consists of a waveform that is zero for $t < 0$ but periodically repeats itself for $t > 0$.   Such a function $p(t)$ is shown in Fig. 5-41a.   It is called "semiperiodic" because it is zero for $t < 0$ and repeats itself every T sec for $t > 0$. T is called the *period* of the function.   We shall express the Laplace transform of this function in terms of the Laplace transform of another function, $p_0(t)$, which is shown in Fig. 5-41b; that is, $p_0(t) = p(t)$ for the first time period but is zero elsewhere. Hence

$$p_0(t) = \begin{cases} p(t) & 0 \le t \le T \\ 0 & t > T \end{cases} \tag{5-259}$$

All the time functions are assumed to be zero for $t < 0$.

Fig. 5-41   (a) A semiperiodic function p(t); (b) a function equal to p(t) for the first cycle and zero elsewhere.

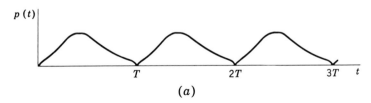

(a)

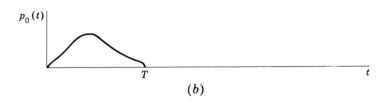

(b)

We can construct $p(t)$ from $p_0(t)$ by taking the sum

$$p(t) = p_0(t) + p_0(t - T) + p_0(t - 2T) + \cdots \tag{5-260}$$

That is, $p_0(t)$ is decayed by 1, 2, . . . times the period, and all these terms are then added.   If

$$\mathcal{L}[p_0(t)] = \mathbf{P}_0(s) \tag{5-261}$$

and $\mathcal{L}[p(t)] = \mathbf{P}(s)$, then

$$\mathbf{P}(s) = \mathbf{P}_0(s)(1 + e^{-st} + e^{-2st} + \cdots) \tag{5-262}$$

We can state this in a more compact form by expressing the series of Eq. (5-262) in closed form as

$$\frac{1}{1 - e^{-sT}} = 1 + e^{-sT} + e^{-2sT} + \cdots \tag{5-263}$$

Then, substituting in Eq. (5-262), we obtain

$$\mathbf{P}(s) = \frac{\mathbf{P}_0(s)}{1 - e^{-sT}} \tag{5-264}$$

5-18   The final-value theorem

In many circumstances, if we know $\mathbf{F}(s)$, we can determine $\lim_{t \to \infty} f(t)$ without evaluating the inverse Laplace transform.   We can obtain this limit very simply, and it often provides us with some useful information.   To obtain a theorem which provides us with the required information we shall work with $df(t)/dt$ and its Laplace transform $s\mathbf{F}(s) - f(0-)$.   If the theorem is to be of use, the function must have a final value ($\lim_{t \to \infty} \sin t$, for example, does not exist).
It can be demonstrated that if $s\mathbf{F}(s)$ does not have poles on the $j\omega$ axis or in the right half plane, then the final value will exist (it should be noted that distribution theory can resolve such difficulties as obtaining the final value of $\sin t$).
From Eq. (5-33) we have, for the Laplace transform of the derivative,

$$\int_0^\infty f'(t)e^{-st}\, dt = s\mathbf{F}(s) - f(0-) \tag{5-265}$$

where $\mathbf{F}(s) = \mathcal{L}[f(t)]$.   We let s approach zero.   Then e^{-st} becomes unity, and

$$\int_0^\infty f'(t)\, dt = \lim_{s \to 0} s\mathbf{F}(s) - f(0-) \tag{5-266}$$

The integral of the derivative of a function is just the function itself.   Therefore

$$\lim_{t \to \infty} f(t) - f(0-) = \lim_{s \to 0} s\mathbf{F}(s) - f(0-)$$

Thus

$$\lim_{t \to \infty} f(t) = \lim_{s \to 0} s\mathbf{F}(s) \qquad (5\text{-}267)$$

Then, if $s\mathbf{F}(s)$ has no poles on the $j\omega$ axis or in the right half plane, the final value of $f(t)$ is given by Eq. (5-267).

As an example let us obtain the final value of the function of time whose Laplace transform is given by

$$\mathbf{F}(s) = \frac{1}{s(s + a)} \qquad a > 0 \qquad (5\text{-}268)$$

{actually, $f(t) = (1/a)(1 - e^{-at})$ and the final value is $1/a$, but we shall ascertain this without taking $\mathcal{L}^{-1}[\mathbf{F}(s)]$}. Then

$$s\mathbf{F}(s) = \frac{1}{s + a} \qquad (5\text{-}269)$$

This has no poles in the right half plane or on the $j\omega$ axis, so the theorem can be applied:

$$\lim_{t \to \infty} f(t) = \lim_{s \to 0} s\mathbf{F}(s) = \lim_{s \to 0} \frac{1}{s + a} = \frac{1}{a} \qquad (5\text{-}270)$$

5-19   The initial-value theorem

At times we are interested in the value of a function of time or its derivative at $t = 0+$. For instance, the value $df(t)/dt \big|_{t=0+}$ gives an indication of the initial rate of response of a function. We shall present a method in this section which enables us to determine the initial value of a function and its derivatives by means of the Laplace transform, but without having to take the inverse transform. Let us start with the assumption that

$$\mathcal{L}\,[f(t)] = \mathbf{F}(s) \qquad (5\text{-}271)$$

and that we have a knowledge of any impulse functions or their derivatives at the origin that are contained in $f(t)$. We shall see later how this information can be obtained. We break up $f(t)$ in the summation

$$f(t) = f_1(t) + K_1\delta(t) + K_2\delta'(t) + K_3\delta''(t) + \cdots \qquad (5\text{-}272)$$

where the primes refer to differentiation. The first of these functions $f_1(t)$, contains no impulse-type functions at $t = 0$. The remaining terms contain any impulse functions or their derivatives at $t = 0$ that are contained in $f(t)$. Usual functions will not contain these impulse functions

$$(K_1 = K_2 = \cdots = 0)$$

Working with Eq. (5-265) here, we have

$$\int_{0-}^{\infty} f'(t)e^{-st}\, dt = s\mathbf{F}(s) - f(0-) \tag{5-273}$$

We break up the integral as follows:

$$\int_{0-}^{\infty} f'(t)e^{-st}\, dt = \int_{0-}^{0+} f'(t)e^{-st}\, dt + \int_{0+}^{\infty} f'(t)e^{-st}\, dt \tag{5-274}$$

Consider the first integral on the right-hand side. Substituting Eq. (5-272), we obtain

$$\int_{0-}^{0+} f'(t)e^{-st}\, dt = \int_{0-}^{0+} f_1'(t)e^{-st}\, dt$$
$$+ \int_{0-}^{0+} K_1\delta'(t)e^{-st}\, dt + \int_{0-}^{0+} K_2\delta''(t)e^{-st}\, dt + \cdots \tag{5-275}$$

Let us evaluate this term by term. In the first integral on the right-hand side $e^{-st} = 1$, since $s = 0$ over the range of integration. The integral of the derivative of a function is just the function itself, so we have

$$\int_{0-}^{0+} f_1'(t)e^{-st}\, dt = \int_{0-}^{0+} f_1'(t)\, dt = f_1(0+) - f_1(0-) \tag{5-276}$$

Actually, $f_1(0-)$ is the limit of $f_1(t)$ as t approaches zero through negative values of t. Similarly, $f_1(0+)$ is the limit as t approaches zero through positive values of t. These limits are the same for $f(t)$ since any impulses (or their derivatives) contained in $f(t)$ will not change these limits. Thus $f_1(0+) = f(0+)$ and $f_1(0-) = f(0-)$ (note that we assume that the impulse starts *after* $t = 0-$ and ends *before* $t = 0+$). Hence Eq. (5-276) becomes

$$\int_{0-}^{0+} f_1'(t)e^{st}\, dt = f(0+) - f(0-) \tag{5-277}$$

Now let us consider the remainder of the integrals of Eq. (5-275). We can represent any one of these by the general form

$$K_m \int_{0-}^{0+} \frac{d^m}{dt^m}\, \delta(t)\, e^{-st}\, dt \qquad m = 1, 2, \ldots \tag{5-278}$$

We saw in Sec. 5-14 that the upper limit of integration of integrals such as Eq. (5-278) could be changed from $0+$ to infinity without changing the integral (heuristically speaking, the impulse and its derivatives are zero for $t \geq 0+$). When the upper limit is changed to infinity, the integral of Eq. (5-278) becomes the definition of the Laplace transform. The Laplace transform of the derivatives of the impulse function is given in Eq. (5-238). Thus

$$K_m \int_{0-}^{0+} \frac{d^m}{dt^m}\, \delta(t)\, e^{-st}\, dt = K_m s^m \qquad m = 1, 2, \ldots \tag{5-279}$$

Substituting Eq. (5-277) and Eq. (5-279) into Eq. (5-274) and then substituting this into Eq. (5-273), we obtain

$$f(0+) - f(0-) + K_1 s + K_2 s^2 + K_3 s^3 + \cdots$$
$$+ \int_{0+}^{\infty} f'(t)e^{-st}\,dt = sF(s) - f(0-)$$

and solving for $f(0+)$ yields

$$f(0+) = s[F(s) - K_1 - K_2 s - K_3 s^2 - \cdots] - \int_{0+}^{\infty} f'(t)e^{-st}\,dt \qquad (5\text{-}280)$$

This relation is true for all values of s. Let us choose a particular one which makes it easy to evaluate $f(0+)$. In the integral of Eq. (5-280) t is always positive, since it ranges from $0+$ to infinity. Hence $\lim\limits_{s\to\infty} f'(t)e^{-st} = 0$ for all t [we assume that $f'(t)$ is of exponential order]. Thus we can eliminate the integral from Eq. (5-279) by letting s approach infinity. This makes $f(0+)$ much easier to evaluate, since we do not have to evaluate the integral.

This reader may have been curious about why the integral was broken in two in Eq. (5-274). This was done to cause the second integral to go to zero as s approaches infinity. If we consider that t lies in the range $0-$ to infinity, then we cannot state that $\lim\limits_{s\to\infty} f(t)e^{-st} = 0$ for all t, since now t can take on the value zero. Then, taking the limit in Eq. (5-280), we obtain

$$f(0+) = \lim_{s\to\infty} s[F(s) - K_1 - K_2 s - K_3 s^2 - \cdots] \qquad (5\text{-}281)$$

We stated at the start that we would obtain the initial value without taking the inverse Laplace transform. However, Eq. (5-280) requires that we know $K_1, K_2, \ldots$. These are the coefficients of any impulse functions (or their derivatives) at $t = 0$ that are contained in $f(t)$. We shall now demonstrate that these functions can be obtained easily from the Laplace transform. In Eqs. (5-62) to (5-64) we demonstrated that with long division we could write the Laplace transform of any ratio of two polynomials as

$$F(s) = d_{m-n}s^{m-n} + \cdots + d_1 s + d_0 + \frac{a_{n-1}s^{n-1} + \cdots + a_1 s + a_0}{b_n s^n + \cdots + b_1 s + b_0}$$
$$(5\text{-}282)$$

where m and n are the highest powers of the numerator and denominator of $F(s)$, respectively. Now we write

$$F(s) = F_1(s) + F_2(s)$$

where

$$F_1(s) = d_{m-1}s^{m-n} + \cdots + d_1 s + d_0 \qquad (5\text{-}283)$$

When we take the inverse Laplace transform, the impulse functions will be contributed by $F_1(s)$ [note that $F_2(s)$ is a proper fraction and can be inverted by partial-fraction-expansion techniques]. Then, using Eq. (5-238) to obtain the inverse Laplace transform of Eq. (5-283) and comparing this with Eq.

(5-272), we obtain

$$K_1 = d_0$$
$$K_2 = d_1 \tag{5-284}$$
$$\cdots \cdots$$

Thus the K_1, K_2, . . . can be obtained by a simple long-division procedure (actually, the inverse transform need not be taken). It should be noted that most of the functions with which we deal will not contain impulse-type functions.

Initial values of the derivative

If the value of $f(t)$ and its derivatives are known at $t = 0-$, then we can use this theorem to evaluate the derivatives of $f(t)$ at $t = 0+$. The procedure is to use Eq. (5-33) to obtain the Laplace transform of the derivative and then apply initial-value theorem to this transform. This yields $[df(t)/dt]_{t=0+}$. Proceeding similarly, we can obtain the initial values of the higher-order derivatives.

Let us now illustrate the initial-value theorem with some examples. The Laplace transform

$$\mathcal{L}[u(t) \cos \omega_0 t] = \frac{s}{s^2 + \omega_0{}^2} \tag{5-285}$$

is a proper fraction, so it contains no impulse functions (or their derivatives). Thus

$$\lim_{t \to 0+} u(t) \cos \omega_0 t = \lim_{s \to \infty} \frac{s^2}{s^2 + \omega_0{}^2} = 1 \tag{5-286}$$

This checks.

Now consider a function which contains an impulse at $t = 0$. From Eq. (5-37) we have

$$\mathcal{L}\left[\frac{d}{dt} u(t) \cos t\right] = \frac{s^2}{s^2 + 1} \tag{5-287}$$

Note that $u(t) \cos t$ has a discontinuity at $t = 0$, so its derivative contains an impulse there (see Sec. 5-14). After long division we obtain

$$\frac{s^2}{s^2 + 1} = 1 - \frac{1}{s^2 + 1}$$

Thus in Eq. (5-272) $K_1 = 1$. Substituting into Eq. (5-281), we have

$$f(0+) = \lim_{s \to \infty} s \left(\frac{s^2}{s^2 + 1} - 1\right) = \lim_{s \to \infty} s \frac{-1}{s^2 + 1} = 0 \tag{5-288}$$

Note that

$$\frac{d}{dt} u(t) \cos t = \sin t \qquad t > 0$$

Thus Eq. (5-288) is valid.

5-20 Time convolution

In this section we shall obtain the Laplace transform of a function of time which is an integral of two functions. This will aid us in obtaining the inverse Laplace transforms of some functions, and in addition, it will enable us to express the response of a network to any function in terms of its response to the impulse function. Let us assume that we have two functions of time, $g(t)$ and $h(t)$, whose Laplace transforms are

$$\mathcal{L}[u(t)g(t)] = \mathbf{G}(s) \qquad\qquad\qquad (5\text{-}289a)$$

$$\mathcal{L}[u(t)h(t)] = \mathbf{H}(s) \qquad\qquad\qquad (5\text{-}289b)$$

We start by forming a function of time $f(t)$ which is defined by the integral relation

$$f(t) = \int_0^\infty u(\tau)g(\tau)u(t - \tau)h(t - \tau) \, d\tau \qquad\qquad (5\text{-}290)$$

Note that t is a constant as far as the integration is concerned [$g(\tau)$ is just $g(t)$ with t replaced by τ, and $h(t - \tau)$ is $h(t)$ with t replaced by $t - \tau$]. Now we obtain the Laplace transform of $f(t)$,

$$\mathbf{F}(s) = \int_0^\infty \int_0^\infty u(\tau)g(\tau)u(t - \tau)h(t - \tau) \, d\tau \, e^{-st} \, dt \qquad (5\text{-}291)$$

We shall assume that $g(t)$ and $h(t)$ are such that the order of integration can be interchanged:

$$\mathbf{F}(s) = \int_0^\infty u(\tau)g(\tau) \int_0^\infty u(t - \tau)h(t - \tau)e^{-st} \, dt \, d\tau \qquad (5\text{-}292)$$

The inner integral is just the Laplace transform of $u(t - \tau)h(t - \tau)$; that is, it is the transform of $h(t)$ delayed by τ sec. Then, from Eqs. (5-289b) and (5-255), we obtain

$$\mathbf{F}(s) = \int_0^\infty u(\tau)g(\tau)\mathbf{H}(s)e^{-st} \, d\tau = \mathbf{H}(s) \int_0^\infty u(\tau)g(\tau)e^{-s\tau} \, d\tau \qquad (5\text{-}293)$$

Note that $\mathbf{H}(s)$ is a constant as far as the integration is concerned. The right-hand integral of Eq. (5-293) is just the Laplace transform of $g(t)$ (it does not matter if we call the variable of integration t or τ). Thus

$$\mathbf{F}(s) = \mathbf{H}(s)\mathbf{G}(s)$$

but $\mathbf{F}(s)$ is the Laplace transform of $f(t)$.   Then substitution of Eq. (5-290) yields

$$\mathcal{L}\left[\int_0^t g(\tau)h(t-\tau)\,d\tau\right] = \mathbf{G}(s)\mathbf{H}(s) \tag{5-294}$$

If we change the upper limit of integration to t, we no longer need the term $u(t-\tau)$ in Eq. (5-290) $[u(t-\tau)=0$ when $\tau>t]$.   Since the lower limit of integration is zero, the $u(\tau)$ term is also unnecessary.   The integral of Eq. (5-290) is called the *convolution* of $g(t)$ and $h(t)$.   It is written as $g(t)*h(t)$. Thus

$$\mathcal{L}[g(t)*h(t)] = \mathbf{G}(s)\mathbf{H}(s) \tag{5-295a}$$

or

$$g(t)*h(t) = \mathcal{L}^{-1}[\mathbf{G}(s)\mathbf{H}(s)] \tag{5-295b}$$

Thus the Laplace transform of the convolution of two time functions is given by the product of their Laplace transforms.   If we have to obtain an inverse Laplace transform of a function which is recognized as the product of two functions whose inverse transforms are known, then the convolution integral can be useful.   For instance, if

$$\mathbf{F}(s) = \frac{1}{s+1}\frac{1}{s+2}$$

then

$$f(t) = e^{-t}*e^{-2t} = \int_0^t e^{\tau}e^{-2(t-\tau)}\,d\tau = \int_0^t e^{-2t+\tau}\,d\tau = e^{-t}-e^{-2t}$$

Now let us consider that we are working with a twoport which has a transfer function $\mathbf{W}(s)$ such that

$$\frac{\mathbf{X}_2(s)}{\mathbf{X}_1(s)} = \mathbf{W}(s) \tag{5-296}$$

where $\mathbf{X}_2(s)$ represents the transform of output current or voltage in response to the input current or voltage $\mathbf{X}_1(s)$.   Suppose that

$$x_1(t) = \delta(t) \tag{5-297}$$

Then, since $\mathcal{L}[\delta(t)]=1$, we have

$$\mathbf{X}_2(s) = \mathbf{W}(s) \tag{5-298}$$

The inverse Laplace transform of $\mathbf{X}_2(s)$ is $x_2(t)$.   Since this is the response to an impulse, we shall call it $w(t)$.   Then

$$w(t) = \mathcal{L}^{-1}[\mathbf{W}(s)] \tag{5-299}$$

We shall assume that these are known quantities.

Let us determine the response of the twoport to an arbitrary $x_1(t)$ whose

Laplace transform is $\mathbf{X}_1(s)$. Substitution in Eq. (5-296) yields

$$\mathbf{X}_2(s) = \mathbf{X}_1(s)\mathbf{W}(s) \tag{5-300}$$

or

$$x_2(t) = \mathcal{L}^{-1}[\mathbf{X}_1(s)\mathbf{W}(s)] \tag{5-301}$$

Then from Eq. (5-295b) we have

$$x_2(t) = x_1(t) * w(t) = \int_0^t x_1(\tau)w(t-\tau)\,d\tau \tag{5-302}$$

Since $\mathbf{X}_1(s)\mathbf{W}(s) = \mathbf{W}(s)\mathbf{X}_1(s)$, we can also write

$$x_2(t) = w(t) * x_1(t) \int_0^t w(\tau)x_1(t-\tau)\,d\tau \tag{5-303}$$

Thus we have expressed the response of a network to an arbitrary input function in terms of its unit-impulse response. This is a further example of the usefulness of the impulse response.

5-21   Nonlinear and time-varying networks

Usually the Laplace transform cannot be applied to the solution of nonlinear and time-varying networks. The use of state-variable techniques, frequently in conjunction with computers, is usually a far superior procedure. Thus we shall defer a solution of these networks until Chap. 7, where we shall discuss state variables.

REFERENCE

[1] L. Schwartz, "Théorie des distributions," vols. I and II, Actualités scientifiques et industrielles, Hermann and Cie., Paris, 1957, 1959.

BIBLIOGRAPHY

Close, C. M.: "The Analysis of Linear Circuits," chap. 10, Harcourt, Brace & World, Inc., New York, 1966.

Javid, M., and E. Brenner: "Analysis Transmission and Filtering of Signals," chap. 10, McGraw-Hill Book Company, New York, 1963.

Ley, B. J., S. G. Lutz, and C. F. Rehberg: "Linear Circuit Analysis," chap. 8, McGraw-Hill Book Company, New York, 1959.

Manning, L. A.: "Electrical Circuits," chaps. 18 and 19, McGraw-Hill Book Company, New York, 1966.

Pearson, S. I., and G. J. Maler: "Introductory Circuit Analysis," chap. 3, John Wiley & Sons, Inc., New York, 1965.

Peskin, E.: "Transient and Steady State Analysis of Electric Networks," chap. 4, D. Van Nostrand Company, Inc., Princeton, N.J., 1961.

Van Valkenburg, M. E.: "Network Analysis," 2d ed., chaps. 7 and 8, Prentice-Hall, Inc., Englewood Cliffs, N.J., 1964.

PROBLEMS

5-1. Obtain the Laplace transform of $u(t)t^n$.

5-2. Obtain the Laplace transform of $u(t)t \sin t$.

5-3. Obtain the inverse Laplace transform of $1/(s+a)^3$.

5-4. Obtain the Laplace transform of $[3 \sin t + e^{-t} \cos t + 3]u(t)$.

5-5. Use Eq. (5-33) to obtain the Laplace transform of $(d/dt)u(t)e^{-2t} \sin t$.

5-6. Use Eq. (5-53) to obtain the Laplace transform of $[\int e^{-2at} \sin t \, dt]u(t)$.

5-7. Obtain the inverse Laplace transform of $(s+4)/(s^2+3s+2)$.

5-8. Obtain

$$\mathcal{L}^{-1}\left[\frac{s^2+s+1}{(s+1)(s+2)(s+3)}\right]$$

5-9. Obtain

$$\mathcal{L}^{-1}\left[\frac{s^2+2s+2}{s(s+1)(s+2)}\right]$$

5-10. Obtain

$$\mathcal{L}^{-1}\left[\frac{s^2+2s+2}{s[(s+1)^2+4]}\right]$$

5-11. Obtain

$$\mathcal{L}^{-1}\left[\frac{s^2+s+1}{(s+1)^2(s+2)}\right]$$

5-12. Obtain

$$\mathcal{L}^{-1}\left[\frac{s^3+4s^2+s+1}{s^3(s+1)^2(s+2)}\right]$$

5-13. Obtain

$$\mathcal{L}^{-1}\left[\frac{s^3+2s^2+1}{[(s+1)^2+4]^3[(s+2)^2+1]^2(s+1)(s+2)}\right]$$

5-14. Obtain

$$\mathcal{L}^{-1}\left[\frac{s^3+2s^2+2s+6}{s^4+3s^3+2s^2+2s+1}\right]$$

5-15. Use the Laplace transform to solve the differential equation $dx^2/dt^2 + 4dx/dt + 2x = u(t) \sin t$, where $x(0-) = 1$ and $(dx/dt)_{t=0-} = 1$.

5-16. Repeat Prob. 5-15 for $dx^2/dt^2 + x = u(t) \sin t$, where $x(0-) = 0$ and $(dx/dt)_{t=0-} = 10$.

5-17. Draw the transformed form of the network of Fig. 4-22.

5-18. Repeat Prob. 5-17 for the network of Fig. 4-23.

5-19. Repeat Prob. 5-17 for the network of Fig. 4-24.

5-20. Repeat Prob. 5-17 for the network of Fig. 4-25.

5-21. Use the Laplace transform to obtain all the loop currents for the network of Fig. 4-22.

5-22. Repeat Prob. 5-21 for the network of Fig. 4-23.

5-23. Use the Laplace transform to obtain all the nodal voltages for the network of Fig. 4-24. Choose a valid set of nodes.

5-24. Repeat Prob. 5-23 for the network of Fig. 4-25.

5-25. Repeat Prob. 5-23, but now use cut-set analysis.

5-26. Repeat Prob. 5-24, but now use cut-set analysis.

5-27. Use the Laplace transform to obtain all the loop currents in the network of Fig. 4-27. Use a valid set of loop currents.

5-28. Find the driving-point impedance of the network of Fig. 5-42.

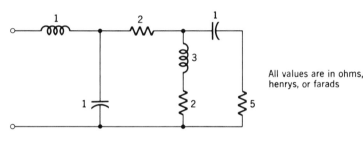

All values are in ohms, henrys, or farads

Fig. 5-42

5-29. Repeat Prob. 5-28 for the network of Fig. 5-43.

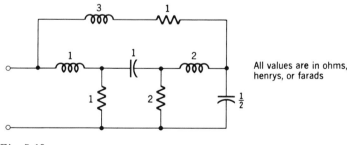

All values are in ohms, henrys, or farads

Fig. 5-43

5-30. Draw a network whose driving-point impedance is

$$\mathbf{Z}(s) = 2s + \frac{1}{4s} + 1$$

5-31. Repeat Prob. 5-30 for

$$Z(s) = \frac{1}{1/2s + 3s + 4}$$

5-32. Repeat Prob. 5-30 for

$$Z(s) = 2s + 3 + \frac{1}{1/3s + 4}$$

5-33. Draw a network whose driving-point admittance is

$$Y(s) = 2s + \frac{1}{4s} + 1$$

5-34. Repeat Prob. 5-33 for

$$Y(s) = \frac{1}{1/2s + 3s + 4}$$

5-35. Repeat Prob. 5-33 for

$$Y(s) = 2s + 3 + \frac{1}{1/3s + 4}$$

5-36. Convert the current generator of Fig. 4-26 into a voltage generator and use loop analysis to obtain the current in the 1-henry inductance.

5-37. Convert the voltage generator of Fig. 4-26 into a current generator and use nodal analysis to obtain the current in the 1-henry coil.

5-38. Convert all the voltage generators of Fig. 4-23 to current generators and use nodal analysis to obtain the current in the 2-henry coil.

5-39. Repeat Prob. 5-38, but now use cut-set analysis.

5-40. Convert all the current generators of Fig. 4-25 into voltage generators and use loop analysis to obtain the current in the 2-farad capacitor. Combine the $\frac{1}{8}$-henry coil and the $\frac{1}{4}$-ohm resistor which are in parallel into a single impedance. Repeat this for the 1-henry coil and the 1-farad capacitor. What is the advantages of doing this?

5-41. Obtain the transfer-voltage ratio $V_2(s)/V_1(s)$ for the network of Fig. 5-44.

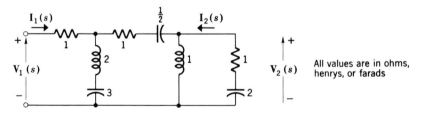

Fig. 5-44

5-42. Obtain the transfer impedance $V_2(s)/I_1(s)$ for the network of Fig. 5-44.

5-43. Obtain the transfer-current ratio $I_2(s)/I_1(s)$ for the network of Fig. 5-44.

5-44. Obtain the transfer admittance $\mathbf{I}_2(s)/\mathbf{V}_1(s)$ for the network of Fig. 5-44.

5-45. Use the results of Prob. 5-41 to obtain $v_2(t)$ if $v_1(t) = u(t)e^{-t}$.

5-46. Use the results of Prob. 5-42 to obtain $v_2(t)$ if $i_1(t) = u(t)\sin t$.

5-47. Draw a pole-zero diagram for

$$\mathbf{W}(s) = \frac{s^2 + 2s + 2}{(s+1)^2(s+2)(s+3)}$$

5-48. Draw a pole-zero diagram for each of the transfer functions obtained in Probs. 5-41 to 5-44.

5-49. Determine by means of both the Hurwitz test and the Routh test which of the following polynomials are Hurwitz polynomials:

$$s^3 + 5s^2 + 8s + 4$$

$$s^4 + 2s^3 + 3s^2 + 2s + 2$$

$$s^4 + s^3 + 14s^2 + 12s + 24$$

5-50. Evaluate the integral

$$\int_{-\infty}^{\infty} \delta(t) \cos t \, dt$$

5-51. Evaluate the integral

$$\int_{-\infty}^{\infty} t \, \delta(t) \, dt$$

5-52. Explain why it is logical to use $0-$ as a lower limit of integration in the Laplace transform integral.

5-53. Obtain $\mathcal{L}^{-1}[s^2 + 2s + 1]$.

5-54. Obtain

$$\mathcal{L}^{-1}\left[\frac{s^3 + 2s^2 + 2s + 2}{s + 1}\right]$$

5-55. In Fig. 5-44, if $v_1(t) = \delta(t)$, find $v_2(t)$.

5-56. For the network of Fig. 5-45, find $i_a(t)$ by loop analysis.

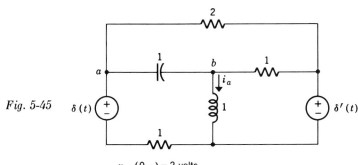

Fig. 5-45

$v_{ab}(0-) = 2$ volts
$i_a(0-) = 1$ amp
All values are in volts, ohms, henrys, or farads

5-57. Repeat Prob. 5-56, but now use nodal analysis. Convert the voltage generators to current generators.

5-58. Evaluate $(d/dt)u(t)e^{-t}$.

5-59. Find the unit-step and unit-impulse responses of the network of Fig. 5-44. Assume that $v_2(t)$ is the output and $v_1(t)$ is the input. Show that the unit-impulse response is the derivative of the unit-step response in this case.

5-60. Find the Laplace transform of

$$f(t) = \begin{cases} \sin t & 0 \le t \le 2\pi \\ 0 & t > 2\pi \text{ or } t < 0 \end{cases}$$

and draw $f(t)$.

5-61. Repeat Prob. 5-60 for

$$f(t) = \begin{cases} t & 0 \le t \le 1 \\ 2 - t & 1 \le t \le 2 \\ 0 & t > 2 \text{ or } t < 0 \end{cases}$$

5-62. If $f(t)$ of Prob. 5-60 is equal to $v_1(t)$ of Fig. 5-44, find $v_2(t)$.

5-63. Given

$$f(t) = \begin{cases} 1 & 0 \le t \le \tfrac{1}{2} \\ 0 & \tfrac{1}{2} \le t \le 1 \end{cases}$$

and $f(t)$ repeats itself periodically thereafter $[f(t + n) = f(t) \text{ for } n = 1, 2, \ldots]$, find $\mathcal{L}[f(t)]$.

5-64. Find the final value of the function of time whose Laplace transform is given by

$$\mathbf{F}(s) = \frac{s^2 + 2s + 1}{s(s + 3)}$$

5-65. Repeat Prob. 5-64 for

$$\mathbf{F}(s) = \frac{s^2 + 2s + 4}{(s + 1)(s + 3)}$$

5-66. Find the initial value $f(0+)$ of the function of time whose Laplace transform is given by

$$\mathbf{F}(s) = \frac{s^2 + 3s + 6}{(s + 1)(s + 2)(s + 3)}$$

5-67. Repeat Prob. 5-66 for

$$\mathbf{F}(s) = \frac{s^2 + 3s + 6}{(s + 1)(s + 2)}$$

5-68. Find the initial value $f'(t)\big|_{t=0+}$ of the first derivative of the function of time of Prob. 5-66. Assume that $f(0-) = f(0+)$.

5-69. Derive relations for the initial values of the first and second derivatives of $f(t)$ in terms of the Laplace transform of $f(t)$.

5-70. Use the convolution theorem to obtain

$$\mathscr{L}^{-1}\left[\frac{1}{s}\frac{1}{s+1}\right]$$

5-71. Repeat Prob. 5-70 for

$$\mathscr{L}^{-1}\left[\frac{1}{(s+1)^2+4}\frac{1}{s+1}\right]$$

5-72. For the network of Fig. 5-44 express $v_2(t)$ as a function of an arbitrary $v_1(t)$ and the impulse response of the network. Use this relation to determine $v_2(t)$ if $v_1(t) = u(t)e^{-t}$.

5-73. Derive a relation for the response of a network to an arbitrary function of time in terms of the unit-step response.

The Sinusoidal Steady State

6

In this chapter we shall consider the response of networks to voltages or currents that vary sinusoidally with time. Almost all the electric power lines into homes, offices, laboratories, and factories supply voltages and currents of this form. In addition, sinusoidal generators are often used to test electric equipment. For instance, the frequency response of audio amplifiers is determined by means of these generators. Almost all communication systems operate by varying sinusoidal waveforms. Thus the response of networks to sinusoidal signals is very important.

The currents and voltages that occur in response to sinusoidal generators will, in general, contain sinusoidal terms plus terms which decay exponentially to zero with time. In this chapter we shall concern ourselves only with the sinusoidal terms and neglect the decaying terms. There are many situations in which it is valid to do this. For instance, suppose we wish to determine the power required to operate an electric heater which consists of a resistance and a small inductance in series. After a fraction of a second the transient terms will have become essentially zero, and the currents and voltages in the circuit will be just sinusoids. If the heater is in operation for more than several seconds, for most of the time of operation the exponential decay terms will be negligible. Of course, a study of the complete time response is also important in many cases. Solutions for the currents and voltages which contain just a sinusoidal term, and in which the decay terms are disregarded, are called *sinusoidal-steady-state solutions*.

We shall begin with a discussion of sinusoids and then obtain a procedure for determining the sinusoidal-steady-state response of a network. In later sections we shall study the applications of sinusoidal-steady-state solutions and some circuits used to perform specific functions.

6-1   Sinusoidal waveforms: phasors and complex algebra

Before we discuss circuits that contain sinusoidal generators, let us discuss sinusoidal waveforms. The simplest sinusoid we shall encounter is given by

$$x(t) = X_{max} \sin \omega_0 t \qquad\qquad (6\text{-}1)$$

where $x(t)$ may represent either a voltage or a current. A plot of this waveform is shown in Fig. 6-1. This function starts at $t = 0$, and in $2\pi/\omega_0$ sec it traces out a waveform which has not, as yet, repeated itself. Thereafter the waveform repeats itself periodically; the waveform for $2\pi/\omega_0 \le t \le 4\pi/\omega_0$ repeats that for $0 \le t \le 2\pi/\omega_0$, and so on. The time

$$T = \frac{2\pi}{\omega_0} \qquad\qquad (6\text{-}2)$$

is called the *period* of the sinusoid. It is also referred to as the time of one *cycle* of the periodic function. The number of cycles that occur in 1 sec is

Fig. 6-1 A plot of $x(t) = X_{max} \sin \omega_0 t$.

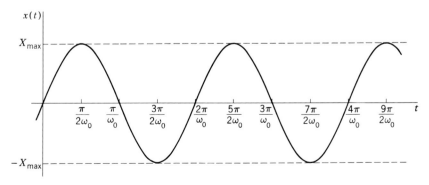

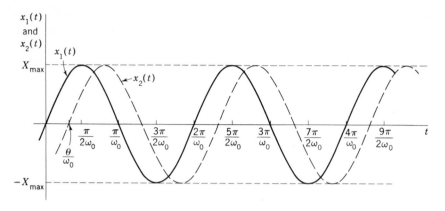

Fig. 6-2   A plot of $x_1(t) = X_{\max} \sin \omega_0 t$ and $x_2(t) = X_{\max} \sin (\omega_0 t - \theta)$.

called the *frequency f_0* of the sinusoid.   Then

$$f_0 = \frac{1}{T} = \frac{\omega_0}{2\pi} \tag{6-3}$$

The unit of frequency is the *hertz* (H_z): 1 hertz = 1 cycle per second.   Other units that are used are kilohertz (kHz), megahertz (mHz), and gigahertz (gHz). These are 10^3, 10^6, and 10^9 times the size of a hertz, respectively (e.g., 1 mHz = 10^6 Hz).

Substituting Eq. (6-3) into Eq. (6-2), we obtain

$$T = \frac{1}{f_0} \tag{6-4}$$

That is, the period is the reciprocal of the frequency. ω_0 is called the *angular frequency*.   Its units are radians per second. $X_{\max}$ is called the *maximum value* or *maximum amplitude* of the sinusoid.   Note that $x(t)$ varies between $X_{\max}$ and $-X_{\max}$.

Now let us assume that we have two sinusoids of the same frequency, as shown in Fig. 6-2.   Here we have

$$x_1(t) = X_{\max} \sin \omega t \tag{6-5a}$$
$$x_2(t) = X_{\max} \sin (\omega t - \theta) = X_{\max} \sin \omega \left(t - \frac{\theta}{\omega} \right) \tag{6-5b}$$

These two sinusoids are essentially the same, except that $x_2(t)$ lags behind $x_1(t)$ by θ/ω sec. $-\theta$ is called the *phase angle* of $x_2(t)$ with respect to $x_1(t)$.   In this case the phase angle is *negative* and is called a *lagging phase angle*. $x_2(t)$ is said to *lag* $x_1(t)$.   It is also possible to have a leading phase angle.   For instance,

$$x_3(t) = X_{\max} \sin (\omega t + \theta) \tag{6-6}$$

Here $x_3(t)$ is said to *lead* $x(t)$, and the phase angle is called a *leading phase angle*. Note that we have dropped the subscript 0 from ω; we shall use it only where it is necessary to avoid confusion.

In the networks we shall often consider all the generators produce sinusoids of the same frequency, although their maximum values and phase angles may be different. As we shall see, the sinusoidal-steady-state solution for the currents and voltages will be sinusoids of the same frequency as the generators. This frequency is known. Thus the only unknowns are the maximum values and the phase angles of the sinusoids. When we speak of a phase angle, we are implying that an arbitrary time has been fixed, while we call $t = 0$. Usually, however, instead of fixing an arbitrary time, we shall follow the equivalent procedure of *establishing one voltage or current as a reference and expressing the phase angles of all the other sinusoids with respect to it.*

For instance, suppose we have three voltages, $x_1(t)$, $x_2(t)$, and $x_3(t)$, and $x_2(t)$ leads $x_1(t)$ by $\pi/3$ rad and $x_3(t)$ leads $x_2(t)$ by $\pi/4$ rad. If we use $x_2(t)$ as reference, then

$$x_2(t) = X_{2,\max} \sin \omega t \tag{6-7a}$$

Thus

$$x_1(t) = X_{1,\max} \sin\left(\omega t - \frac{\pi}{3}\right) \tag{6-7b}$$

$$x_3(t) = X_{3,\max} \sin\left(\omega t + \frac{\pi}{4}\right) \tag{6-7c}$$

In general, the frequency of operation will be a known quantity. Thus the unknowns in sinusoidal-steady-state analysis will consist of the maximum values and the phase angles of the unknown voltages and/or currents.

We can use phase angles to express one sinusoid in terms of another. For instance,

$$\cos \omega t = \sin\left(\omega t + \frac{\pi}{2}\right) \tag{6-8}$$

Let us now discuss some alternative representations of sinusoids and phase angles. Consider the function

$$x(t) = X_{\max} \sin(\omega t + \phi) \tag{6-9}$$

After using the trigonometric identity for the sum of two angles to expand this, we have

$$x(t) = X_{\max} \cos \phi \sin \omega t + X_{\max} \sin \phi \cos \omega t \tag{6-10}$$

Thus $x(t)$ can be considered to be made up of the sum of a sinusoid of maximum value $X_{\max} \cos \phi$ and a cosinusoid of maximum value $X_{\max} \sin \phi$.

Now consider the converse situation. Suppose we are given $x(t)$ in the form

$$x(t) = A \sin \omega t + B \cos \omega t \tag{6-11}$$

and we wish to express $x(t)$ in the form of Eq. (6-9). To do this, we equate Eq. (6-11) to Eq. (6-10),

$$X_{\max} \cos \phi \sin \omega t + X_{\max} \sin \phi \cos \omega t = A \sin \omega t + B \cos \omega t \qquad (6\text{-}12)$$

If this is to be valid for all values of time, then

$$A = X_{\max} \cos \phi \qquad (6\text{-}13a)$$

$$B = X_{\max} \sin \phi \qquad (6\text{-}13b)$$

[consider a time when $\omega t = 2n\pi$, where n is an integer; then Eq. (6-13a) results, and so on]. Now we divide Eq. (6-13b) by Eq. (6-13a). This yields

$$\tan \phi = \frac{B}{A} \qquad (6\text{-}14a)$$

or, equivalently,

$$\phi = \arctan \frac{B}{A} = \tan^{-1} \frac{B}{A} \qquad (6\text{-}14b)$$

Squaring both sides of Eqs. (6-13a) and (6-13b) and adding them gives us

$$A^2 + B^2 = X_{\max}^2 (\cos^2 \phi + \sin^2 \phi)$$

and making use of the trigonometric identity

$$\sin^2 \phi + \cos^2 \phi = 1 \qquad (6\text{-}15)$$

we obtain

$$X_{\max} = \sqrt{A^2 + B^2} \qquad (6\text{-}16)$$

Thus we can use Eqs. (6-14b) and (6-16) to express Eq. (6-11) in the form of Eq. (6-9).

In network analysis we add both voltages and currents (e.g., the voltages generated around a loop are summed in loop analysis). Let us see how this can be done when the voltages and currents are sinusoids. For instance, let us evaluate the sum

$$x(t) = X_{1,\max} \sin (\omega t + \phi_1) + X_{2,\max} \sin (\omega t + \phi_2) \qquad (6\text{-}17)$$

These cannot be added in their present form. We convert each of the sinusoids to the form of Eq. (6-10),

$$x(t) = X_{1,\max} \cos \phi_1 \sin \omega t + X_{1,\max} \sin \phi_1 \cos \omega t$$
$$+ X_{2,\max} \cos \phi_2 \sin \omega t + X_{2,\max} \sin \phi_2 \cos \omega t \qquad (6\text{-}18a)$$

and combine terms to obtain

$$x(t) = (X_{1,\max} \cos \phi_1 + X_{2,\max} \cos \phi_2) \sin \omega t$$
$$+ (X_{1,\max} \sin \phi_1 + X_{2,\max} \sin \phi_2) \cos \omega t \qquad (6\text{-}18b)$$

Then, from Eqs. (6-14*b*) and (6-17), we can write

$$x(t) = X_{\max} \sin (\omega t + \phi) \tag{6-19a}$$

where

$$X_{\max} = \sqrt{(X_{1,\max} \cos \phi_1 + X_{2,\max} \cos \phi_2)^2 + (X_{1,\max} \sin \phi_1 \\ + X_{2,\max} \sin \phi_2)^2} \tag{6-19b}$$

$$\phi = \tan^{-1} \frac{X_{1,\max} \sin \phi_1 + X_{2,\max} \sin \phi_2}{X_{1,\max} \cos \phi_1 + X_{2,\max} \cos \phi_2} \tag{6-19c}$$

Phasors

To make the algebraic operations of trigonometric functions less tedious, we shall approach them from a different viewpoint. In Eqs. (4-55) to (4-58) we developed Euler's relation. Let us restate it here as

$$e^{jx} = \cos x + j \sin x \tag{6-20}$$

where in Eqs. (4-55) to (4-58) we let $x = \omega t$. In this case we let

$$x = \omega t + \phi \tag{6-21}$$

Then

$$e^{j(\omega t + \phi)} = \cos (\omega t + \phi) + j \sin (\omega t + \phi) \tag{6-22}$$

Thus we can state

$$\cos (\omega t + \phi) = \operatorname{Re} e^{j(\omega t + \phi)} \\ \sin (\omega t + \phi) = \operatorname{Im} e^{j(\omega t + \phi)} \tag{6-23}$$

where Re and Im denote the *real part of* and the *imaginary part of*, respectively (note that the imaginary part of a complex function is real).

Now let us study the term $e^{j(\omega t + \phi)}$. Assume that we have a complex plane, similar to the *s* plane (see Sec. 5-1), where there is a real axis and an imaginary axis. Such a plane is shown in Fig. 6-3. Consider that we have drawn an arrow from the origin of length unity and angle ωt, as shown in Fig. 6-3. The real-axis coordinate of this arrow is $\cos \omega t$, and its imaginary-axis coordinate

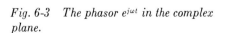

Fig. 6-3   *The phasor $e^{j\omega t}$ in the complex plane.*

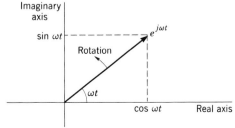

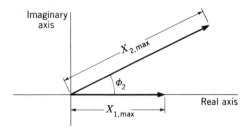

Fig. 6-4 *The phasor representation of Eqs. (6-26).*

is sin ωt. Thus the sum of the real and imaginary parts are cos $\omega t + j$ sin ωt (the real part is that component which is parallel to the horizontal axis, and the imaginary part is the component parallel to the vertical axis). From Eq. (6-20) we see that this arrow represents $e^{j\omega t}$ ($x = \omega t$ here). This arrow is given a special name; it is called a *rotating phasor*. The term "vector" is sometimes used instead of phasor, but a vector represents a magnitude and direction in real space, while the phasor represents the sum of a real and an imaginary component used to express a sinusoid.

As time increases, ωt also increases. The rotating phasor $e^{j\omega t}$ has a magnitude given by

$$|e^{j\omega t}| = \sqrt{\cos^2 \omega t + \sin^2 \omega t} = 1 \tag{6-24}$$

Its angle is just ωt. Thus $e^{j\omega t}$ will always have a magnitude of unity. As ωt increases, the angle ωt shown in Fig. 6-3 will also increase. The net effect is that the phasor rotates in the direction shown. A full revolution is made every time ωt increases by 2π; thus the period of the revolution is

$$T = \frac{2\pi}{\omega} \tag{6-25a}$$

and the frequency is

$$f = \frac{1}{T} = \frac{\omega}{2\pi} \tag{6-25b}$$

which are the same as the period and frequency of the sinusoid. In general, a phasor is drawn at some fixed time.

Now suppose we have two different sinusoids,

$$x_1(t) = X_{1,\text{max}} \sin \omega t \tag{6-26a}$$

$$x_2(t) = X_{2,\text{max}} \sin (\omega t + \phi_2) \tag{6-26b}$$

These can be written as

$$x_1(t) = X_{1,\text{max}} \text{ Im } e^{j\omega t} \tag{6-27a}$$

$$x_2(t) = X_{2,\text{max}} \text{ Im } e^{j(\omega t + \phi_2)} \tag{6-27b}$$

The phasors for these sinusoids are shown in Fig. 6-4.   At the instant of time that

$$\omega t = 2n\pi \qquad n = 0, 1, 2, \ldots \tag{6-28}$$

If the phasors are always drawn this way, then the angle of any phasor is the angle by which its sinusoid leads or lags the reference sinusoid.   Unless otherwise stated, this is the way in which we shall treat phasors; that is, we shall call the phasor that represents $x_2(t)$ in Eq. (6-28) $X_{2,\max}e^{j\phi_2}$.   Hereafter *the word "phasor" will represent* $Xe^{j\phi}$.   *If the* $e^{j\omega t}$ *term is to be included, we shall speak of a "rotating phasor."*

Now let us rewrite Eqs. (6-27) as

$$x_1(t) = \operatorname{Im} X_{1,\max}e^{j\omega t} \tag{6-29a}$$

$$x_2(t) = \operatorname{Im} X_{2,\max}e^{j\phi_2}e^{j\omega t} \tag{6-29b}$$

The quantities $X_{1,\max}$ and $X_{2,\max}e^{j\phi_2}$ are the phasors of Fig. 6-4.   We can write them as

$$\mathbf{X}_{1,\max} = X_{1,\max} = X_{1,\max}e^{j0} \tag{6-30a}$$

$$\mathbf{X}_{2,\max} = X_{2,\max}e^{j\phi_2} \tag{6-30b}$$

where $\mathbf{X}_{\max}$ (boldface type) represents a phasor whose magnitude is $X_{\max}$ and whose angle is ϕ.   These are the maximum value and phase angle of the sinusoid.   That is, we shall call

$$\mathbf{X}_{\max} = X_{\max}e^{j\phi} \tag{6-31a}$$

the phasor of

$$x(t) = X_{\max} \sin{(\omega t + \phi)} \tag{6-31b}$$

Note that a knowledge of the phasor provides us with complete knowledge of the sinusoid, since the frequency is assumed to be known.

Let us now see how the use of phasors simplifies some operations with sinusoids.   Suppose we wish to add the two sinusoids of Eq. (6-17).   This can be written in complex form as

$$x(t) = \operatorname{Im} X_{1,\max}e^{j\phi_1}e^{j\omega t} + \operatorname{Im} X_{2,\max}e^{j\phi_2}e^{j\omega t} \tag{6-32a}$$

Combining terms, we obtain

$$x(t) = \operatorname{Im} (X_{1,\max}e^{j\phi_1} + X_{2,\max}e^{j\phi_2})e^{j\omega t} \tag{6-32b}$$

The phasor that represents $x(t)$ is

$$\mathbf{X}_{\max} = X_{\max}e^{j\phi} = \mathbf{X}_{1,\max} + \mathbf{X}_{2,\max} = X_{1,\max}e^{j\phi_1} + X_{2,\max}e^{j\phi_2} \tag{6-33}$$

Then, to obtain the phasor of $x(t)$, and hence $x(t)$, we need only add the complex numbers as indicated in Eq. (6-33).   This appears to be much simpler than the manipulations of Eqs. (6-17) to (6-19).   The use of phasors does in fact entail a saving, but not as much as appears at first glance, since the algebra of complex numbers can be somewhat tedious.

Complex algebra

In performing sinusoidal-steady-state analyses we shall be manipulating complex numbers. Let us therefore review these manipulations. In general, the rules of ordinary arithmetic apply. We shall be working with quantities that are of the same form as the phasors we have considered. A typical one would be

$$\mathbf{A} = Ae^{j\phi}$$

From Eq. (6-20) we have

$$\mathbf{A} = Ae^{j\phi} = A\cos\phi + jB\sin\phi = \alpha + j\beta \tag{6-34}$$

The form $Ae^{j\phi}$ is known as the *polar form;* here the magnitude and angle of the complex number are specified directly. The form $\alpha + j\beta$ is called the *rectangular form;* here the real and imaginary parts are expressed directly. From Eq. (6-34) we have

$$\alpha = A\cos\phi \tag{6-35a}$$

$$\beta = A\sin\phi \tag{6-35b}$$

Squaring Eqs. (6-35a) and (6-35b), adding them, and using Eq. (6-15), we obtain

$$A = \sqrt{\alpha^2 + \beta^2} \tag{6-36a}$$

The ratio of Eqs. (6-35b) and (6-35a) then yields

$$\phi = \arctan\frac{\beta}{\alpha} = \tan^{-1}\frac{\beta}{\alpha} \tag{6-36b}$$

Thus Eqs. (6-35) and (6-36) can be used to convert from the polar to the rectangular forms, and vice versa.

Addition of complex numbers

Now let us consider the addition or subtraction of complex numbers; that is, let us obtain

$$\mathbf{A}_1 + \mathbf{A}_2 = A_1e^{j\phi_1} \pm A_2e^{j\phi_2}$$

In polar form this addition is difficult. However, if the complex numbers are expressed in rectangular form, the addition or subtraction follow the ordinary rules of addition,

$$\mathbf{A}_1 + \mathbf{A}_2 = \alpha_1 + j\beta_1 \pm (\alpha_2 + j\beta_2) = (\alpha_1 \pm \alpha_2) + j(\beta_1 \pm \beta_2) \tag{6-37}$$

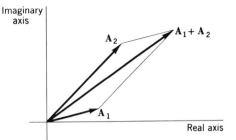

Fig. 6-5 The summation of two complex numbers.

Thus, when complex numbers are added, their real parts are added and their imaginary parts are also added. A graphical representation of this is shown as Fig. 6-5. Adding reals and imaginaries is equivalent to moving one complex phasor parallel to itself until its end touches the arrowhead of the other. The resultant complex number is drawn from the origin to the arrowhead of the moved complex phasor, in accordance with the parallelogram rule for addition of vectors.

Multiplication of complex numbers

To obtain the product

$$\mathbf{A_1A_2} = A_1e^{j\phi_1}A_2e^{j\phi_2}$$

we follow the rules for multiplication of exponentials and arrive at

$$\mathbf{A_1A_2} = A_1A_2e^{j(\phi_1+\phi_2)} \tag{6-38}$$

Thus we multiply the magnitudes and add the phase angles. Multiplication can be carried out in rectangular form, but not as conveniently. For instance, if we apply the ordinary rules of multiplication to

$$\mathbf{A_1A_2} = (\alpha_1 + j\beta_1)(\alpha_2 + j\beta_2)$$

we obtain

$$\mathbf{A_1A_2} = (\alpha_1\alpha_2 - \beta_1\beta_2) + j(\beta_1\alpha_2 + \alpha_1\beta_2) \tag{6-39}$$

The conjugate of a complex number

The conjugate of a complex number is another complex number whose real part is equal to the real part of the complex number and whose imaginary part is equal to the *negative* of the imaginary part of the original number. The conjugate is indicated by a superscript asterisk (*). Thus, if

$$\mathbf{A} = Ae^{j\phi} = \alpha + j\beta \tag{6-40a}$$

then

$$\mathbf{A}^* = \alpha - j\beta \qquad (6\text{-}40b)$$

Also, from Eq. (6-36b) we have

$$\mathbf{A}^* = Ae^{-j\phi} \qquad (6\text{-}40c)$$

The product of a complex number and its conjugate

Let us obtain the product $\mathbf{AA}^*$. Substitution of Eqs. (6-40a) and (6-40c) yields

$$\mathbf{AA}^* = Ae^{j\phi}Ae^{-j\phi} = A^2 \qquad (6\text{-}41a)$$

Thus the product of a number and its conjugate is a real number which is equal to the magnitude of the original number squared. We can also demonstrate this with the rectangular form. In this case

$$\mathbf{AA}^* = (\alpha + j\beta)(\alpha - j\beta) = \alpha^2 + \beta^2 \qquad (6\text{-}41b)$$

Division of complex numbers

To obtain the quotient $\mathbf{A}_1/\mathbf{A}_2$ we apply the usual rules for division of exponentials and arrive at

$$\frac{\mathbf{A}_1}{\mathbf{A}_2} = \frac{A_1 e^{j\phi_1}}{A_2 e^{j\phi_2}} = \frac{A_1}{A_2} e^{j(\phi_1 - \phi_2)} \qquad (6\text{-}42a)$$

Thus the magnitude of the quotient is the quotient of the magnitudes of the original numbers. The angle of the quotient is the differences between the angles of the original numbers. Complex numbers cannot be divided as conveniently when they are in rectangular form. However, division can be accomplished by multiplying both the numerator and the denominator by the conjugate of the denominator. For example,

$$\frac{\mathbf{A}_1}{\mathbf{A}_2} = \frac{\alpha_1 + j\beta_1}{\alpha_2 + j\beta_2} = \frac{\alpha_1 + j\beta_1}{\alpha_2 + j\beta_2}\frac{\alpha_2 - j\beta_2}{\alpha_2 - j\beta_2} = \frac{\alpha_1\alpha_2 + \beta_1\beta_2}{\alpha_2{}^2 + \beta_2{}^2} + j\frac{\beta_1\alpha_2 - \alpha_1\beta_2}{\alpha_2{}^2 + \beta_2{}^2} \qquad (6\text{-}42b)$$

The root of a complex number

Let us consider a procedure for taking the nth root of a complex number. The number should be put into polar form. The nth root of $\mathbf{A}$, for example, is stated as

$$\mathbf{A}^{1/n} = A^{1/n}e^{j(\phi/n)} \qquad (6\text{-}43)$$

It can be demonstrated that this is actually $A^{1/n}$; if this number is multiplied by itself n times, $\mathbf{A} = Ae^{j\phi}$ results. Thus Eq. (6-43) provides a procedure for obtaining the nth root of $\mathbf{A}$.

There is one factor that we must consider here. If we add 2π rad to the angle of a complex number, this is equivalent to rotating it by 2π rad. Thus the same complex number results:

$$\mathbf{A} = Ae^{j\phi} = Ae^{j(\phi+2\pi)} = Ae^{j(\phi+2k\pi)} \qquad k = 0, \pm1, \pm2, \ldots \qquad (6\text{-}44)$$

Ordinarily, this addition of $2k\pi$ does not alter our results, since the resulting complex number is essentially the same. However, in Eq. (6-43), if we divide $\phi + 2k\pi$ (instead of ϕ) by n, the angles of the resultant complex numbers will not differ by an integral multiple of 2π, and different complex numbers will result. Thus all the possible values must be considered. Therefore we write

$$A^{1/n} = A^{1/n}e^{j[(\phi+2k\pi)/n]} \qquad k = 0, 1, 2, \ldots, n-1 \qquad (6\text{-}45)$$

Note that only n values of k are chosen. Additional values of k (such as $k = n, n+1, \ldots$) will yield values of $(\phi + 2k\pi)/n$ which differ from those already obtained by an integral multiple of 2π. Thus these values of $k \geq n$ do not result in new roots.

As an example let us find the cube root of unity. We have

$$1 = 1e^{j2k\pi} \qquad k = 1, 2, 3$$
$$\sqrt[3]{1} = \sqrt[3]{1}\, e^{j2k\pi/3} \qquad k = 1, 2, 3$$

Thus

$$\sqrt[3]{1} = \begin{cases} 1e^{j0} = 1 \\ 1e^{j2\pi/3} \\ 1e^{j4\pi/3} \end{cases}$$

It can be seen that $e^{j6\pi/3}$ is equal to $e^{j2\pi}$, which is equivalent to e^{j0}, and so on.

Logarithms of complex numbers

Suppose we have a complex number in polar form and we take its natural logarithm,

$$\ln \mathbf{A} = \ln Ae^{j\phi} = \ln A + \ln e^{j\phi} \qquad (6\text{-}46)$$

where we have used the fact that the logarithm of a product is equal to the sum of the logarithms of the individual terms. The logarithm is the power to which e must be raised in order to produce the number. Hence

$$\ln e^{j\phi} = j\phi \qquad (6\text{-}47)$$

Consider $\ln A$; this is just the logarithm of a real number. Thus

$$\ln \mathbf{A} = \ln Ae^{j\phi} = \ln A + j\phi \qquad (6\text{-}48)$$

In general, we can write

$$Ae^{j\phi} = Ae^{j(\phi+2k\pi)} \qquad k = 0, 1, 2, \ldots \tag{6-49}$$

Then, substituting into Eq. (6-48), we obtain

$$\ln \mathbf{A} = \ln Ae^{j\phi} = \ln A + j(\phi + 2k\pi) \qquad k = 0, 1, 2, \ldots \tag{6-50}$$

Note that each of the complex numbers corresponding to different values of k is completely different. The value corresponding to $k = 0$ is called the *principal value* of $\ln \mathbf{A}$.

In the preceding operations with complex numbers it was sometimes more convenient to work with the polar forms, and at other times it was more convenient to work with the rectangular forms. In general, if many operations are performed, we may have to convert complex numbers from one form to the other a great many times.

6-2   The sinusoidal-steady-state solution

We shall now consider the Laplace transform form of a typical set of loop, nodal, or cut-set equations in which all the independent generators produce sinusoids of the *same frequency*. The magnitudes and phase angles of the generators will, in general, be different. We shall use these equations to obtain the sinusoidal-steady-state solution. Later we shall simplify this solution by means of the phasors developed in Sec. 6-1.

To start with, let us obtain the Laplace transform of $Y_{\max} \sin (\omega_0 t + \phi)$. From Eq. (6-10) and Table 5-1 we obtain

$$\mathcal{L}[Y_{\max} \sin (\omega_0 + \phi)] = \frac{Y_{\max} \cos \phi \, \omega_0}{s^2 + \omega_0{}^2} + \frac{Y_{\max} \sin \phi \, s}{s^2 + \omega_0{}^2} \tag{6-51}$$

The presence of the phase angle does not alter the fact that sinusoids only produce a pair of simple poles on the $j\omega$ axis. A typical set of loop, nodal, or cut-set-analysis equations in Laplace transform form is given in Eq. (5-142). The characteristic determinant for these equations is shown in Eq. (5-143). From Eq. (5-144) we obtain the solution

$$\mathbf{X}_k(s) = \frac{\Delta_{1k}\mathbf{Y}_1(s) + \Delta_{2k}\mathbf{Y}_2(s) + \cdots + \Delta_{nk}\mathbf{Y}_n(s)}{\Delta} \qquad s = 1, 2, \ldots, n \tag{6-52}$$

In loop analysis $\mathbf{X}_k(s)$ is the Laplace transform of the loop current i_k and $\mathbf{Y}_r(s)$ is the Laplace transform of the sum of the known voltage generators in the rth loop. In nodal or cut-set analysis $\mathbf{X}_k(s)$ is the transform of the kth nodal or cut-set voltage and $\mathbf{Y}_r(s)$ is the sum of known current generators entering the rth node or cut set. Since we are considering the sinusoidal steady state, all the known independent generators will produce sinusoids of the same frequency. We have disregarded initial conditions here, since these generators will not lead to sinusoidal-steady-state terms. We assume that the response to them will be exponentially damped terms. Remember that we wish to obtain only the terms in the solution that are *not* exponentially damped.

The Laplace transforms of the sinusoidal generators will be of the form of Eq. (6-51). Each generator can have a different V_{max} and ϕ. However, all the $\mathbf{Y}_1(s)$, $\mathbf{Y}_2(s)$, . . . , $\mathbf{Y}_n(s)$ terms will contribute *just one* pair of poles at $s = \pm j\omega_0$. Hence, when we clear fractions in Eq. (6-52), we obtain

$$\mathbf{X}_k(s) = \frac{\mathbf{N}(s)}{(s + j\omega_0)(s - j\omega_0)\mathbf{D}(s)} \tag{6-53}$$

where $\mathbf{N}(s)$ and $\mathbf{D}(s)$ are polynomials which do not have roots at $s = \pm j\omega_0$. [It is possible that $\mathbf{N}(s)$ and $\mathbf{D}(s)$ may have roots at $s = \pm j\omega_0$, but we can consider this as a limiting case in the present analysis. That is, we can assume that these roots lie in the left half plane extremely close to the $j\omega$ axis and then let them approach the axis.] The roots of $\mathbf{D}(s)$ are roots of the characteristic determinant.

Now let us expand Eq. (6-53) in partial fractions. This yields

$$\mathbf{X}_k(s) = \frac{\mathbf{K}_{1k}}{s + j\omega_0} + \frac{\mathbf{K}_{2k}}{s - j\omega_0} + \text{other terms} \tag{6-54}$$

The other terms correspond to the roots of $\mathbf{D}(s)$. In practical networks all these roots will be in the left half plane, and when the inverse Laplace transform of Eq. (6-54) is taken, the "other terms" will give rise to exponentially damped terms. Hence, if we are interested in the sinusoidal steady state, we can disregard these terms. We need only consider the inverse Laplace transform of

$$\frac{\mathbf{K}_{1k}}{s + j\omega_0} + \frac{\mathbf{K}_{2k}}{s - j\omega_0}$$

Let us call this $\mathbf{X}_{ks}(s)$ (note that we are disregarding the remaining terms). That is,

$$\mathbf{X}_{ks}(s) = \frac{\mathbf{K}_{1k}}{s + j\omega_0} + \frac{\mathbf{K}_{2k}}{s - j\omega_0} \tag{6-55}$$

The inverse Laplace transform now yields

$$x_{ks}(t) = \mathbf{K}_{1k}e^{-j\omega_0 t} + \mathbf{K}_{2k}e^{j\omega_0 t} \tag{6-56a}$$

and, substituting Euler's relation, we obtain

$$x_{ks}(t) = \mathbf{K}_{1k}(\cos \omega_0 t - j \sin \omega_0 t) + \mathbf{K}_{2k}(\cos \omega_0 t + j \sin \omega_0 t) \tag{6-56b}$$

This is a real voltage or current. Thus $\mathbf{K}_{1k}$ and $\mathbf{K}_{2k}$ must be such that $x_{ks}(t)$ is real. This will occur if, and only if, $\mathbf{K}_{1k}$ and $\mathbf{K}_{2k}$ are conjugates. That

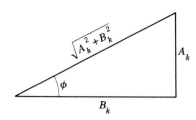

Fig. 6-6 *A right triangle where* $\phi = tan^{-1}$ $(A_K/B_K) = sin^{-1} (A_K/\sqrt{A_k^2 + B_k^2}) = cos^{-1}$ $(B_K/\sqrt{A_k^2 + B_k^2})$.

is, if

$$\mathbf{K}_{1k} = A_k + jB_k \tag{6-57a}$$

then

$$\mathbf{K}_{2k} = A_k - jB_k \tag{6-57b}$$

Substituting in Eq. (6-56b), we obtain

$$x_{ks}(t) = 2A_k \cos \omega_0 t + 2B_k \sin \omega_0 t \tag{6-58}$$

and substitution of Eqs. (6-14) and (6-16) yields

$$x_{ks}(t) = \sqrt{(2A_k)^2 + (2B_k)^2} \sin (\omega_0 t + \phi) \tag{6-59a}$$

$$\phi = \tan^{-1} \frac{A_k}{B_k} \tag{6-59b}$$

Thus the phasor which represents this sinusoid is

$$\mathbf{X}_{ks,\max} = \sqrt{(2A_k)^2 + (2B_k)^2} \ e^{j\phi} \tag{6-60}$$

where ϕ is defined in Eq. (6-59b).

If we can obtain this phasor $\mathbf{X}_{ks,\max}$, then we will have determined all the desired information about $x_{ks}(t)$. Let us see how this can be done. We write $\mathbf{X}_{ks,\max}$ in rectangular form. From Eqs. (6-60) and (6-35) we have

$$\mathbf{X}_{ks,\max} = 2 \sqrt{A_k^2 + B_k^2} (\cos \phi + j \sin \phi)$$

but ϕ is arctan A_k/B_k, which is equal to $\cos^{-1} (B_k/\sqrt{A_k^2 + B_k^2})$, and also to $\sin^{-1} (A_k/\sqrt{A_k^2 + B_k^2})$. To verify this consider the right triangle with sides A_k, B_k, and $\sqrt{A_k^2 + B_k^2}$ shown in Fig. 6-6.

Substituting for $\cos \phi$ and $\sin \phi$, we obtain

$$\mathbf{X}_{ks,\max} = 2(B_k + jA_k) \tag{6-61}$$

Hence [see Eq. (6-57b)]

$$\mathbf{X}_{ks,\max} = 2j\mathbf{K}_{2k} \tag{6-62}$$

Then to find the unknown phasor we need only find the constant $\mathbf{K}_{2k}$ in the partial-fraction expansion and multiply it by $2j$. From Eq. (6-53) and the rules for partial-fraction expansion we have

$$\mathbf{K}_{2k} = \frac{\mathbf{N}(j\omega_0)}{2j\omega_0\mathbf{D}(j\omega_0)} \tag{6-63}$$

Substituting in Eq. (6-62), we obtain

$$\mathbf{X}_{ks,\max} = \frac{\mathbf{N}(j\omega_0)}{\omega_0\mathbf{D}(j\omega_0)} \tag{6-64}$$

Thus we obtain the unknown phasor simply by evaluating Eq. (6-64). Using Eq. (6-53) to substitute for $\mathbf{N}(j\omega_0)/\mathbf{D}(j\omega_0)$, we have

$$\mathbf{X}_{ks,\max} = \left. \frac{\mathbf{X}_k(s)(s+j\omega_0)(s-j\omega_0)}{\omega_0} \right|_{s=j\omega_0} \tag{6-65}$$

That is, we multiply $\mathbf{X}_k(s)$ by

$$\frac{(s+j\omega_0)(s-j\omega_0)}{\omega_0} = \frac{s^2+\omega_0^2}{\omega_0}$$

and *then* let $s = j\omega_0$. This gives us the unknown phasor, and hence the sinusoidal-steady-state solution, without having to evaluate the inverse Laplace transform further.

We now know how to obtain the sinusoidal-steady-state solution. However, before we do this, let us modify the procedure slightly to save us some manipulation. Let us substitute Eq. (6-52) into Eq. (6-65). This yields

$$\mathbf{X}_{ks,\max} =$$
$$\left. \frac{\boldsymbol{\Delta}_{1k}\mathbf{Y}_1(s)[(s+j\omega_0)(s-j\omega_0)/\omega_0] + \boldsymbol{\Delta}_{2k}\mathbf{Y}_2(s)[(s+j\omega_0)(s-j\omega_0)/\omega_0]}{\boldsymbol{\Delta}} \frac{+\cdots+\boldsymbol{\Delta}_{nk}\mathbf{Y}_n(s)[(s+j\omega_0)(s-j\omega_0)/\omega_0]}{} \right|_{s=j\omega_0}$$
$$\tag{6-66}$$

That is, we have multiplied each term of $\mathbf{X}_k(s)$ by $(s+j\omega_0)(s-j\omega_0)/\omega_0$ and then let $s = j\omega_0$. This is a valid procedure, since the poles at $s = \pm j\omega_0$ are introduced by $\mathbf{Y}_k(s)$ [see Eq. (6-51)]. These $\mathbf{Y}_k(s)$ are each sums of the individual generator terms, each of which is in the form of Eq. (6-51). Multiplying the transform of each generator by $(s+j\omega_0)(s-j\omega_0)/\omega_0$ is equivalent to multiplying each $\mathbf{Y}_k(s)$ by this expression. Therefore, if we multiply the Laplace transform of each generator by $(s+j\omega_0)(s-j\omega_0)/\omega_0$ and use these transforms in place of the actual generator transforms in Eq. (6-52), we obtain a new set of functions which we call $\mathbf{X}_{k1}(s)$, where

$$\mathbf{X}_{k1}(s) = \frac{\mathbf{X}_k(s)(s+j\omega_0)(s-j\omega_0)}{\omega_0} \tag{6-67}$$

Thus [see Eq. (6-65)] the desired phasor is

$$\mathbf{X}_{ks,\max} = \mathbf{X}_{k1}(s) \Big|_{s=j\omega_0} \tag{6-68}$$

To obtain $\mathbf{X}_{k1}(s)$ we have multiplied the Laplace transform of each generator by $(s + j\omega_0)(s - j\omega_0)/\omega_0$. Let us substitute in Eq. (6-51) to see what this does to the transform. We have

$$\mathcal{L}[Y_{\max}(\omega_0 t + \phi)]\frac{(s + j\omega_0)(s - j\omega_0)}{\omega_0} = \frac{Y_{\max}\cos\phi\,\omega_0 + Y_{\max}\sin\phi\,s}{\omega_0}$$

(6-69)

Now we let $s = j\omega_0$, as in Eqs. (6-65) or (6-68), and obtain

$$\mathcal{L}[Y_{\max}\sin(\omega_0 t + \phi)]\frac{(s + j\omega_0)(s - j\omega_0)}{\omega_0}\bigg|_{s=j\omega_0}$$

$$= Y_{\max}(\cos\phi + j\sin\phi) = Y_{\max}e^{j\phi} \quad (6\text{-}70)$$

It is important to note that $Y_{\max}e^{j\phi}$ is just the phasor which represents $Y_{\max}\sin(\omega_0 t + \phi)$. Thus, if we replace the Laplace transform of the generator voltages and/or currents by the phasors which represent these generators in the loop, nodal, or cut-set-analysis equations, and then solve for an unknown voltage and/or current, we obtain $\mathbf{X}_{k1}(s)$. Letting $s = j\omega$, we then obtain the desired phasor. Looking at this in an equivalent manner, *if we write the Laplace transform of the loop, nodal, or cut-set equations, but replace s by jω and also replace the Laplace transforms of the generators by their phasors, then the solution for any unknown voltage or current will yield the desired unknown phasor without our having to take the inverse Laplace transform.* Since the unknown phasor contains all the unknown information, we shall have solved the problem.

Note that in the above procedure we have replaced the true generator Laplace transforms by different ones. However, this eliminates the need to write $(s + j\omega_0)(s - j\omega_0)/\omega_0$ whenever the generator terms are encountered. In the solution of multimesh or multinodal circuits this may entail a substantial saving, not only in writing the equations, but, more important, in evaluating the determinants.

Just as we can draw Laplace transformed networks, we can also have sinusoidal-steady-state transformed networks. These will be the same as the Laplace transform form, except that the sinusoidal generators are replaced by their phasors rather than by their Laplace transforms. There are no nonsinusoidal independent generators, initial-condition or otherwise. It is assumed that all the applied generators are sinusoidal of frequency ω_0. It is further assumed that the effects of any initial conditions fall off exponentially. Hence they are not considered here.

Let us illustrate this procedure by obtaining the sinusoidal-steady-state solution for the current in the network of Fig. 6-7. The loop equation for this circuit in Laplace transform form is [see Eq. (6-51)]

$$\frac{V_{\max}\cos\phi\,\omega_0}{s^2 + \omega_0^2} + \frac{Y_{\max}\sin\phi\,s}{s^2 + \omega_0^2} = \left(R + Ls + \frac{1}{Cs}\right)\mathbf{I}(s) \quad (6\text{-}71)$$

The term on the left-hand side is the Laplace transform of the generator voltage. To obtain the sinusoidal-steady-state solution we replace this term by the phasor which represents the generator. In addition, we replace s by

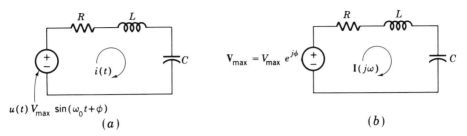

Fig. 6-7   (a) An RLC circuit with a sinusoidal generator; (b) the sinusoidal-steady-state transformed form of this network.

$j\omega_0$ in the remainder of the equation.   Hence

$$V_{\max}e^{j\phi} = \left(R + j\omega_0 L + \frac{1}{j\omega_0 C}\right) \mathbf{I}(j\omega_0) \tag{6-72}$$

This equation could have been obtained from Fig. 6-7b, which is the sinusoidal-steady-state transformed form.   Here the generator has been replaced by its phasor.

Note that if we neglect initial conditions, then the Laplace transforms of the voltage across a resistor, an inductor, or a capacitor, in terms of the Laplace transforms of the current through them are, respectively, given by

$$\mathbf{V}_R(s) = R\mathbf{I}(s) \tag{6-73a}$$
$$\mathbf{V}_L(s) = sL\mathbf{I}(s) \tag{6-73b}$$
$$\mathbf{V}_C(s) = \frac{1}{sC}\,\mathbf{I}(s) \tag{6-73c}$$

To obtain the sinusoidal steady state we let $s = j\omega_0$.   Thus in the sinusoidal-steady-state transformed form

$$\mathbf{V}_R(j\omega_0) = R\mathbf{I}(j\omega_0) \tag{6-74a}$$
$$\mathbf{V}_L(j\omega_0) = j\omega_0 L\mathbf{I}(j\omega_0) \tag{6-74b}$$
$$\mathbf{V}_C(j\omega_0) = \frac{1}{j\omega_0 C}\,\mathbf{I}(j\omega_0) \tag{6-74c}$$

Using Eqs. (6-74) to write the sinusoidal-steady-state transformed form of the voltage drops and Fig. 6-7b to write the loop equation, we can obtain Eq. (6-72) directly.   Thus with the sinusoidal-steady-state transformed form of the network we can obtain the sinusoidal-steady-state equations directly. By *sinusoidal-steady-state equations*, we mean those in which we can solve directly for the unknown phasors.

Let us now solve Eq. (6-72).   This yields

$$\mathbf{I}(j\omega_0) = \frac{V_{\max}e^{j\phi}}{R + j\omega_0 L + 1/j\omega_0 C} = \frac{V_{\max}}{\sqrt{R^2 + (\omega L - 1/\omega C)^2}}\,e^{j(\phi-\theta)} \tag{6-75a}$$

where

$$\theta = \tan^{-1}\frac{\omega_0 L - 1/\omega_0 C}{R} \tag{6-75b}$$

Note that

$$\frac{1}{j} = \frac{1}{j}\frac{j}{j} = -j \tag{6-76}$$

In addition, note that ω_0, as well as L, C, R, $V_{\max}$, and ϕ are given constants. The actual current is

$$i(t) = \frac{V_{\max}}{\sqrt{R^2 + (\omega_0 L - 1/\omega_0 C)^2}} \sin(\omega_0 t + \phi - \theta) \tag{6-77}$$

Note that the sinusoidal-steady-state solution yields phasors [see, for example, Eq. (6-75)]. Thus in this form all voltages and currents, not just the generator ones, are phasors.

Equations (6-74) are useful in performing loop analysis. For nodal or cut-set analysis it is desirable to express the currents in terms of the voltages. This yields

$$\mathbf{I}_R(j\omega_0) = \frac{1}{R}\mathbf{V}_R(j\omega_0) = G\mathbf{V}_R(j\omega_0) \tag{6-78a}$$

$$\mathbf{I}_L(j\omega_0) = \frac{1}{j\omega_0 L}\mathbf{V}_L(j\omega_0) \tag{6-78b}$$

$$\mathbf{I}_C(j\omega_0) = j\omega_0 C\mathbf{V}_C(j\omega_0) \tag{6-78c}$$

We shall explore examples of loop, nodal, and cut-set analyses in the next section and illustrate the solution of simultaneous equations.

6-3 Loop, nodal, and cut-set analysis: solution of simultaneous equations

Let us now apply the procedure developed in the last section to the solution of loop, nodal, and cut-set equations. Actually, all the techniques that we need were developed there. In this section we shall just illustrate them, using more complex circuitry. The use of the sinusoidal-steady-state transformed form of networks to write the equations directly will be demonstrated. From this point on, when we work with sinusoidal steady state, we shall designate the angular frequency as ω rather than ω_0 (we shall not often write the Laplace transform s in sinusoidal-steady-state analysis, so there will be no ambiguity between Im $s = \omega$ and ω_0).

As a first example, let us set up the sinusoidal-steady-state loop equations for the network of Fig. 6-8a. The sinusoidal-steady-state transformed form of this network is given in Fig. 6-8b. Note that this figure conveys all the information of Fig. 6-8a in a more compact form. Often we shall use only the sinusoidal-steady-state form of the network. Writing loop equations for the

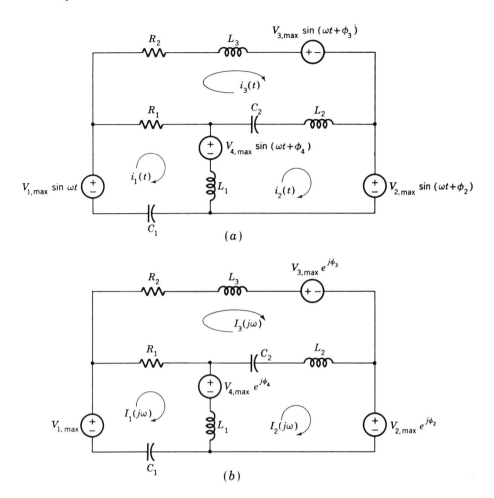

Fig. 6-8   (a) A three-loop network; (b) the sinusoidal-steady-state transformed form of this network.

network, from Eqs. (6-74), we obtain

$$V_{1,\max} - V_{4,\max}e^{j\phi_4} = \left(R_1 + j\omega L_1 + \frac{1}{j\omega C_1} \right) \mathbf{I}_1(j\omega)$$

$$- j\omega L_1 \mathbf{I}_2(j\omega) - R_1 \mathbf{I}_3(j\omega) \quad (6\text{-}79a)$$

$$V_{4,\max}e^{j\phi_4} - V_{2,\max}e^{j\phi_2} = -j\omega L_1 \mathbf{I}_1(j\omega)$$

$$+ \left(j\omega L_1 + j\omega L_2 + \frac{1}{j\omega C_2} \right) \mathbf{I}_2(j\omega) - \left(j\omega L_2 + \frac{1}{j\omega C_2} \right) \mathbf{I}_3(j\omega) \quad (6\text{-}79b)$$

$$- V_{3,\max}e^{j\phi_3} = -R_1 \mathbf{I}_1(j\omega) - \left(j\omega L_2 + \frac{1}{j\omega C_2} \right) \mathbf{I}_2(j\omega)$$

$$+ \left(R_1 + R_2 + j\omega L_2 + j\omega L_3 + \frac{1}{j\omega C_2} \right) \mathbf{I}_3(j\omega) \quad (6\text{-}79c)$$

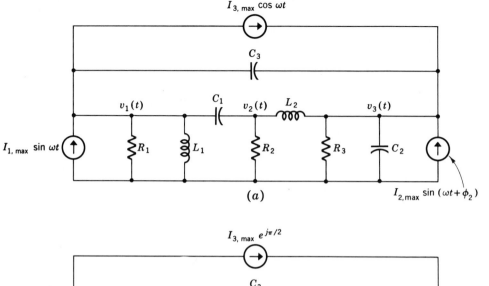

Fig. 6-9   *(a) A three-node network; (b) the sinusoidal-steady-state transformed form of this network.*

These equations can be solved for $\mathbf{I}_1(j\omega)$, $\mathbf{I}_2(j\omega)$, and $\mathbf{I}_3(j\omega)$, the phasors which represent the sinusoidal-steady-state current.   For instance, if

$$\mathbf{I}_1(j\omega) = I_{1,\max}e^{j\phi_{I_1}} \tag{6-80a}$$

then

$$i_1(t) = I_{1,\max}\sin(\omega t - \phi_{I_1}) \tag{6-80b}$$

The actual solution of the set of simultaneous equations will be considered toward the end of this section.

Let us perform a nodal analysis of the network of Fig. 6-9a.   Its sinusoidal-steady-state transformed form is shown in Fig. 6-9b.   Note that we have used

Eq. (6-8) here to obtain the phasor for cos ωt. The nodal-analysis equations for this network are

$$I_{1,\text{max}} - I_{3,\text{max}}e^{j\pi/2} = \left(G_1 + j\omega C_1 + j\omega C_3 + \frac{1}{j\omega L_1}\right)\mathbf{V}_1(j\omega)$$
$$- j\omega C_1\mathbf{V}_2(j\omega) - j\omega C_3\mathbf{V}_3(j\omega) \quad (6\text{-}81a)$$

$$0 = -j\omega C_1\mathbf{V}_1(j\omega) + \left(G_2 + j\omega C_1 + \frac{1}{j\omega L_2}\right)\mathbf{V}_2(j\omega) - \frac{1}{j\omega L_2}\mathbf{V}_3(j\omega) \quad (6\text{-}81b)$$

$$I_{3,\text{max}}e^{j\pi/2} + I_{2,\text{max}}e^{j\phi_2} = -j\omega C_3\mathbf{V}_1(j\omega) - \frac{1}{j\omega L_2}\mathbf{V}_2(j\omega)$$
$$+ \left(G_3 + j\omega C_2 + j\omega C_3 + \frac{1}{j\omega L_2}\right)\mathbf{V}_3(j\omega) \quad (6\text{-}81c)$$

Note that [see Eq. (6-20)]

$$e^{j\pi/2} = j \quad\quad\quad\quad\quad\quad\quad\quad\quad\quad\quad\quad\quad\quad\quad (6\text{-}82)$$

This can be substituted in Eqs. (6-81) to simplify them.

Cut-set analysis follows nodal analysis very closely. The details are left to the reader.

Now let us consider the actual solution of the sinusoidal-steady-state equations of loop, nodal, or cut-set analysis. The analysis exactly parallels that of Sec. 5-7, and the details will not be repeated here. The general form of the simultaneous equations are given by Eq. (5-142), except that s is replaced by $j\omega$. The quantity $\mathbf{Y}_k(j\omega)$ represents the sums of the phasors of the generators. The $\mathbf{X}_k(j\omega)$ are the unknown phasors (loop currents, nodal voltages, or cut-set voltages). The characteristic determinant is as in Eq. (5-143), except that s is replaced by $j\omega$. This determinant and its cofactor are evaluated in accordance with the rules of Sec. 3-9. The unknown phasors are evaluated by Cramer's rule [see Eq. (5-144)].

We shall illustrate this with an example. Let us obtain the current in the 2-ohm resistor of Fig. 6-10a. The sinusoidal-steady-state circuit is shown in

Fig. 6-10   (a) A two-loop network; (b) the sinusoidal-steady-state transformed form of this network. All values are in volts, ohms, henrys, or farads.

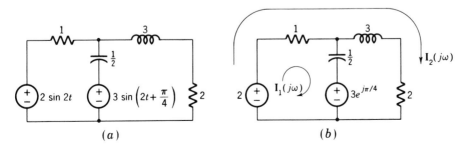

                                (a)   *(b)*

Fig. 6-10*b*.   Note that the frequency is

   $\omega = 2$

The loop equations are

$$2 - 3e^{j\pi/4} = \left(1 + \frac{1}{j}\right)\mathbf{I}_1 + \mathbf{I}_2 \tag{6-83a}$$

$$2 = \mathbf{I}_1 + (3 + j6)\mathbf{I}_2 \tag{6-83b}$$

and the characteristic determinant is

$$\boldsymbol{\Delta} = \begin{vmatrix} 1 + \dfrac{1}{j} & 1 \\ 1 & 3 + j6 \end{vmatrix} = (1 - j)(3 + j6) - 1 \tag{6-84}$$

Ordinarily, it is convenient to convert from rectangular to polar form for multiplying. In this case the numbers are simple enough that this is not necessary. Thus

   $\boldsymbol{\Delta} = 3 + 6 + j(6 - 3) - 1 = 8 + j3$

From Cramer's rule we obtain

$$\mathbf{I}_2 = \frac{2(1 - j) - (2 - 3e^{j\pi/4})}{8 + j3} = \frac{2 - j2 - 2 + 3(0.707 + j0.707)}{8 + j3}$$

$$= \frac{2.121 - j0.121}{8 + j3} = \frac{\sqrt{4.514}\ e^{j\ \tan^{-1} 0.057}}{\sqrt{73}\ e^{j\ \tan^{-1} 0.375}} = 0.248e^{-j0.096\pi} \tag{6-85a}$$

Thus we can state that

$$i_2(t) = 0.248 \sin (2t - 0.096\pi) \tag{6-85b}$$

If dependent generators are included, we consider that their voltages and/or currents, as well as the voltages and/or currents that control them, are phasors. Thus the analysis proceeds as in Eqs. (5-139) to (5-141), except that phasors are used for the sinusoidal-steady-state transforms of the generator voltages and/or currents and s is replaced by $j\omega$. Of course, the independent generators all produce sinusoidal waveforms.

6-4   Impedance and admittance

In Sec. 5-8 we discussed impedance and admittance in terms of the Laplace transform. Most of the material there and in Sec. 5-9 is also applicable here and will not be repeated (it may be desirable to review these sections before proceeding). Remember that a driving-point impedance is the ratio of the Laplace transform of the voltage across a oneport to the transform of the current through it. The oneport cannot contain any independent generators.

A similar definition applies for the sinusoidal steady state.   Here we state that an impedance is the ratio of the *phasor* of the voltage across the oneport to the *phasor* of the current through it.   From Eqs. (6-74) we can determine the impedance of a resistor, inductor, or capacitor in the sinusoidal steady state simply by taking the ratio $\mathbf{V}/\mathbf{I}$.   This yields

$$\mathbf{Z}_R(j\omega) = R \qquad\qquad (6\text{-}86a)$$

$$\mathbf{Z}_L(j\omega) = j\omega L \qquad\qquad (6\text{-}86b)$$

$$\mathbf{Z}_C(j\omega) = \frac{1}{j\omega C} \qquad\qquad (6\text{-}86c)$$

These can be obtained from the impedance in Laplace transform form [see Eqs. (5-158) to (5-160)] simply by replacing s by $j\omega$.   This substitution can be used even if the impedances are more complex than simple elements.   For instance, in Sec. 5-9 we demonstrated that the impedance of any oneport, with no independent generators, can be obtained by applying a voltage (or current) generator to the oneport and determining the resultant current (or voltage). The impedance is then the ratio of the Laplace transform of the voltage to the Laplace transform of the current.

In the sinusoidal steady state we use phasors in place of transforms.   The generators, of course, produce sinusoidal waveforms.   We discussed in Sec. 5-9 that the form of the voltage generator did not affect the impedance.   We ascertained that the driving-point impedance of a oneport could be determined from the relation [see Eqs. (5-190) and (5-192)]

$$\mathbf{Z}(s) = \frac{\triangle_{\mathrm{L}}(s)}{\triangle_{\mathrm{L}\,11}(s)} = \frac{\triangle_{\mathrm{N}\,11}(s)}{\triangle_{\mathrm{N}}(s)} \qquad\qquad (6\text{-}87)$$

where $\triangle_{\mathrm{L}}$ is the characteristic determinant written on a loop basis and $\triangle_{\mathrm{N}}$ is written on a nodal or cut-set basis.   The (s) indicates that these are functions of s.

Let us consider the sinusoidal-steady-state response.   Equation (5-190) was obtained from Eq. (5-189), which gave the Laplace transform of the current into the impedance in terms of the Laplace transform of the voltage across it.   This equation is

$$\mathbf{I}_1(s) = \mathbf{V}_1(s)\frac{\triangle_{\mathrm{L}\,11}(s)}{\triangle_{\mathrm{L}}(s)} \qquad\qquad (6\text{-}88)$$

Dividing both sides of this equation by $\mathbf{V}_1(s)$, we obtain Eq. (6-87).   To obtain the sinusoidal-steady-state response we replace s by $j\omega$ and $\mathbf{V}_1(s)$ by the phasor of the applied voltage,

$$\mathbf{I}_{1p}(j\omega) = \mathbf{V}_{1p}(j\omega)\frac{\triangle_{\mathrm{L}\,11}(j\omega)}{\triangle_{\mathrm{L}}(j\omega)} \qquad\qquad (6\text{-}89)$$

where the subscript p indicates phasors.   Then

$$\mathbf{Z}(j\omega) = \frac{\mathbf{V}_{1p}(j\omega)}{\mathbf{I}_{1p}(j\omega)} = \frac{\triangle_{11}(j\omega)}{\triangle(j\omega)} \tag{6-90}$$

This is the same as Eq. (6-87), except that s has been replaced by $j\omega$.

We have discussed impedance here.   A similar discussion pertains to admittance.   All the statements of Secs. 5-8 and 5-9 can be applied to the sinusoidal steady state by replacing s by $j\omega$ and noting that the transforms of the voltages and currents are now phasors.

Let us discuss some aspects of the simple impedances of Eq. (6-86).   We shall consider the resistance first.   The impedance of a resistor is a real number that is independent of frequency.   The relation between phasors of the current through the resistor and the voltage across it is

$$\mathbf{I}_R(j\omega) = \frac{\mathbf{V}_R(j\omega)}{R} \tag{6-91}$$

Thus, if

$$v_R(t) = V_{\max} \sin \omega t \tag{6-92a}$$

then

$$i_R(t) = \frac{V_{\max}}{R} \sin \omega t \tag{6-92b}$$

Note that the voltage and current have the same phase angle.   They are said to be *in phase*.   Now let us consider the inductor.   The relation between its current and voltage phasors is

$$\mathbf{I}_L(j\omega) = \frac{\mathbf{V}_L(j\omega)}{j\omega L} = \frac{\mathbf{V}_L(j\omega)}{\omega L} e^{-j\pi/2} \tag{6-93a}$$

Thus, if

$$v_L(t) = V_{\max} \sin \omega t$$

then

$$i_L(j\omega) = \frac{V_{\max}}{\omega L} \sin \left(\omega t - \frac{\pi}{2} \right) \tag{6-93b}$$

There are several factors that we should consider here.   The current through an inductor lags the voltage by 90° ($\pi/2$ rad).   This is independent of the frequency.   Now let us consider the magnitude of the impedance, which is ωL.   As ω, the frequency of the sinusoid, increases, so does the magnitude of the impedance (note that the magnitude of the impedance is given by the ratio of the maximum magnitude of the voltage to the maximum of the current).   Thus, if the frequency is small (or large), the magnitude of $\mathbf{Z}_L(j\omega)$ will be small (or large).

Now let us consider the impedance of the capacitor. From Eq. (6-86c) we have

$$\mathbf{I}_C(j\omega) = j\omega C \mathbf{V}_C(j\omega) = \omega C \mathbf{V}_C(j\omega)e^{j\pi/2} \tag{6-94}$$

Equivalently, if

$$v_C(t) = V_{\max} \sin \omega t \tag{6-95}$$

then

$$i_C(t) = \omega C V_{\max} \sin \left(\omega t + \frac{\pi}{2} \right) \tag{6-96}$$

Thus the current leads the voltage by 90° ($\pi/2$ rad). This may be disconcerting, since the current appears to start before the voltage is applied. Actually, this is not the case. In sinusoidal-steady-state analysis we disregard the exponentially damped terms. However, for very small values of time these terms do influence the solution, and their effect is such that the current does not start before the voltage does. After a time, therefore, the relationships given by the sinusoidal steady state are established.

The magnitude of the capacitive impedance is given by $1/\omega C$. Thus it behaves in a fashion which is the inverse of the inductive impedance.

The admittance of a simple resistance, inductance, or capacitance can be obtained by taking the reciprocals of Eqs. (6-86). This yields

$$\mathbf{Y}_R(j\omega) = \frac{1}{R} = G \tag{6-97a}$$

$$\mathbf{Y}_L(j\omega) = \frac{1}{j\omega L} \tag{6-97b}$$

$$\mathbf{Y}_C(j\omega) = j\omega C \tag{6-97c}$$

Let us consider somewhat more complex impedances. For instance, we shall obtain the impedance of the oneport of Fig. 6-11. In Sec. 5-9 we demonstrated that the impedance which results from the parallel interconnection of impedances is the reciprocal of the sum of the reciprocals of the impedances. Thus

$$\mathbf{Z}(j\omega) = \frac{1}{1/R + 1/j\omega L} = \frac{j\omega LR}{R + j\omega L} \tag{6-98a}$$

Multiplying the numerator and denominator of this expression by the conju-

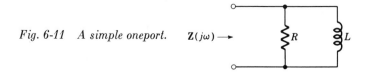

Fig. 6-11   A simple oneport. $\mathbf{Z}(j\omega) \longrightarrow$

gate of the denominator, $R - j\omega L$, we obtain

$$\mathbf{Z}(j\omega) = \frac{\omega^2 L^2 R}{R^2 + \omega^2 L^2} + j\frac{\omega L R^2}{R^2 + \omega^2 L^2} \tag{6-98b}$$

Note that the impedance has a real part and an imaginary part. In general this is the case, and the real part of the impedance is called the *resistive component* or the *resistance*, denoted by $R(\omega)$. In this case it is given by

$$R(\omega) = \frac{\omega^2 L^2 R}{R^2 + \omega^2 L^2} \tag{6-99}$$

In any but the simplest of impedances the resistive component will be a function of frequency, as $R(\omega)$ indicates. Note also that the function of frequency is indicated as ω rather than $j\omega$, since $R(\omega)$ is always real. There is no conflict of terminology here. If we work with a simple resistance R, its resistive component is just R, which is also equal to its impedance.

The imaginary component of the impedance is called the *reactive component* or the *reactance*, indicated by the symbol $X(\omega)$. In this case

$$X(\omega) = \frac{\omega L R^2}{R^2 + \omega^2 L^2} \tag{6-100}$$

Note that the reactance is often a negative quantity. For instance, the impedance of a capacitor is $1/j\omega C = -j/\omega C$.

In general, we can write

$$\mathbf{Z}(j\omega) = R(\omega) + jX(\omega) \tag{6-101}$$

The sum of two impedances can be represented physically by the series interconnection of the impedances. Thus Eq. (6-101) can be considered to come about from the series interconnection of an impedance $R(\omega)$ and another impedance $jX(\omega)$. For instance, the impedance of Eq. (6-98b) could be represented as the series interconnection of $\mathbf{Z}_1$ and $\mathbf{Z}_2$, as shown in Fig. 6-12. The values of $\mathbf{Z}_1$ and $\mathbf{Z}_2$ are given by

$$\mathbf{Z}_1(j\omega) = \frac{\omega^2 L^2 R}{R^2 + \omega^2 L^2} \tag{6-102a}$$

$$\mathbf{Z}_2(j\omega) = \frac{j\omega L R^2}{R^2 + \omega^2 L^2} \tag{6-102b}$$

Note that the sum of $\mathbf{Z}_1(j\omega)$ and $\mathbf{Z}_2(j\omega)$ yields the impedance of Eq. (6-98b). Let us consider that ω is a constant, that is, that we are working at only one frequency. $\mathbf{Z}_1(j\omega)$ is a real number, so it can be represented physically by a resistance whose numerical value is given by Eq. (6-102a). This is shown in Fig. 6-12b. In addition, $\mathbf{Z}_2(j\omega)$ is a *positive* imaginary number, so it can be represented by an inductance (if it were a negative imaginary number, we could represent it by a capacitance). Since the impedance of an inductance is $j\omega$ times the inductance, an inductor of $LR^2/(R^2 + \omega^2 L^2)$

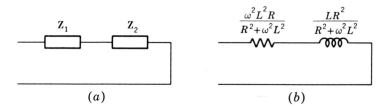

Fig. 6-12   (a) A representation of Eq. (6-98b), where $\mathbf{Z}_1 = \omega^2 L^2 R/(R^2 + \omega^2 L^2)$ and $\mathbf{Z}_2 = j\omega L R^2/(R^2 + \omega^2 L^2)$; (b) an alternative representation; the values given are the resistance in ohms and the inductance in henrys.

henrys will produce the required $\mathbf{Z}_2$ of Eq. (6-102b). This inductance is also shown in Fig. 6-12b. The network of Fig. 6-12b is equivalent to that of Fig. 6-11 if the frequency is constant at ω. Note that the resistance and inductance of Fig. 6-12b are functions of frequency. Consider that we used an ordinary resistance and inductance of the values given in Fig. 6-12b, which were evaluated for a fixed ω ($\omega = \omega_0$). Then this circuit would be equivalent to that of Fig. 6-11 only at the single frequency ω_0. It would not be equivalent at any other frequency. This is *different* from the equivalent circuits that we have encountered before, which were equivalent for all input signals.

Now let us consider admittance. For all but the simplest networks, the admittance will be a complex number. Thus we can write

$$\mathbf{Y}(j\omega) = G(\omega) + jB(\omega) \tag{6-103}$$

The real part of the admittance $G(\omega)$ is called the *conductive component* of the admittance, or simply the *conductance*. The imaginary part $B(\omega)$ is called the *susceptive component* or the *susceptance*. As an illustration let us obtain the admittance of the network of Fig. 6-11. This consists of two admittances in parallel. Thus the admittance is the sum of the individual admittances

$$\mathbf{Y}(j\omega) = \frac{1}{R} + \frac{1}{j\omega L} = G - \frac{j}{\omega L} \tag{6-104}$$

The conductance here is G, and the susceptance is $-1/\omega L$. Note that an inductance will have a positive reactance but a negative susceptance. The converse will be true for a capacitance.

An impedance can be represented as a series interconnection of two elements equal to its resistive and reactive components, respectively. Similarly, an admittance can be represented by the parallel interconnection of two elements equal to its conductive and susceptive components. Thus in the sinusoidal steady state any impedance can be represented by the series interconnection of a resistance and a reactance or the parallel interconnection of a conductance and a susceptance. In general, these equivalences will be valid only at the single frequency at which the element values are calculated.

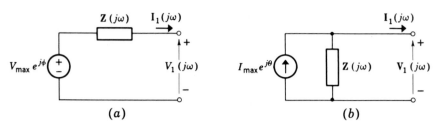

Fig. 6-13 (a) A voltage generator; (b) a current generator. These are equivalent as far as external conditions are concerned if $I_{max}e^{j\theta} = V_{max}e^{j\phi}/\mathbf{Z}(j\omega)$ and the impedances are equal in both circuits.

6-5 Equivalent voltage and current generators

A voltage generator in series with an impedance can be made equivalent to a current generator in shunt with an impedance on a sinusoidal-steady-state basis. Thus loop analysis can conveniently be performed on circuits containing current generators, and nodal or cut-set analysis can conveniently be performed on circuits with voltage generators. In Sec. 5-10 we discussed that this equivalence was valid on a Laplace transform basis. The entire discussion of that section is applicable to the sinusoidal steady state if we replace s by $j\omega$ and the transforms of the generators by their phasors. As always in the sinusoidal steady state, we assume that all the generators produce sinusoids of the same frequency and that initial-condition generators are neglected. We shall not repeat all the details of Sec. 5-10 here but shall demonstrate the equivalence of two basic circuits.

Consider the two generators shown in Figs. 6-13a and 6-13b. To show that their external conditions can be made equivalent, we must demonstrate that the relations between their terminal voltages and currents can be made identical. From Fig. 6-13a we have

$$\mathbf{V}_1(j\omega) = V_{max}e^{j\phi} - \mathbf{I}_1(j\omega)\mathbf{Z}(j\omega) \tag{6-105a}$$

and from Fig. 6-13b we have

$$\mathbf{V}_1(j\omega) = I_{max}e^{j\theta}\mathbf{Z}(j\omega) - \mathbf{I}_1(j\omega)\mathbf{Z}(j\omega) \tag{6-105b}$$

Equations (6-105a) and (6-105b) will be identical if the impedances are the same in each case and if

$$V_{max}e^{j\phi} = I_{max}e^{j\theta}\mathbf{Z}(j\omega) \tag{6-106}$$

Thus, if the above conditions hold, then these two generators will be equivalent as far as external conditions are concerned.

Examples involving interchange of voltage- and current-generator sources are very similar to those of Sec. 5-10 and will not be repeated here.

6-6   Transfer functions

We work with transfer functions on a sinusoidal-steady-state basis as well as on a Laplace transform basis.   The discussions of Sec. 5-11 are applicable, almost to the word, to the sinusoidal steady state if we replace s by $j\omega$, and we shall not repeat them here.

6-7   Phasor diagrams

In many instances, especially when simple circuits are involved, it is informative to draw all the phasors of a network.   For instance, Kirchhoff's voltage law states that the sum of the voltage drops around a closed loop is equal to zero.   Thus the diagram which indicates the sum of the phasors representing the voltages around a closed loop should be a closed polygon (it is assumed that the phasors are added by the vector-addition rule; that is, the end of one phasor is placed in contact with the arrowhead of the other).   Similarly, Kirchhoff's current law states that the net current into a node, or cut set, is zero.   Thus the sum of the phasors representing the current in a node must be zero.   Hence the diagram of the sum of all the phasors representing these currents will be a closed polygon.

Let us illustrate these ideas with some examples.   In Fig. 6-14*a* we have a simple series RC circuit.   The loop equation for this circuit is

$$V_{\max}e^{j\phi} = RI_{\max} + j\omega LI_{\max} \tag{6-107}$$

Note that we have assumed, for convenience, that the reference phasor is the current. ϕ can then be considered to be an unknown quantity.   The phasors $RI_{\max}$ and $j\omega LI_{\max}$ represent the voltage drops across the resistance and inductance, respectively.   The sum of these phasors is equal to the generator-voltage phasor $V_{\max}e^{j\phi}$. $RI_{\max}$ will be in phase with the current, while $j\omega LI_{\max}$ will lead it by 90°.   Note that $j = e^{j\pi/2}$.   The phasor diagram is illustrated in Fig. 6-14*b*.   The resultant of the two phasors represents $V_{\max}e^{j\phi}$.   This is also

Fig. 6-14   (a) A simple RL series circuit; (b) its phasor diagram.

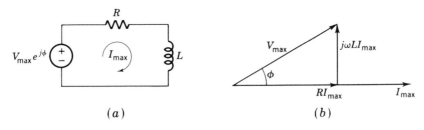

(a)   (b)

shown.   Note that, depending upon the ratio of R and ωL, the angle ϕ, which is called the *phase angle*, can vary between 0 and 90°.

Let us consider the phasor diagrams of some other simple networks. Figure 6-15a is a simple series RC circuit.   Its phasor diagram is drawn in Fig. 6-15b.   The current is taken as the reference here.   The voltage across the capacitor is

$$\frac{1}{j\omega C}\,I_{\max} = -\frac{j}{\omega C}\,I_{\max} \tag{6-108}$$

Thus the voltage across the capacitor lags the current by 90°.   The phasor representing $V_{\max}e^{j\phi}$ is drawn as shown.   Note that the phase angle ϕ can vary between 0 and $-90°$, depending upon the relative values of $1/\omega C$ and R. An RLC series circuit and its phasor diagram are shown in Figs. 6-15c and d. Note that the phasors representing the voltage drop across the inductor and the voltage drop across the capacitor are 180° out of phase.   Thus one is subtracted from the other.   If

$$\omega L = \frac{1}{\omega C} \tag{6-109}$$

then the two phasors will be equal in magnitude and 180° out of phase.   Thus their net sum will be zero.   In this case

$$V_{\max} = I_{\max}R \tag{6-110}$$

Fig. 6-15   *Some simple networks and their phasor diagrams: (a) an RC series circuit; (b) its phasor diagram; (c) an RLC series circuit; (d) its phasor diagram.*

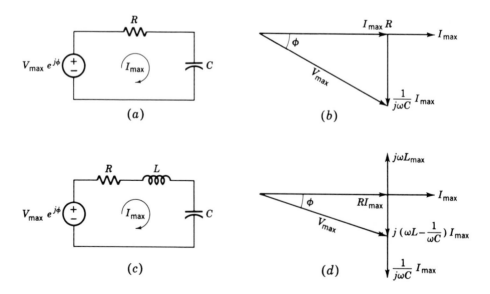

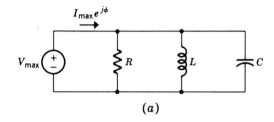

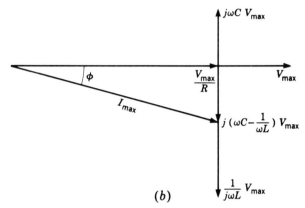

Fig. 6-16 (a) An RLC parallel circuit; (b) its phasor diagram.

That is, the presence of inductance and capacitance will not affect the current if Eq. (6-109) is satisfied.   This is a condition called *resonance*.   We shall study it further in subsequent sections.

As a final example let us draw a phasor diagram for a circuit where we apply Kirchhoff's current law at a node.   We shall use the circuit of Fig. 6-16a here. The current in the resistance, inductance, and capacitance branches are V_{max}/R, $V_{max}/j\omega L$, and $j\omega C V_{max}$, respectively.   Thus the current in the resistive branch is in phase with the voltage, while the currents in the inductive and capacitive branches lag and lead the voltage by 90°, respectively.   The phasor diagram is drawn in Fig. 6-16b.   We have chosen the voltage as a reference here.   Note that the currents through the inductance and capacitance are 180° out of phase.   If the element values and the frequency are such that Eq. (6-109) holds, then the sum of the currents in the capacitive and inductive branches will be zero (even though the individual inductive and capacitive branch currents are not).   This phenomenon will be discussed further when we consider resonance.

6-8   Average power and effective values

The power dissipated by an electric circuit is an important quantity.   For instance, we often consider the power supplied by a radio transmitter to an

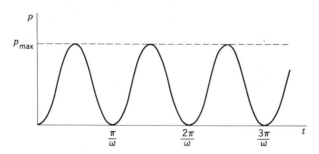

Fig.   *6-17 Instantaneous power in a resistive circuit.*

antenna, or the output power of a high-fidelity amplifier, or the power dissipated by an electric heater.   In this section we shall consider the power supplied to a "load" in the special case when the voltages and currents are sinusoids.

We have demonstrated [see Eq. (1-27)] that the instantaneous power supplied to a oneport circuit element is

$$p = vi \qquad\qquad (6\text{-}111)$$

where v is the voltage across the element and i is the current through it.   If the voltages and/or currents vary with time, then the power will also be a function of time.   We shall consider that the voltage and current are sinusoids.   Then

$$v = V_{max} \sin \omega t \qquad\qquad (6\text{-}112a)$$

$$i = I_{max} \sin \omega t \qquad\qquad (6\text{-}112b)$$

In this section we shall assume that the phase angle between the voltage and current is 0°, that is, that they are *in phase*.   This is the case if the circuit element in question is a resistance.   In the next section we shall consider the case of power in general impedances.   Substituting Eqs. (6-112) into Eq. (6-111), we obtain

$$p = V_{max}I_{max} \sin^2 \omega t = P_{max} \sin^2 \omega t \qquad\qquad (6\text{-}113)$$

The power periodically varies between $V_{max}I_{max}$ and zero.   Note that in this case it is never negative.   A typical plot of this instantaneous power is shown in Fig. 6-17.

We often do not speak of the instantaneous power, but of the *average power*. This is what we mean when we speak of a 60-watt light bulb.   The average power is the total energy supplied during one cycle divided by the time of the period.   That is, it is just the average of the power supplied to the element for a time equal to one period.   The average power is a useful and practical quantity.   For instance, suppose, as is often the case, that the voltage and current supplied from the generating station has a frequency of 60 Hz, and that this is used to drive a motor. Although the electric power varies essentially as in Eq. (6-113), the mechanical power supplied by the motor is essentially constant because of the inertia of the motor and load. Thus the average input power times the motor's efficiency will yield the output power of the motor. Similar effects occur in heating elements and in incandescent lamps because of thermal inertia. The average power times the time of operation is essentially the total energy supplied to the circuit.

If T is the time of one period, then the average power is defined as

$$P = \frac{1}{T} \int_0^T p \, dt \tag{6-114}$$

Let us substitute Eq. (6-113) into Eq. (6-114). This yields

$$P = \frac{1}{T} \int_0^T V_{\max} I_{\max} \sin^2 \omega t \, dt \tag{6-115}$$

Noting that $T = 2\pi/\omega$, we obtain

$$P = \frac{\omega}{2\pi} \int_0^{2\pi/\omega} V_{\max} I_{\max}(\tfrac{1}{2} - \tfrac{1}{2} \cos 2\omega t) \, dt = \frac{V_{\max} I_{\max}}{2} \tag{6-116}$$

where we have used the trigonometric identity

$$\sin^2 \omega t = \tfrac{1}{2} - \tfrac{1}{2} \cos 2\omega t$$

Let us compare the result of Eq. (6-116) with the power when the voltage and current are constant (direct voltage and current). Then the average power over *any* T sec is given by

$$P = \frac{1}{T} \int_0^T V_{dc} I_{dc} \, dt \tag{6-117a}$$

$$P = V_{dc} I_{dc} \tag{6-117b}$$

Note that the relation for average power is a function of the waveform used. Since we have been considering power dissipated in a resistance, let us write this power in terms of the resistance. In general, if an impedance is a pure resistance, then

$$V_{\max} = \frac{I_{\max}}{R} \tag{6-118}$$

Substituting in Eq. (6-116), we obtain

$$P = \frac{1}{2} \frac{V_{\max}^2}{R} \tag{6-119a}$$

$$P = \frac{1}{2} I_{\max}^2 R \tag{6-119b}$$

For the direct-current case we have

$$P = \frac{V_{dc}{}^2}{R} \qquad\qquad (6\text{-}120a)$$

$$P = I_{dc}{}^2 R \qquad\qquad (6\text{-}120b)$$

It is convenient to be able to use the same relation for power dissipated in a resistor regardless of the waveform of the voltage or the current. For this reason, we define an *effective voltage* V_{eff} and *effective current* I_{eff}. These are such that

$$P = \frac{V_{eff}^2}{R} \qquad\qquad (6\text{-}121a)$$

or

$$P = I_{eff}^2 R \qquad\qquad (6\text{-}121b)$$

regardless of the waveform. That is, the effective voltage and current are defined for each waveform such that the average power is given by Eqs. (6-121). For instance, comparison of Eqs. (6-121) and (6-120) shows that for the direct case

$$V_{eff} = V_{dc} \qquad\qquad (6\text{-}122a)$$

$$I_{eff} = I_{dc} \qquad\qquad (6\text{-}122b)$$

For the sinusoidal case compare Eqs. (6-121) and (6-119). This yields

$$V_{eff} = \frac{V_{max}}{\sqrt{2}} = 0.707 V_{max} \qquad\qquad (6\text{-}123a)$$

$$I_{eff} = \frac{I_{max}}{\sqrt{2}} = 0.707 I_{max} \qquad\qquad (6\text{-}123b)$$

Thus for a sinusoidal waveform the effective value of the voltage or the current is the maximum value of the voltage or current divided by $\sqrt{2}$.

If the periodic waveform is not sinusoidal, then the effective value will not be given by Eq. (6-123). For instance, suppose we have a periodic voltage $v(t)$ of period T. Let us determine its effective value. The instantaneous power dissipated in an R-ohm resistance when $v(t)$ is across it is

$$p = \frac{v^2(t)}{R} \qquad\qquad (6\text{-}124)$$

Thus the average power is [see Eq. (6-114)]

$$P = \frac{1}{T} \int_0^T \frac{v^2(t)}{R} \, dt \qquad\qquad (6\text{-}125)$$

Equating this with Eq. (6-121a), we obtain

$$V_{eff} = \sqrt{\frac{1}{T} \int_0^T v^2(t) \, dt} \qquad\qquad (6\text{-}126)$$

The integral within the square-root sign is just the average (or mean) value of $v^2(t)$ over one period. Thus the effective value of a voltage (or current) is the square root of the mean value of the voltage (or current). This is often called the *root-mean-square* (*rms*) value. We often write

$$V_{rms} = V_{eff} \tag{6-127a}$$

$$I_{rms} = I_{eff} \tag{6-127b}$$

Where the identifying subscript is omitted, effective value is indicated; for instance, V_2 will refer to $V_{2,rms}$. We shall indicate maximum value by the subscript max (as in $V_{2,max}$).

We have expressed phasors in terms of maximum values, but we can also use effective values. For instance, if

$$v_1 = \sqrt{2}\, V_{1,eff} \sin (\omega t + \phi) = V_{1,max} \sin (\omega t + \phi) \tag{6-128a}$$

then this can be characterized by either of the phasors

$$\mathbf{V}_1 = \mathbf{V}_{1,eff} = V_1 e^{j\phi} = V_{1,eff} e^{j\phi} \tag{6-128b}$$

or

$$\mathbf{V}_{1,max} = V_{1,max} e^{j\phi} \tag{6-128c}$$

We shall use the effective value and the effective-value phasor very often. The effective value is usually used when the voltage or current is stated. For instance, a (sinusoidal) 115-volt power line produces 115 volts rms, or a peak voltage of $115\sqrt{2} = 162.6$ volts.

6-9   Power factor

In the last section we considered power dissipated in purely resistive loads. Now let us discuss power supplied to an impedance which has reactive components as well as resistive ones. For instance, consider the impedance of Fig. 6-18. If the voltage across it is given by

$$v = V_{max} \sin \omega t \tag{6-129a}$$

then the current through it will be

$$i = I_{max} \sin (\omega t + \phi) \tag{6-129b}$$

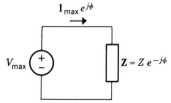

Fig. 6-18   A oneport impedance.

The average power dissipated in this impedance is

$$P = \frac{1}{T} \int_0^T V_{max} I_{max} \sin \omega t \sin (\omega t + \phi) \, dt \tag{6-130}$$

Substituting $T = 2\pi/\omega$ and the trigonometric identity of Eqs. (6-9) and (6-10), we obtain

$$P = \frac{\omega}{2\pi} \int_0^{2\pi/\omega} V_{max} I_{max} (\cos \phi \sin^2 \omega t + \sin \phi \sin \omega t \cos \omega t) \, dt$$

Integration yields

$$P = \frac{V_{max} I_{max}}{2} \cos \phi \tag{6-131}$$

Substituting the effective values of Eqs. (6-123), we have

$$P = V_{eff} I_{eff} \cos \phi \tag{6-132}$$

Thus, when the voltage and current are not in phase, the power is not given by the product of their effective values, but their product must be multiplied by the *cosine of the phase angle between them.* The cosine of this phase angle, cos ϕ, is called the *power factor.*

If the impedance has a reactive component, then the product of the effective value of the voltage across it and the current through it *does not* yield the power. This product $V_{eff} I_{eff}$ is sometimes called the *apparent power.* That is,

$$A_P = V_{eff} I_{eff} \tag{6-133}$$

The true power is given by the product of the apparent power and the power factor. The quantity $V_{eff} I_{eff} \sin \phi$ is sometimes called the *reactive power.* It units are reactive volt amperes (vars). Vars are used rather than watts because reactive power is *not* true power. Let

$$Q = V_{eff} I_{eff} \sin \phi \tag{6-134}$$

We can then write

$$B = P + jQ = V_{eff} I_{eff} (\cos \phi + j \sin \phi) = V_{eff} I_{eff} e^{j\phi} \tag{6-135}$$

B is called the *complex power.* Its magnitude is the apparent power, and its real part is the true power. Note carefully that the only true power is P. *The other quantities—reactive power, complex power, and apparent power—are not the true power supplied to the element.*

In the preceding development we chose the voltage as the reference to establish the phase angle. Actually, it does not matter what we use as the reference. The power is given by Eq. (6-132), where ϕ is the phase angle between the voltage and the current. If the phase angle of the voltage is not zero, then we start integrating in Eq. (6-130) at a time when the voltage is zero and is increasing positively. We integrate for one full period. The function integrated over the period will be identical with that integrated in Eq. (6-130). If the voltage phasor is given by $\mathbf{V}_{\text{eff}} = V_{\text{eff}} e^{j\theta_1}$, the current phasor is given by $\mathbf{I}_{\text{eff}} = I_{\text{eff}} e^{j\theta_2}$, and we define

$$\theta_1 - \theta_2 = \phi \tag{6-136}$$

then $\cos \phi$ is the power factor, and Eq. (6-132) can be used to compute the power.

Let us consider the product

$$\mathbf{V}_{\text{eff}}\mathbf{I}_{\text{eff}}^* = V_{\text{eff}} e^{j\theta_1} I_{\text{eff}} e^{-j\theta_2} = V_{\text{eff}} I_{\text{eff}} e^{j(\theta_1 - \theta_2)} \tag{6-137}$$

where the asterisk denotes the conjugate. Substituting Eq. (6-136) and comparing the result with that of Eq. (6-132), we obtain

$$P = \text{Re } \mathbf{V}_{\text{eff}}\mathbf{I}_{\text{eff}}^* \tag{6-138}$$

Consider the phase angle ϕ between the voltage and the current. From Eq. (6-132) we see that, if

$$-\frac{\pi}{2} \le \phi \le \frac{\pi}{2} \tag{6-139}$$

then the power will be positive. However, if

$$\pi \ge \phi \ge \frac{\pi}{2}$$

or

$$-\frac{\pi}{2} \ge \phi \ge -\pi \tag{6-140}$$

then $\cos \phi$ will be negative, and the power will also be negative. A negative P means that, on the average, the load supplies power to the generator. Thus there will be a net flow of energy from the load to the generator. If there are no generators in the load, this is impossible (note that the net energy flow cannot be accounted for by initial conditions, since the energy flow persists for an indefinite time, and thus the energy is infinite). Therefore for ordinary circuit elements the power-factor angle will be restricted by relation (6-139).

Let us now consider the case where $\phi = \pm\pi/2$. In this case the load is purely reactive (it contains only inductors and capacitors). Then Eq. (6-132) yields

$$P = 0 \tag{6-141}$$

Let us study the instantaneous power to see why the average power is zero. The instantaneous power is

$$p = V_{\text{max}} I_{\text{max}} \sin \omega t \sin\left(\omega t \pm \frac{\pi}{2}\right) = \pm V_{\text{max}} I_{\text{max}} \sin \omega t \cos \omega t$$

or, equivalently,

$$p = \pm\tfrac{1}{2}V_{max}I_{max} \sin 2\omega t \qquad (6\text{-}142)$$

Thus, for the one half of the cycle the instantaneous power is positive, but for the next it is negative, and so on. This gives an average power of zero. That is, the reactive elements take power and store energy for one half of the cycle and then return it to the circuit in the next half cycle (this is discussed in further detail in Sec. 1-13). If the power-factor angle is not zero, but has a magnitude smaller than $\pi/2$, then the instantaneous power will be negative for some part, but less than half, of the cycle.

6-10   Frequency-response plots

In our previous discussions of the sinusoidal steady state we assumed that we were working only at a single frequency. Often this is the case. However, at times we may require the response of a network to many frequencies. We could accomplish this by obtaining the sinusoidal-steady-state response at one frequency ($\omega = \omega_0$) and then assume that the generator (or generators) is shifted to a new frequency $\omega = \omega_1$ and obtain the response there. We can repeat this procedure at all frequencies of interest. This is not as tedious as it sounds. We can usually perform the analysis in terms of a general ω and obtain the solution in terms of it. Then we need only substitute all the desired values of ω to obtain all the required solutions. Only one analysis is required. For instance, for the network of Fig. 6-19, we have

$$\mathbf{I}(j\omega) = \frac{V_1}{R + 1/j\omega C} = \frac{j\omega C V_1}{1 + j\omega RC} \qquad (6\text{-}143)$$

$\mathbf{I}(j\omega)$ can be found for any desired value of ω by substituting that value into Eq. (6-143).

Let us consider some applications in which we might want the sinusoidal-steady-state response of a network to more than one frequency. Audio devices such as high-fidelity amplifiers, for instance, are rated in terms of their frequency response; that is, their sinusoidal-steady-state response to all frequencies in the audible range is studied. The response to each of these frequencies should be the same if the amplifier is to be of good quality. A simple way of presenting this information is in a graph of the response versus

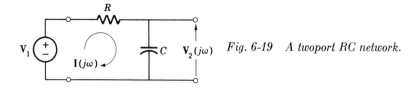

Fig. 6-19   A twoport RC network.

frequency. This is called a *frequency-response plot*. Frequency-response plots are also used to analyze tuned amplifiers, the devices that allow radio and television receivers to receive one signal and reject all others. Such plots are also used for general analysis procedures. We shall also see in Chap. 11 that the frequency-response plot can be used to obtain the response of a network to an arbitrary function of time.

The response of a network consists of two parts, a magnitude and a phase angle (usually, phasor notation is used). We can also use the real and imaginary parts of the phasor. In any event, there are two variables that must be plotted against frequency. This is a total of three quantities. Three-dimensional plots are cumbersome, and various types of two-dimensional plots are used to avoid them. These will be discussed in the next few sections.

6-11   Amplitude and phase plots

A simple way of presenting frequency-response information is to use two graphs. A common procedure consists of plotting the magnitude of the frequency response vs. the frequency on one graph and the phase angle of the frequency response vs. the frequency on the other. We shall illustrate this procedure with the transfer-voltage ratio of the network of Fig. 6-19. From Eq. (6-143) and the fact that the phasor of the voltage $\mathbf{V}_2(j\omega)$ is given by $\mathbf{I}(j\omega)/j\omega C$, we obtain

$$\mathbf{K}(j\omega) = \frac{\mathbf{V}_2(j\omega)}{\mathbf{V}_1(j\omega)} = \frac{1}{1 + j\omega RC} \tag{6-144a}$$

Writing this in polar form, we have

$$\mathbf{K}(j\omega) = K(\omega)e^{j\phi(\omega)} \frac{1}{\sqrt{1 + \omega^2 R^2 C^2}} e^{-j\tan^{-1}\omega RC} \tag{6-144b}$$

Thus the magnitude and phase of this expression are

$$K(\omega) = \frac{1}{\sqrt{1 + (\omega RC)^2}} \tag{6-144c}$$

$$\phi(\omega) = -\tan^{-1}\omega RC \tag{6-144d}$$

Let us consider the plots of these functions, which are shown in Fig. 6-20a and b. When ω is small, so that $\omega RC \ll 1$, then $K(\omega) \approx 1$ and $\phi(\omega) \approx 0$. As ω becomes large, $K(\omega)$ decreases and $\phi(\omega)$ departs from zero. For very large ω, $K(\omega) \approx 1/\omega RC$ and falls to zero asymptotically, while the phase shift approaches $-90°$ asymptotically.

Plots of this general form are often obtained for transistor and vacuum-tube amplifiers. For instance, Figs. 6-20 could represent the magnitude and phase angle of the amplification of a high-fidelity audio amplifier [the ampli-

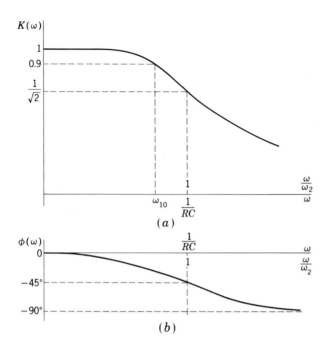

$K(\omega)$

1

0.9

$\dfrac{1}{\sqrt{2}}$

ω_{10} $\dfrac{1}{RC}$ $\dfrac{\omega}{\omega_2}$ ω

(a)

$\phi(\omega)$

0

$-45°$

$-90°$

$\dfrac{1}{RC}$ ω $\dfrac{\omega}{\omega_2}$

(b)

Fig. 6-20   The frequency-response plots of the open-circuit transfer-voltage ratio of the network of Fig. 6-19: (a) amplitude-response plot; (b) phase-response plot. Normalized frequency axes, as well as absolute ones, are shown; the half-power frequency is used as the normalizing constant.

fication is just the transfer-voltage (or current) ratio of the amplifier network]. These curves could also represent the amplification of an amplifier used in an electronic voltmeter. Such a device can measure very small sinusoidal voltages, since the amplifier increases their magnitudes. In such devices it is conventional to speak of a *bandwidth*, which is the useful range of frequencies. Ideally, the magnitude $K(\omega)$ would be constant over all the bandwidth. In addition, $\phi(\omega)$ would be zero. Thus all frequencies would be amplified equally (we shall discuss this further below). In general, $K(\omega)$ and $\phi(\omega)$ are not constant over any range of frequencies. Thus we define the bandwidth as that range of frequencies where $K(\omega)$ is constant and $\phi(\omega)$ is zero for all practical purposes. The bandwidth will depend upon the application for which the device is used. For instance, the response for an audio amplifier might be considered acceptable if it does not vary by more than 10 percent. Thus the bandwidth would consist of those frequencies between zero and ω_{10} on Fig. 6-20a. In this case we say that the bandwidth is ω_{10}. For the electronic voltmeter we might consider anything more than a 1 percent variation unacceptable; here the bandwidth would be considerably less than ω_{10}.

We stated above that $K(\omega)$ should be constant and $\phi(\omega)$ should be zero if the network is to be ideal. We can demonstrate this on a transient basis and then extend the results somewhat. In Sec. 5-15 we discussed the fact that in an ideal amplifier the input and output should be related by

$$v_2(t) = k v_1(t)$$

and their Laplace transforms would be

$$\mathbf{V}_2(s) = k\mathbf{V}_1(s)$$

Thus the transfer-voltage ratio of this network is

$$\mathbf{K}(s) = k \qquad\qquad\qquad\qquad (6\text{-}145a)$$

Since this is a constant, on a sinusoidal-steady-state basis we have

$$\mathbf{K}(j\omega) = k \qquad\qquad\qquad\qquad (6\text{-}145b)$$

Thus the ideal frequency response has a constant amplitude and zero phase shift.

There is another fact that should be considered. If the output voltage has the same waveform as the input but is delayed in time, the response is often considered to be ideal (see Sec. 5-15). Then (see Sec. 5-16) we can have

$$\mathbf{V}_2(s) = k e^{-\tau s}\mathbf{V}_1(s)$$

Thus the transfer-voltage ratio is

$$\mathbf{K}(s) = k e^{-\tau s} \qquad\qquad\qquad\qquad (6\text{-}146a)$$

Hence on a sinusoidal-steady-state basis we have

$$\mathbf{K}(j\omega) = k e^{-j\omega\tau} \qquad\qquad\qquad\qquad (6\text{-}146b)$$

Therefore, if the amplitude of $\mathbf{K}(j\omega)$ is constant and its phase varies linearly with frequency, there will be no distortion. Equations (6-145) and (6-146) indicate that an ideal device would have a transfer function whose amplitude never varies with frequency. Actually, this need not be the case. Very often the input signal $v_1(t)$ can be shown to be made up of a limited range of frequencies. For instance, the input signal to an audio amplifier usually contains only frequencies in the range 20 to 20,000 Hz. Thus the response of the device outside this range will not affect the output.

Often, when a specific application is not considered, and the frequency response has the general shape of Fig. 6-20, bandwidth is defined as the range of frequencies between zero and the frequency at which the response has fallen off to $1/\sqrt{2}$ the "zero-frequency" (direct-voltage) value. This is called the *half-power bandwidth*. If the voltage falls off by $1/\sqrt{2}$, then the power, which is proportional to voltage squared, will be halved. There is nothing special about the figure $1/\sqrt{2}$; it is merely a convenient one to use. Let us obtain the half-power bandwidth for Eq. (6-144c). If $K(\omega) = 1/\sqrt{2}$, then

$$\sqrt{1 + \omega_2{}^2 R^2 C^2} = 1$$

or equivalently,

$$\omega_2{}^2 R^2 C^2 = 1$$

where ω_2 is the specific value of ω that satisfies this equation.   Hence the half-power bandwidth is given by

$$\omega_2 = \frac{1}{RC} \qquad\qquad (6\text{-}147a)$$

or

$$f_2 = \frac{1}{2\pi RC} \qquad\qquad (6\text{-}147b)$$

Note that at the half-power frequency f_2 the phase shift is $-45°$ [see Eq. (6-144d)].   It is often convenient to normalize the frequency response of the network in terms of f_2.   For instance, substituting it into Eq. (6-144) and noting that $f = \omega/2\pi$, we obtain

$$\mathbf{K}(j\omega) = \frac{1}{1 + jf/f_2} = \frac{1}{\sqrt{1 + (f/f_2)^2}}\, e^{-j\tan^{-1} f/f_2} \qquad\qquad (6\text{-}148a)$$

or, equivalently,

$$\mathbf{K}(j\omega) = \frac{1}{1 + j\omega/\omega_2} = \frac{1}{\sqrt{1 + (\omega/\omega_2)^2}}\, e^{-j\tan^{-1}\omega/\omega_2} \qquad\qquad (6\text{-}148b)$$

The frequency axis is often plotted as ω/ω_2 or f/f_2 to take advantage of this normalization.   Such normalized axes are also shown in Fig. 6-20.

Often a logarithmic axis is used for the frequency axis.   This allows us to present a very large range of frequencies on a single graph without having to crowd the low frequencies together.   As an example of this Eqs. (6-148) are again plotted in Fig. 6-21a and b.   Now we have used semilog graph paper. Note that a much wider range of frequencies can be indicated here.

The curves that we have considered had a zero-frequency response of unity (zero frequency corresponds to a direct voltage or a direct current), and the bandwidth was determined in terms of this zero-frequency response. Now let us consider a curve for which the zero-frequency value of $\mathbf{K}(j\omega)$ is not unity.   For instance, we could have

$$\mathbf{K}(j\omega) = \frac{K_0}{1 + j\omega/\omega_2} \qquad\qquad (6\text{-}149)$$

$K(0) = K_0$, and in this case it is common to normalize with respect to K_0. That is, we work with $\mathbf{K}(j\omega)/K_0$.   All the results then proceed as before.

Very often in working with electronic amplifiers the response falls off to zero at low frequencies as well as at high ones.   In this case we do not normalize with respect to the zero-frequency response.   The usable region of amplification is now a *midband region*, which lies above the very low and below the very high frequencies.   The amplification should be essentially constant in

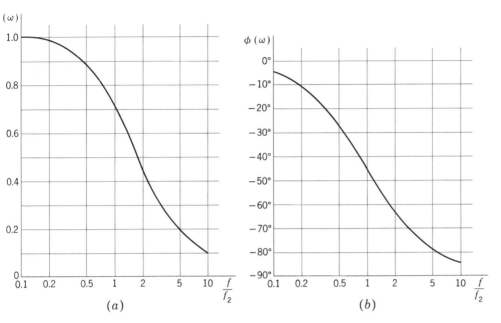

Fig. 6-21   The frequency response, on a logarithmic-frequency axis, of the open-circuit transfer-voltage ratio of the network of Fig. 6-19: (a) amplitude response; (b) phase response.

this region.   In such cases the response is usually normalized with respect to the midband value, and the bandwidth is determined in terms of the midband response.

Our discussions have been in terms of the transfer-voltage ratio.   Actually, any transfer function could have been used.

6-12   Polar plots

We can plot *both* the magnitude and phase of a complex function against frequency on a two-dimensional plot if we use the set of axes shown in Fig. 6-22, which are its real and imaginary parts [we have assumed that the function we are plotting is $\mathbf{K}(j\omega)$, although it can be any complex function of frequency]. Now consider the point P.   The length of the phasor from the origin to P gives the magnitude of $\mathbf{K}(j\omega)$ [that is, $K(\omega)$].   Similarly, the angle of $\mathbf{K}(j\omega)$ [$\phi(\omega)$] is also shown.   The real and imaginary parts of $\mathbf{K}(j\omega)$ can be obtained from the horizontal- and vertical-axis coordinates of point P.   If we evaluate $\mathbf{K}(j\omega)$ for a sequence of points (for frequency from $\omega = 0$ to $\omega = \infty$) and plot each of these as in Fig. 6-22, a curve will result.   The frequency does not

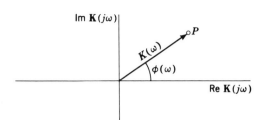

Fig. 6-22   *The axes used in a polar plot of* **K**$(j\omega)$.

appear on any axis, but the frequency used to calculate any point on the curve can be marked next to that point.

Let us illustrate the procedure with an example. We shall again use the open-circuit transfer-voltage ratio for the network of Fig. 6-19. From Eq. (6-144) we have

$$\mathbf{K}(j\omega) = \frac{1}{1 + j\omega RC} = \frac{1}{\sqrt{1 + (\omega RC)^2}}\, e^{-j\tan^{-1}\omega RC} \qquad (6\text{-}150a)$$

Alternatively, we can write

$$\mathbf{K}(j\omega) = \mathrm{Re}\ \mathbf{K}(j\omega) + j\ \mathrm{Im}\ \mathbf{K}(j\omega) = \frac{1}{1 + \omega^2 R^2 C^2} - \frac{j\omega RC}{1 + \omega^2 R^2 C^2} \qquad (6\text{-}150b)$$

Plotting either of these equations in a polar plot, we obtain the graph of Fig. 6-23. Three frequencies are marked on the graph as $\omega = 0$, $\omega = 1/RC$, and $\omega = \infty$. Other points might also be marked. Note that for the network of Fig. 6-19 the polar plot is a semicircle. The following manipulation will show this. Consider $[\mathrm{Re}\ \mathbf{K}(j\omega) - \frac{1}{2}]^2 + [\mathrm{Im}\ \mathbf{K}(j\omega)]^2$. Substituting Eq. (6-150b), we obtain

$$[\mathrm{Re}\ \mathbf{K}(j\omega) - \tfrac{1}{2}]^2 + [\mathrm{Im}\ \mathbf{K}(j\omega)]^2 = \tfrac{1}{4} \qquad (6\text{-}151)$$

This is the equation of a circle whose radius is $\frac{1}{2}$ and whose center is at $\mathrm{Re}\ \mathbf{K}(j\omega) = \frac{1}{2}$ and $\mathrm{Im}\ \mathbf{K}(j\omega) = 0$.

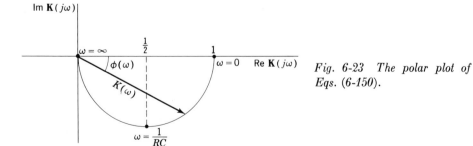

Fig. 6-23   *The polar plot of Eqs. (6-150).*

The magnitude and phase of $\mathbf{K}(j\omega)$ at any frequency can be read directly from the polar plot by drawing a phasor from the origin to the point on the graph which corresponds to the frequency in question. Note that when $\omega = 1/RC$, then $K(j\omega) = \frac{1}{2}e^{-j\pi/4}$, as it should. The polar plots provide essentially the same information about frequency as do the amplitude and phase plots. They are just an alternative means of providing it. In studies of network stability special polar plots called *Nyquist diagrams* are used. In many applications these Nyquist diagrams can replace the Routh and Hurwitz tests discussed in Sec. 5-13.

6-13 The relationship between frequency response and the pole-zero diagram

We shall now discuss a simple graphical procedure that can be used to obtain the frequency response of a network function from the location of its poles and zeros. We shall work with the Laplace transform of the network transfer function

$$\mathbf{W}(s) = \frac{K(s - s_{01})(s - s_{02}) \cdots (s - s_{0m})}{(s - s_1)(s - s_2) \cdots (s - s_n)} \tag{6-152}$$

To obtain the sinusoidal-steady-state transfer function we need only replace s by $j\omega$ (see Sec. 6-6),

$$\mathbf{W}(j\omega) = W(\omega)e^{j\phi(\omega)} = \frac{K(j\omega - s_{01})(j\omega - s_{02}) \cdots (j\omega - s_{0m})}{(j\omega - s_1)(j\omega - s_2) \cdots (j\omega - s_n)} \tag{6-153}$$

Let us obtain the magnitude and phase of this expression. From Eq. (6-38) we have

$$W(\omega) = K\frac{|j\omega - s_{01}|\,|j\omega - s_{02}| \cdots |j\omega - s_{0m}|}{|j\omega - s_1|\,|j\omega - s_2| \cdots |j\omega - s_n|} \tag{6-154a}$$

$$\phi(\omega) = \measuredangle(j\omega - s_{01}) + \measuredangle(j\omega - s_{02}) + \cdots + \measuredangle(j\omega - s_{0m})$$
$$- [\measuredangle(j\omega - s_1) + \measuredangle(j\omega - s_2) + \cdots + \measuredangle(j\omega - s_n)] \tag{6-154b}$$

where $\measuredangle(j\omega - s_{01})$ is read as "the phase angle of $j\omega - s_{01}$." Note that $s_{01} \cdots s_{0m}$ and $s_1 \cdots s_n$ can be complex numbers.

Let us now consider a pole-zero diagram to see how Eqs. (6-154) can be simply evaluated by graphical means. Before we study a complete diagram, let us consider one with a single zero, at $s = s_{01}$. We shall determine the magnitude and phase angle of $j\omega_0 - s_{01}$, where ω_0 is a particular value of ω. Figure 6-24 shows the single zero s_{01} and $j\omega_0$. The dashed phasor from the origin to point s_{01} is the phasor of s_{01}. That is, its magnitude is equal to the magnitude of s_{01}, and its phase angle is the angle of s_{01}. The vertical phasor from the origin to the point $j\omega_0$ is the phasor $j\omega_0$. Thus, according to the rules for the subtraction of phasors, the phasor from the point s_{01} to the point $j\omega_0$ is

$j\omega_0 - s_{01}$. The magnitude and phase angle of this phasor can be read with a ruler and a protractor, without the need for any calculations. Thus, by varying the point $j\omega_0$, by simple graphical means we can determine the magnitude and phase angle of $j\omega_0 - s_{01}$ for any desired frequencies.

To solve for the magnitude and phase of $\mathbf{W}(j\omega)$, which has many poles and zeros [see Eq. (6-154)], we can measure with a ruler and protractor the magnitude and phase angle of each of the terms. Then, to obtain the magnitude $W(\omega_0)$ we multiply the magnitudes of all the phasors drawn from $j\omega_0$ to the zeros and divide this by the product of the magnitudes of all the phasors drawn from $j\omega_0$ to the poles. If there is a constant multiplier, the result of this calculation should be multiplied by it. The phase angle $\phi(\omega_0)$ is obtained by taking the sum of the angles of all the phasors drawn from the zeros ($s_{01} \cdot \cdot \cdot s_{0m}$) to the point $j\omega_0$ and then subtracting from this sum the sum of the angles of all the phasors drawn from all the poles ($s_1 \cdot \cdot \cdot s_n$) to $j\omega_0$. The construction for a typical pole-zero diagram is shown in Fig. 6-25. If multiple poles or zeros occur, then these are counted in order of their multiplicity. For instance, if there is a triple zero at s_{01}, then the magnitude product will contain the factor $|j\omega_0 - s_{01}|^3$, and three times the angle of $j\omega_0 - s_{01}$ will be used in computing the phase angle.

The graphical construction that we have been considering is useful not only because it permits us to obtain the frequency response easily, but also because it provides insight into the relative effect of different poles and zeros on the frequency response. For instance, in Fig. 6-25, suppose we are most interested in the response to frequencies between ω_a and ω_b. Note that the magnitude and phase angle of the phasor $j\omega - s_1$ will change more rapidly than any of the other phasors as ω varies from ω_a to ω_b. In general, as ω is varied over any frequency range of interest, the phasors drawn from poles or zeros near the frequency range will vary more rapidly than those drawn from poles or zeros far from the range. Thus the poles and zeros closest to

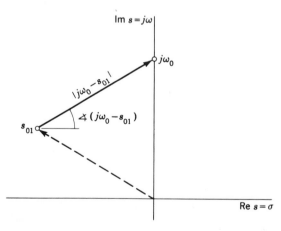

Fig. 6-24   *A graphical construction of* $j\omega_0 - s_{01}$. *The solid-line phasor represents* $j\omega_0 - s_{01}$ *and the dashed-line phasor is* s_{01}.

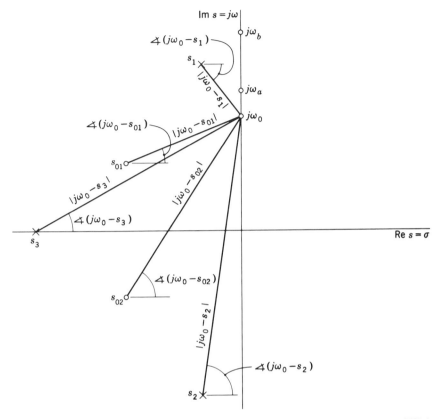

Fig. 6-25   *A pole-zero diagram of* $\mathbf{W}(s)$ *illustrating the graphical construction of* $W(\omega)$ *and* $\phi(\omega)$.

the range of interest have the greatest effect on the shape of the frequency-response curve. These poles and zeros are called the *dominant poles* and *dominant zeros*. At times, when the frequency range is limited, the phasors drawn from the nondominant poles need only be calculated at a single frequency chosen near the center of the range of interest. These phasors can be considered constant for all values of ω within the range of interest. The validity of this approximation should be checked against the end points of the range.

6-14   Decibel notation

We often find it desirable to express the transfer function of a twoport in terms of logarithms. This is done in analyzing audio devices, for example, because

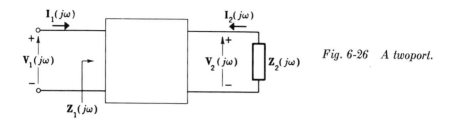

Fig. 6-26   A twoport.

the ear functions logarithmically.   We shall also see that the use of logarithms simplifies the plotting of frequency-response curves.   Let us use the twoport of Fig. 6-26 to establish some fundamental definitions.   Let P_2 be the average power supplied to the load impedance $\mathbf{Z}_2(j\omega)$ and P_1 be the average power entering the twoport.   Then the number of *bels of power gain* of the twoport is given by

$$\text{No. of bels} = \log_{10} \frac{P_2}{P_1} \tag{6-155}$$

The bel is, in general, too large a unit for our purposes, and the *decibel*, which is $\frac{1}{10}$ bel, is usually used.   The number of decibels is given by

$$\text{No. of decibels} = 10 \log_{10} \frac{P_2}{P_1} \tag{6-156}$$

Now let us consider some special cases.   If $\mathbf{Z}_2(j\omega) = R_2$ and $\mathbf{Z}_1(j\omega) = R_1$ (that is, if the input impedance and load impedance of the twoport are purely resistive), then the number of decibels is [see Eqs. (6-121)]

$$\text{No. of decibels} = 10 \log_{10} \frac{V_2{}^2/R_2}{V_1{}^2/R_1} = 10 \log_{10} \frac{I_2{}^2 R_2}{I_1{}^2 R_1} \tag{6-157}$$

where V_1, V_2, I_1, and I_2 are the magnitudes of the effective values of $\mathbf{V}_1$, $\mathbf{V}_2$, $\mathbf{I}_1$, and $\mathbf{I}_2$, respectively.   If

$$R_1 = R_2 \tag{6-158}$$

then Eq. (6-157) becomes

$$\text{No. of decibels} = 20 \log_{10} \frac{V_2}{V_1} \tag{6-159a}$$

$$\text{No. of decibels} = 20 \log_{10} \frac{I_2}{I_1} \tag{6-159b}$$

Strictly speaking, the only time that Eqs. (6-159a) or (6-159b) can be used is when both $\mathbf{Z}_1(j\omega)$ and $\mathbf{Z}_2(j\omega)$ are pure resistances and Eq. (6-158) holds.   However, it is common to express the transfer-voltage ratio or transfer-current ratio in decibels with Eq. (6-159a) or Eq. (6-159b) even if Eq. (6-158) is not true.   In fact, this is done even if $\mathbf{Z}_1(j\omega)$ and $\mathbf{Z}_2(j\omega)$ are not purely resistive.

In such cases the number of decibels given by Eqs. (6-156), (6-159a), or (6-159b) will *all* be different.   It is permissible to use decibels in this way, provided it is understood that we are talking about a power ratio *or* a voltage ratio *or* a current ratio, but not all three.

When $P_2 = \frac{1}{2}P_1$ [see Eq. (6-156)], then the number of decibels is

$$-10 \log_{10}2 = -3.0103 \approx -3 \text{ db}$$

Thus half-power frequencies (see Sec. 6-11) are often called 3-db frequencies.

6-15   Logarithmic frequency plots—Bode plots

We shall now plot the amplitude and phase of a transfer function of the form of Eq. (6-152) on a decibel basis.   Such plots are called *Bode plots*, after the man who developed them.   We shall often find that these plots are very convenient to use.   They are also used extensively in the analysis and design of feedback amplifiers.[1]   For the time being we shall restrict ourselves to the case where the poles and zeros all lie on the real (σ) axis.   Thus from Eq. (6-152) we have

$$\mathbf{W}(s) = K \frac{s_{01}s_{02} \, \cdots \, s_{0m}}{s_1 s_2 \, \cdots \, s_n} \frac{(s/s_{01} - 1)(s/s_{02} - 1) \, \cdots \, (s/s_{0m} - 1)}{(s/s_1 - 1)(s/s_2 - 1) \, \cdots \, (s/s_n - 1)} \tag{6-160}$$

For convenience let us normalize this relation as

$$\mathbf{W}_n(s) = \mathbf{W}(s) \frac{s_1 s_2 \, \cdots \, s_n}{K s_{01}s_{02} \, \cdots \, s_{0m}} \tag{6-161}$$

Hence

$$\mathbf{W}_n(j\omega) = W_n(\omega)e^{j\phi(\omega)} = \frac{(j\omega/s_{01} - 1)(j\omega/s_{02} - 1) \, \cdots \, (j\omega/s_{0m} - 1)}{(j\omega/s_1 - 1)(j\omega/s_2 - 1) \, \cdots \, (j\omega/s_n - 1)} \tag{6-162}$$

The magnitude and phase angle of this expression are given by

$$W_n(\omega) = \frac{\sqrt{(\omega/s_{01})^2 + 1} \, \sqrt{(\omega/s_{02})^2 + 1} \, \cdots \, \sqrt{(\omega/s_{0m})^2 + 1}}{\sqrt{(\omega/s_1)^2 + 1} \, \sqrt{(\omega/s_2)^2 + 1} \, \cdots \, \sqrt{(\omega/s_n)^2 + 1}} \tag{6-163a}$$

$$\pm \phi(\omega) = \tan^{-1}\frac{\omega}{s_{01}} + \tan^{-1}\frac{\omega}{s_{02}} + \cdots + \tan^{-1}\frac{\omega}{s_{0m}}$$
$$- \left(\tan^{-1}\frac{\omega}{s_1} + \tan^{-1}\frac{\omega}{s_2} + \cdots + \tan^{-1}\frac{\omega}{s_n} \right) \tag{6-163b}$$

Now let us obtain $W_n(\omega)$ on a decibel basis.   This is given by

$$W_{n,\text{db}}(\omega) = 20 \log_{10} W_n(\omega) \tag{6-164}$$

It is assumed that $W_n(\omega)$ represents a transfer-voltage or transfer-current ratio or a transfer admittance or transfer impedance [if it represented a transfer-power ratio, the multiplying factor of Eq. (6-164) would be 10]. Then, substituting Eq. (6-163a) into Eq. (6-164), we obtain

$$
\begin{aligned}
W_{n,\,\mathrm{db}}(\omega) = 10 \left\{ \log_{10} \left[\left(\frac{\omega}{s_{01}}\right)^2 + 1 \right] + \log_{10} \left[\left(\frac{\omega}{s_{02}}\right)^2 + 1 \right] + \cdots \right. \\
+ \log_{10} \left[\left(\frac{\omega}{s_{0m}}\right)^2 + 1 \right] - \log_{10} \left[\left(\frac{\omega}{s_{1}}\right)^2 + 1 \right] - \log_{10} \left[\left(\frac{\omega}{s_{2}}\right)^2 + 1 \right] \\
\left. - \cdots - \log_{10} \left[\left(\frac{\omega}{s_{n}}\right)^2 + 1 \right] \right\} \quad (6\text{-}165)
\end{aligned}
$$

The use of logarithms has converted Eq. (6-163a) into a sum of terms. Let us consider one of these terms and discuss its frequency response. The frequency response of the entire function can then be obtained by taking the sum and differences of similar terms,

$$
H_{0k} = 10 \log_{10} \left[\left(\frac{\omega}{s_{0k}}\right)^2 + 1 \right] \quad (6\text{-}166)
$$

Before we plot this curve, let us determine its asymptotes. If

$$
\frac{\omega}{s_{0k}} \ll 1 \quad (6\text{-}167)
$$

then

$$
H_{0k}(\omega) \approx 10 \log_{10} 1 = 0 \text{ db} \quad (6\text{-}168)
$$

However, if

$$
\frac{\omega}{s_{0k}} \gg 1 \quad (6\text{-}169)
$$

then

$$
H_{0k}(\omega) \approx 10 \log_{10} \left(\frac{\omega}{s_{0k}}\right)^2 = 20 \log_{10} \frac{\omega}{s_{0k}} = 20 \log_{10} \omega - 20 \log_{10} s_{0k} \quad (6\text{-}170)
$$

If we use semilog paper to plot this graph, or equivalently, if we use a $10 \log_{10} \omega$ scale for the frequency axis, then the curve of Eq. (6-170) will be a straight line of the form $20x + b$, where $x = \log_{10} \omega$. The asymptote, as well as the actual curves are shown in Fig. 6-27.

We can use the asymptotes to sketch the curve in quickly. Let us consider them further. From Eq. (6-170) we have, for the high-frequency asymptote at $\omega = s_{0k}$,

$$
H(s_{01}) = 20 \log_{10} 1 = 0 \text{ db}
$$

Thus the high-frequency asymptote intersects the low-frequency asymptote (the horizontal axis) at $\omega = s_{01}$. In Fig. 6-27 the axis is shown normalized so that the point of intersection is unity. Let us consider the slope of this straight-line asymptote. From Eq. (6-170) we have that the slope is 20 on a

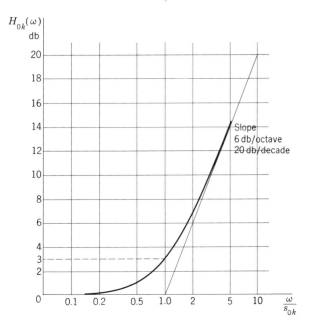

$H_{0k}(\omega)$ db

Fig. 6-27   A plot of $H_{0k}(\omega)$
$= 10 \log_{10} [(\omega/s_{0k})^2 + 1]$ and
its asymptotes.

Slope
6 db/octave
20 db/decade

log frequency scale.   Let us interpret this.   Comparing the response at two frequencies, ω_b and ω_d, we have

$$H_{01}(\omega_b) - H_{01}(\omega_a) = 20 \log_{10} \omega_b - 20 \log_{10} \omega_a = 20 \log_{10} \frac{\omega_b}{\omega_2} \qquad (6\text{-}171)$$

If $\omega_b = 2\omega_a$, then

$$H_{01}(\omega_b) - H_{01}(\omega_a) = 20 \log_{10} 2 = 20(0.30103) \approx 6 \text{ db}$$

A two-to-one range of frequencies is termed an *octave*.   Thus the slope of the high-frequency asymptote is 6 db/octave.   Similarly, if $\omega_b = 10\omega_a$, then

$$H_{01}(\omega_b) - H_{01}(\omega_a) = 20 \log_{10} 10 = 20 \text{ db}$$

A 10-to-1 range of frequencies is called a *decade*.   Thus the slope of this asymptote is also 20 db/decade.   Let us see how the actual curve departs from the asymptotes.   From Eq. (6-166) we see that if $\omega = s_{01}$, then

$$H_{01}(s_{01}) = 10 \log_{10} 2 \approx 3 \text{ db}$$

Thus at the point $s = s_{01}$ the curve is 3 db from its asymptote.   The actual deviation of the curve from its asymptotes at other frequencies is given in Fig. 6-27.

The frequency $\omega = s_{01}$ is called the *break point* or *break frequency*, so termed because the asymptote "breaks" here.   If we know the break frequency, we can draw the asymptote and then sketch the curve in quickly.   This is one of the reasons that Bode plots are often used.

Now let us obtain the graph of a more complex function.   For example, suppose that

$$\mathbf{W}(j\omega) = \frac{(j\omega - 1)(j\omega - 3)}{(j\omega - 2)(j\omega - 4)^2} \tag{6-172}$$

This can be written as

$$\mathbf{W}(j\omega) = \frac{3}{32} \frac{(j\omega - 1)(j\omega/3 - 1)}{j(\omega/2 - 1)(j\omega/4 - 1)^2}$$

Thus in normalized form

$$\mathbf{W}_n(\omega) = \frac{(j\omega - 1)(j\omega/3 - 1)}{(j\omega/2 - 1)(j\omega/4 - 1)^2}$$

Putting this into the form of Eq. (6-165), we obtain

$$W_{n,\,\mathrm{db}}(\omega) = 10 \log_{10}(\omega^2 + 1) + 10 \log_{10}\left[\left(\frac{\omega}{3}\right)^2 + 1\right] - 10 \log_{10}\left[\left(\frac{\omega}{2}\right)^2 + 1\right]$$
$$- 20 \log_{10}\left[\left(\frac{\omega}{4}\right)^2 + 1\right] \quad (6\text{-}173)$$

Note that the multiplying factor of the last term is 20, because it is squared in Eq. (6-172).   Thus we have a sum of four terms, each of which is of the form of Eq. (6-166).   The asymptotes for each of these is drawn in Fig. 6-28a.   The asymptotes for the complete $W_{n,\,\mathrm{db}}(\omega)$, drawn in Fig. 6-28$b$, are obtained by adding the asymptotes of Fig. 6-28a on a point-by-point basis. The desired curve can then be sketched in, as shown by the dashed curve of Fig. 6-28b.   Note that the actual curve departs from the break points by values other than 3 db.   This is because all four terms must be considered at all points.   However, at points far removed from its break point each term is closely approximated by its asymptotes.   To plot the response accurately, the curves (not just the asymptotes) for each of the functions in Eq. (6-167) can be drawn in Fig. 6-28a using Fig. 6-27.   The sum of these four curves is taken on a point-by-point basis.   Often sufficient accuracy is obtained just by drawing the asymptotes and rounding them off.

Note that at each break point the asymptote changes its slope by $6n$ db/octave, where n is an integer.   The value of n depends upon the power of the particular factor that contains the break point.   That is, the asymptote will have a break point at $\omega = \omega_0$, and its slope will change by $6n$ db/octave if the expression in question has a factor $(j\omega/\omega_0 - 1)^n$.

It is very convenient to be able to use straight lines to sketch curves.   Let us see how this can be done for phase response.   From Eq. (6-163b) we see that phase functions of the form $\tan^{-1}(\omega/s_{0k})$ will be encountered.   When a log frequency axis is used, this curve can be approximated closely by a curve whose

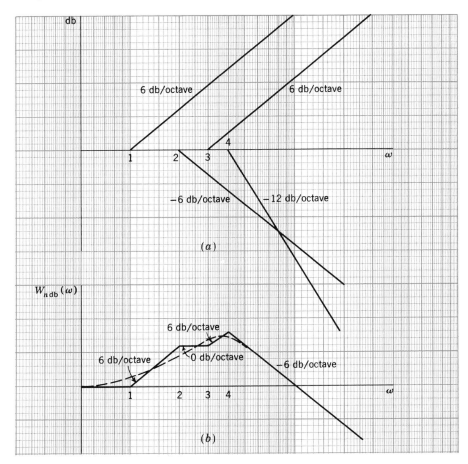

Fig. 6-28   (a) The asymptotes of each of the terms of Eq. (6-117); (b) the asymptotes of the actual response; a sketch of the actual curve is shown by dashes.

slope is 45°/decade and two horizontal straight lines.   These straight lines and

$$\phi_{0k}(\omega) = \tan^{-1} \frac{\omega}{s_{0k}} \tag{6-174}$$

are plotted in Fig. 6-29.   Note that the curve is closely approximated by the straight lines.   Thus we can use the straight-line asymptotes to rapidly sketch the phase response of a network.

We have assumed so far that all the poles and zeros of the function in question are real.   Now let us consider a pair of complex-conjugate zeros (or poles).   We shall work with a function of the form

$$\mathbf{H}_{0k_1, k_2}(s) = \frac{s^2}{\omega_0{}^2} + \frac{2d}{\omega_0} s + 1 \tag{6-175}$$

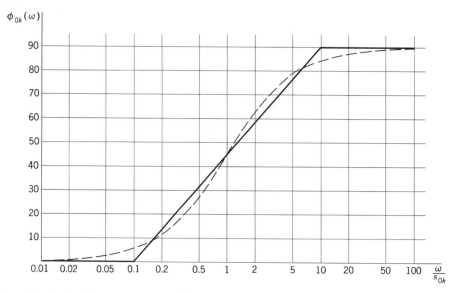

Fig. 6-29   A plot of $\phi_{0k} = \tan^{-1}(\omega/s_{0k})$ and its asymptotes.

where d and ω_0 are as defined in Eqs. (4-140), (4-141) and (4-144). The expression has been normalized so that $H_{0k}(0) = 1$.   Then

$$\mathbf{H}_{0k_1,k_2}(j\omega) = 1 - \frac{\omega^2}{\omega_0^2} + j2d\frac{\omega}{\omega_0} \tag{6-176}$$

The magnitude and phase angle of this expression are

$$H_{0k_1,k_2}(\omega) = \sqrt{\left(1 - \frac{\omega^2}{\omega_0^2}\right)^2 + 4d^2\left(\frac{\omega}{\omega_0}\right)^2} \tag{6-177a}$$

$$\phi_{0k_1,k_2} = \tan^{-1}\frac{2d\omega/\omega_0}{1 - (\omega/\omega_0)^2} \tag{6-177b}$$

On a decibel basis Eq. (6-171a) can be written as

$$H_{0k_1,k_2,\,\text{db}} = 10\log_{10}\left[\left(1 - \frac{\omega^2}{\omega_0^2}\right)^2 + 4d^2\left(\frac{\omega}{\omega_0}\right)^2\right] \tag{6-178}$$

For very small ω the asymptotic response is given by

$$H_{0k_1,k_2,\,\text{db}}(\omega) = 10\log_{10}1 = 0 \text{ db} \tag{6-179a}$$

and for very large ω the asymptotic response is given by

$$H_{0k_1,k_2,\,\text{db}}(\omega) = 10\log_{10}\left(\frac{\omega}{\omega_0}\right)^4 = 40\log_{10}\frac{\omega}{\omega_0} = 40\log_{10}\omega - 40\log_{10}\omega_0 \tag{6-179b}$$

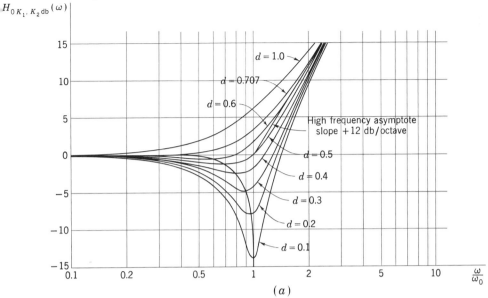

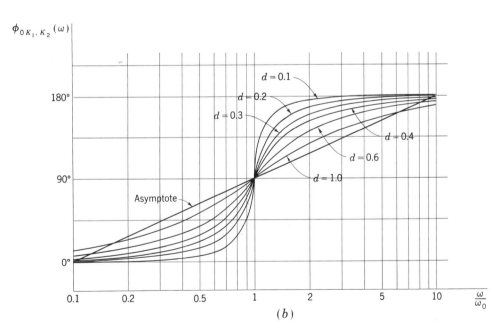

Fig. 6-30   *(a) A plot of $H_{0k_1k_2, db}(\omega)$; (b) a plot of $\phi_{0k_1k_2}(\omega)$. (By permission from M. E. Van Valkenburg, "Network Analysis," 2d ed., Prentice-Hall, Inc., Englewood Cliffs, N.J., © 1964.)*

Comparing this with Eq. (6-166) and its asymptotic slopes, we find that the high-frequency asymptotic slope is 12 db/octave, or 40 db/decade.   The break point occurs at $\omega = \omega_0$.   Note that this asymptotic slope is essentially the same as the one given for Eq. (6-166), where one zero gave us 6 db/octave. In Eq. (6-175) we have two zeros (or poles).   Thus we have twice the slope. The asymptotic straight lines for a pair of complex poles or zeros are drawn on a frequency-response curve in essentially the same way as for a real pole or zero.   The departure of the actual curve from the asymptotic value is given in Fig. 6-30a.   Note that the departure of the curve from its asymptote can be *large*, especially in the vicinity of $\omega = \omega_0$.   Figure 6-30a *should* be used to ascertain the deviation of the actual curve from its asymptotic value.

The curves of $\phi_{0k_1,k_2}(\omega)$ versus ω are shown in Fig. 6-30b.   These can be approximated by two horizontal lines and a line whose slope is 90°/decade, as shown on the diagram.   Figure 6-30b should be used to obtain the deviation of the response from the asymptotes.   In general, the curves of Fig. 6-30 will depart further from their asymptotes than those for simple poles and zeros.   Thus care should be taken in the case of a pair of complex roots to correct for deviations from the asymptotes.   In other respects, however, the procedures for drawing the frequency-response curves is essentially the same as for real poles and zeros.

6-16   Parallel resonance

In this section and the next two we shall discuss the frequency response of some relatively simple circuits.   These are usually used in tuned amplifiers, that is, in amplifiers that are designed to amplify a specific range of frequencies and reject all others.   Such amplifiers are used in every radio and television receiver.   Their purpose is to allow only one station of all the hundreds that are broadcasting to be received at a time.   In addition to their importance in their own right, the study of these circuits will provide us with some important insight into substitutions and approximations.

The simplest resonant circuit that we shall consider is shown in Fig. 6-31.   It consists of a coil in parallel with a capacitor.   The resistor R is

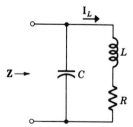

Fig. 6-31   *A parallel resonant circuit.*

often not one that is placed there, but one that comes about because of the resistance of the wire of the coil. A quantity used to characterize a coil is its *quality factor* Q, defined on a sinusoidal-steady-state basis as

$$Q = \frac{2\pi \text{ maximum energy stored in the coil}}{\text{energy dissipated in the resistor in one cycle}} \tag{6-180}$$

If the current through the coil $\mathbf{I}_L$ is given by

$$\mathbf{I}_L = I_L e^{j\phi} \tag{6-181}$$

then the maximum current in the coil is $\sqrt{2}\, I_L$; that is,

$$i_L = I_{L,\max} \sin(\omega t + \phi) = \sqrt{2}\, I_L \sin(\omega t + \phi)$$

Thus from Eq. (1-129) we obtain

$$Q = \frac{2\pi \tfrac{1}{2}L(\sqrt{2}\, I_L)^2}{I_L{}^2 R T} \tag{6-182a}$$

where T is the period. Then, from the relation $T = 2\pi/\omega$ we have

$$Q = \frac{\omega L}{R} \tag{6-182b}$$

Let us obtain the input impedance of the circuit of Fig. 6-31. Combining elements as discussed in Sec. 5-9, we obtain

$$\mathbf{Z} = \frac{1/j\omega C (R + j\omega L)}{R + j(\omega L - 1/\omega C)} \tag{6-183a}$$

and after manipulation we have

$$\mathbf{Z} = \frac{L/C(1 - jR/\omega L)}{R[1 + j(\omega L/R)(1 - 1/\omega^2 LC)]} \tag{6-183b}$$

To simplify this expression and make it more understandable, we shall make some substitutions. Let

$$\omega_0 = \frac{1}{\sqrt{LC}} \tag{6-184a}$$

or

$$f_0 = \frac{1}{2\pi \sqrt{LC}} \tag{6-148b}$$

Also,

$$Q_0 = \frac{\omega_0 L}{R} \tag{6-185a}$$

f_0 is called the *resonant frequency*. Substitution of Eqs. (6-184) into Eq. (6-185a) yields

$$Q_0 = \frac{1}{\omega_0 RC} = \frac{1}{R}\sqrt{\frac{L}{C}} \tag{6-185b}$$

Substitution of Eqs. (6-184) and (6-185) into Eqs. (6-183) yields, after some manipulation,

$$\mathbf{Z} = \frac{Q_0{}^2 R(f/f_0 - j1/Q_0)}{f/f_0 + jQ_0(f^2/f_0{}^2 - 1)} \tag{6-186}$$

In most tuned amplifiers Q_0 will be a large number, often greater than 100. Thus the second term in the denominator is an important one. Usually we are interested in frequencies near f_0, so that f/f_0 will be close to unity. The term $(f/f_0)^2$ must be obtained to a very high degree of accuracy, since we are subtracting two nearly equal numbers. For instance, in the difference

$$100 - 99 = 1$$

if we make a 1 percent error in one of the numbers and write $101 - 99 = 2$, we obtain a 100 percent error in the answer. Thus Eq. (6-186) must be evaluated with great accuracy.

By making an appropriate substitution we can eliminate the need for this great accuracy. Let

$$\delta = \frac{f - f_0}{f_0} = \frac{f}{f_0} - 1 \tag{6-187}$$

Then

$$\frac{f^2}{f_0{}^2} - 1 = (1 + \delta)^2 - 1 = \delta^2 + 2\delta + 1 - 1 = \delta(\delta + 2) \tag{6-188}$$

Note that the two nearly equal numbers that are subtracted are $(1 + \delta)^2$ and 1. However, the subtraction is carried out exactly in Eq. (6-188) (note the term $1 - 1$). The remaining term does not have this subtraction. Hence a small error in δ will not result in a large error in $\delta(\delta + 2)$. Thus the substitution of Eq. (6-188) into Eq. (6-186) eliminates the need for extreme accuracy (note that $f - f_0$ can easily be obtained accurately, so there will be no large errors in δ). Substituting in this way and manipulating, we have

$$\mathbf{Z} = \frac{Q_0{}^2 R[1 + \delta + j1/Q_0]}{1 + \delta + jQ_0\delta(\delta + 2)} \tag{6-189}$$

In general, for tuned amplifiers

$$Q_0 \gg 1 \tag{6-190}$$

In addition, δ is usually close to unity. As a result,

$$1 + \delta \gg \frac{1}{Q_0}$$

We can then neglect the $j1/Q_0$ term in the numerator (note that there is no subtraction of nearly equal terms here). After doing this and manipulating, we have

$$\mathbf{Z} = Ze^{j\phi} = \frac{Q_0{}^2R}{1 + jQ_0\delta(\delta + 2)/(\delta + 1)} \tag{6-191}$$

The magnitude of this expression is given by

$$Z = \frac{Q_0{}^2R}{\sqrt{1 + Q_0{}^2\delta^2(\delta + 2)^2/(\delta + 1)^2}} \tag{6-192a}$$

and its phase angle is

$$\phi = -\tan^{-1}\frac{Q_0\delta(\delta + 2)}{\delta + 1} \tag{6-192b}$$

The maximum value of Z occurs when $\delta = 0$ $(f = f_0)$ and is given by

$$Z_{\max} = Q_0{}^2R \tag{6-193a}$$

This is a resistance, so we shall designate it by R_0. Then, substituting Eq. (6-185a), we obtain

$$R_0 = Q_0{}^2R = (\omega_0L)Q_0 = \frac{Q_0}{\omega_0C} \tag{6-193b}$$

Normalization of Eq. (6-192a) with respect to R_0 yields

$$\frac{Z}{R_0} = \frac{1}{\sqrt{1 + Q_0{}^2\delta^2(\delta + 2)^2/(\delta + 1)^2}} \tag{6-194}$$

Typical curves for various values of Q_0 are given in Fig. 6-32. Note that the curves vary more rapidly with frequency as Q_0 is increased. Note also that R_0 is increased as Q_0 is increased. Although we have been studying the impedance of a parallel resonant circuit, we shall see that the frequency response of circuits using parallel resonant circuits can have the same form as Fig. 6-32.

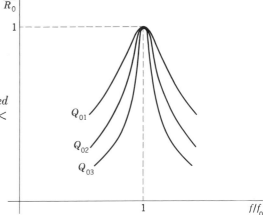

Fig. 6-32 Typical curves of the normalized impedance of a parallel resonant circuit $Q_{01} < Q_{02} < Q_{03}$.

The bandwidth of a parallel resonant circuit is the range of frequency for which Z/R_0 varies from R_0 by less than some specified amount. The specified amount depends upon the application for which the circuit is used. Much of the discussion of bandwidth in Sec. 6-11 is also applicable here. For convenience we shall use the half-power bandwidth B:

$$B = f_2 - f_1 \tag{6-195}$$

where

f_1 = lower frequency   where $\dfrac{Z}{R} = \dfrac{1}{\sqrt{2}}$ (6-196a)

f_2 = upper frequency   where $\dfrac{Z}{R} = \dfrac{1}{\sqrt{2}}$ (6-196b)

It will be convenient to work with f rather than with δ in this case.

Substituting Eq. (6-187) into Eq. (6-194), we obtain

$$\frac{Z}{R_0} = \frac{1}{\sqrt{1 + Q_0^2(f/f_0 - f_0/f)^2}}$$

At $f = f_1$ and $f = f_2$, $Z/R_0 = 1/\sqrt{2}$. Thus

$$\frac{1}{\sqrt{2}} = \frac{1}{\sqrt{1 + Q_0^2(f_2/f_0 - f_0/f_2)^2}} \tag{6-197a}$$

$$\frac{1}{\sqrt{2}} = \frac{1}{\sqrt{1 + Q_0^2(f_1/f_0 - f_0/f_1)^2}} \tag{6-197b}$$

Each of these equations will have two solutions—a positive one and a negative one. Choosing the positive solutions, we have

$$Q_0\left(\frac{f_2}{f_0} - \frac{f_0}{f_2}\right) = 1 \tag{6-198a}$$

$$Q_0\left(\frac{f_0}{f_1} - \frac{f_1}{f_0}\right) = 1 \tag{6-198b}$$

Equating and solving, we have

$$f_1 f_2 = f_0^2 \tag{6-199}$$

Then, substituting Eq. (6-199) into Eq. (6-198a) and manipulating, we obtain

$$B = f_2 - f_1 = \frac{f_0}{Q_0} \tag{6-200}$$

Thus the frequencies f_2 and f_1 have geometric symmetry about f_0. The bandwidth varies directly with f_0 and inversely with Q_0.

Let us now obtain an expression for f_2 and f_1. We solve Eq. (6-199) for f_1 and substitute it into Eq. (6-200). This yields

$$f_2 = \frac{f_0}{2Q_0} + \sqrt{f_0^2\left(1 + \frac{1}{4Q_0^2}\right)} \tag{6-201a}$$

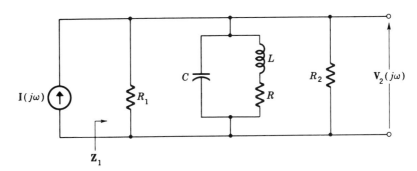

Fig. 6-33   A tuned network.

Similarly,

$$f_1 = -\frac{f_0}{2Q_0} + \sqrt{f_0{}^2\left(1 + \frac{1}{4Q_0{}^2}\right)} \tag{6-201b}$$

where we have chosen the positive solutions. If $Q_0 \gg 1$, we can make some approximations to simplify these expressions. Expansion of Eq. (6-201a) in a power series yields

$$f_2 = \frac{f_0}{2Q_0} + f_0\left(1 - \frac{1}{8Q_0{}^2} + \cdots\right) \tag{6-202}$$

If $Q_0 \gg 1$, we can neglect all the terms containing Q_0 except the first one (for example, $\frac{1}{2}Q_0 \gg \frac{1}{8}Q_0{}^2$). Thus

$$f_2 \approx f_0\left(1 + \frac{1}{2Q_0}\right) \tag{6-203a}$$

Proceeding similarly, we have

$$f_1 \approx f_0\left(1 - \frac{1}{2Q_0}\right) \tag{6-203b}$$

Equations (6-203a) and (6-203b) demonstrate that when Q_0 is large, f_1 and f_2 exhibit arithmetic symmetry about f_0; that is, they essentially are equally spaced about f_0.

Let us now demonstrate that a parallel resonant circuit can be used to produce a network whose transfer function will vary with frequency in accordance with Fig. 6-32. Consider the circuit given in Fig. 6-33. This is an equivalent circuit for many tuned electronic amplifiers. Let us call $\mathbf{Z}$ the impedance of just the parallel resonant circuit. The output voltage is given by the product $\mathbf{IZ}_1$, where $\mathbf{Z}_1$ is the impedance of R_1, R_2, and $\mathbf{Z}$ in parallel. Combining these three impedances in parallel, we have

$$\mathbf{V}_2(j\omega) = \mathbf{I}(j\omega)\frac{1}{1/R_1 + 1/\mathbf{Z} + 1/R_2} \tag{6-204}$$

The transfer function for this network is $\mathbf{Y}_T(j\omega) = \mathbf{V}_2(j\omega)/\mathbf{I}(j\omega)$. Then, substituting Eqs. (6-191) and (6-193b) into Eq. (6-204) and manipulating, we obtain

$$\mathbf{Y}_T(j\omega) = \frac{R_{\text{sh}}}{1 + j(Q_0 R_{\text{sh}}/R_0)[\delta(\delta + 2)/(\delta + 1)]} \tag{6-205}$$

where

$$\frac{1}{R_{\text{sh}}} = \frac{1}{R_1} + \frac{1}{R_2} + \frac{1}{R_0} \tag{6-206}$$

That is, R_{sh} represents the parallel combination of R_1, R_2, and R_0, the resistance of the resonant circuit at the resonant frequency.

Now let us define

$$Q_{\text{eff}} = \frac{Q_0 R_{\text{sh}}}{R_0} \tag{6-207}$$

Then, substituting in Eq. (6-205) and normalizing, we have

$$\frac{\mathbf{Y}_T(j\omega)}{R_{\text{sh}}} = \frac{1}{1 + jQ_{\text{eff}}[\delta(\delta + 2)/(\delta + 1)]} \tag{6-208}$$

We see that after normalization this equation is identical with Eq. (6-191), except that Q_0 is replaced by Q_{eff}. For this reason we call Q_{eff} the *effective Q* of the circuit. Thus all our previous discussions about the shape of the resonance curve can be applied to the transfer function $\mathbf{Y}_T(j\omega)$, and we need only replace Q_0 by Q_{eff}.

Power-factor correction

There is another application employing parallel resonant circuits which differs from the preceding one in that the Q of the circuit is very low and only one frequency is considered. Electric induction motors draw the same current as though an inductance in series with a resistance was connected across the power line. Such a circuit, which is electrically equivalent to the motor, is shown in Fig. 6-34a. For this circuit

$$I = Ie^{j\theta} = \frac{V}{Z} e^{-j\phi} \tag{6-209}$$

where

$$\mathbf{Z} = Ze^{j\phi} = R + j\omega L = \sqrt{R^2 + \omega^2 L^2}\, e^{j\tan^{-1}\omega L/R} \tag{6-210}$$

The power supplied to the motor is

$$P = VI \cos\theta = VI \cos\phi \tag{6-211}$$

If the power factor was unity, then the same power could be supplied to the motor at a lower value of current. In general, the user pays on the basis

Fig. 6-34 (a) The equivalent circuit of an induction motor; (b) the same circuit with a power-factor-correcting capacitor added.

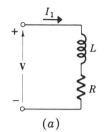

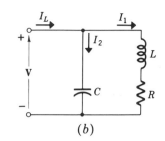

(a)   (b)

of power. However, if the power factor is low, then the current will be higher then is necessary to supply this power. This "excess" current produces an excessive power loss in the resistance of the transmission lines that run from the generating station to the user and in the resistance of the electrical generators. Thus it is desirable to operate as close to unity power factor as possible.

If we place a capacitor of the appropriate size in parallel with the motor, as shown in Fig. 6-34b, we can reduce the magnitude of I_L, the line current (since the voltage V across the motor has not changed, the motor current I_1 will not change). Let us demonstrate that this can be done. The motor current is [see Eqs. (6-209) and (6-210)]

$$\mathbf{I}_1 = I_1 e^{j\theta} = I_1 e^{-j\phi} = I \cos\phi - jI \sin\phi \tag{6-212}$$

We choose C such that

$$I_2 = jI \sin\phi \tag{6-213}$$

That is,

$$j\omega C V = jI \sin\phi$$

or, equivalently,

$$C = \frac{I \sin\phi}{\omega V} \tag{6-214}$$

In general,

$$\mathbf{I}_L = \mathbf{I}_1 + \mathbf{I}_2 \tag{6-215a}$$

Substituting Eqs. (6-212) and (6-213), we obtain

$$\mathbf{I}_L = I \cos\phi \tag{6-215b}$$

The line voltage and line current are now in phase, and the magnitude of the line current is the minimum that will supply the motor power. Note that the current of the capacitor is 180° out of phase with the out-of-phase component of I_1 and thus substracts from it.

The circuit of Fig. 6-34b is also used in large generating stations to "correct" the power factor of the current supplied by the generators. In such cases the current drawn by the capacitor can be very large, and very large capacitors are needed. To obtain large capacitors, synchronous generators which are not in use can be operated as unloaded motors. Under appropriate operating conditions their equivalent circuits are essentially capacitances. Such devices are called *synchronous capacitors* and are used for power-factor correction.

6-17   Series resonance

Let us consider the circuit shown in Fig. 6-35, which is called a *series resonant circuit.* Its input impedance $\mathbf{Z}(j\omega)$ is given by

$$\mathbf{Z}(j\omega) = R + j\omega L + \frac{1}{j\omega C} = R + j\left(\omega L - \frac{1}{\omega C}\right) \tag{6-216a}$$

After manipulation we obtain

$$\mathbf{Z}(j\omega) = R\left[1 + j\frac{\omega L}{R}\left(1 - \frac{1}{\omega^2 LC}\right)\right] \tag{6-216b}$$

The accuracy required here is the same as in the parallel resonant circuit. Note that Eq. (6-216*b*) is the same as the denominator of Eq. (6-183*b*). To eliminate the need for this great accuracy we substitute Eq. (6-187). Then we substitute Eqs. (6-184*a*) and (6-185*a*) and manipulate. This yields

$$\mathbf{Z}(j\omega) = R\left(1 + jQ_0\delta \frac{\delta + 2}{\delta + 1}\right) \tag{6-217}$$

At the resonant frequency $f = f_0$ [see Eq. (6-184)], $\delta = 0$, and $Z = R$, a resistance. At other frequencies there is a reactive component given by $RQ_0\delta(\delta + 2)/(\delta + 1)$. Thus the magnitude of the impedance of the series resonant circuit is a minimum at $f = f_0$, in contrast to this parallel resonant circuit, where the magnitude of the impedance is maximum at the resonant frequency (this assumes that $Q_0 \gg 1$).

Let us obtain the transfer-voltage ratio of the network of Fig. 6-35. We

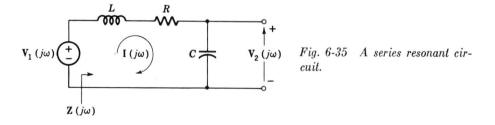

Fig. 6-35   A series resonant circuit.

have

$$\mathbf{V}_2(j\omega) = \frac{\mathbf{I}(j\omega)}{j\omega C}$$

$$\mathbf{I}(j\omega) = \frac{\mathbf{V}_1(j\omega)}{\mathbf{Z}(j\omega)}$$

Thus the transfer-voltage ratio is given by

$$\mathbf{K}(j\omega) = \frac{\mathbf{V}_2(j\omega)}{\mathbf{V}_1(j\omega)} = \frac{1/j\omega C}{R[1 + jQ_0\delta(\delta + 2)/(\delta + 1)]} \qquad (6\text{-}218)$$

Usually, in using circuits we are interested in frequencies close to ω_0. For instance, δ may vary from -0.01 to $+0.01$. Thus the change in $1/\omega C$ will be very small, and the factor in the *numerator* of Eq. (6-218) can be closely approximated by $1/j\omega_0 C$. For instance, if ω_0 varies only from 1.01×10^6 rad/sec to 0.99×10^6 rad/sec, and if, in the numerator of Eq. (6-218), we approximate $1/\omega$ by the constant 10^{-6}, then only a 1 percent error will result over the frequency range.

A great deal of care should be taken in making approximations in resonant circuits. For instance, in Eq. (6-216a), we *cannot* approximate $1/\omega C$ by $1/\omega_0 C$, because there we are working with the difference of two nearly equal numbers, $\omega L - 1/\omega C$. A small error in either of them can result in a very large error in the answer. Hence no approximation is made. However, the $1/\omega C$ in the numerator of Eq. (6-218) multiplies the entire expression, and so a small error in $1/\omega C$ there merely results in the same small error in the answer.

With this approximation Eq. (6-218) becomes

$$\mathbf{K}(j\omega) = \frac{1/j\omega_0 RC}{1 + jQ_0\delta(\delta + 2)/(\delta + 1)} \qquad (6\text{-}219)$$

At resonance $\omega_0 L = 1/\omega_0 C$. Hence

$$\frac{1}{\omega_0 RC} = \frac{\omega_0 L}{R} = Q_0 \qquad (6\text{-}220)$$

Thus

$$\mathbf{K}(j\omega) = \frac{-jQ_0}{1 + jQ_0\delta(\delta + 2)/(\delta + 1)} \qquad (6\text{-}221)$$

The normalized magnitude of this expression is given by

$$\frac{K(\omega)}{Q_0} = \frac{1}{\sqrt{1 + [Q_0\delta(\delta + 2)/(\delta + 1)]^2}} \qquad (6\text{-}222a)$$

where we have normalized with respect to Q_0. The phase angle of Eq. (6-221) is

$$\phi(\omega) = -\left[\frac{\pi}{2} + \tan^{-1}\frac{Q_0\delta(\delta + 2)}{\delta + 1}\right] \qquad (6\text{-}222b)$$

Comparison of Eqs. (6-222) with Eqs. (6-192b) and (6-194) for the impedance of the parallel resonant circuit shows that, with the exception of the $\pi/2$ rad phase shift, the expressions are the same. Thus the magnitude of the normalized frequency response of the transfer-voltage ratio is given by Fig. 6-32. In addition, Eqs. (6-195) through (6-203) can be used here to determine the bandwidth.

The maximum value of the transfer-voltage ratio is Q_0. In general, $Q_0 \gg 1$. Thus at resonance the magnitude of the output voltage can be much greater than that of the input voltage. This does not violate any basic physical laws (note that no power is dissipated in the capacitor). In fact, if the current is considered on a transient basis (note that in the sinusoidal steady state we have neglected the exponential decay terms), the total energy supplied by the generator $v_1(t)$ at *any* time will equal the sum of the energy dissipated in the resistance plus the energy stored in the electric and magnetic fields of the capacitor and inductor, respectively, at that time.

6-18   Other resonant circuits

We have considered the simple cases of parallel and series resonance. At times more complex resonant circuits are utilized in electronic amplifiers. The type of circuit and the approximations used depend upon the electronic devices themselves. The reader is referred to electronics texts for a discussion of these circuits.

6-19   Mutual-inductance coupling: ideal transformers

In this section we shall develop and discuss the ideal transformer. The transformer is an extremely important device that is used extensively in electronic and power applications. As we shall see, it can be used to step voltage, current, and impedance levels up or down in a very simple way. Transformers make possible the efficient transmission of electric energy over long distances by stepping up the voltage and stepping down the current used in the transmission lines (the power dissipated in the transmission line is given by I^2R, where R is the series resistance of the transmission line).

Before we consider transformers, let us briefly review the analysis of mutual-inductance-coupled circuits and then apply this analysis to the ideal transformer (it is assumed that the reader is familiar with the discussions of mutual-inductance-coupled circuits in Secs. 1-11, 1-13, 3-4, and 5-5). Let us consider the network of Fig. 6-36, which uses mutual-inductance coupling, and set up its sinusoidal-steady-state simultaneous equations. Using the convention for mutual-inductance voltage drops established in Sec. 5-5, and replacing

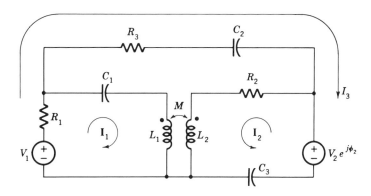

Fig. 6-36   *A three-loop circuit.*

s by $j\omega$, we obtain the loop equations

$$V_1 = \left(R_1 + j\omega L_1 + \frac{1}{j\omega C_1}\right)\mathbf{I}_1 + j\omega M\mathbf{I}_2 + R_1\mathbf{I}_3 \qquad (6\text{-}223a)$$

$$V_2 e^{j\phi_2} = j\omega M\mathbf{I}_1 + \left(R_2 + j\omega L_2 + \frac{1}{j\omega C_3}\right)\mathbf{I}_2 - \frac{1}{j\omega C_3}\mathbf{I}_3 \qquad (6\text{-}223b)$$

$$V_1 - V_2 e^{j\phi_2} = R_1\mathbf{I}_1 - \frac{1}{j\omega C_3}\mathbf{I}_2 + \left(R_1 + R_3 + \frac{1}{j\omega C_2} + \frac{1}{j\omega C_3}\right)\mathbf{I}_3 \qquad (6\text{-}223c)$$

Note that these equations can also be obtained from the equivalent circuit for a pair of coupled coils given in Fig. 3-20.

Now we shall work with the much simpler circuit of Fig. 6-37 and develop the ideal transformer from it. This circuit could be considered to be part of a larger network. The loop equations are

$$\mathbf{V}_1(j\omega) = j\omega L_1\mathbf{I}_1(j\omega) + j\omega M\mathbf{I}_2(j\omega) \qquad (6\text{-}224a)$$

$$\mathbf{V}_2(j\omega) = j\omega M\mathbf{I}_1(j\omega) + j\omega L_2\mathbf{I}_2(j\omega) \qquad (6\text{-}224b)$$

Let us idealize this network. In Sec. 1-13 we defined the coefficient of coupling k [see Eq. (1-134)] and demonstrated that its maximum value was unity. Hence

$$M \leq \sqrt{L_1 L_2} \qquad (6\text{-}225)$$

Fig. 6-37   *A pair of coupled coils.*

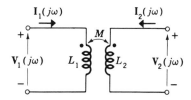

Let us assume that $k = 1$. The coils are then called *unity-coupled coils*, and relation (6-225) is satisfied with the equals sign. Substituting Eq. (6-225), with the equals sign, into Eqs. (6-224) and factoring, we obtain

$$\mathbf{V}_1(j\omega) = \sqrt{L_1}\,[j\omega\,\sqrt{L_1}\,\mathbf{I}_1(j\omega) + j\omega\,\sqrt{L_2}\,\mathbf{I}_2(j\omega)] \qquad (6\text{-}226a)$$

$$\mathbf{V}_2(j\omega) = \sqrt{L_2}\,[j\omega\,\sqrt{L_1}\,\mathbf{I}_1(j\omega) + j\omega\,\sqrt{L_2}\,\mathbf{I}_2(j\omega)] \qquad (6\text{-}226b)$$

Now we take the ratio of Eq. (6-226a) to Eq. (6-226b). This yields

$$\frac{\mathbf{V}_1(j\omega)}{\mathbf{V}_2(j\omega)} = \sqrt{\frac{L_1}{L_2}} \qquad (6\text{-}227)$$

This is an important result. In the ideal case of a pair of unity-coupled coils the input and output voltages $\mathbf{V}_1(j\omega)$ and $\mathbf{V}_2(j\omega)$ will differ only by a real multiplying constant. This is, one will be a real constant times the other.

Now let us consider another idealization. Let L_1 and L_2 increase without limit, but keep the ratio L_1/L_2 constant. We shall assume that both $\mathbf{V}_1$ and $\mathbf{V}_2$ are finite. Then, as L_1 and L_2 approach infinity, if Eqs. (6-226) are not to be violated, either $\mathbf{I}_1$ and $\mathbf{I}_2$ must both become zero or the following equation must be satisfied:

$$j\omega\,\sqrt{L_1}\,\mathbf{I}_1(j\omega) + j\omega\,\sqrt{L_2}\,\mathbf{I}_2(j\omega) = 0 \qquad (6\text{-}228)$$

If we are to obtain a nontrivial solution (one with a nonzero current), then Eq. (6-228) must hold. Manipulation of this equation yields

$$\frac{\mathbf{I}_2(j\omega)}{\mathbf{I}_1(j\omega)} = \sqrt{\frac{L_1}{L_2}} \qquad (6\text{-}229)$$

Combining this with Eq. (6-227), we obtain

$$\frac{\mathbf{V}_1(j\omega)}{\mathbf{V}_2(j\omega)} = \frac{\mathbf{I}_2(j\omega)}{\mathbf{I}_1(j\omega)} = \sqrt{\frac{L_1}{L_2}} \qquad (6\text{-}230)$$

Thus, if we have the double idealization of unity-coupled coils and infinite inductances, then the voltages and currents will be related by Eq. (6-230). A device which satisfies this equation is called an *ideal transformer*.

Let us consider this from a somewhat different viewpoint. The voltage induced in an inductor is given by the rate of change of flux linkages [see Eqs. (1-92) and (1-93)] as

$$v = L\frac{di}{dt} = \frac{d\phi_1}{dt} \qquad (6\text{-}231)$$

where ϕ_1 are the flux linkages. In addition, it can be shown that the coefficient of coupling is equal to the fraction of the flux set up by one coil which links the second one. In a pair of unity-coupled coils all the flux set up by one coil links the other one as well as itself. The amount of flux set up by a coil is proportional to the number of its turns. In addition, if the flux is uniform

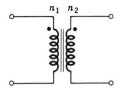

Fig. 6-38   A symbol for the ideal transformer.

throughout the space of the coil, then the total voltage induced in a coil will be proportional to the number of its turns (each turn will have the same voltage induced in it).   Thus in the ideal case we can state that inductance is proportional to the number of the turns of the coil squared,

$$L_1 = Kn_1{}^2 \tag{6-232a}$$

$$L_2 = Kn_2{}^2 \tag{6-232b}$$

where n_1 and n_2 are the number of turns of L_1 and L_2, respectively, and K is a constant of proportionality.   In the case of coupled coils the flux set up by one coil is proportional to the number of its turns, while the voltage induced in the other one will be proportional to the number of its turns.   The mutual inductance is then proportional to the product of these numbers,

$$M = Kn_1n_2 \tag{6-233}$$

It can be demonstrated that in the ideal case the constants of proportionality of Eqs. (6-232) and (6-233) are equal.   Substituting these equations into Eq. (6-230), we obtain

$$\frac{\mathbf{V}_1(j\omega)}{\mathbf{V}_2(j\omega)} = \frac{\mathbf{I}_2(j\omega)}{\mathbf{I}_1(j\omega)} = \frac{n_1}{n_2} \tag{6-234}$$

The quantity n_1/n_2 is called the *turns ratio* of the transformer.   Thus the ratios of input to output voltage and output to input current are proportional to the turns ratio.   A symbol for the ideal transformer is given in Fig. 6-38.

The preceding discussion was on a sinusoidal-steady-state basis.   If we replace $j\omega$ by s and replace the phasors by Laplace transforms in the previous discussion, the equations become valid on a Laplace transform basis.   Thus in the time domain $v_1(t)$ and $v_2(t)$ will have the same waveform except for a constant multiplier.   The same statements can be made about $i_1(t)$ and $i_2(t)$.   Note that $i_1(t)$ and $v_1(t)$ need not have the same waveform.

Impedance transformation

In addition to stepping voltages and currents up or down, the ideal transformer can be used to step impedance levels up or down.   This property is utilized often in electronic devices.   For instance, suppose we have an audio amplifier which is to drive a loudspeaker.   The loudspeaker may essentially appear as a 4-ohm resistor, whereas the amplifier, if it is to function properly, requires a

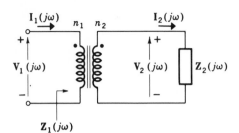

Fig. 6-39 A circuit which is used to illustrate the impedance-transforming properties of an ideal transformer.

5,000-ohm resistance connected to its output. We shall demonstrate how a transformer can be used to eliminate this "mismatch" of impedance levels (usually this transformer is included within the amplifier).

Consider the circuit of Fig. 6-39. The impedance $\mathbf{Z}_2(j\omega)$ is connected to the output terminal of the transformer. From the definition of impedance (see Sec. 6-4),

$$\mathbf{Z}_2(j\omega) = \frac{\mathbf{V}_2(j\omega)}{\mathbf{I}_2(j\omega)} \tag{6-235}$$

The effective input impedance of the transformer is

$$\mathbf{Z}_1(j\omega) = \frac{\mathbf{V}_1(j\omega)}{\mathbf{I}_1(j\omega)} \tag{6-236}$$

Substituting Eq. (6-234) into Eq. (6-236), we obtain

$$\mathbf{Z}_1(j\omega) = \frac{(n_1/n_2)\mathbf{V}_2(j\omega)}{(n_2/n_1)\mathbf{I}_2(j\omega)} = \left(\frac{n_1}{n_2}\right)^2 \frac{\mathbf{V}_2(j\omega)}{\mathbf{V}_1(j\omega)} \tag{6-237}$$

Substituting Eq. (6-235), we have

$$\mathbf{Z}_1(j\omega) = \left(\frac{n_1}{n_2}\right)^2 \mathbf{Z}_2(j\omega) \tag{6-238}$$

Thus the input impedance is equal to the turns ratio squared times the load impedance. By adjusting the turns ratio, then, we can set the input impedance level at any desired value.

Again, we could have worked here with a Laplace transform rather than on a sinusoidal-steady-state basis.

6-20   Equivalent circuits for actual transformers

The ideal transformer cannot actually be built, because we cannot construct either unity-coupled coils or infinite inductances. However, actual transformers often closely approximate ideal ones over certain ranges of frequency. In this section we shall develop an equivalent circuit, or a *model*, which performs in essentially the same way as does an actual transformer. The equivalent circuit of an actual device, if it is to be completely accurate, often requires an infinite number of elements.　Such a circuit is impractical to work with, so one with a smaller number of elements must be used.　This represents a compromise between accuracy and practicality, but such compromises usually result in equivalent circuits that are accurate enough for most practical purposes.

We shall draw the equivalent circuit that will be used and then explain the functions of the circuit elements.　The circuit is shown in Fig. 6-40.　It consists of an ideal transformer plus other circuit elements.　The inductances of the ideal transformer are infinite.　Thus in an ideal transformer the input current will be zero when the output current is zero [see Eq. (6-234)].　However, in an actual transformer the input current will not be zero when the output current is zero, because the inductances are not infinite.　To account for this we put the inductance L_m, called the *magnetizing inductance*, in parallel with the input of the transformer.　At low frequencies the reactance of this inductance, ωL_m, is very small, and it effectively short circuits the transformer.　The presence of the finite magnetizing inductance is the reason that actual transformers cannot be used at very low frequencies.

Practical transformers often have iron cores.　The varying flux induces currents in these cores called *eddy currents*, which cause a heating of the core. In addition, the varying flux produces a *hysteresis loss* in the iron.　To account for the power dissipated in the core, the resistor R_c is included in the circuit. The coils of an actual transformer are not unity-coupled.　Thus some flux set up by the primary will *not* link the secondary, and vice versa.　There will be some flux which links only the primary and induces a voltage in it which is equivalent to the voltage set up in an ordinary inductance.　There is a similar effect in the secondary.　These effects are accounted for by the inductors L_1 and L_2, called *leakage inductances*.　The windings of the transformer will have some resistance, which is accounted for by R_1 and R_2.　Any two conductors will have a capacitance between them.　The capacitors C_1 and C_2 account for

Fig. 6-40　An equivalent circuit for an actual transformer.

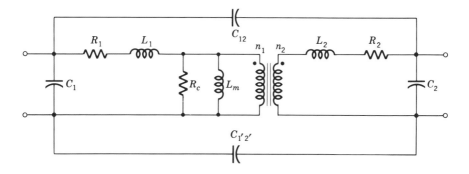

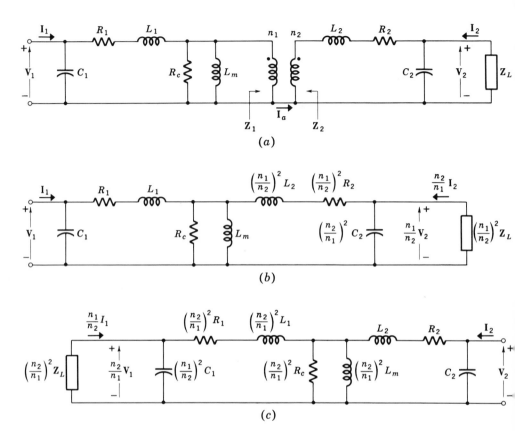

Fig. 6-41   (a) A simplified equivalent circuit for a transformer; (b) the equivalent circuit referred to the primary side; (c) the equivalent circuit referred to the secondary side.

capacitance *between parts* of the primary and secondary windings. The capacitors C_{12} and $C_{1'2'}$ account for capacitance between the primary and secondary windings.

Actually, there is no unique placement of these elements, and different placements could have been used. At times the capacitors C_{12} and $C_{1'2'}$ are omitted, and C_1 and C_2 are increased to account approximately for their omission. This sometimes greatly simplifies calculations with no substantial sacrifice in accuracy.

The equivalent circuit of Fig. 6-41 has been drawn with the capacitors C_{12} and $C_{1'2'}$ omitted. In addition, we have assumed that the primary and secondary of the transformer have one wire in common. This connection is often used in electronic devices. We now can manipulate this circuit to simplify it. Let us assume that only the impedance Z_L is connected to the secondary of the transformer. In so far as the primary side is concerned, the secondary manifests itself in the impedance $\mathbf{Z}_1$. This is given by the impedance connected to the secondary multiplied by $(n_1/n_2)^2$ [see Eq. (6-238)]. Thus, in so far as the primary side of the transformer is concerned, Fig. 6-41b is equivalent to Fig. 6-41a (note that the capacitor is multiplied by $n_2{}^2/n_1{}^2$, since impedance is *inversely* proportional to capacitance). The voltage across and the current into the primary of the ideal transformer are related to the secondary voltage and current by Eq. (6-234). Thus the voltage across and the current into the load $(n_1/n_2)^2\mathbf{Z}_L$ will be as given in Fig. 6-41b. This is called an *equivalent circuit referred to the primary side*.

Figure 6-41c shows an *equivalent circuit referred to the secondary side*. Here it should be assumed that the *only* connection to the primary side is an impedance $\mathbf{Z}_L$, and that the generator network is connected to the secondary. The discussion then follows that for Fig. 6-41b.

6-21 Three-phase circuits

Most electric power transmission is at 50 or 60 Hz. These alternating frequencies are employed so that transformers can be used to step the voltage up for efficient transmission (see Sec. 6-19). In addition, the electric generators are usually constructed so that they produce *three-phase voltages* and currents. That is, they produce three voltages, each of which differs by $2\pi/3$ rad in phase angle. This is shown diagrammatically in Fig. 6-42. Studies of three-phase transmission systems with four wires indicate that they are more efficient than single-phase systems. Moreover, three-phase motors operate more efficiently and supply more constant torque than do single-phase ones. Ordinary sinusoidal-steady-state analyses can be used to analyze three-phase circuits. Other more systematic techniques are also available.

Let us consider the network of Fig. 6-42 and determine some of the voltages. The wire labeled $00'$ is called the *neutral*. The wires aa', bb', and cc' are called the *lines*. The line to neutral voltages all have a magnitude equal

Fig. 6-42 The representation of a three-phase generator.

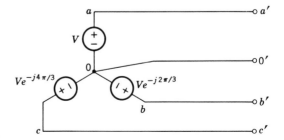

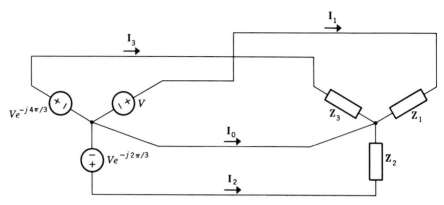

Fig. 6-43   A three-phase circuit with a Y-connected load and generators.

to V and differ in phase by 120°, or $2\pi/3$ rad.   Now let us obtain the line-to-line voltages.   For instance,

$$V_{a'b'} = V - Ve^{-j2\pi/3} = \sqrt{3}\ Ve^{-j\pi/6} \tag{6-239a}$$

Similarly,

$$V_{b'c'} = \sqrt{3}\ Ve^{-j(\pi/6-2\pi/3)} \tag{6-239b}$$

$$V_{c'a'} = \sqrt{3}\ Ve^{-j(\pi/6-4\pi/3)} \tag{6-239c}$$

Thus the line-to-line voltages also are three-phase voltages (their phase angles differ by 120°).   Their magnitudes are $\sqrt{3}$ times the line-to-line voltages.

In home power-distribution systems two lines and a neutral are often used. Typically, 120 volts and 208 volts are then available; that is, a single phase is brought into the house.   These voltages are obtained from the secondaries of three-phase transformers which are used to step down the voltages from the high voltages in the main distribution system.   An alternative procedure often used in home distribution systems is the *three-wire* system.   In this case an ordinary transformer is connected between one line and a neutral or from line to line.   The secondary of the transformer is *center-tapped;* that is, a wire is connected to its midpoint.   The voltages between the center tap and either end of the winding will be equal in magnitude but will differ by 180°.   Thus the magnitude of the voltage across the entire secondary winding will be twice the magnitude of the voltage between the center tap and one side of the transformer.   Typically, 120 volts and 240 volts are then available.

Let us consider the currents in a three-phase circuit.   A typical one is shown in Fig. 6-43.   The configuration of the load is called a Y connection because of its shape.   Each load impedance has a generator connected directly across it. Thus we can write

$$\mathbf{I}_1 = \frac{V}{\mathbf{Z}_1} \qquad\qquad (6\text{-}240a)$$

$$\mathbf{I}_2 = \frac{V e^{-j2\pi/3}}{\mathbf{Z}_2} \qquad\qquad (6\text{-}240b)$$

$$\mathbf{I}_3 = \frac{V e^{-j4\pi/3}}{\mathbf{Z}_3} \qquad\qquad (6\text{-}240c)$$

The neutral current is

$$\mathbf{I}_0 = -(\mathbf{I}_1 + \mathbf{I}_2 + \mathbf{I}_3) \qquad\qquad (6\text{-}240d)$$

Now let us assume that the three loads are equal,

$$\mathbf{Z}_1 = \mathbf{Z}_2 = \mathbf{Z}_3 = \mathbf{Z} \qquad\qquad (6\text{-}241)$$

In this case the load is said to be *balanced*. Then $\mathbf{I}_0$ is given by

$$\mathbf{I}_0 = \frac{V}{\mathbf{Z}}(1 + e^{-j2\pi/3} + e^{-j4\pi/3}) = 0 \qquad\qquad (6\text{-}242)$$

That is, the sum of the terms in the parentheses is zero. This illustrates one of the advantages of three-phase power transmission. Under balanced conditions the current in the neutral wire is zero. Thus no power is lost there.

We have not considered that the wires between the generator and loads have resistance. However, in general, they do. Thus there is a voltage drop across the wires and power dissipated in them. This voltage drop is undesirable, since it causes the voltage across the loads ($\mathbf{Z}_1$, $\mathbf{Z}_2$, and $\mathbf{Z}_3$) to be less than the generator voltages. In a balanced three-phase system three generators are connected to three loads, but only four wires are used, and there is no power dissipated in the neutral, nor is there any voltage drop across it. In an ordinary connection of three generators to three loads we would require six wires, each of which would have a voltage drop and dissipate power.

In a large electrical-distribution system the loads $\mathbf{Z}_1$, $\mathbf{Z}_2$, and $\mathbf{Z}_3$ could each represent the parallel connection of all the electrical equipment in a single home, group of homes, factories, etc. They would not be exactly equal, but on the average they would be almost equal. Thus, in general, $\mathbf{I}_0$ will be small, and the power dissipated in the neutral wire and the voltage drop across it will both be small.

At times three-phase systems are operated without the neutral. Again, this network can be solved, for both balanced and unbalanced loads, by simple loop analysis. Impedances can also be included in the wires between the generators and the loads.

If there is no neutral connection, then the configuration of Fig. 6-44 can be used. The load and generator are said to be *delta-connected*, since this

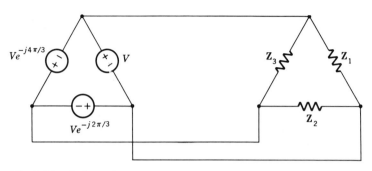

Fig. 6-44   A three-phase circuit with delta-connected load and generators.

configuration resembles the Greek letter delta. This circuit can be solved by ordinary loop analysis.

In large three-phase power-distribution systems a procedure called the *method of symmetrical components* is often used to solve for the voltages and currents.

6-22   Distributed-parameter systems: transmission lines

In most of our discussions we have assumed that we were working with lumped circuit elements—resistors, inductors, capacitors, and mutual inductances. However, as we have also discussed (Sec. 1-14), there are times when these lumped representations cannot be used. This occurs both in transmission lines that are used to send signals from one point to another (e.g., from an antenna to a receiver) and in some of the very small circuit elements used in integrated electronic circuits. In this section we shall analyze a distributed-parameter transmission line. This analysis can also be applied directly to distributed integrated electronic circuits (see Sec. 6-25).

The transmission line that we shall analyze, shown in Fig. 6-45*a*, consists of two wires. The total resistance of a 1-m length of the line is R ohms. This is the sum of the resistances of the upper and lower wires. R is called the *resistance per unit length*. That is, if we connect a 1-m piece of the upper wire in series with a 1-m piece of the lower wire and consider just the resistance of the wires, then the resistance of the series connection is R ohms. Similarly, if we consider just inductance, there is an inductance of L henrys/m. Any two conductors have a capacitance between them. The capacitance between the two wires is C farads/m of length. The dielectric between the two wires will not be perfect (there will not be zero conductivity between them), thus we have a conductance of G mhos/m between the wires.

To analyze the transmission line we approximate a very short length Δx of it by the circuit of Fig. 6-45*b*. This has the correct total series impedance and shunt admittance of a length Δx. This circuit just approximates a length of transmission line. However, in the limit, as Δx approaches zero, it becomes exact. Now let us obtain $\mathbf{V}(x + \Delta x,\ j\omega) - \mathbf{V}(x,j\omega)$. From Fig. 6-45$b$ we have

$$\mathbf{V}(x + \Delta x,\ j\omega) - \mathbf{V}(x,j\omega) = -\left(\frac{R\ \Delta x}{2} + j\frac{\omega L}{2}\ \Delta x\right)[\mathbf{I}(x,j\omega) + \mathbf{I}(x + \Delta x,\ j\omega)]$$

$$(6\text{-}243)$$

In the limit, as Δx approaches zero, $\mathbf{I}(x + \Delta x,\ j\omega)$ approaches $\mathbf{I}(x,j\omega)$. Hence we can write

$$\lim_{\Delta x \to 0} \frac{\mathbf{V}(x + \Delta x,\ j\omega) - \mathbf{V}(x,j\omega)}{\Delta x} = -(R + j\omega L)\mathbf{I}(x,j\omega) \qquad (6\text{-}244)$$

The left-hand side of this equation is just the definition of the derivative. Hence Eq. (6-244) becomes

$$\frac{d\mathbf{V}(x,j\omega)}{dx} = -(R + j\omega L)\mathbf{I}(x,j\omega) \qquad (6\text{-}245)$$

Again, applying Kirchhoff's laws to Fig. 6-45b, we obtain

$$\mathbf{I}(x + \Delta x,\ j\omega) - \mathbf{I}(x,j\omega) = -\mathbf{V}_{ab}(G\ \Delta x + j\omega C\ \Delta x) \qquad (6\text{-}246)$$

Fig. 6-45 (a) A transmission line; (b) a lumped-parameter approximation to a short length Δx of this transmission line.

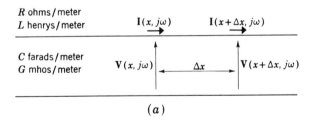

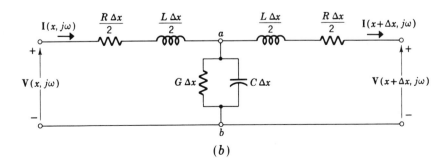

As Δx approaches zero, $\mathbf{V}(x + \Delta x,\ j\omega)$ approaches $\mathbf{V}(x,j\omega)$, which also approaches $\mathbf{V}_{ab}$.   Hence

$$\lim_{\Delta x \to 0} \frac{\mathbf{I}(x + x,\ j\omega) - \mathbf{I}(x,j\omega)}{\Delta x} = -(G + j\omega C)\mathbf{V}(x,j\omega) \tag{6-247}$$

Taking the limit, we obtain

$$\frac{d\mathbf{I}(x,j\omega)}{dx} = -(G + j\omega C)\mathbf{V}(x,j\omega) \tag{6-248}$$

Equations (6-245) and (6-248) characterize the behavior of the transmission line.   Let us now manipulate these equations so that we can obtain solutions.   We differentiate Eq. (6-245) with respect to x and then substitute Eq. (6-248).   This yields

$$\frac{d^2\mathbf{V}(x,j\omega)}{dx} = (R + j\omega L)(G + j\omega C)\mathbf{V}(x,j\omega) \tag{6-249}$$

Similarly, we can differentiate Eq. (6-248) and substitute Eq. (6-245), to obtain

$$\frac{d^2\mathbf{I}(x,j\omega)}{dx} = (R + j\omega L)(G + j\omega C)\mathbf{I}(x,j\omega) \tag{6-250}$$

Equations (6-249) and (6-250) are linear differential equations with constant coefficients.   They can be solved by the procedures of Chap. 4.   Thus

$$\mathbf{V}(x,j\omega) = \mathbf{A}_1 e^{-\gamma x} + \mathbf{A}_2 e^{\gamma x} \tag{6-251a}$$

$$\mathbf{I}(x,j\omega) = \mathbf{B}_1 e^{-\gamma x} + \mathbf{B}_2 e^{\gamma x} \tag{6-251b}$$

where

$$\gamma = \sqrt{(R + j\omega L)(G + j\omega C)} \tag{6-252}$$

γ is called the *propagation constant*.   We shall study its significance subsequently.

The $\mathbf{A}_1$, $\mathbf{A}_2$, $\mathbf{B}_1$, and $\mathbf{B}_2$ terms are arbitrary constants.   However, they are related by Eq. (6-245) or Eq. (6-248).   Substituting Eqs. (6-251) into Eq. (6-245), we obtain

$$-\gamma\mathbf{A}_1 e^{-\gamma x} + \gamma\mathbf{A}_2 e^{\gamma x} = (R + j\omega L)(\mathbf{B}_1 e^{-\gamma x} + \mathbf{B}_2 e^{-\gamma x}) \tag{6-253a}$$

or, equivalently,

$$[-\gamma\mathbf{A}_1 + (R + j\omega L)\mathbf{B}_1]e^{-\gamma x} + [\gamma\mathbf{A}_2 + (R + j\omega L)\mathbf{B}_2]e^{\gamma x} = 0 \tag{6-253b}$$

$\mathbf{A}_1$, $\mathbf{A}_2$, $\mathbf{B}_1$, and $\mathbf{B}_2$ are constants.   Equations (6-253) must be valid for *all* values of x, so each bracketed term must be zero (let x become very large; then the second bracketed term must be zero; and so on). Hence

$$\mathbf{B}_1 = \frac{\gamma \mathbf{A}_1}{R + j\omega L} = \sqrt{\frac{G + j\omega C}{R + j\omega L}} \, \mathbf{A}_1 \qquad\qquad (6\text{-}254a)$$

$$\mathbf{B}_2 = -\frac{\gamma \mathbf{A}_2}{R + j\omega L} = -\sqrt{\frac{G + j\omega C}{R + j\omega L}} \, \mathbf{A}_2 \qquad\qquad (6\text{-}254b)$$

where $\sqrt{(R + j\omega L)/(G + j\omega C)}$ has the dimension of an impedance. We call it the *characteristic impedance* $\mathbf{Z}_0$, where

$$\mathbf{Z}_0 = \sqrt{\frac{R + j\omega L}{G + j\omega C}} \qquad\qquad (6\text{-}255)$$

We shall discuss the significance of the characteristic impedance in Sec. 6-23.

If we substitute Eqs. (6-251) into Eq. (6-248), Eqs. (6-254) result. Thus no new information is obtained. Substituting Eq. (6-255) into Eqs. (6-254), we obtain

$$\mathbf{B}_1 = \frac{\mathbf{A}_1}{\mathbf{Z}_0} \qquad\qquad (6\text{-}256a)$$

$$\mathbf{B}_2 = \frac{-\mathbf{A}_2}{\mathbf{Z}_0} \qquad\qquad (6\text{-}256b)$$

Thus Eqs. (6-251) become

$$\mathbf{V}(x,j\omega) = \mathbf{A}_1 e^{-\gamma x} + \mathbf{A}_2 e^{\gamma x} \qquad\qquad (6\text{-}257a)$$

$$\mathbf{I}(x,j\omega) = \frac{\mathbf{A}_1}{\mathbf{Z}_0} e^{-\gamma x} - \frac{\mathbf{A}_2}{\mathbf{Z}_0} e^{\gamma x} \qquad\qquad (6\text{-}257b)$$

The constants $\mathbf{A}_1$ and $\mathbf{A}_2$ are determined from the boundary conditions, which are obtained from the connections made to the input and output ends of the line. We shall determine these constants subsequently.

6-23   The infinite transmission line and lossless lines

To explore the significance of the quantities determined in the last section we shall consider the case of a transmission line which is infinitely long. Such a line is symbolically shown in Fig. 6-46. A voltage generator whose phasor is $\mathbf{V}_0$ is connected to the input. Now let us determine the constants $\mathbf{A}_1$ and $\mathbf{A}_2$. The propagation constant γ is given by Eq. (6-252). It will be a complex number whose real part is positive. Note that the maximum angle of $R + j\omega L$ is $\pi/2$ rad. Similarly, $G + j\omega C$ has a maximum angle of $\pi/2$ rad. Thus

$$(R + j\omega L)(G + j\omega C)$$

has a maximum angle of π rad. Hence γ has a maximum angle of $\pi/2$ rad.

*Fig. 6-46   An infinite
transmission line with a
voltage-generator input.*

We let

$$\gamma = \gamma_1 + j\gamma_2 \qquad (6\text{-}258)$$

γ_1 is called the *attenuation constant* and γ_2 is called the *phase constant*.   Thus

$$e^{\gamma x} = e^{\gamma_1 x}e^{j\gamma_2 x} \qquad (6\text{-}259)$$

Note that γ_1 determines the variation of the magnitude of $e^{\gamma x}$, while γ_2 determines the variation of the phase of $e^{\gamma x}$.   Since γ_1 is positive, $e^{\gamma_1 x}$ will become infinite as x approaches infinity.   This is impossible, because the voltage and current must also become infinite [see Eq. (6-251)].   Hence infinite power will be dissipated in the resistance and conductance of the transmission line. Note that the input voltage and current will be finite.   Hence in the *infinite* transmission line, we must state

$$\mathbf{A}_2 = 0 \qquad (6\text{-}260)$$

Thus Eqs. (6-257) become

$$\mathbf{V}(x,j\omega) = \mathbf{A}_1 e^{-\gamma x} \qquad (6\text{-}261a)$$

$$\mathbf{I}(x,j\omega) = \frac{\mathbf{A}_1}{\mathbf{Z}_0} e^{-\gamma x} \qquad (6\text{-}261b)$$

At $x = 0$ the input to the line $\mathbf{V}(0,j\omega) = V_0$.   Thus

$$\mathbf{A} = V_0 \qquad (6\text{-}262)$$

and, substituting into Eq. (6-261), we obtain

$$\mathbf{V}(x,j\omega) = V_0 e^{-\gamma x} \qquad (6\text{-}263a)$$

$$\mathbf{I}(x,j\omega) = \frac{V_0}{\mathbf{Z}_0} e^{-\gamma x} \qquad (6\text{-}263b)$$

To see the significance of γ let us substitute Eq. (6-252) into Eq. (6-263a). This yields

$$\mathbf{V}(x,j\omega) = V_0 \exp\left[-x\sqrt{(R + j\omega L)(G + j\omega C)}\right] \qquad (6\text{-}264)$$

In general, as x increases, the magnitude of V will fall off *exponentially* and the phase shift will vary *linearly* with x.   If the *frequency* ω of the input signal is *varied*, then both the attenuation and the phase shift will vary in accordance with Eq. (6-264).   In Sec. 6-11 we saw that if a transfer function was not to introduce distortion, the amplitude of its response to all frequencies should be constant with frequency, and its phase shift should vary linearly with frequency. In general, Eq. (6-264) does not satisfy this. However, we shall see later some special cases that do.

Now let us consider the special case of a lossless transmission line. In this case there are no dissipative elements. Hence

$$R = 0 \qquad\qquad\qquad\qquad\qquad\qquad (6\text{-}265a)$$

$$G = 0 \qquad\qquad\qquad\qquad\qquad\qquad (6\text{-}265b)$$

Then γ becomes

$$\gamma = \sqrt{(j\omega L)(j\omega C)} = \sqrt{-\omega^2 LC} = j\omega \sqrt{LC} \qquad\qquad (6\text{-}266)$$

Substitution in Eq. (6-264) yields

$$\mathbf{V}(x,j\omega) = V_0 \exp\left(-j\omega x \sqrt{LC}\right) \qquad\qquad\qquad (6\text{-}267)$$

Then the transmission from the input to any point x on the infinite transmission line will be distortionless.

In general (see Sec. 6-11), a transfer function of $e^{-j\omega\tau}$ is produced by a network which just delays the signal by τ sec. Thus on a lossless transmission line the signal will take $x \sqrt{LC}$ sec to travel a length of line x m long. That is, the signal travels along the transmission line with a velocity of $1/\sqrt{LC}$ m/sec.

The transmission line need not be lossless to have distortionless transmission. Suppose that

$$G + j\omega C = K^2(R + j\omega L) \qquad\qquad\qquad\qquad (6\text{-}268)$$

where K is a positive constant. Then [see Eq. (6-252)]

$$\gamma = K(R + j\omega L) \qquad\qquad\qquad\qquad\qquad (6\text{-}269)$$

Substitution in Eq. (6-264) yields

$$\mathbf{V}(x,j\omega) = V_0 e^{-KRx} e^{-j\omega LKx} \qquad\qquad\qquad\qquad (6\text{-}270)$$

Thus the attenuation is independent of frequency, and the phase shift varies linearly with frequency at any point on the line. Note, however, that the signal is attenuated as it propagates down the line.

To determine the significance of the characteristic impedance let us determine the input impedance of the infinite transmission line (note that we are considering the general case here). We have

$$\mathbf{Z}_{\text{in}} = \frac{\mathbf{V}(0,j\omega)}{\mathbf{I}(0,j\omega)} \qquad\qquad\qquad\qquad\qquad (6\text{-}271)$$

Substituting Eqs. (6-263), we obtain

$$\mathbf{Z}_{\text{in}} = \mathbf{Z}_0 \qquad\qquad\qquad\qquad\qquad\qquad (6\text{-}272)$$

Thus the characteristic impedance is equal to the input impedance of a transmission line that is infinitely long. From *measurements at the input terminals* we cannot tell an infinite transmission line from an impedance equal to its characteristic impedance (the voltage-current relations will be the same). Thus, if we terminate a finite length of transmission line in its characteristic impedance, the voltage-current relations on that finite line will be the same as if the line were infinitely long (i.e., they will act as though they were terminated in an infinite length of transmission line).

Let us determine the characteristic impedance for a lossless transmission line. Substituting Eqs. (6-265) into Eq. (6-255), we obtain

$$\mathbf{Z}_0 = \sqrt{\frac{L}{C}} \tag{6-273}$$

That is, it is a resistance. A resistance dissipates power. It may seem odd that a lossless device can dissipate power. Actually, however, energy is fed into the transmission line, and this energy propagates down the line. If the line were finite, the energy would be reflected back from the output end (this is similar to a capacitor or inductor taking power for half of a cycle and giving it back during the next half cycle). However, the line is infinite, and the signals never reach the output end to be reflected back.

6-24   The transmission line with arbitrary termination

Now let us discuss a transmission line of finite length D which is terminated in an arbitrary impedance $\mathbf{Z}$, as shown in Fig. 6-47. The voltage and current are given by Eqs. (6-257). Thus

$$\mathbf{V}(x,j\omega) = \mathbf{A}_1 e^{-\gamma x} + \mathbf{A}_2 e^{\gamma x} \tag{6-274a}$$

$$\mathbf{I}(x,j\omega) = \frac{\mathbf{A}_1}{\mathbf{Z}_0} e^{-\gamma x} - \frac{\mathbf{A}_2}{\mathbf{Z}_0} e^{\gamma x} \tag{6-274b}$$

We cannot say that $\mathbf{A}_2$ is zero here, because the line is finite. At $x = 0$, $\mathbf{V}(0,j\omega) = V_0$, so

$$\mathbf{A}_1 + \mathbf{A}_2 = V_0 \tag{6-275}$$

Fig. 6-47   *A finite transmission line terminated in an impedance Z.*

$x = 0$ $x = D$

Thus we have one equation with two unknowns. To determine the other unknown we must work with boundary conditions at the other end of the transmission line. From the definition of impedance,

$$\frac{\mathbf{V}(D,j\omega)}{\mathbf{I}(D,j\omega)} = \mathbf{Z}(j\omega) \tag{6-276}$$

Then, substituting Eqs. (6-274), we obtain

$$\frac{\mathbf{A}_1 e^{-\theta} + \mathbf{A}_2 e^{\theta}}{(\mathbf{A}_1/\mathbf{Z}_0)e^{-\theta} - (\mathbf{A}_2/\mathbf{Z}_0)e^{\theta}} = \mathbf{Z}(j\omega) \tag{6-277}$$

where we have substituted

$$\theta = \gamma D \tag{6-278}$$

Manipulation yields

$$\mathbf{A}_1 e^{-\theta}\left(1 - \frac{\mathbf{Z}}{\mathbf{Z}_0}\right) + \mathbf{A}_2 e^{\theta}\left(1 + \frac{\mathbf{Z}}{\mathbf{Z}_0}\right) = 0 \tag{6-279}$$

Solving Eqs. (6-275) and (6-279) simultaneously, we obtain

$$\mathbf{A}_1 = \frac{V_0}{1 + [(\mathbf{Z} - \mathbf{Z}_0)/(\mathbf{Z} + \mathbf{Z}_0)]e^{-2\theta}} \tag{6-280a}$$

$$\mathbf{A}_2 = \frac{V[(\mathbf{Z} - \mathbf{Z}_0)/(\mathbf{Z} + \mathbf{Z}_0)]e^{-2\theta}}{1 + [(\mathbf{Z} - \mathbf{Z}_0)/(\mathbf{Z} + \mathbf{Z}_0)]e^{-2\theta}} \tag{6-280b}$$

and, substituting in Eqs. (6-274), we have

$$\mathbf{V}(x,j\omega) = \frac{V_0}{1 + [(\mathbf{Z} - \mathbf{Z}_0)/(\mathbf{Z} + \mathbf{Z}_0)]e^{-2\theta}}\left(e^{-\gamma x} + \frac{\mathbf{Z} - \mathbf{Z}_0}{\mathbf{Z} + \mathbf{Z}_0}e^{-2\theta}e^{\gamma x}\right) \tag{6-281a}$$

$$\mathbf{I}(x,j\omega) = \frac{V_0/\mathbf{Z}_0}{1 + [(\mathbf{Z} - \mathbf{Z}_0)/(\mathbf{Z} + \mathbf{Z}_0)]e^{-2\theta}}\left(e^{-\gamma x} - \frac{\mathbf{Z} - \mathbf{Z}_0}{\mathbf{Z} + \mathbf{Z}_0}e^{-2\theta}e^{\gamma x}\right) \tag{6-281b}$$

In Sec. 6-23 we demonstrated that the $e^{-\gamma x}$ term indicated that signals were propagated down the transmission line. Similarly, $e^{\gamma x}$ (where x is replaced by $-x$) indicates that signals are propagated back up the transmission line. On a *transient* basis a signal is set up by the input generator and travels down the transmission line. When it reaches the termination, some of it is *reflected* and travels back up the line, from $x = D$ to $x = 0$. Actually, many reflections can take place at both ends of the transmission line as the signal is reflected up and back. The component of the voltage

$$\mathbf{V}_i(x,j\omega) = \frac{V_0 e^{-\gamma x}}{1 + [(\mathbf{Z} - \mathbf{Z}_0)/(\mathbf{Z} + \mathbf{Z}_0)]e^{-2\theta}} \tag{6-282a}$$

is called the *incident voltage*, while

$$\mathbf{V}_r(x,j\omega) = \frac{V_0[(\mathbf{Z} - \mathbf{Z}_0)/(\mathbf{Z} + \mathbf{Z}_0)]e^{-2\theta}e^{\gamma x}}{1 + [(\mathbf{Z} - \mathbf{Z}_0)/(\mathbf{Z} + \mathbf{Z}_0)]e^{-2\theta}} \tag{6-282b}$$

is called the *reflected voltage*. Similarly, we can speak of incident and reflected components of current.

If $\mathbf{Z} = \mathbf{Z}_0$, then $\mathbf{V}_r = 0$. There is no reflected voltage, and the relations become the same as those for the infinite transmission line.

We can define a quantity called the reflection coefficient $\boldsymbol{\Gamma}$, as the ratio

$$\boldsymbol{\Gamma} = \frac{\mathbf{V}_r(D,j\omega)}{\mathbf{V}_i(D,j\omega)}$$

This indicates how much of the incident signal is reflected and how much is "absorbed" by the load impedance. From Eqs. (6-282) we have

$$\boldsymbol{\Gamma} = \frac{\mathbf{Z} - \mathbf{Z}_0}{\mathbf{Z} + \mathbf{Z}_0} \tag{6-283}$$

(note that $\gamma D = \boldsymbol{\theta}$). When $\mathbf{Z}_0 = \mathbf{Z}$, then $\boldsymbol{\Gamma} = 0$.

6-25   Distributed integrated circuits: *RC* transmission lines

In integrated electronic circuits we often encounter distributed circuits of the form shown in Fig. 6-48*a*. They consist of three thin films, a dielectric layer separating a layer of essentially zero resistance from one of relatively high resistance. The connections are made as shown. The symbol for this circuit is shown in Fig. 6-48*b*. This circuit, called a *thin-film RC-distributed network*, usually behaves as a transmission line that has zero inductance and

Fig. 6-48   (a) A thin-film RC-distributed network; (b) its symbol.

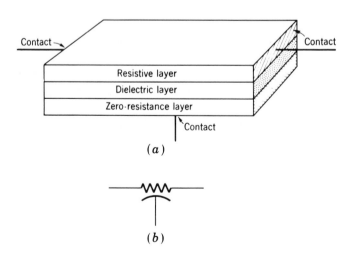

(a)

(b)

zero conductance (the capacitance comes about because of the capacitance between the resistive layer and the zero resistance layer). Thus the relations of Secs. 6-22 and 6-24 are valid here. γ and Z_0 will be [see Eqs. (6-252) and (6-255)]

$$\gamma = \sqrt{j\omega RC} = \sqrt{\omega RC}\ e^{j\pi/4} = \sqrt{\frac{\omega RC}{2}}\ (1+j) \qquad (6\text{-}284a)$$

$$Z_0 = \sqrt{\frac{R}{j\omega C}} = \sqrt{\frac{R}{\omega C}}\ e^{-j\pi/4} = \sqrt{\frac{R}{2\omega C}}\ (1-j) \qquad (6\text{-}284b)$$

All the previously developed relations can be used if Eqs. (6-284) are used for γ and Z_0.

The value of γ given by Eq. (6-284a) will not result in distortionless transmission. However, if the signals are restricted to appropriate ranges of frequency, the distortion can be kept as small as desired.

REFERENCE

[1] H. W. Bode, "Network Analysis and Feedback Amplifier Design," chap. 14, D. Van Nostrand Company, Inc., Princeton, N.J., 1945.

BIBLIOGRAPHY

Chirlian, P. M.: "Analysis and Design of Electronic Circuits," pp. 283–306, McGraw-Hill Book Company, New York, 1965.

Chirlian, P. M.: "Integrated and Active Network Analysis and Synthesis," chap. 4, Prentice-Hall, Inc., Englewood Cliffs, N.J., 1967.

Clement, P. R., and W. C. Johnson: "Electrical Engineering Science," chaps. 10 and 11, McGraw-Hill Book Company, New York, 1960.

Close, C. M.: "The Analysis of Linear Circuits," chaps. 5, 7, and 8, Harcourt, Brace & World, Inc., New York, 1966.

Guillemin, E. A.: "Introductory Circuit Theory," chaps. 6, 7, and 8, John Wiley & Sons, Inc., New York, 1953.

Javid, M., and E. Brenner: "Analysis, Transmission, and Filtering of Signals," chaps. 11 and 12, McGraw-Hill Book Company, New York, 1963.

Manning, L. A.: "Electrical Circuits," chaps. 4 and 6, McGraw-Hill Book Company, New York, 1966.

Pearson, S. I., and G. J. Maler: "Introductory Circuit Analysis," chaps. 5, 6, and 8, John Wiley & Sons, Inc., New York, 1965.

Skilling, H. H.: "Electrical Engineering Circuits," 2d ed., chaps. 3, 4, 6, and 10, John Wiley & Sons, Inc., New York, 1965.

Van Valkenburg, M. E.: "Network Analysis," 2d ed., chaps. 12, 13, and 14, Prentice-Hall, Inc., Englewood Cliffs, N.J., 1964.

PROBLEMS

6-1. Draw the waveforms $v = 1 \sin 3t$, $v = 2 \sin (3t + \pi/4)$, and $v = 3 \cos 3t$.

6-2. Obtain the sum $1 \sin 2t + 3 \sin (2t + \pi/4)$ in the form $A \sin (2t + \phi)$.

6-3. Obtain the phasors for the sinusoids of Prob. 6-1.

6-4. Repeat Prob. 6-2, but now use phasors.

6-5. Perform the following operations:

$$(2 + j3) + 4e^{j\pi/6} - 3e^{j\pi/5}$$
$$(1 + j) + 4e^{j\pi/6}(j3e^{j\pi/2})$$
$$(3 + j4)(6 + j8)$$
$$\frac{4 + j3}{2 + j1}$$
$$\frac{2e^{j\pi/4}}{3e^{-j\pi/6}}$$

Express all the answers in both polar and rectangular form.

6-6. Obtain all possible values of $2^{1/5}$.

6-7. Obtain $\ln (3 + j4)$.

6-8. Discuss, using equations, why the sinusoidal-steady-state transformed form of a network can be used to obtain the sinusoidal-steady-state solution.

6-9. For the network of Fig. 6-49 the generators are applied at $t = 0$ and there is no initial storage of energy in the inductors or capacitors. Obtain the complete solution for all the currents in the network. How does this differ from the sinusoidal-steady-state solution?

6-10. Evaluate

$$\begin{vmatrix} 2 + j3 & 4 - j \\ 4 - j & 6 + j15 \end{vmatrix}$$

6-11. Evaluate

$$\begin{vmatrix} 4 + j8 & 2 + j3 & 3 + j4 \\ 2 + j3 & 9 - j16 & 4 - j2 \\ 3 + j4 & 4 - j2 & 15 + j6 \end{vmatrix}$$

6-12. Use loop analysis to solve for all the currents in Fig. 6-49 on a sinusoidal-steady-state basis.

Fig. 6-49

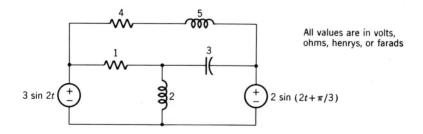

All values are in volts, ohms, henrys, or farads

3 sin 2t

2 sin $(2t + \pi/3)$

6-13. Repeat Prob. 6-12, but now use the network of Fig. 6-50.

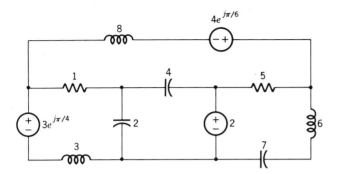

All values are in volts,
ohms, henrys, or farads
The phasor magnitude
represents the maximum
value of the sinusoids
The frequency of the
sinusoids is $f = 4/2\pi$

Fig. 6-50

6-14. Use nodal analysis to solve for all the branch voltages in the network of Fig. 6-51 on a sinusoidal-steady-state basis.

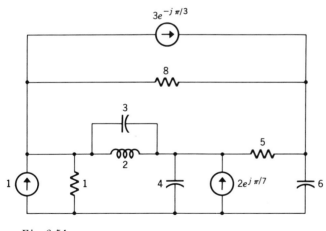

All values are in amperes,
ohms, henrys, or farads
The phasor magnitudes
represent the maximum
values of the sinusoids
The frequency of the
sinusoids is $f = 3/2\pi$

Fig. 6-51

6-15. Repeat Prob. 6-14, but now use the network of Fig. 6-52.

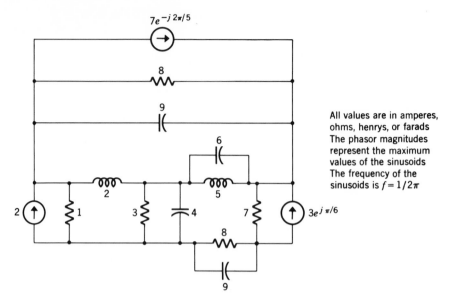

$7e^{-j\,2\pi/5}$

8

9

6

2

5

2 | 1 | 3 | 4 | 7 | $3e^{j\,\pi/6}$

8

9

All values are in amperes,
ohms, henrys, or farads
The phasor magnitudes
represent the maximum
values of the sinusoids
The frequency of the
sinusoids is $f = 1/2\pi$

Fig. 6-52

6-16. Repeat Prob. 6-14, but now use cut-set analysis.

6-17. Repeat Prob. 6-15, but now use cut-set analysis.

6-18. On a sinusoidal-steady-state basis, determine the driving-point imped-ance and driving-point admittance of the network of Fig. 5-42.   Use $\omega = 2$.

6-19. Repeat Prob. 6-18 for the network of Fig. 5-43.

6-20. Determine the resistance, reactance, conductance, and susceptance of the network of Prob. 6-18.   Draw two networks that are equivalent at $\omega = 2$. Are these networks equivalent at other frequencies?

6-21. Repeat Prob. 6-20 for the network of Fig. 5-43.

6-22. Use nodal analysis to determine all the branch voltages in the network of Fig. 6-49.   Convert all voltage generators to current generators.   Note that some elements must be considered in the original network to determine their voltages.

6-23. Repeat Prob. 6-22 for the network of Fig. 6-50.

6-24. Use loop analysis to obtain all the branch currents in the network of Fig. 6-51.   Convert all current generators to voltage generators.   Note that some elements must be considered in the original network to determine their currents.

6-25. Repeat Prob. 6-24 for the network of Fig. 6-52.

6-26. Obtain the transfer-voltage ratio of the network of Fig. 5-44 on a sinusoidal-steady-state basis.

6-27. Repeat Prob. 6-26 for the transfer-current ratio.

6-28. Repeat Prob. 6-26 for the transfer impedance.

6-29. Repeat Prob. 6-26 for the transfer admittance.

6-30. Draw the phasor diagram for the network of Fig. 6-49.

6-31. The voltage across a 10-ohm resistor is $10 \sin (\omega t + \pi/3)$ volts. What is the average power dissipated in the resistance?

6-32. Find the effective value of $v = V_{max} \sin^2 \omega t$ and $v = V_1 \sin \omega_1 t + V_2 \sin 2\omega_1 t$.

6-33. The voltage across an impedance and the current through it are given by $v = 10 \sin (\omega t + \pi/6)$ volts and $i = 3 \sin (\omega t + \pi/7)$ amps. What is the average power dissipated in the impedance?

6-34. What is the average power supplied by the 3-volt generator of Fig. 6-49?

6-35. Derive an expression for the average power dissipated in an impedance in terms of the current through it, the resistance, and the conductance.

6-36. Repeat Prob. 6-35, but use the voltage across the impedance rather than the current through it.

6-37. Derive an expression for the average power dissipated in an admittance in terms of the voltage across it, the conductance, and the susceptance.

6-38. Repeat Prob. 6-37, but use the current through the admittance rather than the voltage across it.

6-39. Draw amplitude and phase plots for the transfer-voltage ratio of the network of Fig. 6-53.

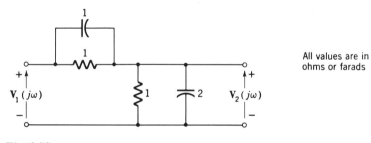

All values are in ohms or farads

Fig. 6-53

6-40. Repeat Prob. 6-39, but now use semilog paper.

6-41. Repeat Prob. 6-39, but now use a polar plot.

6-42. Determine the poles and zeros for the transfer-voltage ratio of the network of Fig. 6-53. Draw the pole-zero diagram and use this to construct graphical amplitude and phase plots for the network.

6-43. The input power to a twoport is 10 watts. What is the output power if its power gain is -100 db?

6-44. Repeat Prob. 6-39, but draw the amplitude response on a decibel basis. Use semilog paper for both the amplitude and phase plots. Use the techniques of Sec. 6-15 here and draw all straight-line asymptotes.

6-45. Repeat Prob. 6-44 for the network of Fig. 6-54.

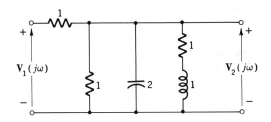

All values are in ohms,
henrys, or farads

Fig. 6-54

6-46. For the circuit of Fig. 6-31 $L = 1 \times 10^{-6}$ henry, $C = 1 \times 10^{-6}$ farad, and $R = 0.01$ ohms. Draw the frequency and phase response of this network, using $f_0 = 10^{-6}/2\pi$ Hz as the center frequency.

6-47. The network of Fig. 6-33 is to have a half-power bandwidth of 10^4 Hz. The resonant frequency is to be $f_0 = 10^6$ Hz. The capacitance is 0.05×10^{-6} farads, and the coil and its resistor are such that $Q_0 = 200$. If $R_2 = 10^6$ ohms, what should the values of R_1 and L be to achieve the design? What is the value of R?

6-48. Discuss the use of the substitution of Eq. (6-187).

6-49. For the circuit of Fig. 6-34a $\mathbf{I}_1 = 10e^{-j\pi/3}$ amps rms, $f = 60$ Hz, and $\mathbf{V} = 100$ volts rms. It is desired to add a capacitor, as in Fig. 6-34b, for power-factor correction. What value of C should be used?

6-50. Draw curves of $|\mathbf{Z}(j\omega)|$, $R(\omega)$, and $X(\omega)$ versus frequency for the network of Fig. 6-35. Plot about the center frequency $f_0 = 1/2\pi\sqrt{LC}$.

6-51. Use loop analysis to solve for all the branch currents of Fig. 6-55 on a sinusoidal-steady-state basis.

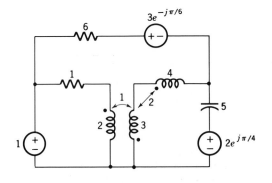

All values are in volts,
ohms, henrys, or farads
The frequency of the
sinusoids is $f = 8/2\pi$

Fig. 6-55

6-52. In the circuit of Fig. 6-39, $\mathbf{Z}_2 = 3 + j4$ and $n_1/n_2 = 1,000$. Find $\mathbf{Z}_1$.

6-53. The response of an ideal transformer is independent of frequency. Discuss in qualitative terms the response of the circuit of Fig. 6-40 as a function of frequency. Neglect C_{12} and $C_{1'2'}$; assume that $L_m \gg L_1$, $L_m \gg L_2$ and that C_1 and C_2 are small.

6-54. For the circuit of Fig. 6-43 $V = 120$ volts rms, $\mathbf{Z}_1 = 3 + j4$ ohms, $\mathbf{Z}_2 = 4 + j6$ ohms, and $\mathbf{Z}_3 = 7 + j1$ ohms. Compute $\mathbf{I}_1$, $\mathbf{I}_2$, and $\mathbf{I}_3$, the power supplied by each of the generators, the load voltages, and the power dissipated in the loads. Assume that each of the wires from the generator to the loads has an impedance of $1 + j1$ ohms.

6-55. Repeat Prob. 6-54, but now assume that the neutral wire is not connected.

6-56. For the circuit of Fig. 6-44 $V = 120$ volts rms, $\mathbf{Z}_1 = 3 + j4$ ohms, $Z_2 = 4 + j6$ ohms, and $Z_3 = 7 + j1$ ohms. Compute the power supplied by each generator, the voltage across the loads, and the power dissipated in the loads. Assume that the wires from the generators to the loads have an impedance of $1 + j1$ ohms.

6-57. For the transmission line of Fig. 6-45a $R = 10^{-7}$ ohms/m, $L = 1.2 \times 10^{-6}$ henry/m, $C = 10 \times 10^{-12}$ farad/m $= 10$ pf/m, and $G = 10^{-10}$ mho/m. Compute $\boldsymbol{\gamma}$ and $\mathbf{Z}_0$ for this transmission line.

6-58. An infinite transmission line has the parameters given in Prob. 6-57. A voltage whose phasor is 1 volt is connected to the input to the line. Compute the voltage at $x = 1, 2, 100, 10^4$, and 10^{10} m. Assume that $\omega = 1$.

6-59. Repeat Prob. 6-58, but now assume that $R = G = 0$.

6-60. Repeat Prob. 6-58, but now assume that $\omega = 10, 10^3, 10^6$, and 10^{12} rad/sec.

6-61. A transmission line has the parameters $R = 10^{-7}$ ohm/m, $L = 1.2 \times 10^{-6}$ henry/m, and $C = 10$ pf/m. What must G be if the transmission is to be distortionless?

6-62. The transmission line of Fig. 6-47 is lossless, and $L = 1.2 \times 10^{-6}$ henry/m and $C = 10$ pf/m. The line is 10 m long, and $\mathbf{Z} = (3 + j4) \times 10^2$ ohms. If $\omega = 2\pi \times 30 \times 10^6$ and $V = 1.0$ volts, compute the voltage and current at all points along the line.

6-63. Repeat Prob. 6-62, but now assume that $\mathbf{Z}$ is an open circuit.

6-64. The transmission line of Fig. 6-47 is 10 m long and lossless. Its parameters are such that $1/\sqrt{LC} = 3 \times 10^8$ m/sec and $\sqrt{L/C} = 50$ ohms. If $\mathbf{Z} = 100$ ohms and $f = 30 \times 10^6$ Hz, find the input impedance of the transmission line.

6-65. Repeat Prob. 6-64, but now assume that $f = 15 \times 10^6$ Hz.

6-66. Repeat Prob. 6-64, but now use a 2.5-m length of line and let $\mathbf{Z} = 0$.

6-67. Repeat Prob. 6-66 with $\mathbf{Z} = \infty$.

6-68. For the transmission line of Prob. 6-64 compute the voltage and current at all points along the transmission line.

6-69. Repeat Prob. 6-68, but now assume that the generator has an internal series resistance of 30 ohms. *Hint:* Use the input impedance of the transmission line.

State Space

In this chapter we shall discuss another technique for the solution of electric networks, or systems characterized by differential equations. We have already considered classical and Laplace transform techniques to solve these problems (Chaps. 4 and 5). There are many reasons for considering a new technique, called the *state-space technique* or the *state-variable technique*. Large, complex problems are generally solved with digital or analog computers, and the state-variable technique is more easily applied to computer solutions than other procedures. In addition, state-space techniques are very effective in analyzing nonlinear and/or time-varying networks. This is due, in part, to the relative ease with which these procedures can be used with computers. The Laplace transform is usually of no use here.

The above discussion does not mean that Laplace transform techniques are outmoded. Indeed, for a great many of the problems encountered by the electrical engineer the Laplace transform is in fact the best procedure. Thus the two procedures augment each other.

7-1   States, state equations, state space, and trajectory

When classical or Laplace transform techniques are used to solve a network, we generally obtain a set of m simultaneous equations with m unknowns. We can then use Cramer's rule to obtain a set of m equations, each of which has one unknown. Each of these equations can be of order $2m$. That is, in classical procedures, there can be a $2m$th-order derivative, or the highest power of s in the Laplace transform procedure can be $2m$. The facts we need in order to solve for the unknowns are the network configuration, the element values, the independent generator values, and the initial conditions.

In state-variable procedures we shall define a new set of unknowns, called *state variables*. These are characterized by a set of *first-order differential equations* of a special form. Before we develop general results, let us consider a specific example to clarify some of these ideas. For the simple network of Fig. 7-1, for $t > 0$ the classical integral differential equation is

$$Ri(t) + L\frac{di(t)}{dt} + \frac{1}{C}\int i(t)\,dt = V \tag{7-1}$$

Differentiating, we obtain

$$\frac{d^2i(t)}{dt^2} + \frac{R}{L}\frac{di(t)}{dt} + \frac{1}{LC}i(t) = 0 \tag{7-2}$$

Thus we have a second-order equation which characterizes this network. This equation was solved in Sec. 4-4. Let us now characterize the network of Fig. 7-1 in terms of a new set of unknowns. We shall choose $i_L(t)$, the current through the inductor, and $v_C(t)$, the voltage across the capacitor and solve for each of these quantities. We can write Eq. (7-1) as

$$Ri_L(t) + L\frac{di_L(t)}{dt} + v_C(t) = V \tag{7-3}$$

and, manipulating this, we have

$$\frac{di_L(t)}{dt} = -\frac{R}{L}i_L(t) - \frac{1}{L}v_C(t) + \frac{V}{L} \tag{7-4}$$

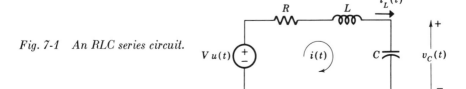

Fig. 7-1   An RLC series circuit.

We also know that

$$v_C(t) = \frac{1}{C} \int i_L(t)\, dt \tag{7-5}$$

and after differentiation we obtain

$$\frac{dv_C(t)}{dt} = \frac{1}{C} i_L(t) \tag{7-6}$$

Equations (7-4) and (7-6) are now in the proper form to constitute the state equations for the network. We rewrite them as

$$\frac{di_L(t)}{dt} = -\frac{R}{L} i_L(t) - \frac{1}{L} v_C(t) + \frac{V}{L} \tag{7-7a}$$

$$\frac{dv_C(t)}{dt} = \frac{1}{C} i_L(t) \tag{7-7b}$$

From the loop equations for the network we have obtained two *first-order* differential equations which characterize the system. In the next section we shall discuss general techniques for obtaining these equations. The variables of these first-order differential equations, in this case $i_L(t)$ and $v_C(t)$, are called the *state variables*. The set of numerical values of all the state variables at any time is said to be the *state* of the network at that time.

The initial conditions are important in the solution of the circuit. Note that the two initial conditions with which we must work in this circuit are $v_C(0-)$ and $i_L(0-)$. These are the initial values of the state variables. The initial values of the state variables will, in general, be specified. The state gives the value of all the state variables at an arbitrary time t. At the initial time $(t = 0-)$ we designate the state as the *initial state*. Thus in a network problem the initial state will be specified, since the initial conditions are specified. If all the initial conditions are zero, we say that the circuit is in the *zero state*.

We shall develop procedures to solve the equations in the state-variable form in Sec. 7-5. However, at the present time we can obtain the solution of Eqs. (7-7) (i.e., the state variables), since we have solved Eq. (7-2). We shall use this solution to illustrate some additional definitions. Consider that the initial state has both $v_C(0-)$ and $i_L(0-)$ equal to zero; then we can use the solutions of Sec. 4-4. We shall consider two typical and simple solutions to Eq. (7-2). The first of these is the critically damped case [case 2, Eq. (4-160)],

$$i_L(t) = \frac{V}{L} t e^{-\omega_0 t} \tag{7-8}$$

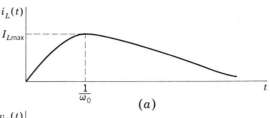

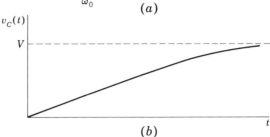

Fig. 7-2 (a) A plot of $i_L(t)$ given by Eq. (7-8); (b) a plot of $v_c(t)$ given by Eq. (7-10).

where

$$\omega_0 = \frac{1}{\sqrt{LC}} \qquad (7\text{-}9)$$

To obtain $v_C(t)$ we can use Eq. (7-5). Carrying out this integration and adjusting the constant of integration so that $v_C(0) = 0$, we have

$$v_C(t) = V[1 - e^{-\omega_0 t}(\omega_0 t + 1)] \qquad (7\text{-}10)$$

We could represent these two variables by two separate graphs of $i_L(t)$ versus time and $v_C(t)$ versus time, as shown in Figs. 7-2a and b. We can also represent both state variables on a *single* graph by using $i_L(t)$ and $v_C(t)$ axes, as shown in Fig. 7-3. That is, corresponding to each value of time, we plot a point $(i_L(t_1), v_C(t_1))$. When we do this for all time, a curve results. Time is not indicated on any of the axes, but we can write next to any point the time to which it corresponds (this curve is analogous to the polar plots of Sec. 6-12, with t the variable instead of ω). Since the state variables are plotted, the entire region (which in this case is a plane) is called the *state space*.

Fig. 7-3 State space and trajectory for the network of Fig. 7-1 for the critically damped case. It is assumed that the initial conditions are zero.

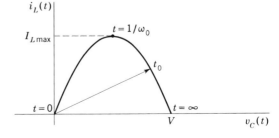

Note that if there are three state variables, then a three-dimensional plot is required. If there are more than three state variables, then a space of more than three dimensions will be required to display them. Of course, such a space cannot be drawn. However, the general concept of a state space can be applied. In the example we have a two-dimensional state space. This is a plane which is often called the *phase plane*. The actual curve in the state space is called the *trajectory*. Each point on the trajectory gives the state of the network at that time (the values of all the state variables at that time). If we draw a line from the origin to some point on the trajectory corresponding to $t = t_0$ in Fig. 7-3, then the vertical component of the line gives $i_L(t_0)$, and the horizontal component is $v_C(t_0)$. Such a line can be considered to be a *vector;* each of its components gives one of the state variables. In general, a vector can be represented by a *one-column matrix* (see Sec. 3-10 for a discussion of matrices and matrix operations). That is, we write an array of numbers, each of which corresponds to one of the state variables (or to one of the vector components). For example, if we designate the vector by $[q(t)]$, then at a particular time t_0

$$[q(t_0)] = \begin{bmatrix} i_L(t_0) \\ v_C(t_0) \end{bmatrix} \tag{7-11}$$

This is merely a shorthand notation for the representation of the state variables. The state space represents all the possible values of the state variables. The trajectory represents the actual values of these variables.

Before discussing these definitions in more general terms, let us consider another example to illustrate a different trajectory. We shall again analyze the network of Fig. 7-1, but now we assume that $R = 0$. From Eqs. (4-162),

Fig. 7-4 *State space and trajectory for the network of Fig. 7-1 for the case $R = 0$. It is assumed that the initial conditions are zero, and in the curve $n = 0, 1, 2, \ldots$.*

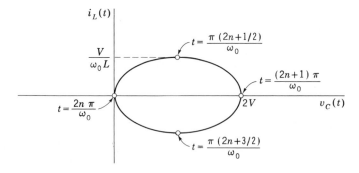

(4-144), and (7-5) we have

$$i_L(t) = \frac{V}{\omega_0 L} \sin \omega_0 t \tag{7-12a}$$

$$v_C(t) = V(1 - \cos \omega_0 t) \tag{7-12b}$$

The state-space trajectory is given in Fig. 7-4. Note that the trajectory starts at the origin and in $2\pi/\omega_0$ sec returns there; hence the curve repeats itself each $2\pi/\omega_0$ sec. This is a periodic function. If the network is underdamped, but R is not zero, then the curve of Fig. 7-4 will be modified into a spiral which encircles the point $(i_L = 0, v_C = V)$ and eventually converges to it.

Finally, it should be noted that the usual variables can be expressed in terms of the state variables. In this case the loop current $i(t)$ [see Fig. 7-1] can be expressed in terms of only one of the two state variables,

$$i(t) = i_L(t) \tag{7-13}$$

We can also express other quantities in terms of the state variables. For instance, the voltages across the inductor and resistor are given by

$$v_L(t) = -Ri_L(t) - v_C(t) + V \tag{7-14a}$$

$$v_R(t) = Ri_L(t) \tag{7-14b}$$

In general, the variables of the network can be expressed in terms of the independent generators, constants, and state variables.

We can now formulate the definitions of this section in general terms. It may not be obvious from the discussion how the state variables are obtained, but in Secs. 7-2 to 7-4 we shall discuss a general procedure for obtaining the state-variable characterization of an electric network. We shall also see there how the unknown loop currents and/or nodal or cut-set voltages, as well as other network voltages and currents, can be obtained from the state variables.

Suppose we have a general network in which the independent generators are designated by $y_i(t)$ $(i = 1,2, \ldots ,k)$. In general, these will be voltage generators when loop analysis is used and current generators when nodal or cut-set analysis is used, although there may also be a mixture of generator types. The unknowns of the network will be designated by $x_i(t)$ $(i = 1,2, \ldots ,m)$. These are, in general, loop currents or nodal or cut-set voltages. However, if, for instance, a voltage is desired, it could be included in the unknowns even if loop analysis were used. We shall also assume that the initial currents in the inductors and the initial voltages across the capacitors are specified.

We now choose a new set of variables $q_i(t)$ $(i = 1,2, \ldots ,n)$ which are the *state variables*. In the next section we shall see that these can be the voltages across the capacitors and the currents through the inductors of the network and that we can characterize the behavior of the network in terms of these variables.

Note that in the previous examples of this section we were able to characterize the network in terms of $i_L(t)$ and $v_C(t)$. The set of state-variable equations will be written in the form

$$\frac{dq_1(t)}{dt} = f_1[q_1(t), q_2(t), \ldots, q_n(t), y_1(t), y_2(t), \ldots, y_k(t), t]$$

$$\frac{dq_2(t)}{dt} = f_2[q_1(t), q_2(t), \ldots, q_n(t), y_1(t), y_2(t), \ldots, y_k(t), t] \qquad (7\text{-}15)$$

$$\cdots \cdots \cdots \cdots \cdots \cdots \cdots \cdots \cdots \cdots \cdots$$

$$\frac{dq_n(t)}{dt} = f_n[q_1(t), q_2(t), \ldots, q_n(t), y_1(t), y_2(t), \ldots, y_k(t), t]$$

That is, the derivative of each of the state variables will be a function of all the state variables, including itself, the independent generators, and time. The initial conditions are incorporated in the initial state of the system. Note that each of the functions $f_1, f_2, \ldots$ in Eqs. (7-15) is, in general, different. However, these functions are restricted *not* to contain any derivatives with respect to time of the unknown state variables [for example, see Eqs. (7-7)]. In nonlinear or time-varying circuits the functions of Eqs. (7-15) will be nonlinear or time varying [for example, $q_i^2(t)$ or $tq_i(t)$ may be present].

Matrix notation can be used to express these equations in a compact form (we assume that the reader is familiar with Sec. 3-10, which describes basic matrix operations). We define the matrices

$$[q(t)] = \begin{bmatrix} q_1(t) \\ q_2(t) \\ \cdot \\ \cdot \\ \cdot \\ q_n(t) \end{bmatrix} \qquad (7\text{-}16)$$

$$[y(t)] = \begin{bmatrix} y_1(t) \\ y_2(t) \\ \cdot \\ \cdot \\ \cdot \\ y_k(t) \end{bmatrix} \qquad (7\text{-}17)$$

The use of brackets to indicate matrices is in many circumstances a simple notation to use. However, there are times when it is cumbersome. In such cases we shall designate matrices by a "hat" over the symbol; for instance,

$$[q(t)] = \hat{q}(t) \qquad (7\text{-}18)$$

Thus we can define

$$
\hat{f}[\hat{q}(t),\hat{y}(t),t] = \begin{bmatrix} f_1[q_1(t),\, q_2(t),\, \ldots\,,\, q_n(t),\, y_1(t),\, y_2(t),\, \ldots\,,\, y_k(t),\, t] \\ f_2[q_1(t),\, q_2(t),\, \ldots\,,\, q_n(t),\, y_1(t),\, y_2(t),\, \ldots\,,\, y_k(t),\, t] \\ \cdots\cdots\cdots\cdots\cdots\cdots\cdots\cdots\cdots\cdots\cdots\cdots\cdots\cdots \\ f_n[q_1(t),\, q_2(t),\, \ldots\,,\, q_n(t),\, y_1(t),\, y_2(t),\, \ldots\,,\, y_k(t),\, t] \end{bmatrix}
$$

$$(7\text{-}19)$$

Thus the set of equations of (7-15) can be written in compact form as

$$
\frac{d\hat{q}(t)}{dt} = \hat{f}[\hat{q}(t),\hat{y}(t),t] \tag{7-20}
$$

where Eq. (7-20) is *defined* as equivalent to Eq. (7-15). The matrix $\hat{q}(t)$ is a vector which gives the state of the network at time t. The path traced by the tip of the vector is the trajectory in the n-dimensional state space. Note that $\hat{y}(t)$ also represents a vector in k-dimensional space.

In general, we shall demonstrate in the next few sections that the network unknowns $x_1(t),\, \ldots\,,\, x_m(t)$ can be expressed in terms of the state variables and the independent generators as

$$
\begin{aligned}
x_1(t) &= g_1[q_1(t),\, q_2(t),\, \ldots\,,\, q_n(t),\, y_1(t),\, y_2(t),\, \ldots\,,\, y_k(t),\, t] \\
x_2(t) &= g_2[q_1(t),\, q_2(t),\, \ldots\,,\, q_n(t),\, y_1(t),\, y_2(t),\, \ldots\,,\, y_k(t),\, t] \\
&\cdots\cdots\cdots\cdots\cdots\cdots\cdots\cdots\cdots\cdots\cdots\cdots \\
x_m(t) &= g_m[q_1(t),\, q_2(t),\, \ldots\,,\, q_n(t),\, y_1(t),\, y_2(t),\, \ldots\,,\, y_k(t),\, t]
\end{aligned}
\tag{7-21}
$$

where $g_1,\, g_2,\, \ldots\,,\, g_m$ are functions of the state variables, the independent generators, and time. If we define an $\hat{x}(t)$ matrix (or vector) as

$$
\hat{x}(t) = \begin{bmatrix} x_1(t) \\ x_2(t) \\ \cdot \\ \cdot \\ \cdot \\ x_m(t) \end{bmatrix}
\tag{7-22}
$$

then we can write Eqs. (7-21) in matrix form as

$$
\hat{x}(t) = \hat{g}[\hat{q}(t),\hat{y}(t),t] \tag{7-23}
$$

In the case of linear time-invariant networks the functions $f_1, f_2, \ldots, f_n$ and $g_1, g_2, \ldots, g_n$ of Eqs. (7-15) and (7-21), respectively, become simple linear relations. That is, the functions become *linear sums* of their terms. The right-hand sides of Eqs. (7-7), for instance, consist of just a linear sum of the state variables and the generator terms.   In such cases we can replace the general functional relation of Eqs. (7-15) and (7-21) by simple equations. For instance, Eqs. (7-15) will become

$$\frac{dq_1(t)}{dt} = a_{11}q_1(t) + a_{12}q_2(t) + \cdots + a_{1n}q_n(t) + b_{11}y_1(t) + b_{12}y_2(t)$$
$$+ \cdots + b_{1k}y_k(t)$$

$$\frac{dq_2(t)}{dt} = a_{21}q_1(t) + a_{22}q_2(t) + \cdots + a_{2n}q_n(t) + b_{21}y_1(t) + b_{22}y_2(t)$$
$$+ \cdots + b_{2k}y_k(t) \quad (7\text{-}24)$$

$$\cdots\cdots\cdots\cdots\cdots\cdots\cdots\cdots\cdots\cdots\cdots\cdots$$

$$\frac{dq_n(t)}{dt} = a_{n1}q_1(t) + a_{n2}q_2(t) + \cdots + a_{nn}q_n(t) + b_{n1}y_1(t) + b_{n2}y_2(t)$$
$$+ \cdots + b_{nk}y_k(t)$$

where the a's and b's are constants.   We can write this in matrix form by defining two matrices

$$\hat{a} = \begin{bmatrix} a_{11} & a_{12} & \cdots & a_{1n} \\ a_{21} & a_{22} & \cdots & a_{2n} \\ \cdots\cdots\cdots\cdots\cdots \\ a_{n1} & a_{n2} & \cdots & a_{nn} \end{bmatrix} \quad (7\text{-}25)$$

$$\hat{b} = \begin{bmatrix} b_{11} & b_{12} & \cdots & b_{1k} \\ b_{21} & b_{22} & \cdots & b_{2k} \\ \cdots\cdots\cdots\cdots\cdots \\ b_{n1} & b_{n2} & \cdots & b_{nk} \end{bmatrix} \quad (7\text{-}26)$$

Then

$$\frac{d\hat{q}(t)}{dt} = \hat{a}\hat{q}(t) + \hat{b}\hat{y}(t) \quad (7\text{-}27)$$

For instance, consider Eqs. (7-7).   Here

$$\hat{q}(t) = \begin{bmatrix} i_L(t) \\ v_C(t) \end{bmatrix} \quad (7\text{-}28a)$$

$$\hat{a} = \begin{bmatrix} \dfrac{-R}{L} & \dfrac{-1}{L} \\ \dfrac{1}{C} & 0 \end{bmatrix} \quad (7\text{-}28b)$$

$$\hat{b} = \begin{bmatrix} \dfrac{1}{L} \\ 0 \end{bmatrix} \quad (7\text{-}28c)$$

$$\hat{y}(t) = [V] \quad (7\text{-}28d)$$

Thus Eq. (7-27) for this case can be written as

$$\frac{d}{dt}\begin{bmatrix} i_L(t) \\ v_C(t) \end{bmatrix} = \begin{bmatrix} \dfrac{-R}{L} & \dfrac{-1}{L} \\ \dfrac{1}{C} & 0 \end{bmatrix}\begin{bmatrix} i_L(t) \\ v_C(t) \end{bmatrix} + \begin{bmatrix} \dfrac{1}{L} \\ 0 \end{bmatrix}[V] \tag{7-28e}$$

and, carrying out the rules for matrix manipulation, we obtain Eqs. (7-7). Note that *taking the derivative of a matrix means differentiating each element of the matrix.*

In the linear time-invariant case the network unknowns $x_1(t), \ldots, x_m(t)$ will be expressed as linear combinations of the state variables and the known generator functions. Thus we can write Eqs. (7-21) in the simplified form

$$x_1(t) = c_{11}q_1(t) + c_{12}q_2(t) + \cdots + c_{1n}q_n(t) + d_{11}y_1(t) + d_{12}y_2(t)$$
$$+ \cdots + d_{1k}y_k(t)$$

$$x_2(t) = c_{21}q_1(t) + c_{22}q_2(t) + \cdots + c_{2n}q_n(t) + d_{21}y_1(t) + d_{22}y_2(t)$$
$$+ \cdots + d_{2k}y_k(t) \tag{7-29}$$

$$\cdots \cdots \cdots \cdots \cdots \cdots \cdots \cdots \cdots \cdots \cdots$$

$$x_m(t) = c_{m1}q_1(t) + c_{m2}q_2(t) + \cdots + c_{mn}q_n(t) + d_{m1}y_1(t) + d_{m2}y_2(t)$$
$$+ \cdots + d_{mk}y_k(t)$$

where the c's and d's are constants. Let us define the matrices

$$\hat{c} = \begin{bmatrix} c_{11} & c_{12} & \cdots & c_{1n} \\ c_{21} & c_{22} & \cdots & c_{2n} \\ \cdots & \cdots & \cdots & \cdots \\ c_{m1} & c_{m2} & \cdots & c_{mn} \end{bmatrix} \tag{7-30}$$

$$\hat{d} = \begin{bmatrix} d_{11} & d_{12} & \cdots & d_{1k} \\ d_{21} & d_{22} & \cdots & d_{2k} \\ \cdots & \cdots & \cdots & \cdots \\ d_{m1} & d_{m2} & \cdots & d_{mk} \end{bmatrix} \tag{7-31}$$

Then, in matrix form,

$$\hat{x}(t) = \hat{c}\hat{q}(t) + \hat{d}\hat{y}(t) \tag{7-32}$$

As an example let us assume that the desired network unknowns are given by Eqs. (7-13) and (7-14). Thus

$$\hat{x}(t) = \begin{bmatrix} i(t) \\ v_L(t) \\ v_R(t) \end{bmatrix} \tag{7-33a}$$

$$\hat{c} = \begin{bmatrix} 1 & 0 \\ -R & -1 \\ R & 0 \end{bmatrix} \tag{7-33b}$$

$$\hat{d} = \begin{bmatrix} 0 \\ 1 \\ 0 \end{bmatrix} \tag{7-33c}$$

Thus Eqs. (7-13) and (7-14) can be represented by

$$
\begin{bmatrix} i(t) \\ v_L(t) \\ v_R(t) \end{bmatrix} = \begin{bmatrix} 1 & 0 \\ -R & -1 \\ R & 0 \end{bmatrix} \begin{bmatrix} i_L(t) \\ v_C(t) \end{bmatrix} + \begin{bmatrix} 0 \\ 1 \\ 0 \end{bmatrix} [V] \tag{7-33d}
$$

7-2   State-variable equations of networks

In this section we shall develop a technique for writing the state-variable equations of electric networks. We shall also express all the network voltages and currents in terms of the state variables.

At the start we shall restrict ourselves to networks which satisfy the following two conditions: (1) there can be *no* loop which contains *only* independent voltage generators and capacitors, and (2) there can be *no* cut set which contains *only* independent current generators and inductors. The reasons for these restrictions will become clear when we discuss improper networks at the end of this section.

A network which satisfies conditions 1 and 2 is called a *proper network.* We shall assume that we are working with a proper network. Then the state variables will be *all* the currents through the inductors and *all* the voltages across the capacitors. We must demonstrate that this represents a valid choice; that is, we must show that all the state variables can be characterized by equations of the form of Eqs. (7-15). In addition, we must demonstrate that all the network currents and/or voltages can be expressed in terms of the state variables and the independent generators, that is, that they can be characterized by equations of the form of Eqs. (7-21). If the networks are linear and time invariant, then we must be able to represent the state variables by a set of equations of the form of Eqs. (7-24). Similarly, for the linear time-invariant case the network voltages and/or currents must be characterizable by equations of the form of Eqs. (7-29). The set of state variables that we shall use here is not the only set that can be used. In Sec. 7-8 we shall illustrate this by choosing another valid set of state variables.

In order to apply these procedures let us develop a simple equivalent circuit. Consider Fig. 7-5a, which represents any element that is part of a circuit. Let us assume that we know $v(t)$, the voltage across the element. Then, as far as external conditions are concerned, we can replace the element by a voltage generator that produces $v(t)$, as shown in Fig. 7-5b. To demonstrate that this is true, consider loop analysis. Each term in the equations represents the voltage drop across an element. In Fig. 7-5b this voltage drop is represented directly. Thus the loop-analysis equations will not change if Fig. 7-5b is substituted for Fig. 7-5a. Hence Figs. 7-5a and b are equivalent for conditions external to the replaced element.

If we know the current through an element, we can replace it by a current

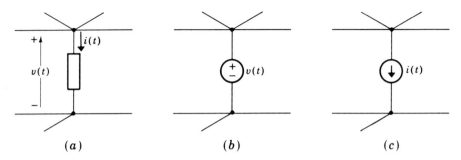

Fig. 7-5   (a) *A general element in a network;* (b) *a voltage-generator circuit that is equivalent to* (a) *as far as external conditions are concerned;* (c) *a current-generator circuit that is equivalent to* (a) *as far as external conditions are concerned.*

generator which produces this current. Such a substitution is shown in Fig. 7-5c. The proof of the validity of this equivalence is the same as that for Fig. 7-5b, except that we use nodal or cut-set analysis instead of loop analysis and work with the currents in elements rather than the voltages across them.

To obtain the state variables and state-variable equations with proper networks let us first define state variables as *all* the currents through the inductors and *all* the voltages across the capacitors. Now we treat these voltages and currents as *though they were known.* We replace the inductors by current generators whose currents are equal to the currents through the inductors. For instance, we replace L_1 by a current generator whose current is given by the symbol $i_L(t)$. In addition, we replace all the capacitors by voltage generators whose voltages are the voltages across the capacitors. The remaining network consists only of known independent generators, generators whose voltages and/or currents are the state variables, and resistances. If we treat all generators as though they were known [for example, if we treat $i_L(t)$ just as if it were a known quantity], then we have a network with generators and resistors, and we can perform a loop, nodal, or cut-set analysis on this *equivalent network* to obtain any desired current or voltage. These will be expressed in terms of the known resistors, known generators, and the generators, which are expressed in terms of the state variables. Thus all the network unknowns can be expressed in terms of these quantities in the form of Eqs. (7-21). If the network is linear and time invariant, then the unknown voltages and/or currents will be linear time-invariant functions of the generator voltages. Thus the network unknowns will be expressed in the form of Eqs. (7-29).

We must now demonstrate that we can obtain the state-variable equations in the form of Eqs. (7-15). Let us work with the capacitor voltage terms first. With loop, nodal or cut-set analyses of the equivalent network we can determine the *current* through any capacitor. Thus we can write

$$i_{C_k}(t) = \mu_{C_k}[q_1(t), q_2(t), \ldots, q_n(t), y_1(t), y_2(t), \ldots, y_k(t), t] \qquad (7\text{-}34)$$

where the q_i $(i = 1,2, \ldots ,n)$ are the state variables, the $y_i(t)$ $(i = 1,2, \ldots ,k)$ are the known generators, and μ_1 is just some function of these variables. If the *resistances* are linear and time invariant, then $i_{C_k}(t)$ will be a linear function of these variables (only the resistances need be linear, since the equivalent network we are working with consists of only the resistors, the given generators, and the equivalent generators). Now let us assume that the capacitor C_k is linear and time invariant. Then

$$i_{C_k}(t) = C_k \frac{dv_{C_k}(t)}{dt} \tag{7-35}$$

Substituting in Eq. (7-34), we obtain

$$\frac{dv_{C_k}(t)}{dt} = \frac{1}{C_k} \mu_{C_k}[q_1(t), \ldots , q_n(t), y_1(t), y_2(t), \ldots , y_k(t), t] \tag{7-36}$$

where $(1/C_k)\mu_{C_k}[\quad]$ represents one of the functions in Eqs. (7-15). We can do this for each one of the capacitors in turn. Thus we have expressed the capacitor voltages in the state-variable form.

We now apply loop, nodal, or cut-set analysis to the equivalent network to obtain the *voltage* across the inductors. This will be of the form

$$v_{L_k}(t) = \mu_{L_k}[q_1(t), \ldots , q_n(t), y_1(t), \ldots , y_k(t), t] \tag{7-37}$$

If the inductors are linear and time invariant, then

$$v_{L_k} = L_k \frac{di_{L_k}(t)}{dt} \tag{7-38}$$

Substituting in Eq. (7-37) and manipulating, we obtain

$$\frac{di_{L_k}(t)}{dt} = \frac{1}{L_k} \mu_{L_k}[q_1(t), \ldots , q_n(t), y_1(t), \ldots , y_k(t), t] \tag{7-39}$$

where $(1/L_k)\mu_{L_k}[\quad]$ represents one of the functions in Eqs. (7-15). Repeating this for each of the inductors, we obtain the state-variable equations for the inductor currents. If the network is linear and time invariant, then the functions of Eqs. (7-36) and (7-39) will be linear sums of the $q_k(t)$ and $y_i(t)$. In this section we shall be concerned primarily with linear time-invariant networks. Time-varying and nonlinear networks will be discussed in Secs. 7-3 and 7-4, respectively.

As an example consider the linear time-invariant network of Fig. 7-6a. The state variables are $i_L(t)$, the current through the inductor, and the voltage across the capacitor, $v_C(t)$. We replace the inductor by a current generator whose current is $i_L(t)$, and we replace the capacitor by a voltage generator whose voltage is $v_C(t)$. The resultant network is shown in Fig. 7-6b. Let us now solve for the unknown loop currents. We treat all generators as knowns. Note that we have only a resistance network to work with. The current generator could be converted to a voltage generator, but this is not necessary.

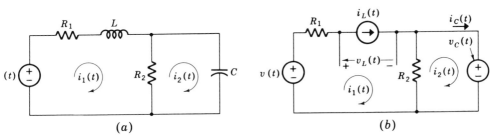

Fig. 7-6   (a) A two-loop proper network; (b) an equivalent network used in obtaining the state variables.   The generator voltage v(t) is known.

Since $i_L(t)$ is the only loop current through the current generator, we can write

$$i_1(t) = i_L(t) \tag{7-40}$$

Then, writing a loop equation for the $i_2(t)$ loop, we have

$$-v_C(t) = -R_2 i_1(t) + R_2 i_2(t) \tag{7-41a}$$

and after rearranging and substituting Eq. (7-40), we have

$$i_2(t) = i_L(t) - \frac{v_C(t)}{R_2} \tag{7-41b}$$

Equations (7-40) and (7-41b) are of the form of Eqs. (7-29).

Now let us obtain the state-variable equations.   We solve Fig. 7-6b for the voltage $v_L(t)$ across the inductor.   Apply Kirchhoff's voltage law to the $i_1(t)$ loop.   This yields

$$v(t) = R_1 i_1(t) + v_L(t) + R_2[i_1(t) - i_2(t)] \tag{7-42a}$$

Substituting Eqs. (7-40) and (7-41b) and manipulating, we have

$$v_L(t) = -R_1 i_L(t) - v_C(t) + v(t) \tag{7-42b}$$

and, substituting Eq. (7-38) and manipulating, we obtain

$$\frac{di_L(t)}{dt} = -\frac{R_1}{L} i_L(t) - \frac{1}{L} v_C(t) + \frac{1}{L} v(t) \tag{7-43}$$

Now we use Fig. 7-6b to solve for $i_C(t)$.   We see from the figure that

$$i_C(t) = i_2(t) \tag{7-44}$$

Then, substituting Eqs. (7-35) and (7-41b) and manipulating, we have

$$\frac{dv_C(t)}{dt} = \frac{1}{C} i_L(t) - \frac{1}{R_2 C} v_C(t) \tag{7-45}$$

Equations (7-43) and (7-45) are the state-variable equations for this network. We shall repeat them here:

$$\frac{di_L(t)}{dt} = -\frac{R_1}{L} i_L(t) - \frac{1}{L} v_C(t) + \frac{1}{L} v(t) \tag{7-46a}$$

$$\frac{dv_C(t)}{dt} = \frac{1}{C} i_L(t) - \frac{1}{R_2 C} v_C(t) \tag{7-46b}$$

Using the notation of Eqs. (7-24) to (7-27), we have

$$\hat{q}(t) = \begin{bmatrix} i_L(t) \\ v_C(t) \end{bmatrix} \tag{7-47a}$$

$$\hat{a} = \begin{bmatrix} -\dfrac{R_1}{L} & -\dfrac{1}{L} \\ \dfrac{1}{C} & -\dfrac{1}{R_2 C} \end{bmatrix} \tag{7-47b}$$

$$\hat{b} = \begin{bmatrix} \dfrac{1}{L} \\ 0 \end{bmatrix} \tag{7-47c}$$

$$\hat{y}(t) = [v(t)] \tag{7-47d}$$

In addition, with the notation of Eqs. (7-29) to (7-32), we have

$$\hat{x}(t) = \begin{bmatrix} i_1(t) \\ i_2(t) \end{bmatrix} \tag{7-47e}$$

$$\hat{c} = \begin{bmatrix} 1 & 0 \\ 1 & \dfrac{-1}{R_2} \end{bmatrix} \tag{7-47f}$$

$$\hat{d} = \begin{bmatrix} 0 \\ 0 \end{bmatrix} \tag{7-47g}$$

Topological considerations

Let us now relate some aspects of network topology to our procedure. We demonstrated in Sec. 3-1 that the tree-branch voltages uniquely determine *all* the branch voltages in a connected network, and that the chord currents uniquely determine *all* the branch currents of a connected network. We shall assume that we are working with connected networks or can make them connected by adding branches that have no current in them (see Fig. 3-12). The network is to be characterized by state variables which are the voltages across the capacitors and the currents through the inductors. Thus we should be able to choose a tree for the network which contains *all* the capacitors and *none* of the inductors; that is, the inductors are all in branches which are chords.

There may be resistive elements in both the tree branches and in the chords.

However, the currents through the chord resistances and the voltages across the tree-branch resistances can be found by the procedures we have indicated (see the network of Fig. 7-6b). Any independent voltage generators should be in the tree branches, and any independent current generators should be in the chords. Then all the tree-branch voltages can be expressed in terms of known voltages or state variables, and the chord currents can be expressed in terms of known currents or state variables (we can still convert current generators to voltage generators, and vice versa). Thus we can determine all the network voltages and currents in terms of these quantities. A tree that contains all the capacitors and voltage generators of a network and none of the inductors or current generators is called a *proper tree*. If a network has at least one proper tree, then it is a proper network.

Let us demonstrate this. A proper network is characterized by the two conditions that (1) there can be no loop which contains only independent voltage generators and capacitors and (2) there can be no cut sets which contain only independent current generators and inductors. Consider condition 1. If a loop does not *only* contain independent voltage generators and capacitors, then we can choose each voltage-generator branch and each capacitor branch as a tree branch, since no loop will be formed by this choice (at least one branch of each loop must be omitted, since we have a proper network). Similarly, for condition 2, each inductor branch and independent-current-generator branch of the cut set can be chosen as a chord, since there will always be at least one other branch (the tree branch) remaining which will connect the two parts of the network separated by the cut set. For example, a proper tree for Fig. 7-6c consists of the branches containing $v(t)$, R_1, R_2, and C.

Improper networks

We shall demonstrate that improper networks cause trouble and see what can be done to eliminate it. Figure 7-7 is an improper network, since there is a loop which contains only $v(t)$, C_1, and C_2. Now let us proceed in the usual way and set up the equivalent network shown in Fig. 7-7b. An immediate problem is that the voltage generators are not independent. Kirchhoff's voltage law must be satisfied around the outer loop. Thus, if we treat $v_{C_1}(t)$ and $v(t)$ as "independent" generators, then $v_{C_2}(t)$ must be such that

$$v_{C_2}(t) = v(t) - v_{C_1}(t) \tag{7-48}$$

In general, if we have improper loops of this type, we must specify one of the capacitor voltage generators in terms of the other generators of the loop. Similarly, if we have an improper cut set, one of the inductor current generators must be specified in terms of the others. However, doing this does not solve our problems. Let us try to solve the network of Fig. 7-7b for the loop currents in terms of the state variables and the independent generators. We can write

$$i_1(t) = i_L(t) \tag{7-49}$$

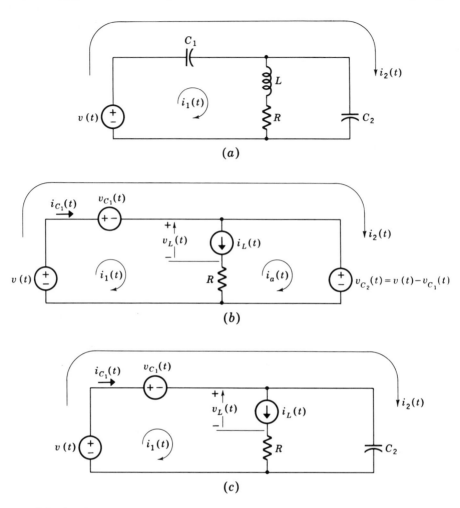

Fig. 7-7 (a) *An improper network;* (b) *an equivalent circuit which cannot be used to obtain the state variables;* (c) *an equivalent circuit which can be used to obtain the state variables.*

However, we cannot write an equation for $i_2(t)$ in Fig. 7-7b, since it does not pass through any impedance. Thus we cannot go on with the procedure. It may seem that a different choice of loop currents would rectify this problem. However, this is not the case. For instance, suppose $i_a(t)$ had been chosen instead of $i_2(t)$. Then we could write

$$i_1(t) - i_a(t) = i_L(t) \tag{7-50}$$

for the first loop. However, we cannot write an equation in terms of generators $i_1(t)$ and $i_a(t)$ for the second loop, since the voltage drop across the inductor is unknown.

To eliminate this difficulty, we replace *all but one* of the capacitors of the improper loop by generators. The voltage of this remaining capacitor voltage will *not* be a state variable. In the case of a cut set that comprises only inductors and current generators, we replace *all but one* of the inductors by a current generator in the equivalent network. The current of the remaining inductor does *not* become a state variable. This is illustrated in Fig. 7-7c for the network of Fig. 7-7a. Now we can write

$$i_1(t) = i_L(t) \tag{7-51}$$

$$v(t) = v_{C_1}(t) + \frac{1}{C_2} \int i_2(t)\, dt \tag{7-52a}$$

Solving for $i_2(t)$, we obtain

$$i_2(t) = -C_2 \frac{dv_{C_1}(t)}{dt} + C_2 \frac{dv(t)}{dt} \tag{7-52b}$$

We have expressed the loop currents in terms of the state variables and the known generators. However, derivatives are present, so that we may not be able to express the state-variable equations in the proper form (often additional manipulation allows this to be done). Let us attempt to obtain the state-variable equations. From Fig. 7-7c, the voltage across the inductor is

$$v_L(t) = -Ri_L(t) - v_{C_1}(t) + v(t) \tag{7-53}$$

Substituting Eq. (7-38), we obtain

$$\frac{di_L(t)}{dt} = -\frac{R}{L} i_L(t) - \frac{1}{L} v_{C_1}(t) + \frac{1}{L} v(t) \tag{7-54}$$

The current through C_1 is $i_{C_1} = i_1 + i_2$. Substituting Eqs. (7-51), (7-52b), and (7-35), we have

$$C_1 \frac{dv_{C_1}(t)}{dt} = i_L(t) - C_2 \frac{dv_{C_1}(t)}{dt} + C_2 \frac{dv(t)}{dt} \tag{7-55a}$$

After manipulation we have

$$\frac{dv_{C_1}(t)}{dt} = \frac{1}{C_1 + C_2} i_L(t) + \frac{C_2}{C_1 + C_2} \frac{dv(t)}{dt} \tag{7-55b}$$

Equations (7-54) and (7-55b) are in the proper form. In this case the procedure works, and the state-variable equations have been obtained. Note that the equations are not exactly in state-variable form, since a derivative of the input quantity (i.e., generator) appears in the right-hand side of the equation. However, this derivative is a known quantity. The difficulty can be resolved by mathematically considering that not only is $v(t)$ an input, but also $dv(t)/dt$ is an input quantity.

This procedure has one disadvantage. The equivalent network that we must solve (Fig. 7-7c) is no longer just a resistance-generator network. It may now contain capacitors and inductors. Then its solution is more difficult. This is especially true of nonlinear and time-varying networks.

An improper network can be converted to a proper one by the following procedure. We insert a resistor in series with *one* of the capacitors in *each* of the improper loops (for example, in Fig. 7-7a we place a resistor in series with C_2); then we place a resistor in shunt with *one* of the inductors of *each* improper cut set. There will no longer be any improper loops or cut sets, and the network becomes a proper network. We can now solve the network and let the series resistances approach zero and the shunt resistors approach infinity. This procedure will always work, but it has the disadvantage of complicating the network by adding extra elements. In addition, it complicates the calculations, since the added resistors must be written as letters and carried through the solution. These complications usually prevent the use of computer techniques.

Mutual-inductance coupling

We have neglected mutual-inductance-coupled circuits in our discussions thus far. To analyze such circuits we can replace them by the equivalent circuits of Figs. 3-20 and 3-23. It may seem that extra state variables are introduced by this process. They can be, but often they are not. For instance, the network of Fig. 3-20b is an improper one, since there are only three inductances and no other elements are connected to one node. Thus the current in M is not made a state variable. In general, after we replace the inductances by their equivalent circuits, the circuit is analyzed using the procedures discussed in this section.

7-3 State-variable equations for time-varying networks

For proper time-varying networks the procedure used to obtain the state-variable equations is no more difficult than if the elements were time invariant. In fact, the procedure follows that for the time-invariant network very closely. We replace the inductors and capacitors by current and voltage generators as before, and thus we have a resistive network to analyze. Then the loop, nodal, or cut-set analysis proceeds as it would for a time-invariant network, except that now the resistors may be functions of time. For instance, in the example of Fig. 7-6, if R_1 and R_2 varied with time, we would simply replace them by $R_1(t)$ and $R_2(t)$ whenever they occurred. Thus there would be essentially no greater difficulty in formulating the equations than in the time-invariant case. (Note that we shall use capital letters for time-varying circuit elements here.)

Now let us consider that the capacitors and inductors are time varying. This does not affect the equivalent network analysis at all, since the capacitors and inductors only enter in as voltage or current generators. Thus the general *form* of the expression for the current through the capacitors and the voltage across the inductors, given by Eqs. (7-34) and (7-37), will be unchanged by the fact that they are time varying. Note that in the equivalent network we do not actually specify the value of the state-variable generators (the solution of the equations and the actual function characterized by μ_{C_k} and μ_{L_k} will change, however). The current through a time-varying capacitor $C_k(t)$ is given by [see Eq. (1-65)]

$$i_{C_k}(t) = C_k(t) \frac{dv_{C_k}(t)}{dt} + v_{C_k}(t) \frac{dC_k(t)}{dt} \tag{7-56}$$

Substitution in Eq. (7-34) and manipulation yields

$$\frac{dv_{C_k}(t)}{dt} = \frac{\mu_{C_k}}{C_k(t)} [q_1(t), \ldots, q_n(t), y_1(t), \ldots, y_k(t), t] - \frac{v_{C_k}(t)}{C_k(t)} \frac{dC_k(t)}{dt}$$
$$\tag{7-57}$$

This is just a function of all the state variables [note that one of the $q_i(t) = v_{C_k}(t)$], the generator voltages, and time. Note that $C_k(t)$, and hence its derivative, are assumed to be known functions. The form of Eq. (7-57) is correct. Note that there are no time derivatives of the state variables on the right-hand side.

We can proceed similarly to obtain the state-variable equations for the currents through the inductors. The current through a time-varying inductor $L_k(t)$ is given by Eq. (1-105) as

$$v_{L_k}(t) = L_k(t) \frac{di_{L_k}(t)}{dt} + i_{L_k}(t) \frac{dL_k(t)}{dt} \tag{7-58}$$

Substituting into Eq. (7-37), we obtain

$$\frac{di_{L_k}(t)}{dt} = \frac{\mu_{L_k}}{L_k(t)} [q_1(t), \ldots, q_n(t), y_1(t), \ldots, y_k(t), t] - \frac{1}{L_k(t)} \frac{dL_k(t)}{dt} i_L(t)$$
$$\tag{7-59}$$

This is the correct form for a state-variable equation.

Consider Figs. 7-6 again, but now assume that L and C are time varying and that they are known functions of time. The equivalent circuit of Fig. 7-6b is still used. Thus Eqs. (7-40) to (7-42b) and Eq. (7-44) are still valid. The resistors may now be functions of time. Thus, substituting Eq. (7-58) into Eq. (7-42b), we obtain

$$L(t) \frac{di_L(t)}{dt} + i_L(t) \frac{dL(t)}{dt} = -R_1 i_L(t) - v_C(t) + v(t) \tag{7-60a}$$

and, after manipulation, we have

$$\frac{di_L(t)}{dt} = -\frac{1}{L} \left[R_1 + \frac{dL(t)}{dt} \right] i_L(t) - \frac{1}{L} v_C(t) + \frac{1}{L} v(t) \tag{7-60b}$$

Substituting Eq. (7-56) into Eq. (7-41*b*), and then substituting Eq. (7-48) and manipulating, we obtain

$$\frac{dv_C(t)}{dt} = \frac{1}{C} i_L(t) - \frac{1}{C}\left[\frac{1}{R_2} + \frac{dC(t)}{dt}\right] v_C(t) \tag{7-61}$$

Then Eqs. (7-60*b*) and (7-61) are the state-variable equations for the network.

Note that the introduction of time-varying elements hardly complicates the *formulation* of the state-variable equations at all. It may, however, complicate their solution.

If the network is improper, we can apply the procedures of the last section. Note, however, that although the concepts involved may not be more difficult, the manipulation may be far more tedious when time-varying improper networks are encountered, since we now have to work with an equivalent network containing time-varying capacitors and inductors.

7-4 State-variable equations for nonlinear networks

Let us now consider the state-variable equations for networks which have nonlinear circuit elements. We shall have to impose some restrictions on these networks, but in a great many practical cases these restrictions do not limit the applicability of the procedure. We shall discuss the restrictions as we come to them. Let us assume at the start that we are dealing with a proper network; then the state variables will be the currents through all the inductors and the voltages across all the capacitors. We form the equivalent network by replacing all the inductors by current generators and the capacitors by voltage generators, as in Sec. 7-2. Now we must solve a purely resistive network, as before. The resistors may be nonlinear, and this can complicate the procedure.

In Sec. 3-8 we defined current-controlled and voltage-controlled nonlinear resistances. If the circuit contains a voltage-controlled (or current-controlled) nonlinear resistor, we may not be able to express its voltage (or current) as a function of the current through it (or voltage across it). Many nonlinear resistors are both voltage controlled and current controlled, so that this problem does not arise. At times, however, we may not be able to perform an analysis of the nonlinear resistor circuit. In general, if all the voltage-controlled nonlinear resistors lie in the chords (of one proper tree), then the voltage across them will be expressible in terms of tree-branch voltages. Thus the current through these resistors will be defined in terms of tree-branch voltages. Similarly, if all the current-controlled nonlinear resistors lie in the tree branches, then the current through them, and thus the voltage across them, will be expressible in terms of the chord currents. If these conditions are met, the circuit can usually be solved. The discussion of Sec. 3-8 also applies to the solution of nonlinear resistor circuits. We shall assume that the networks are solvable.

Now let us consider nonlinear inductors. Here we shall restrict ourselves to inductors whose flux linkages are functions of the current through them,

$$\phi = f_L(i) \tag{7-62}$$

In general, most practical nonlinear inductors are of this type (that is, the flux linkages are functions of the current through them and not of the voltage across them). The voltage drop across the inductor is given by

$$v_L(t) = \frac{df_L(i)}{di}\bigg|_i \frac{di_L(t)}{dt} \tag{7-63}$$

[see Eq. (3-69)]. Note that the derivative of $f_L(i)$ is evaluated at the instantaneous current in the inductance. It is assumed that $f_L(i)$ is a known function. It may, however, be represented graphically. The graphical information can then either be approximated by an algebraic function or graphical techniques can be used to solve the equations. Digital-computer procedures can be used here (procedures for the solution of state-variable equations are given in Secs. 7-5 and 7-6).

Now let us obtain the state-variable equations. The solution of the equivalent network (e.g., Fig. 7-6*b*) will yield a relationship of the form of Eq. (7-37). Substituting Eq. (7-63), we obtain

$$\frac{df_{L_k}(i)}{di}\bigg|_i \frac{di_L(t)}{dt} = \mu_{L_k}[q_1(t), \ \ldots \ , q_n(t), y_1(t), \ \ldots \ , y_k(t), t] \tag{7-64}$$

Manipulating, we have

$$\frac{di_L(t)}{dt} = \frac{1}{df_{L_k}(i)/di\bigg|_i} \mu_{L_k}[q_1(t), \ \ldots \ , q_n(t), y_1(t), \ \ldots \ , y_k(t), t] \tag{7-65}$$

This is in the state-variable form. Note that $df_{L_k}(i)/di$ is a function of current but is not a time derivative. For instance, if $\phi = i^3$, then

$$\frac{df_{L_k}(i)}{di_{L_k}}\bigg|_i = 3i_{L_k}{}^2 \tag{7-66}$$

Thus this is just a (nonlinear) function of the state variable i_{L_k}.

If we have a nonlinear capacitor, then we shall restrict ourselves to those capacitors in which the charge transferred is a function of the voltage across the capacitor [see Eq. (3-72)],

$$q_c = f_c(v) \tag{7-67}$$

In general, most nonlinear capacitors are of this form. Thus [see Eq. (3-73)] the current through the capacitor will be

$$i_C(t) = \frac{df_C(v)}{dv}\bigg|_v \frac{dv(t)}{dt} \tag{7-68}$$

Substituting Eq. (7-68) into Eq. (7-34) and manipulating, we obtain

$$\frac{dv_{C_k}}{dt} = \frac{1}{df_{C_k}(v)/dv\bigg|_v} \mu_{C_k}[q_1(t), \ldots, q_n(t), y_1(t), \ldots, y_k(t), t] \tag{7-69}$$

which is the correct form for the state-variable equation.

Now let us consider an example of this procedure. We shall again use the network of Fig. 7-6a, but with the assumption that all the elements are nonlinear. The equivalent circuit is set up exactly as in Fig. 7-6b. The state variables are $i_L(t)$ and $v_C(t)$. We shall assume that R_1 is current controlled and that the voltage across it is

$$v_{R_1} = f_{R_1}(i_1) \tag{7-70}$$

We shall assume that R_2 is voltage controlled and the current through it (in a downward direction) is

$$i_{R_2} = f_{R_2}(v_C) \tag{7-71}$$

Thus we can write

$$i_1(t) = i_L(t) \tag{7-72}$$
$$i_2(t) = i_1(t) - f_{R_2}(v_C) \tag{7-73}$$

Then the voltage across the inductance is

$$v_L(t) = -f_{R_1}(i_L) - v_C(t) + v(t) \tag{7-74}$$

Substituting Eq. (7-63) and manipulating, we obtain

$$\frac{di_L(t)}{dt} = -\frac{1}{df_L(i_L)/di_L\bigg|_{i_L}} f_{R_1}(i_L) - \frac{1}{df_L(i_L)/di_L\bigg|_{i_L}} v_C(t) + \frac{1}{df_L(i_L)/di_L\bigg|_{i_L}} v(t) \tag{7-75}$$

This is the state-variable equation for $i_L(t)$. The current through the capacitor is $i_2(t)$. Then, substituting Eq. (7-68) into Eq. (7-73) and manipulating, we obtain the state-variable equation

$$\frac{dv_C(t)}{dt} = \frac{1}{df_C(v_C)/dv_C\bigg|_{v_C}} i_L(t) - \frac{1}{df_C(v_C)/dv_C\bigg|_{v_C}} f_{R_2}(v_C) \tag{7-76}$$

To clarify these equations let us consider some specific functions. For the resistors let

$$f_{R_1}(i_L) = i_L + \alpha_2 i_L{}^2 \tag{7-77a}$$
$$f_{R_2}(v_C) = v_C{}^3 \tag{7-77b}$$

and for the inductor and capacitor, respectively, let

$$\phi = i_L + \beta_3 i_L{}^3 \tag{7-77c}$$

$$q = v_C + \gamma_4 v_C{}^4 \tag{7-77d}$$

Substitution in Eqs. (7-75) and (7-76) yields

$$\frac{di_L(t)}{dt} = -\frac{i_L(t) + \alpha_2 i_L{}^2(t)}{1 + 3\beta_3 i_L{}^2(t)} - \frac{v_C(t)}{1 + 3\beta_3 i_L{}^2(t)} + \frac{v(t)}{1 + 3\beta_3 i_L{}^2(t)} \tag{7-78}$$

$$\frac{dv_C(t)}{dt} = \frac{i_L(t)}{1 + 4\gamma_4 v_C{}^3(t)} - \frac{v_C{}^3(t)}{1 + 4\gamma_4 v_C{}^3(t)} \tag{7-79}$$

These are the nonlinear relationships for the state variables.

Note that the nonlinearities of the inductance and the capacitance introduces no real difficulty in the *formulation* of the state-variable equations. The nonlinear resistors do not introduce much difficulty here either. One of the advantages of the state-variable technique is that the equations can be formulated quickly. The nonlinearities can introduce great difficulties, however, in the *solution* of these equations. A computer can be very helpful here.

If we are dealing with improper networks, then the procedures given in Sec. 7-2 for these networks can be applied. In this case a nonlinear equivalent network containing resistors, inductors, and capacitors may have to be solved, and this can complicate matters greatly.

7-5   The solution of state-variable equations for linear time-invariant networks: classical methods and Laplace transform techniques

So far we have considered procedures only for the formulation of state-variable equations. In this section we shall discuss the solution of the state-variable equations of linear networks. A procedure for nonlinear or time-varying networks will be presented in the next section. Here we shall consider linear networks whose state-variable equations are given by Eqs. (7-24) or whose matrix form is given by Eq. (7-27) as

$$\frac{d\hat{q}(t)}{dt} = \hat{a}\hat{q}(t) + \hat{b}\hat{y}(t) \tag{7-80}$$

Let us consider the solution of some simplified forms of this equation before we study the general solution.

Suppose there is only one state variable. Then the matrices of Eq. (7-80) just become scalar quantities (i. e., single terms). For instance,

$$\frac{dq_1(t)}{dt} = a_{11}q_1(t) + b_{11}y_1(t) \tag{7-81}$$

For our initial study let us assume that $y_1(t) = 0$.   Then we are working with the homogeneous equation

$$\frac{dq_1(t)}{dt} = a_{11}q(t) \tag{7-82}$$

We can solve this by the procedures of Chap. 4.   However, let us obtain a more general procedure for its solution so that we can apply it to the solution of the nonhomogeneous matrix equation.

We multiply both sides of Eq. (7-82) by $e^{-ta_{11}}$ and rearrange.   This yields

$$e^{-ta_{11}} \frac{dq_1(t)}{dt} - a_{11}q(t)e^{-ta_{11}} = 0 \tag{7-83}$$

Consider the left-hand side of this equation.   It can be written as

$$\frac{d[e^{-ta_{11}}q_1(t)]}{dt}$$

Thus

$$\frac{d[e^{-ta_{11}}q_1(t)]}{dt} = 0 \tag{7-84}$$

[note that in applying the rule for carrying out the derivative of a product to Eq. (7-84), we obtain Eq. (7-83)].   We multiply through by dt and integrate. This yields

$$\int d[e^{-ta_{11}}q_1(t)] = 0 \tag{7-85}$$

and, carrying out the integration, we obtain

$$e^{-ta_{11}}q_1(t) = K \tag{7-86}$$

where K is a constant of integration.   Then, rearranging Eq. (7-86), we have

$$q_1(t) = Ke^{ta_{11}} \tag{7-87}$$

At $t = 0-$, $q_1(t) = q_1(0-)$, the initial state.   Thus $K = q_1(0-)$, or

$$q_1(t) = q_1(0-)e^{ta_{11}} \tag{7-88}$$

Note that the initial condition is easily introduced.

Now let us consider the homogeneous matrix equation of Eq. (7-80), with $\hat{y}(t) = 0$.   That is, let us solve

$$\frac{d\hat{q}(t)}{dt} = \hat{a}\hat{q}(t) \tag{7-89}$$

Remember that we are solving equations of the form of Eqs. (7-24) here, with all $b = 0$.   Equations (7-82) and (7-89) seem to be similar, except that one is a matrix equation.   Since Eq. (7-88) is the solution to Eq. (7-82), we could guess that the solution to Eq. (7-89) is

$$\hat{q}(t) = e^{t\hat{a}}\hat{q}(0-) \tag{7-90}$$

where the matrices are defined in Eqs. (7-16) and (7-25). Note that the right-hand side of Eq. (7-90) must be written in this order to make the matrix multiplications conformable (see Sec. 3-10). Equation (7-90) is just a guess, so we must verify it. In addition, we must define what is meant by $e^{t\hat{a}}$ (note that $\hat{a}$ is a matrix). We shall define this by analogy with scalar quantities. The power series for an exponential is

$$e^{ta} = 1 + ta + \frac{(ta)^2}{2!} + \frac{(ta)^3}{3!} + \frac{(ta)^4}{4!} + \cdots$$

Then for a square matrix $\hat{a}$ we define

$$e^{t\hat{a}} = u + t\hat{a} + \frac{t^2}{2!}\hat{a}^2 + \frac{t^3}{3!}\hat{a}^3 + \frac{t^4}{4!}\hat{a}^4 + \cdots \tag{7-91}$$

where u is the unit matrix of the same order as $\hat{a}$. The quantities t, $t^2/2!$, $t^3/3!$, . . . are scalars, so they just multiply each element of the appropriate matrix. The matrix $\hat{a}^k$ is merely $\hat{a}$ multiplied by itself k times. Note that each matrix is square.

Now we are in a position to verify Eq. (7-89). We substitute Eqs. (7-90) and (7-91) into the left-hand side of Eq. (7-89). This yields

$$\frac{d\hat{q}(t)}{dt} = \frac{d}{dt}\left(u + t\hat{a} + \frac{t^2}{2!}\hat{a}^2 + \frac{t^3}{3!}\hat{a}^3 + \cdots\right)q(0-) \tag{7-92a}$$

Differentiating, we obtain

$$\frac{d\hat{q}(t)}{dt} = \left(\hat{a} + t\hat{a}^2 + \frac{t^2}{2!}\hat{a}^3 + \frac{t^3}{3!}\hat{a}^4 + \cdots\right)\hat{q}(0-)$$

$$= \hat{a}\left(u + t\hat{a} + \frac{t^2\hat{a}^2}{2!}\right)\hat{q}(0-) \tag{7-92b}$$

(note that $\hat{a}$ is a matrix of constant terms). Comparing this with Eq. (7-91), we have

$$\frac{d\hat{q}(t)}{dt} = \hat{a}e^{t\hat{a}}q(0-) \tag{7-92c}$$

and if we substitute Eq. (7-90), we obtain

$$\frac{d\hat{q}(t)}{dt} = \hat{a}\hat{q}(t)$$

Thus we have obtained Eq. (7-89) and have verified that Eq. (7-90) is a solution of Eq. (7-89). The matrix $e^{t\hat{a}}$ is called the *transition matrix* and is often written as

$$\hat{\phi}(t) = e^{t\hat{a}} \tag{7-93}$$

Note that [see Eq. (7-91)]

$$\hat{\phi}(0) = \mathsf{u} \tag{7-94}$$

Now let us consider the solution of the nonhomogeneous equation

$$\frac{d\hat{q}(t)}{dt} = \hat{a}\hat{q}(t) + \hat{b}\hat{y}(t) \tag{7-95}$$

We shall use a procedure analogous to that for solving Eq. (7-82). We multiply both sides of Eq. (7-95) by $e^{-t\hat{a}}$. Then, after rearranging, we have

$$e^{-t\hat{a}}\frac{d\hat{q}(t)}{dt} - e^{-t\hat{a}}\hat{a}\hat{q}(t) = e^{-t\hat{a}}\hat{b}\hat{y}(t) \tag{7-96}$$

By analogy with Eqs. (7-83) and (7-84), we would guess that

$$\frac{d[e^{-t\hat{a}}\hat{q}(t)]}{dt} = e^{-t\hat{a}}\frac{d\hat{q}(t)}{dt} - e^{-t\hat{a}}\hat{a}\hat{q}(t) \tag{7-97}$$

Let us now verify that this is true. Substituting Eq. (7-91) into the left-hand side of Eq. (7-97), we obtain

$$\frac{d[e^{-t\hat{a}}\hat{q}(t)]}{dt} = \frac{d}{dt}\left[\left(\mathsf{u} - t\hat{a} + \frac{t^2\hat{a}^2}{2!} - \frac{t^3\hat{a}^3}{3!} + \cdots\right)\hat{q}(t)\right] \tag{7-98a}$$

Noting that the derivative of a matrix is the derivative of each term of the matrix and substituting Eq. (7-91), we obtain

$$\frac{d[e^{-t\hat{a}}\hat{q}(t)]}{dt} = e^{-t\hat{a}}\frac{d\hat{q}(t)}{dt} + \left(-\hat{a} + t\hat{a}^2 - \frac{t^2\hat{a}^3}{2!} + \cdots\right)\hat{q}(t) \tag{7-98b}$$

$$\frac{d[e^{-t\hat{a}}\hat{q}(t)]}{dt} = e^{-t\hat{a}}\frac{d\hat{q}(t)}{dt} - \left(\mathsf{u} - t\hat{a} + \frac{t^2}{2!}\hat{a}^2 - \cdots\right)\hat{a}\hat{q}(t) \tag{7-98c}$$

Then, substituting Eq. (7-91) into Eq. (7-98c), we obtain Eq. (7-97). Thus Eq. (7-97) it is verified. Now we can substitute Eq. (7-97) into Eq. (7-96). This yields

$$\frac{d[e^{-t\hat{a}}\hat{q}(t)]}{dt} = e^{-t\hat{a}}\hat{b}\hat{y}(t) \tag{7-99}$$

Since the derivative of a matrix is just the derivative of each term, we can "multiply through" by dt and integrate both sides of the equation from $-\infty$ to t (note that we have modified the previous procedure slightly). This yields

$$e^{-t\hat{a}}\hat{q}(t) = \int_{-\infty}^{t} e^{-\tau\hat{a}}\hat{b}\hat{y}(\tau)\, d\tau \tag{7-100a}$$

where τ is used as the variable of integration. To take the integral of a matrix means integrating each term in the matrix.

We have assumed in the integration that $e^{-t\hat{a}}\hat{q}(t) = 0$ at $t = -\infty$. In general, the integral $\int_{-\infty}^{0-} e^{-t\hat{a}}\hat{b}\hat{y}(t)\, dt$ is just a constant matrix, which we shall designate as $\hat{K}$. Thus we can write

$$e^{-t\hat{a}}\hat{q}(t) = \int_{0-}^{t} e^{-\tau\hat{a}}\hat{b}\hat{y}(\tau)\,d\tau + \hat{K} \tag{7-100b}$$

To obtain the $\hat{q}(t)$ we must have the inverse of $e^{-t\hat{a}}$. This is given by

$$[e^{-t\hat{a}}]^{-1} = [e^{t\hat{a}}] \tag{7-101}$$

This is not as obvious as it looks, since these are matrices. Equation (7-101) can be verified by demonstrating that $e^{-t\hat{a}}e^{t\hat{a}} = \mathsf{u}$. This can be done by substituting Eq. (7-91) into the relation $e^{-t\hat{a}}e^{t\hat{a}}$. This yields

$$\left(\mathsf{u} + t\hat{a} + \frac{t^2\hat{a}^2}{2!} + \cdots\right)\left(\mathsf{u} - t\hat{a} + \frac{t^2\hat{a}^2}{2!} - \cdots\right)$$
$$= \mathsf{u} + t\hat{a} - t\hat{a} + t^2\hat{a}^2 - t^2\hat{a}^2 + \cdots = \mathsf{u} \tag{7-102}$$

Then, premultiplying both sides of Eq. (7-100) by $e^{t\hat{a}}$, we obtain

$$\hat{q}(t) = e^{t\hat{a}}\hat{K} + e^{t\hat{a}}\int_{0-}^{t} e^{-\tau\hat{a}}\hat{b}\hat{y}(\tau)\,d\tau \tag{7-103}$$

Now we let $t = 0-$ and assume that all generators are zero at $t = 0-$ [they are all multiplied by $u(t)$]. Hence

$$\hat{q}(0-) = \mathsf{u}\hat{K} = \hat{K} \tag{7-104}$$

Note that $e^{t\hat{a}} = \mathsf{u}$ when $t = 0$ [see Eq. (7-91)]. Substituting Eq. (7-104) into Eq. (7-103), we obtain

$$\hat{q}(t) = e^{t\hat{a}}\hat{q}(0-) + e^{t\hat{a}}\int_{0}^{t} e^{-\tau\hat{a}}\hat{b}\hat{y}(\tau)\,d\tau \tag{7-105}$$

Thus we have obtained the solution of the state-variable equations.

Let us illustrate this with an example. For the network of Fig. 7-1, whose state variables are given in Eq. (7-7), we shall consider the case $R = 0$ [we can then compare the solution with Eqs. (7-12)]. Equation (7-7) becomes

$$\frac{di_L}{dt} = -\frac{1}{L}v_C(t) + \frac{V}{L} \tag{7-106a}$$

$$\frac{dv_C}{dt} = \frac{1}{C}i_L(t)\,dt \tag{7-106b}$$

Thus the various matrices are

$$\hat{q}(t) = \begin{bmatrix} i_L(t) \\ v_C(t) \end{bmatrix} \tag{7-107a}$$

$$\hat{a} = \begin{bmatrix} 0 & -1/L \\ 1/C & 0 \end{bmatrix} \tag{7-107b}$$

$$\hat{b} = \begin{bmatrix} 1/L \\ 0 \end{bmatrix} \tag{7-107c}$$

$$\hat{y}(t) = [V] \tag{7-107d}$$

Then, substituting in Eq. (7-105), we have

$$\hat{q}(t) = \left\{ \exp\left(-t \begin{bmatrix} 0 & -1/L \\ 1/C & 0 \end{bmatrix} \right) \right\} \hat{q}(0-) + \left\{ \exp\left(t \begin{bmatrix} 0 & -1/L \\ 1/C & 0 \end{bmatrix} \right) \right\}$$

$$\times \int_0^t \left\{ \exp\left(-\tau \begin{bmatrix} 0 & -1/L \\ 1/C & 0 \end{bmatrix} \right) \right\} \begin{bmatrix} 1/L \\ 0 \end{bmatrix} [V] \, d\tau \quad (7\text{-}108)$$

To simplify the manipulations we shall assume that $q(0-) = 0$. This yields

$$\hat{q}(t) = \left\{ \exp\left(t \begin{bmatrix} 0 & -1/L \\ 1/C & 0 \end{bmatrix} \right) \right\} \int_0^t \left(\mathsf{u} - \tau \begin{bmatrix} 0 & -1/L \\ 1/C & 0 \end{bmatrix} \right.$$

$$\left. + \frac{\tau^2}{2!} \begin{bmatrix} 0 & -1/L \\ 1/C & 0 \end{bmatrix} \begin{bmatrix} 0 & -1/L \\ 1/C & 0 \end{bmatrix} + \cdots \right) \begin{bmatrix} V/L \\ 0 \end{bmatrix} dt$$

Manipulation yields

$$\hat{q}(t) = \left\{ \exp\left(t \begin{bmatrix} 0 & -1/L \\ 1/C & 0 \end{bmatrix} \right) \right\} \int_0^t \left\{ \begin{bmatrix} 1 & 0 \\ 0 & 1 \end{bmatrix} - \tau \begin{bmatrix} 0 & -1/L \\ 1/C & 0 \end{bmatrix} \right.$$

$$\left. - \frac{\tau^2}{2!} \begin{bmatrix} 1/LC & 0 \\ 0 & 1/LC \end{bmatrix} + \cdots \right\} \begin{bmatrix} V/L \\ 0 \end{bmatrix} dt$$

$$= \left\{ \exp\left(t \begin{bmatrix} 0 & -1/L \\ 1/C & 0 \end{bmatrix} \right) \right\} \left\{ t \begin{bmatrix} 1 & 0 \\ 0 & 1 \end{bmatrix} - \frac{t^2}{2!} \begin{bmatrix} 0 & -1/L \\ 1/C & 0 \end{bmatrix} \right.$$

$$\left. - \frac{t^3}{3!} \begin{bmatrix} 1/LC & 0 \\ 0 & 1/LC \end{bmatrix} + \cdots \right\} \begin{bmatrix} V/L \\ 0 \end{bmatrix}$$

$$= \left\{ \exp\left(t \begin{bmatrix} 0 & -1/L \\ 1/C & 0 \end{bmatrix} \right) \right\} \left\{ t \begin{bmatrix} V/L \\ 0 \end{bmatrix} - \frac{t^2}{2!} \begin{bmatrix} 0 \\ V/LC \end{bmatrix} \right.$$

$$\left. - \frac{t^3}{3!} \begin{bmatrix} V/L^2C \\ 0 \end{bmatrix} + \cdots \right\}$$

Substituting Eq. (7-91), we have

$$\hat{q}(t) = \left\{ \begin{bmatrix} 1 & 0 \\ 0 & 1 \end{bmatrix} + t \begin{bmatrix} 0 & -1/L \\ 1/C & 0 \end{bmatrix} - \frac{t^2}{2!} \begin{bmatrix} 1/LC & 0 \\ 0 & 1/LC \end{bmatrix} + \cdots \right\}$$

$$\left\{ t \begin{bmatrix} V/L \\ 0 \end{bmatrix} - \frac{t^2}{2!} \begin{bmatrix} 0 \\ V/CL \end{bmatrix} - \frac{t^3}{3!} \begin{bmatrix} V/L^2C \\ 0 \end{bmatrix} - \cdots \right\}$$

$$= t \begin{bmatrix} V/L \\ 0 \end{bmatrix} + t^2 \begin{bmatrix} 0 \\ V/2LC \end{bmatrix} - \frac{t^3}{3!} \begin{bmatrix} V/L^2C \\ 0 \end{bmatrix} + \cdots$$

$$= \begin{bmatrix} Vt/L + 0 - Vt^3/3!CL^2 + \cdots \\ 0 + Vt^2/2LC + 0 + \cdots \end{bmatrix} \quad (7\text{-}109)$$

Then, substituting Eq. (7-107a), we obtain

$$i_L(t) = V\left(\frac{1}{L} t - \frac{t^3}{3!L^2C} + \cdots \right)$$

$$v_C(t) = V\left(0 + \frac{t^2}{2!LC} + \cdots \right)$$

Substitution of $\omega_0 = 1/LC$ yields

$$i_L(t) = \frac{V}{\omega_0 L}\left(\omega_0 t - \frac{\omega_0{}^3 t^3}{3!} + \cdots\right)$$

$$v_C(t) = V\left(\frac{\omega_0{}^2 t^2}{2!} - \cdots\right)$$

If we had evaluated more terms in these series, we would have seen that they can be obtained in closed form as Eqs. (7-12a) and (7-12b). Thus we have verified the results of this analysis. The state-variable solution seems to be far more tedious than the classical or Laplace transform procedures. In this example it is. However, state variables are often applied to systems whose solutions must be expressed in series terms, and in such cases there are no less tedious forms. The state-variable technique would usually be applied if computer procedures were to be used, or for time-varying or nonlinear networks, and here the technique has distinct advantages. For linear systems application of the Laplace transform to the solution of the state-variable equations often greatly reduces the work.

Use of the Laplace transform

The matrix equations of Eqs. (7-80) represent a set of linear differential equations with constant coefficients [see Eqs. (7-24)]. Thus we can use the Laplace transform to solve them. In analyzing linear systems this often permits a great saving in work (unless digital computers are used to solve the equations). As an example let us define the Laplace transform

$$\mathcal{L}\hat{q}(t) = \mathcal{L}\begin{bmatrix} q_1(t) \\ \cdot \\ \cdot \\ \cdot \\ q_n(t) \end{bmatrix} = \hat{\mathbf{Q}}(s) = \begin{bmatrix} \mathbf{Q}_1(s) \\ \cdot \\ \cdot \\ \cdot \\ \mathbf{Q}_n(s) \end{bmatrix} \tag{7-110}$$

We take the Laplace transform of both sides of Eq. (7-80). This yields

$$s\hat{\mathbf{Q}}(s) - \hat{q}(0-) = \hat{a}\hat{\mathbf{Q}}(s) + \hat{b}\hat{\mathbf{Y}}(s) \tag{7-111a}$$

where $\hat{\mathbf{Y}}(s)$ is the Laplace transform matrix of $\hat{y}(t)$. Manipulating Eq. (7-111a), we obtain

$$(s\mathsf{u} - \hat{a})\hat{\mathbf{Q}}(s) = \hat{b}\hat{\mathbf{Y}}(s) + \hat{q}(0-) \tag{7-111b}$$

[note that $s\mathsf{u}\hat{\mathbf{Q}}(s) = s\hat{\mathbf{Q}}(s)$]. Assuming that $(s\mathsf{u} - \hat{a})^{-1}$ exists, we premultiply by it; this yields

$$\hat{\mathbf{Q}}(s) = (s\mathsf{u} - \hat{a})^{-1}[\hat{b}\hat{\mathbf{Y}}(s) + \hat{q}(0-)] \tag{7-112}$$

Thus we need only take the inverse Laplace transform to obtain the solution.

Consider the previous example, where the $\hat{a}$ and $\hat{b}$ matrices are given by Eqs. (7-107b) and (7-107c). We have assumed that $\hat{q}(0-) = 0$. The voltage generator is a unit step times V. Hence [see Eq. (7-107d)]

$$\hat{\mathbf{Y}}(s) = \left[\frac{V}{s} \right] \tag{7-113}$$

Substituting into Eq. (7-112), we obtain

$$\hat{\mathbf{Q}}(s) = \left(s \begin{bmatrix} 1 & 0 \\ 0 & 1 \end{bmatrix} - \begin{bmatrix} 0 & -\dfrac{1}{L} \\ \dfrac{1}{C} & 0 \end{bmatrix} \right)^{-1} \begin{bmatrix} \dfrac{V}{Ls} \\ 0 \end{bmatrix} \tag{7-114a}$$

and after manipulation we have

$$\hat{\mathbf{Q}}(s) = \begin{bmatrix} s & \dfrac{1}{L} \\ -\dfrac{1}{C} & s \end{bmatrix}^{-1} \begin{bmatrix} \dfrac{V}{Ls} \\ 0 \end{bmatrix} = \begin{bmatrix} \dfrac{s}{s^2 + 1/LC} & \dfrac{-1/L}{s^2 + 1/LC} \\ \dfrac{1/C}{s^2 + 1/LC} & \dfrac{s}{s^2 + 1/LC} \end{bmatrix} \begin{bmatrix} \dfrac{V}{Ls} \\ 0 \end{bmatrix} \tag{7-114b}$$

and

$$\hat{\mathbf{Q}}(s) = \begin{bmatrix} \dfrac{V/L}{s^2 + 1/LC} \\ \dfrac{V}{CLs(s^2 + 1/LC)} \end{bmatrix} = \begin{bmatrix} \dfrac{V/L}{s^2 + 1/LC} \\ V\left(\dfrac{1}{s} - \dfrac{s}{s^2 + 1/LC} \right) \end{bmatrix} \tag{7-114c}$$

where we have used a partial-fraction expansion. Taking the inverse Laplace transform of each element of the matrix, we obtain

$$\hat{q}(t) = \begin{bmatrix} \dfrac{V}{\omega_0 L} \sin \omega_0 t \\ V(1 - \cos \omega_0 t) \end{bmatrix} \tag{7-115}$$

where $\omega_0 = 1/\sqrt{LC}$. These results check with the previous ones.

Although the Laplace transform procedure is often considerably less tedious than the classical one, computer techniques are often more suited to modifications of classical procedures.

7-6 An approximate procedure for the solution of state-variable equations: time-varying networks and nonlinear networks

In this section we shall discuss an approximation technique that can be used to solve state-variable equations. Approximation techniques are usually more tedious than others, but they are often the only ones that can be used with nonlinear or time-varying networks. Moreover, digital computers work

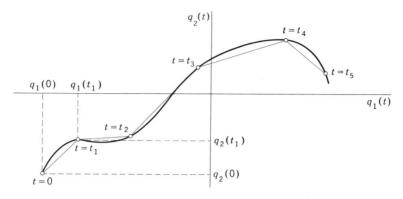

Fig. 7-8   The approximation of a trajectory by straight-line segments.

on the basis of approximation procedures. Thus a knowledge of these pro-cedures is necessary if digital computers are to be used to solve the equations.

The procedure we shall use is based on the approximation of the trajectory by straight-line segments. For instance, consider the (two-dimensional) trajectory of Fig. 7-8, approximated by straight-line segments as shown. For convenience we shall choose

$$t_1 - 0 = t_2 - t_1 = t_3 - t_2 = \cdots = \Delta t \tag{7-116}$$

(note that the spacing on the diagram need not be uniform). On any straight-line segment of the approximate trajectory we assume that dq_j/dt is constant, that is, that Δt is small enough that the derivatives can be considered constant over each interval. Note that if the derivatives are constant, then the trajectory will be a straight line. Thus

$$\frac{dq_1(t)}{dt} = K_1$$

$$\frac{dq_2(t)}{dt} = K_2 \tag{7-117}$$

$$\cdots \cdots \cdots$$

$$\frac{dq_n(t)}{dt} = K_n$$

where $K_1, K_2, \ldots, K_n$ are constants; that is, all the derivatives are constants. In matrix form Eq. (7-117) can be written as

$$\frac{d\hat{q}(t)}{dt} = \hat{K} \tag{7-118}$$

As Δt approaches zero, the approximate trajectory approaches the actual trajectory.

Now let us consider the actual procedure.   We shall assume that the state-variable equation [see Eqs. (7-15) and (7-20)]

$$\frac{d\hat{q}(t)}{dt} = \hat{f}[\hat{q}(t),\hat{y}(t),t] \tag{7-119}$$

and the initial state $\hat{q}(0-)$ are known.   Then, at $t = 0-$ we know all the state variables.   The $\hat{y}(t)$ represent known generators.   Thus we can substitute in Eq. (7-119) and obtain all the derivatives evaluated at $t = 0-$:

$$\frac{d\hat{q}(t)}{dt}\bigg|_{t=0-} = \hat{f}[\hat{q}(0-),\hat{y}(0-),0-] \tag{7-120}$$

This substitution is not difficult, even in the case of nonlinear or time-varying networks.   For instance, consider Eqs. (7-78) and (7-79).   The initial values of the state variables can be obtained by simple substitution of the known values $i_L(0-)$, $v_C(0-)$, and $v(0-)$.   We assume that $d_q(t)/dt$ is constant in the range $0 \le t \le t_1$.   Then for $0 \le t \le t_1$ on the straight-line segment we have

$$\hat{q}(t) = t\frac{d\hat{q}(0-)}{dt} + \hat{q}(0-) \tag{7-121}$$

where we have used the somewhat improper notation

$$\frac{d\hat{q}(t)}{dt}\bigg|_{t=t_0} = \frac{d\hat{q}(t_0)}{dt} \tag{7-122}$$

Note that Eq. (7-121) actually represents, for $0 \le t \le t_1$,

$$q_1(t) = t\frac{dq_1(0-)}{dt} + q_1(0-)$$

$$q_2(t) = t\frac{dq_2(0-)}{dt} + q_2(0-) \tag{7-123}$$

. . . .

$$q_n(t) = t\frac{dq_n(0-)}{dt} + q_n(0-)$$

Then at $t = t_1$ we can write

$$\hat{q}(t_1) = t_1\frac{d\hat{q}(0-)}{dt} + \hat{q}(0-) \tag{7-124}$$

Substituting these values in the state-variable equation of Eq. (7-119), we find

$$\frac{d\hat{q}(t_1)}{dt} = \hat{f}[\hat{q}(t_1),\hat{y}(t_1),t_1] \tag{7-125}$$

Thus $d\hat{q}(t_1)/dt$ has been obtained by simple substitution.   Note that $\hat{q}(t_1)$ has been obtained in Eq. (7-124).   Thus we know all the derivatives at $t = t_1$, and for $t_1 \leq t \leq t_2$ we can write

$$\hat{q}(t) = (t - t_1) \frac{d\hat{q}(t_1)}{dt} + \hat{q}(t_1) \tag{7-126}$$

Then we can use this equation to calculate $\hat{q}(t_2)$. Substituting $\hat{q}(t_2)$ and $\hat{y}(t_2)$ in Eq. (7-119) yields $d\hat{q}(t_2)/dt$, and for $t_2 \leq t \leq t_3$ we have

$$\hat{q}(t) = (t - t_2) \frac{d\hat{q}(t_2)}{dt} - \hat{q}(t_2) \tag{7-127}$$

Proceeding in this manner, for $t_k \leq t \leq t_{k+1}$ we obtain

$$\hat{q}(t) = (t - t_k) \frac{d\hat{q}(t_k)}{dt} + \hat{q}(t_k) \qquad k = 0, 1, 2, \ldots \tag{7-128}$$

where $t_0 = 0-$. Since we know that the trajectory consists of a series of straight-line segments, we need only calculate $\hat{q}(0-)$, $\hat{q}(t_1)$, $\hat{q}(t_2)$, $\ldots$ and connect these points by straight lines to obtain the trajectory.

As an example of this procedure let us solve the nonlinear state-variable equation given by Eqs. (7-78) and (7-79), where we shall assume that

$$\alpha = 0 \tag{7-129a}$$

$$\beta = \tfrac{1}{3} \tag{7-129b}$$

$$\gamma = 0 \tag{7-129c}$$

and

$$v(t) = 1 \text{ volt}$$

[for simplicity and accuracy we shall also assume that $v(0-) = 1$ since 1 is its value for "most" of the first interval]. Equations (7-78) and (7-79), the state-variable equations, become

$$\frac{di_L(t)}{dt} = -\frac{i_L(t)}{1 + i_L{}^2(t)} - \frac{v_C(t)}{1 + i_L{}^2(t)} + \frac{1}{1 + i_L{}^2(t)} \tag{7-130a}$$

$$\frac{dv_C(t)}{dt} = i_L(t) - v_C{}^3(t) \tag{7-130b}$$

We shall assume that the initial state is

$$i_L(0-) = 0 \tag{7-131a}$$

$$v_C(0-) = 0 \tag{7-131b}$$

Substitution in Eqs. (7-130) then yields

$$\frac{di_L(0-)}{dt} = 1 \tag{7-132a}$$

$$\frac{dv_C(0-)}{dt} = 0 \tag{7-132b}$$

Let us choose $\Delta t = 0.1$. Actually, the accuracy depends upon the choice of Δt. The smaller its value, the greater the accuracy. When the solution is obtained, its accuracy should be checked by repeating the calculations with a smaller Δt. If this gives substantially different values, then the calculation should be repeated with the smaller value of Δt. The accuracy of this calculation should also be checked.

Proceeding with the example, we have

$$i_L(0.1) = 0.1 \frac{di_L(0-)}{dt} + i_L(0-) = 0.1 \qquad (7\text{-}133a)$$

$$v_C(0.1) = 0 \qquad (7\text{-}133b)$$

Substituting Eqs. (7-133) into Eqs. (7-130) and evaluating at $t = 0.1$, we obtain

$$\frac{di_L(0.1)}{dt} = 0.891 \qquad (7\text{-}134a)$$

$$\frac{dv_C(0.1)}{dt} = 0.1 \qquad (7\text{-}134b)$$

Now we use these derivatives to calculate the state variables at $t = 0.2$. Thus

$$i_L(0.2) = 0.1(0.891) + 0.1 = 0.1891 \qquad (7\text{-}135a)$$
$$v_C(0.2) = 0.1(0.1) + 0.0 = 0.01 \qquad (7\text{-}135b)$$

Then substitution in Eqs. (7-130) gives us

$$\frac{di_L(0.2)}{dt} = 0.773 \qquad (7\text{-}136a)$$

$$\frac{dv_C(0.2)}{dt} = 0.1891 \qquad (7\text{-}136b)$$

Then

$$i_L(0.3) = 0.1(0.773) + 0.1891 = 0.2664 \qquad (7\text{-}137a)$$

$$v_C(0.3) = 0.1(0.1891) + 0.01 = 0.02891 \qquad (7\text{-}137b)$$

This process can be continued for as long as desired. In most networks a final equilibrium state is obtained. That is, the calculation should continue until the state variables approach a constant value. Of course, there are trajectories, such as that of Fig. 7-4, where this will not occur. In general, however, even in nonlinear networks, these trajectories will usually approach a repeating path, and the calculations can stop once the trajectory begins to trace such a repeating path. There are times when the trajectory will be an increasing spiral or some other curve that increases without limit. In such cases the trajectory should be calculated for as long a time as practical or desired.

In this example, to reduce the work involved, we have not carried out the trajectory to its final value.   The accuracy should also be checked.

The procedures of this section can be easily programmed for digital computers.   Graphical information, as well as specific nonlinear functions, can be used to characterize the nonlinear elements.

7-7   Stability and oscillation

In Sec. 5-13 we discussed the fact that certain circuits were unstable and that in linear circuits the outputs contain components which build up indefinitely with time.   Usually terms of the form $e^{at} \sin (bt + \phi)$ are obtained.   In actual oscillatory circuits the voltages and currents cannot build up indefinitely. Such large voltages either will destroy the circuit elements or circuit nonlinearities will limit the size of the oscillations.   At sufficiently large signal levels all electronic devices (such as transistors) become nonlinear.   Thus a study of oscillating circuits should be made on a nonlinear as well as on a linear basis.   In this section we shall consider stability and oscillation in terms of state variables.

Linear circuits

Let us discuss linear circuits first.   This will provide us with a fundamental understanding which we can apply to the nonlinear circuits.   As a specific example consider the circuit of Fig. 7-1.   Its state-variable equations are given in Eqs. (7-7).   A trajectory for this circuit when the operation is stable is shown in Fig. 7-3.   The response consists of constants plus exponentially damped terms.   The trajectory thus approaches the finite point in the state space,

$$i_L(\infty) = 0 \tag{7-138a}$$

$$v_C(\infty) = V \tag{7-138b}$$

Now let us study the case $R = 0$.   This is borderline instability.   The poles of the voltage and the current lie on the $j\omega$ axis.   In this case the state variables are given by the sinusoidal terms of Eq. (7-12), and the trajectory is the ellipse of Fig. 7-4.   The trajectory continuously retraces itself; the response never reaches a final value.   This elliptical trajectory (in two dimensions) characterized sinusoids.   The period of the sinusoid is the time required for the trajectory to complete one ellipse.

Now let us consider the same circuit, but with the assumption that R is negative.   The state-variable equations are given by Eqs. (7-7) as before, but R is replaced by $-R$.   If we solve for the state variables, we find that they consist of sinusoidal terms multiplied by an increasing exponential.   The trajectory will have the general form shown in Fig. 7-9a, a spiral that increases

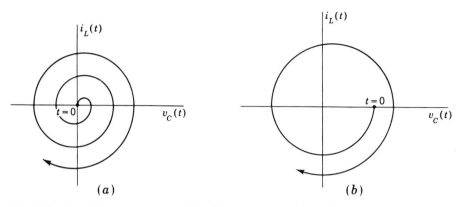

Fig. 7-9   The trajectory of an unstable linear network: (a) with zero initial state; (b) with nonzero initial state.

without limit.   The curve of Fig. 7-9a is drawn for zero initial conditions. In this case the voltage V of Fig. 7-1 cannot be zero, since something is needed to initiate the signal (i.e., the transform of the output of the network is the transform of the voltage V times the transfer function).   In actual circuits there is always some signal.   For instance, the "noise" caused by stray pickup or the random motion of electrons in the resistances of the circuit is usually a sufficient signal to start the oscillation.   In Fig. 7-9b we have assumed that $v_C(0-) \neq 0$.   In this case we have an "initial-condition voltage generator"; then the actual voltage V can be zero, and oscillations will still build up.

These ideas can be carried over to general networks.   We find that if the trajectory approaches a finite point in the state space as t approaches infinity, then the network is stable.   If the trajectory approaches infinite values as t approaches infinity, usually in a spiraling fashion, then the network is unstable. If the trajectory does not approach a finite value, but continuously retraces itself, then for a *linear* network the network is on the borderline of oscillation.

Nonlinear circuits

Most nonlinear circuits act as linear ones when the signal levels are very small. Thus, if they are unstable, the currents and voltages will initially build up as though the circuit were linear.   When the signals become larger, then the nonlinearities usually limit the amplitude of the oscillation.

As an illustration let us again study the circuit of Fig. 7-1, but now we shall assume that the resistor is nonlinear and its resistance is given by

$$R = i^2 - 1 \tag{7-139}$$

A sketch of this resistance is given in Fig. 7-10.   Note that it is negative for

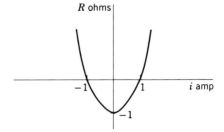

Fig. 7-10 *The resistance of the resistor given in Eq. (7-139).*

small current levels but becomes positive when $|i| > 1$. Note also that R increases without limit as $|i|$ increases. Actual resistances usually do not do this. However, this circuit will not operate far into the region where R is positive; hence Eq. (7-139) approximates a practical resistance over its range of operation. The voltage across the resistor is given by iR. Thus

$$v_R(t) = i^3(t) - i(t) \tag{7-140}$$

The state-variable equations for this network are

$$\frac{di_L(t)}{dt} = -\frac{1}{L}[i_L{}^3(t) - i_L(t)] - \frac{1}{L}v_C(t) + \frac{1}{L}V \tag{7-141a}$$

$$\frac{dv_C(t)}{dt} = \frac{1}{C}i_L(t) \tag{7-141b}$$

These equations can be solved by the procedures of Sec. 7-6. A typical trajectory is shown in Fig. 7-11. The trajectory approaches a final curve, which it repeats over and over again. This final curve is called a *limit cycle*.

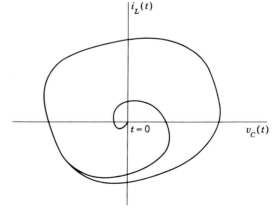

Fig. 7-11 *A trajectory for the nonlinear oscillator whose state-variable equations are given by Eqs. (7-141).*

In general, most nonlinear oscillators will have the same limit cycle, independently of the initial conditions. The trajectory taken from the initial-state point to the limit cycle does depend upon the initial conditions. The time required for the trajectory to trace out one limit cycle is the period of the oscillation. In nonlinear devices the limit cycle will not be elliptical (in two dimensions). This shows that the periodic function produced by the oscillator is not a sinusoid (the sinusoid is distorted by the nonlinearities in the circuit).

In general, we can state that *if a nonlinear circuit builds up to a limit cycle, then the circuit is unstable.* This means that at very low levels the circuit acts linearly and the currents and voltages start to build up exponentially. The nonlinearities limit this buildup, and the final response is the continuous tracing of the limit cycle.

7-8   Another set of state-variable equations

In Secs. 7-2, 7-3, and 7-4 we wrote the state-variable equations of networks with the currents through the inductors and the voltages across the capacitors as the state variables. However, this is *not* the only set of state variables that can be used. In fact, there are a great many other sets, and at times one set may be more convenient to use than another. In this section we shall consider another procedure for writing the state-variable equations.

At first we shall demonstrate this procedure by considering a specific linear differential equation with only one variable and then replacing this equation by a set of state variable equations. The linear differential equation is

$$\frac{d^3x(t)}{dt^3} + \alpha_2 \frac{d^2x(t)}{dt^2} + \alpha_1 \frac{dx(t)}{dt} + \alpha_0 x(t) = y(t) \tag{7-142}$$

We shall define the state variables as $x(t)$ and its derivatives. For instance,

$$q_1(t) = x(t) \tag{7-143a}$$

$$q_2(t) = \frac{dx(t)}{dt} \tag{7-143b}$$

$$q_3(t) = \frac{d^2x(t)}{dt^2} \tag{7-143c}$$

We must now demonstrate that these are actually state variables, that is, that they can be characterized by a set of equations of the form of Eqs. (7-15) or (7-20). Differentiating Eq. (7-143a), we obtain

$$\frac{dq_1(t)}{dt} = \frac{dx(t)}{dt} = q_2(t) \tag{7-144}$$

This is in the proper form. Differentiation of Eq. (7-143*b*) yields

$$\frac{dq_2(t)}{dt} = q_3(t) \tag{7-145}$$

This supplies the second state-variable equation. We substitute Eqs. (7-144), (7-145), and (7-143*c*) into Eq. (7-142), and, after manipulating, we obtain

$$\frac{dq_3(t)}{dt} = -\alpha_0 q_1(t) - \alpha_1 q_2(t) - \alpha_2 q_3 + y(t) \tag{7-146}$$

Equations (7-144) to (7-146) are in the form of Eqs. (7-15), so they constitute a set of state variables for the system characterized by Eq. (7-142).

Since we have been working with a linear time-invariant system, we can write the state-variable equation in the form of Eq. (7-27). In this case the matrices are

$$\hat{q}(t) = \begin{bmatrix} q_1(t) \\ q_2(t) \\ q_3(t) \end{bmatrix} \tag{7-147a}$$

$$\hat{y}(t) = [y(t)] \tag{7-147b}$$

$$\hat{a} = \begin{bmatrix} 0 & 1 & 0 \\ 0 & 0 & 1 \\ -\alpha_0 & -\alpha_1 & -\alpha_2 \end{bmatrix} \tag{7-147c}$$

$$\hat{b} = \begin{bmatrix} 0 \\ 0 \\ 1 \end{bmatrix} \tag{7-147d}$$

Let us now generalize this example so that we may consider a linear differential equation with constant coefficients of arbitrary order. For instance, let us obtain the state-variable equations which characterize

$$\alpha_n \frac{d^n x(t)}{dt^n} + \alpha_{n-1} \frac{d^{n-1} x(t)}{dt^{n-1}} + \cdots + \alpha_1 \frac{dx(t)}{dt} + \alpha_0 x(t) = y(t) \tag{7-148}$$

The state variables are now chosen as

$$q_1(t) = x(t)$$

$$q_2(t) = \frac{dx(t)}{dt} = \frac{dq_1(t)}{dt}$$

$$q_3(t) = \frac{d^2 x(t)}{dt^2} = \frac{dq_2(t)}{dt} \tag{7-149}$$

$$\cdots \cdots \cdots \cdots$$

$$q_n(t) = \frac{d^{n-1} x(t)}{dt^{n-1}} = \frac{dq_{n-1}(t)}{dt}$$

Then, proceeding as in Eqs. (7-142) to (7-146), we obtain

$$\frac{dq_1(t)}{dt} = q_2(t)$$

$$\frac{dq_2(t)}{dt} = q_3(t) \qquad\qquad\qquad (7\text{-}150)$$

$$\cdot \ \cdot \ \cdot \ \cdot \ \cdot \ \cdot \ \cdot$$

$$\frac{dq_{n-1}(t)}{dt} = q_n(t)$$

Thus

$$\frac{dq_n(t)}{dt} = -\frac{\alpha_0}{\alpha_n} q_1(t) - \frac{\alpha_1}{\alpha_n} q_2(t) - \cdot \cdot \cdot - \frac{\alpha_{n-1}}{\alpha_n} q_n(t) + \frac{1}{\alpha_n} y(t)$$

If we have a set of m simultaneous linear differential equations with constant coefficients and unknowns, these can be solved to yield a set of linear differential equations with constant coefficients each of which has only one unknown (see Sec. 4-6). It may seem that a set of state-variable equations of the form of Eqs. (7-150) can be written for each of these equations. However, a complication arises. When the simultaneous equations are solved to obtain the set of equations each of which has only one unknown, the equations can contain terms which are the derivatives of the known $y(t)$ terms [see Eq. (4-172)]. For instance, solving the simultaneous equations could result in a differential equation of the form

$$\alpha_2 \frac{d^2x(t)}{dt^2} + \alpha_1 \frac{dx(t)}{dt} + \alpha_0 x(t) = \beta_2 \frac{d^2y(t)}{dt^2} + \beta_1 \frac{dy(t)}{dt} + \beta_0 y(t) \qquad (7\text{-}151)$$

If we use the procedure that we have just discussed to obtain the state variables, then the resulting equation will not be of the form of Eq. (7-20). This is because $q(t)$ would be a function of $dy(t)/dt$ as well as of $y(t)$. That is, the state-variable equations should be in terms of $y(t)$ but not of its derivatives.

We can overcome this difficulty by modifying our definitions of the state variable. Instead of using Eq. (7-149) to define the first state variable, we choose

$$q_1(t) = x(t) - \frac{\beta_2}{\alpha_2} y(t) \qquad\qquad\qquad (7\text{-}152a)$$

Solving for $x(t)$, we obtain

$$x(t) = q_1(t) + \frac{\beta_2}{\alpha_2} y(t) \qquad\qquad\qquad (7\text{-}152b)$$

and substitution in Eq. (7-151) gives us

$$\alpha_2 \frac{d^2q_1(t)}{dt^2} + \alpha_1 \frac{dq_1(t)}{dt} + \alpha_0 q_1(t) = \left(\beta_1 - \frac{\alpha_1}{\alpha_2} \beta_2 \right) \frac{dy(t)}{dt} + \left(\beta_0 - \frac{\alpha_0}{\alpha_2} \beta_2 \right) y(t)$$

$$(7\text{-}153)$$

Note that the highest-order derivative of $y(t)$ has been cancelled from the equation. In general, instead of just defining $q_1(t)$ as $x(t)$, we now add a function of $y(t)$ to it, so that the derivative of $y(t)$ whose order is the same as the order of the highest-order derivative of $x(t)$ is cancelled when $q_1(t)$ is substituted in the equation. Now, instead of defining $q_2(t)$ as in Eq. (7-149), we add a function of $y(t)$, so that the derivative of $y(t)$ whose order is one less than the one previously considered is canceled from the equation. In this case we let

$$q_2(t) = \frac{dq_1(t)}{dt} - \frac{\beta_1 - \alpha_1\beta_2/\alpha_2}{\alpha_2} y(t) \tag{7-154}$$

Then, substituting in Eq. (7-153), we obtain

$$\alpha_2 \frac{dq_2(t)}{dt} + \alpha_1 q_2(t) + \alpha_0 q_1(t) = \left[\beta_0 - \frac{\alpha_0}{\alpha_2}\beta_2 - \frac{\alpha_1}{\alpha_2}\left(\beta_1 - \frac{\alpha_1\beta_2}{\alpha_2}\right)\right] y(t) \tag{7-155}$$

Equations (7-154) and (7-155) define the state-variable equations for the system. We rewrite them here

$$\frac{dq_1(t)}{dt} = q_2(t) + \frac{\beta_1 - \alpha_1\beta_2/\alpha_2}{\alpha_2} y(t) \tag{7-156a}$$

$$\frac{dq_2(t)}{dt} = -\frac{\alpha_0}{\alpha_2} q_1(t) - \frac{\alpha_1}{\alpha_2} q_2(t) + \frac{1}{\alpha_2}\left[\beta_0 - \frac{\alpha_0}{\alpha_2}\beta_2 - \frac{\alpha_1}{\alpha_2}\left(\beta_1 - \frac{\alpha_1\beta_2}{\alpha_2}\right)\right] y(t) \tag{7-156b}$$

In general, this procedure can be extended to higher-order differential equations. Equations (7-149) are used as a starting point in defining the state variables. Then $y(t)$, multiplied by the appropriate constant, is added to the first state variable. The constant is chosen such that the derivative of $y(t)$ whose order is the same as the highest-order derivative of the unknown is canceled from the equation when the state variable is substituted. The procedure is then repeated with the subsequent equations. This technique applies as long as the order of the highest derivative of $y(t)$ is equal to or less than the order of the highest derivative of $x(t)$. This will usually be the case with the simultaneous equations of linear time-invariant networks.

Let us illustrate this procedure with the network of Fig. 7-6a. The differential equations for this network are

$$v(t) = (R_1 + R_2 + Lp)i_1(t) - R_2 i_2(t) \tag{7-157a}$$

$$0 = -R_2 i_1(t) + \left(R_2 + \frac{1}{Cp}\right)i_2(t) \tag{7-157b}$$

where we have used the operator notation of Eqs. (3-12) and (3-13). Solving these simultaneous equations (see Sec. 4-6), we obtain

$$\left(R_2 Lp + R_1 R_2 + \frac{L}{C} + \frac{R_1 + R_2}{Cp}\right)i_1(t) = \left(R_2 + \frac{1}{Cp}\right)v(t) \tag{7-158a}$$

$$\left(R_2 Lp + R_1 R_2 + \frac{L}{C} + \frac{R_1 + R_2}{Cp}\right)i_2(t) = R_2 v(t) \tag{7-158b}$$

Differentiating both equations, we have

$$R_2L\frac{d^2i_1(t)}{dt^2} + \left(R_1R_2 + \frac{L}{C}\right)\frac{di_1(t)}{dt} + \frac{R_1 + R_2}{C}i_1(t) = \frac{1}{C}v(t) + R_2\frac{dv(t)}{dt}$$

$$(7\text{-}159a)$$

$$R_2L\frac{d^2i_2(t)}{dt^2} + \left(R_1R_2 + \frac{L}{C}\right)\frac{di_2(t)}{dt} + \frac{R_1 + R_2}{C}i_2(t) = R_2\frac{dv(t)}{dt} \qquad (7\text{-}159b)$$

Let us consider Eq. (7-159a). We choose the first state variable as

$$q_1(t) = i_1(t) \qquad (7\text{-}160)$$

Note that there is no $v(t)$ term here. This is because Eq. (7-159a) does not contain a $d^2y(t)/dt^2$ term. Substituting into Eq. (7-159a), we obtain

$$R_2L\frac{d^2q_1(t)}{dt^2} + \left(R_1R_2 + \frac{L}{C}\right)\frac{dq_1(t)}{dt} + \frac{R_1 + R_2}{C}q_1(t) = R_2\frac{dv(t)}{dt} + \frac{1}{C}v(t)$$

$$(7\text{-}161)$$

Now we choose

$$q_2(t) = \frac{dq_1(t)}{dt} - \frac{1}{L}v(t) \qquad (7\text{-}162)$$

Substituting into Eq. (7-161) and manipulating, we have

$$\frac{dq_2(t)}{dt} = -\frac{R_1R_2 + L/C}{LR_2}q_2(t) - \frac{R_1 + R_2}{R_2LC}q_1(t) + \left(\frac{1}{C} - \frac{R_1R_2 + L/C}{L}\right)v(t)$$

$$(7\text{-}163)$$

Equations (7-162) and (7-163) constitute the state-variable representation of Eq. (7-159a).

Now let us consider Eq. (7-159b). We choose a state variable as

$$q_3(t) = i_2(t) \qquad (7\text{-}164)$$

and, substituting in Eq. (7-159b), we have

$$R_2L\frac{d^2q_3(t)}{dt^2} + \left(R_1R_2 + \frac{L}{C}\right)\frac{dq_3(t)}{dt} + \frac{R_1 + R_2}{C}q_3(t) = R_2\frac{dv(t)}{dt} \qquad (7\text{-}165)$$

Then we define

$$q_4(t) = \frac{dq_3(t)}{dt} - \frac{1}{L}v(t) \qquad (7\text{-}166)$$

Substituting in Eq. (7-165) and manipulating, we have

$$\frac{dq_4(t)}{dt} = -\frac{R_1 + R_2 + L/C}{LR_2}q_4(t) - \frac{R_1 + R_2}{R_2LC}q_3(t) - \frac{R_1R_2 + L/C}{L}v(t)$$

$$(7\text{-}167)$$

Equations (7-162), (7-163), (7-166), and (7-167) define the state-variable equations. Rewriting these yields

$$\frac{dq_1(t)}{dt} = q_2(t) + \frac{1}{L} v(t) \tag{7-168a}$$

$$\frac{dq_2(t)}{dt} = -\frac{R_1 + R_2}{R_2 LC} q_1(t) - \frac{R_1 R_2 + L/C}{LR_2} q_2(t) + \left(\frac{1}{C} - \frac{R_1 R_2 + L/C}{L}\right) v(t) \tag{7-168b}$$

$$\frac{dq_3(t)}{dt} = q_4(t) + \frac{1}{L} v(t) \tag{7-168c}$$

$$\frac{dq_4(t)}{dt} = -\frac{R_1 + R_2}{R_2 LC} q_3(t) - \frac{R_1 R_2 + L/C}{LR_2} q_4(t) - \frac{R_1 R_2 + L/C}{L} v(t) \tag{7-168d}$$

Note that these can be treated as two sets of simultaneous equations with two unknowns rather than as a set of simultaneous equations with four unknowns. This type of result occurs because we have dealt with state variables derived from a set of equations each of which has only one unknown.

The procedures of Sec. 7-5 can be used to solve the state-variables equations obtained using the procedure of this section. However, there is one added complexity. The initial conditions are usually specified in terms of the voltage across the capacitors and the currents through the inductors. When these quantities are the state variables, then the initial state is specified (this is the case when the procedure of Sec. 5-2 is used). However, when the procedure of the present section is used, the initial state (for example, the initial values of the derivatives) will not generally be specified. In many instances the techniques of Sec. 4-2 can be used to obtain these initial states. This requires extra work.

The procedure described in this section may appear to have little value, since it is so much more cumbersome than the one discussed in Secs. 7-2 to 7-4. This is especially true in the case of nonlinear or time-varying networks. However, there are circumstances where this technique, as well as others for obtaining a set of state variables, provides more insight into the problem or leads to simpler computer solutions.

BIBLIOGRAPHY

Kuo, B. C.: "Linear Networks and Systems," chaps. 5 and 6, McGraw-Hill Book Company, New York, 1967.

O'N. Roe, P. H.: "Networks and Systems," chap. 5, Addison-Wesley Publishing Company, Reading, Mass., 1966.

Schwarz, R. J., and B. Friedland: "Linear Systems," pp. 51–60, McGraw-Hill Book Company, New York, 1965.

PROBLEMS

7-1. For the circuit of Fig. 7-1 $L = 1$ henry, $C = 4$ farads, and $R = 3$ ohms. Plot the trajectory in state space.

7-2. Repeat Prob. 7-1, but now use $R = 1$ ohm, and then use $R = 0.5$ ohm.

7-3. Write, in matrix form, the state-variable equations for the network of Fig. 4-22. Then write, in matrix form, the equations which express all the branch currents and voltages in terms of the state variables, generator voltages, and element values.

7-4. Repeat Prob. 7-3 for the network of Fig. 4-23.

7-5. Repeat Prob. 7-3 for the network of Fig. 4-24.

7-6. Repeat Prob. 7-3 for the network of Fig. 4-25.

7-7. Repeat Prob. 7-3 for the network of Fig. 4-27. Note that the dependent generators should be expressed in terms of state variables, circuit elements, and independent generators.

7-8. Repeat Prob. 7-3 for the network of Fig. 7-12.

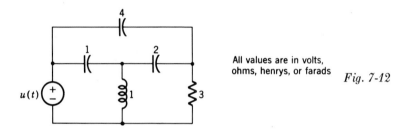

All values are in volts, ohms, henrys, or farads

Fig. 7-12

7-9. Repeat Prob. 7-3 for the network of Fig. 7-13.

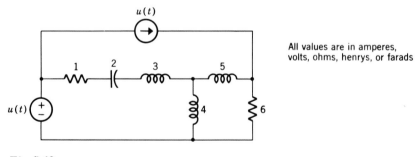

All values are in amperes, volts, ohms, henrys, or farads

Fig. 7-13

7-10. Repeat Prob. 7-3 for the network of Fig. 7-14.

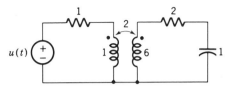

Fig. 7-14

All values are in volts, ohms, henrys, or farads

7-11. Repeat Prob. 7-3, but now assume that in Fig. 4-22 the 2-farad capacitor is replaced by one whose capacitance is given by $C(t) = 2 + e^{-t}$ farads and that the 1-henry inductance is replaced by one whose inductance is $L(t) = 1 + 0.5 \sin 2t$ henrys.

7-12. Repeat Prob. 7-4, but now assume that in Fig. 4-23 the 3-henry inductor is replaced by one whose inductance is $3 + 2e^{-t}$ henrys, the 2-henry inductor is replaced by one whose inductance is $2 + \cos t$ henrys, and the $\frac{1}{2}$-farad capacitor is replaced by one whose capacitance is $\frac{1}{2} + \frac{1}{4} \sin 2t$ farads.

7-13. Repeat Prob. 7-3, but now assume that in Fig. 4-22 the 2-farad capacitor is replaced by one whose charge is given by $q = 2v + \frac{1}{2}v^3$, where v is the voltage across the capacitor, and that the 1-henry inductor is replaced by one whose flux linkages are given by $\phi = 2i^3$.

7-14. Repeat Prob. 7-13, but in addition assume that the 1-ohm resistor is replaced by one whose current is given by $i = \frac{1}{2}v^3$, where v is the voltage across the resistor.

7-15. Solve the state-variable equations $dq_1(t)/dt = 2q_1(t) + q_2(t) + 3$ and $dq_2(t)/dt = q_1(t) - 3q_2(t) + 1$, where the initial state is given by $q_1(0-) = 0$ and $q_2(0-) = 0$.

7-16. Repeat Prob. 7-15, but now assume that the initial state is given by $q_1(0-) = 1$ and $q_2(0-) = -1$.

7-17. Solve the state-variable equations of Prob. 7-3 by classical procedures.

7-18. Solve the state-variable equations of Prob. 7-4 by classical procedures.

7-19. Solve the state-variable equations of Prob. 7-5 by classical procedures.

7-20. Solve the state-variable equations of Prob. 7-6 by classical procedures.

7-21. Repeat Prob. 7-17, but now use Laplace transform procedures.

7-22. Repeat Prob. 7-18, but now use Laplace transform procedures.

7-23. Repeat Prob. 7-19, but now use Laplace transform procedures.

7-24. Repeat Prob. 7-20, but now use Laplace transform procedures.

7-25. Repeat Prob. 7-15, but now use the approximation procedure of Sec. 7-6. Compare your results with those of Prob. 7-15.

7-26. Repeat Prob. 7-25, but now use the initial state given in Prob. 7-16. Compare your results with those of Prob. 7-16.

7-27. Solve the state-variable equations for the network of Prob. 7-11. Assume that all initial conditions are zero.

7-28. Repeat Prob. 7-27 for the network of Prob. 7-12.

7-29. Repeat Prob. 7-27 for the network of Prob. 7-13.

7-30. Repeat Prob. 7-27 for the network of Prob. 7-14.

7-31. For the circuit of Fig. 7-1 $V = 10$ volts, $R = -1$ ohm, $L = 1$ henry, and $C = 1$ farad.   Write the state-variable equations, solve them, and draw the trajectory.   Assume that the initial state is $i_L(0-) = 0$ and $v_C(0-) = 0$.

7-32. Repeat Prob. 7-31, but now use the initial state $i_L(0-) = -1$ amp and $v_C(0-) = -20$ volts.

7-33. Repeat Prob. 7-31, but now assume that the voltage across the resistance, in terms of the current through it, is $v = -i + 0.1i^3$ (the resistor is negative for small currents).   Determine the limit cycle.   Plot $v_C(t)$ versus time for one limit cycle.   What is the period of the oscillation?

7-34. Repeat Prob. 7-33, but now assume that the initial state is $i_L(0-) = 1$ amp and $v_C(0-) = 15$ volts.   Compare the limit cycle with that of Prob. 7-28.

7-35. Repeat Prob. 7-31, but now assume that the voltage across the resistance in terms of the current through it is $v = -i + 0.1i^3$ and that the flux linkages of the inductor in terms of its current are $\phi = i + 0.1i^3$.

7-36. Repeat Prob. 7-3, but now use a different set of state variables.

7-37. Repeat Prob. 7-4, but now use a different set of state variables.

7-38. Repeat Prob. 7-5, but now use a different set of state variables.

7-39. Repeat Prob. 7-6, but now use a different set of state variables.

7-40. Solve the state-variable equations of Prob. 7-36 by classical procedures.

7-41. Repeat Prob. 7-40, but now use Laplace transform procedures.

7-42. Solve the state-variable equation of Prob. 7-37 by classical procedures.

7-43. Repeat Prob. 7-42, but now use Laplace transform procedures.

7-44. Solve the state-variable equation of Prob. 7-38 by classical procedures.

7-45. Repeat Prob. 7-44, but now use Laplace transform procedures.

7-46. Solve the state-variable equation of Prob. 7-39 by classical procedures.

7-47. Repeat Prob. 7-46, but now use Laplace transform procedures.

Twoport Networks

8

In this chapter we shall discuss the properties of networks with two defined pairs of terminals. These are called *twoport networks*, or simply *twoports*. Since a great many practical devices are twoports, these networks merit special attention. In addition, twoports are often used to obtain equivalent circuits for electronic devices such as transistors and vacuum tubes. We shall extend our results to networks that have more than two ports.

In general, in this chapter we shall work with the Laplace transform form of networks. The sinusoidal steady state can be obtained by replacing s by $j\omega$ and the transformed generator voltages and currents by phasors (see Sec. 6-2).

8-1 Twoports

In a great many applications we work with electric networks which have one pair of terminals designated as the input and another pair of terminals designated as the output, with no *external* connections between these pairs of terminals. For instance, in an audio amplifier a microphone is connected to the input terminal and a loudspeaker is connected to the output terminals. How-

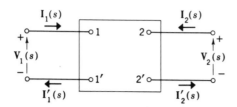

Fig. 8-1   *A four-terminal twoport.*

ever, there is no connection between the input and the output outside the amplifier. The audio amplifier then can be classified as a *twoport* or a *twoport network*, because it has "two ports of entry." The mode of operation discussed here guarantees that the device will operate as a twoport. However, as we shall demonstrate, other connections may be used with twoports.

To work with twoports we must define them in a more rigorous manner. We shall use Fig. 8-1 to aid in this definition. A twoport, in its most general sense, has four terminals, which are arranged in two pairs of terminals as shown. *If a four-terminal network is to behave as a twoport, then the current entering one terminal of a pair must equal the current leaving the other terminal of that pair.* That is, in Fig. 8-1

$$\mathbf{I}_1(s) = \mathbf{I}_1'(s) \tag{8-1a}$$

$$\mathbf{I}_2(s) = \mathbf{I}_2'(s) \tag{8-1b}$$

Equations (8-1) are called the *port conditions.* If they are satisfied in a four-terminal network, then the network is a twoport. Note that we do *not* require that $\mathbf{I}_1(s)$ and $\mathbf{I}_2(s)$ be equal.

A network with four terminals can, in general, have three independent currents (Kirchhoff's current law states that on a volume basis the net current into any volume is zero). *A twoport has only two independent currents.* This is the important property which the port conditions specify. We shall see that the behavior of twoports can be characterized in terms of only two currents. It is this fact, rather than the port conditions, which can be considered to be fundamental (actually, the two conditions are equivalent). In addition, in a twoport we are interested only in the two voltages $\mathbf{V}_1(s)$ and $\mathbf{V}_2(s)$.

Fig. 8-2   *A set of external conditions for which the four-terminal network will behave as a twoport.*

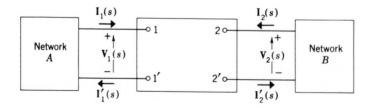

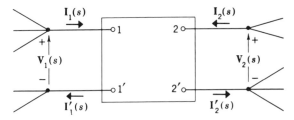

Fig. 8-3 A four-terminal network embedded in a general network.

Often the external connections of a four-terminal network determine whether or not it acts as a twoport. For instance, in Fig. 8-2 the external connections are such that the port conditions are satisfied and the four-terminal network behaves as a twoport. No matter what the oneports of network A and network B contain, the port conditions, Eqs. (8-1), must hold, since the current entering a oneport must equal the current leaving it. Often, however, if a four-terminal network is embedded in a general network, as shown in Fig. 8-3, we cannot tell from inspection whether the port conditions are satisfied or not. The only way to verify them is to analyze the *entire* network to see if $I_1(s) = I_1'(s)$, and so on. Note that we need check only *one* of Eqs. (8-1*a*) and (8-1*b*). If one of these is satisfied, then Kirchhoff's current law requires that the other also be satisfied.

Three-terminal twoports

Frequently, instead of dealing with a four-terminal network, we work with one that has only three terminals, as in Fig. 8-4. In this case there *are* only two independent currents. Thus the three-terminal network always behaves as a twoport regardless of the circuit in which it is embedded, and we do not have to verify that port conditions are satisfied.

8-2 Twoport parameters

Consider that we are working with a twoport of the form of either Fig. 8-1 or Fig. 8-4. We shall characterize this network by a set of simultaneous equations and equivalent circuits. In general, there are two independent currents, $I_1(s)$ and $I_2(s)$, and two independent voltages, $V_1(s)$ and $V_2(s)$ [in

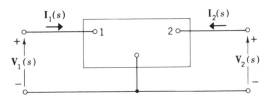

Fig. 8-4 A three-terminal twoport.

the case of a four-terminal network, as in Fig. 8-1, we do not concern ourselves with $\mathbf{V}_{12}(s)$ or $\mathbf{V}_{1'2'}(s)$]. Usually, we can express any two of the independent variables in terms of the other two. Thus two of $\mathbf{V}_1(s)$, $\mathbf{V}_2(s)$, $\mathbf{I}_1(s)$, and $\mathbf{I}_2(s)$ can be considered to be independent variables, while the other two can be considered dependent. The resulting parameters and equivalent circuits depend upon which variables are chosen as dependent. We shall assume in this chapter that the networks are linear and time invariant.

The open-circuit impedance parameters

In the twoport of Fig. 8-1 (or 8-4) the voltages $\mathbf{V}_1(s)$ and $\mathbf{V}_2(s)$ can be expressed as linear functions of $\mathbf{I}_1(s)$ and $\mathbf{I}_2(s)$,

$$\mathbf{V}_1(s) = \mathbf{z}_{11}(s)\mathbf{I}_1(s) + \mathbf{z}_{12}(s)\mathbf{I}_2(s) \tag{8-2a}$$

$$\mathbf{V}_2(s) = \mathbf{z}_{21}(s)\mathbf{I}_1(s) + \mathbf{z}_{22}(s)\mathbf{I}_2(s) \tag{8-2b}$$

These equations can be found by means of the following procedure. We connect a current generator $\mathbf{I}_1(s)$ to terminals 1 and 1' of Fig. 8-1 and connect a current generator $\mathbf{I}_2(s)$ to terminals 2 and 2'. Then we perform a nodal or cut-set analysis to find $\mathbf{V}_1(s)$ and $\mathbf{V}_2(s)$. Using Cramer's rule, we can now express the voltages as linear functions of the current generators, as shown in Eqs. (8-2).

The $\mathbf{z}_{ij}(s)$ ($i = 1, 2; j = 1, 2$) are called the *z parameters* of the network. We shall see that a knowledge of these enables us to determine the effect of the twoport on any network into which it is interconnected as long as the port conditions are satisfied.

Equations (8-2) are often expressed in matrix form. We define

$$\hat{\mathbf{V}}(s) = \begin{bmatrix} \mathbf{V}_1(s) \\ \mathbf{V}_2 \end{bmatrix} \tag{8-3}$$

$$\hat{\mathbf{I}}(s) = \begin{bmatrix} \mathbf{I}_1(s) \\ \mathbf{I}_2(s) \end{bmatrix} \tag{8-4}$$

$$\hat{\mathbf{z}}(s) = \begin{bmatrix} \mathbf{z}_{11}(s) & \mathbf{z}_{12}(s) \\ \mathbf{z}_{21}(s) & \mathbf{z}_{22}(s) \end{bmatrix} \tag{8-5}$$

The matrix $\hat{\mathbf{z}}(s)$ is called the *z-parameter matrix*. Equations (8-2) can be written as

$$\hat{\mathbf{V}} = \hat{\mathbf{z}}\hat{\mathbf{I}} \tag{8-6}$$

We use a "hat" over a symbol to designate it as a matrix [see Eq. (7-18)]. Note that $\hat{\mathbf{V}}$ and $\hat{\mathbf{I}}$ are also vectors, that is, they are single-column matrices.

The z parameters can be found by the procedure outlined following Eqs. (8-2). However, there are far less tedious methods. Since the z parameters are independent of the current, if we find them for any value of current, we know them for all currents.   Thus we should use the currents that make the solution easiest.   Consider Fig. 8-5*a*.   Here a current generator $\mathbf{I}_1(s)$ is applied at the input terminals, and the output terminals are open-circuited.   Hence

$$\mathbf{I}_2(s) = 0 \tag{8-7}$$

Substituting this in Eqs. (8-2), we obtain

$$\mathbf{V}_1(s) = \mathbf{z}_{11}(s)\mathbf{I}_1(s) \tag{8-8a}$$
$$\mathbf{V}_2(s) = \mathbf{z}_{21}(s)\mathbf{I}_1(s) \tag{8-8b}$$

Thus, once we have solved for $\mathbf{V}_1(s)$ and $\mathbf{V}_2(s)$, we can obtain $\mathbf{z}_{11}(s)$ and $\mathbf{z}_{21}(s)$ immediately.   Manipulating Eqs. (8-8), we have

$$\mathbf{z}_{11}(s) = \left.\frac{\mathbf{V}_1(s)}{\mathbf{I}_1(s)}\right|_{\mathbf{I}_2(s)\,=\,0} \tag{8-9}$$

$$\mathbf{z}_{21}(s) = \left.\frac{\mathbf{V}_2(s)}{\mathbf{I}_1(s)}\right|_{\mathbf{I}_2(s)\,=\,0} \tag{8-10}$$

Let us consider the physical significance of Eqs. (8-9) and (8-10). $\mathbf{z}_{11}(s)$ is the driving-point impedance of terminals 1 and 1′ when the output terminals are open-circuited.   Thus we call $\mathbf{z}_{11}(s)$ the *open-circuit input driving-point impedance*.   As the word "input" indicates, this impedance is taken at the input terminals (terminals 1 and 1′ are called the *input terminals*, and terminals 2 and 2′ are called the *output terminals*). $\mathbf{z}_{21}(s)$ is a *transfer impedance*.   That is, it is the ratio of a voltage at one part of the network to the current, applied at another part of the network, which causes it. $\mathbf{z}_{21}(s)$ is called the *open-circuit forward transfer impedance*.   The word "forward" indicates that this function gives the voltage at the output in response to a current at the input terminals.

To measure the other two *z* parameters we use the circuit of Fig. 8-5*b*. Here the input is open-circuited so that

$$\mathbf{I}_1(s) = 0 \tag{8-11}$$

Fig. 8-5   Circuits used for the determination of the z parameters: (a) open-circuited output; (b) open-circuited input.

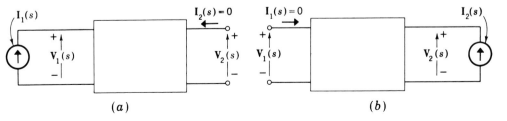

and the current generator is applied at the output port. Substitution of Eq. (8-11) into Eqs. (8-2) yields

$$\mathbf{V}_1(s) = \mathbf{z}_{12}(s)\mathbf{I}_2(s) \tag{8-12a}$$

$$\mathbf{V}_2(s) = \mathbf{z}_{22}(s)\mathbf{I}_2(s) \tag{8-12b}$$

Then

$$\mathbf{z}_{12}(s) = \frac{\mathbf{V}_1(s)}{\mathbf{I}_2(s)}\bigg|_{\mathbf{I}_1(s)=0} \tag{8-13}$$

$$\mathbf{z}_{22}(s) = \frac{\mathbf{V}_2(s)}{\mathbf{I}_2(s)}\bigg|_{\mathbf{I}_1(s)=0} \tag{8-14}$$

Then we call $\mathbf{z}_{12}(s)$ the *open-circuit reverse transfer impedance* and $\mathbf{z}_{22}(s)$ the *open-circuit output driving-point impedance*.

Another useful quantity is the determinant of the z-parameter matrix,

$$\Delta_{\mathbf{z}} = \begin{vmatrix} \mathbf{z}_{11}(s) & \mathbf{z}_{12}(s) \\ \mathbf{z}_{21}(s) & \mathbf{z}_{22}(s) \end{vmatrix} = \mathbf{z}_{11}(s)\mathbf{z}_{22}(s) - \mathbf{z}_{12}(s)\mathbf{z}_{21}(s) \tag{8-15}$$

Once we know the z parameters, we can use Eqs. (8-2) to characterize the network. However, it is usually more convenient to obtain an equivalent circuit. Note that such a circuit is equivalent only as far as conditions *external* to the twoport are concerned (see Sec. 2-4). Hence it can be used to calculate the effect of the twoport on the rest of the network. That is, we wish to obtain a circuit which has the same terminal equations as Eqs. (8-2). Then we can replace the twoport by the equivalent circuit and apply all the network-analysis procedures to the resulting network. There are several advantages in replacing one network by another. The equivalent network may be much simpler than the actual one. The actual network may be an electronic device, such as a transistor, which is not composed of an interconnection of actual circuit elements. However, it often does behave as a linear circuit, and its z parameters can be measured making use of Eqs. (8-9), (8-10), (8-13) and (8-14). Special precautions should be taken in making open- and short-circuit measurements of electronic devices. These will be discussed in Sec. 8-8.

Now let us discuss the z-parameter equivalent circuits given in Fig. 8-6. Network analysis of these figures indicates that the terminal relations between their voltages and currents are given by Eqs. (8-2) (this analysis is left to the reader). Thus as far as external conditions are concerned, these circuits are all equivalent to the twoport. Note that these equivalent circuits employ dependent generators. Analysis of this type of circuit was discussed in Secs. 3-6, 5-6, and 6-3. The use of these equivalent circuits will be discussed in Sec. 8-8.

We can replace *any* three-terminal network or four-terminal network which satisfies the port conditions by any one of the networks of Fig. 8-6. This is often a great help in analysis procedures. As an example let us determine the z parameters of the network shown in Fig. 8-7a. To determine z_{11} and z_{21} we use the network of Fig. 8-7b. Analyzing it, we obtain

$$\mathbf{V}_1(s) = [\mathbf{Z}_1(s) + \mathbf{Z}_2(s) + r]\mathbf{I}_1(s) \tag{8-16a}$$

$$\mathbf{V}_2(s) = [\mathbf{Z}_2(s) + r]\mathbf{I}_1(s) \tag{8-16b}$$

Then, substituting in Eqs. (8-9) and (8-10), we have

$$\mathbf{z}_{11}(s) = \mathbf{Z}_1(s) + \mathbf{Z}_2(s) + r \tag{8-17a}$$

$$\mathbf{z}_{21}(s) = \mathbf{Z}_2(s) + r \tag{8-17b}$$

Similarly, for Fig. 8-7b we have [note that $\mathbf{I}_1(s) = 0$, so the dependent generator produces zero voltage]

$$\mathbf{V}_1(s) = \mathbf{Z}_2(s)\mathbf{I}_2(s) \tag{8-18a}$$

$$\mathbf{V}_2(s) = [\mathbf{Z}_3(s) + \mathbf{Z}_2(s)]\mathbf{I}_2(s) \tag{8-18b}$$

Fig. 8-6   z-parameter equivalent circuits: (a) two-dependent-generator form; (b) output-circuit-dependent-generator form; (c) input-circuit-dependent-generator form.

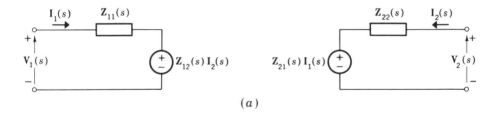

(a)

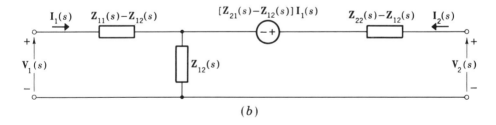

(b)

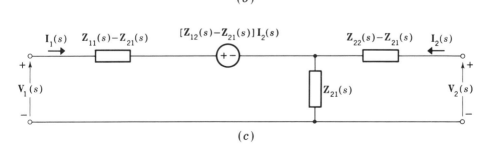

(c)

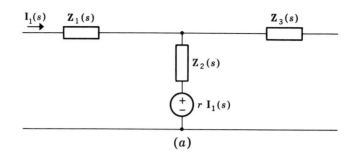

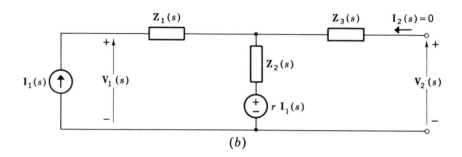

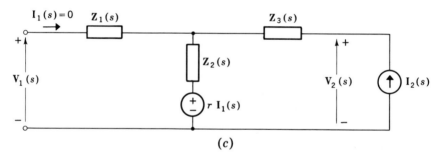

Fig. 8-7   (a) A network containing a dependent generator; (b) a network used to calculate $z_{11}(s)$ and $z_{21}(s)$; (c) a network used to calculate $z_{22}(s)$ and $z_{12}(s)$.

and substitution in Eqs. (8-13) and (8-14) yields

$$z_{12}(s) = Z_2(s) \tag{8-19a}$$
$$z_{22}(s) = Z_2(s) + Z_3(s) \tag{8-19b}$$

Every network does not have to have a set of z parameters. For instance, in a network that has an open-circuited output, z_{22} does not exist, since it always is infinite.

The parameters we shall introduce in the rest of this section will be similar in concept to the z parameters, and we shall omit many of the details of the discussion.

The short-circuit admittance parameters

Let us now express the currents of the twoport in terms of its voltages as

$$\mathbf{I}_1(s) = \mathbf{y}_{11}(s)\mathbf{V}_1(s) + \mathbf{y}_{12}(s)\mathbf{V}_2(s) \qquad (8\text{-}20a)$$
$$\mathbf{I}_2(s) = \mathbf{y}_{21}(s)\mathbf{V}_1(s) + \mathbf{y}_{22}(s)\mathbf{V}_2(s) \qquad (8\text{-}20b)$$

The $\mathbf{y}_{ij}$ are called the y *parameters.* They are characterized by a y-parameter matrix

$$\hat{\mathbf{y}}(s) = \begin{bmatrix} \mathbf{y}_{11}(s) & \mathbf{y}_{12}(s) \\ \mathbf{y}_{21}(s) & \mathbf{y}_{22}(s) \end{bmatrix} \qquad (8\text{-}21)$$

In matrix form Eqs. (8-20) become

$$\hat{\mathbf{I}}(s) = \hat{\mathbf{y}}(s)\hat{\mathbf{V}}(s) \qquad (8\text{-}22)$$

We also define the determinant of $\mathbf{y}(s)$,

$$\Delta_{\mathbf{y}} = \begin{vmatrix} \mathbf{y}_{11}(s) & \mathbf{y}_{12}(s) \\ \mathbf{y}_{21}(s) & \mathbf{y}_{22}(s) \end{vmatrix} = \mathbf{y}_{11}(s)\mathbf{y}_{22}(s) - \mathbf{y}_{12}(s)\mathbf{y}_{21}(s) \qquad (8\text{-}23)$$

Some simplified circuits that can be used to determine the y parameters are shown in Fig. 8-8. Here the output and input are alternately short-circuited. Thus, for Fig. 8-8a $\mathbf{V}_2(s) = 0$, while for Fig. 8-8b $\mathbf{V}_1(s) = 0$. Then for the network of Fig. 8-8a Eqs. (8-20) become

$$\mathbf{I}_1(s) = \mathbf{y}_{11}(s)\mathbf{V}_1(s) \qquad (8\text{-}24a)$$
$$\mathbf{I}_2(s) = \mathbf{y}_{21}(s)\mathbf{V}_1(s) \qquad (8\text{-}24b)$$

Fig. 8-8 (a) *A circuit used to determine* $\mathbf{y}_{11}(s)$ *and* $\mathbf{y}_{21}(s)$; (b) *a circuit used to determine* $\mathbf{y}_{12}(s)$ *and* $\mathbf{y}_{22}(s)$.

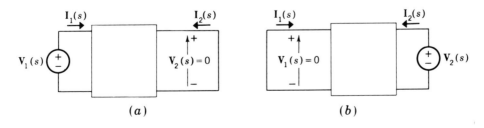

Hence

$$y_{11}(s) = \frac{I_1(s)}{V_1(s)}\bigg|_{V_2(s)=0} \qquad (8\text{-}25a)$$

$$y_{21}(s) = \frac{I_2(s)}{V_1(s)}\bigg|_{V_2(s)=0} \qquad (8\text{-}25b)$$

Thus $y_{11}(s)$ is called the *short-circuit input driving-point admittance*, and $y_{21}(s)$ is called the *short-circuit forward transfer admittance*. Similarly, from Fig. 8-8*b* and Eqs. (8-20) we obtain

$$y_{12}(s) = \frac{I_1(s)}{V_2(s)}\bigg|_{V_1(s)=0} \qquad (8\text{-}26a)$$

$$y_{22}(s) = \frac{I_2(s)}{V_2(s)}\bigg|_{V_1(s)=0} \qquad (8\text{-}26b)$$

Hence $y_{12}(s)$ is called the *short-circuit reverse transfer admittance*, and $y_{22}(s)$ is called the *short-circuit output driving-point admittance*.

Equivalent circuits with y parameters are shown in Fig. 8-9. Remember that these are equivalent only for conditions external to the twoport.

The hybrid parameters

Let us now express the input voltage and output current of the twoport in terms of the input current and the output voltage:

$$V_1(s) = h_{11}(s)I_1(s) + h_{12}(s)V_2(s) \qquad (8\text{-}27a)$$

$$I_2(s) = h_{21}(s)I_1(s) + h_{22}(s)V_2(s) \qquad (8\text{-}27b)$$

The h_{ij}, called the *hybrid parameters*, are often used in the analysis of transistor circuits. The h-parameter matrix is

$$\hat{h}(s) = \begin{bmatrix} h_{11}(s) & h_{12}(s) \\ h_{21}(s) & h_{22}(s) \end{bmatrix} \qquad (8\text{-}28)$$

and its determinant is

$$\Delta_h = \begin{vmatrix} h_{11}(s) & h_{12}(s) \\ h_{21}(s) & h_{22}(s) \end{vmatrix} = h_{11}(s)h_{22}(s) - h_{12}(s)h_{21}(s) \qquad (8\text{-}29)$$

To determine the parameters $h_{11}(s)$ and $h_{21}(s)$ we short-circuit the output and apply a current generator at the input. Because of the short circuit

$$V_2(s) = 0$$

Thus

$$h_{11}(s) = \frac{V_1(s)}{I_1(s)}\bigg|_{V_2(s)=0} \qquad (8\text{-}30a)$$

$$h_{21}(s) = \frac{I_2(s)}{I_1(s)}\bigg|_{V_2(s)=0} \qquad (8\text{-}30b)$$

Then $\mathbf{h}_{11}(s)$ is called the *short-circuit input driving-point impedance*, and $\mathbf{h}_{21}(s)$ is called the *short-circuit forward-transfer-current ratio*.

To calculate the parameters $\mathbf{h}_{12}(s)$ and $\mathbf{h}_{22}(s)$ we open-circuit the input and connect a voltage generator to the output.   Then

$$\mathbf{I}_1(s) \,=\, 0$$

Thus

$$\mathbf{h}_{12}(s) \;=\; \frac{\mathbf{V}_1(s)}{\mathbf{V}_2(s)}\bigg|_{\mathbf{I}_1(s)\,=\,0} \tag{8-30c}$$

$$\mathbf{h}_{22}(s) \;=\; \frac{\mathbf{I}_2(s)}{\mathbf{V}_2(s)}\bigg|_{\mathbf{I}_1(s)\,=\,0} \tag{8-30d}$$

Hence $\mathbf{h}_{12}(s)$ is called the *open-circuit reverse-transfer-voltage ratio*, and $\mathbf{h}_{22}(s)$ is called the *open-circuit output driving-point admittance*.   Note that $\mathbf{h}_{11}$ has the dimensions of an impedance, $\mathbf{h}_{22}$ has the dimensions of an admittance, and

Fig. 8-9   y-parameter equivalent circuits: (a) two-dependent-generator form; (b) output-circuit-dependent-generator form; (c) input-circuit-dependent-generator form.

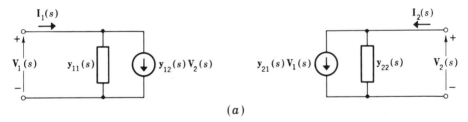

(a)

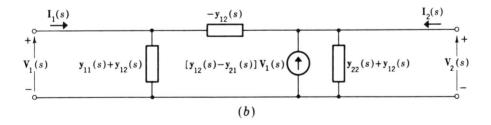

(b)

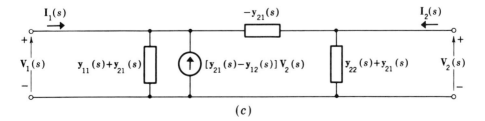

(c)

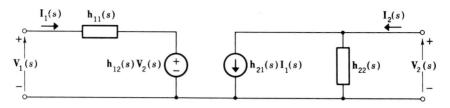

Fig. 8-10 The h-parameter equivalent circuit. Note that $\mathbf{h}_{11}(s)$ is an impedance and $\mathbf{h}_{22}(s)$ is an admittance.

$\mathbf{h}_{12}$ and $\mathbf{h}_{21}$ are dimensionless. Because of these differing dimensions, they are called hybrid parameters.

An *h*-parameter equivalent circuit is given in Fig. 8-10. The impedance levels of the transistor are such that the *h* parameters can be measured especially accurately for them. Thus this equivalent circuit is commonly used in the analysis of transistor circuits.

The inverse hybrid parameters

We can proceed in a manner similar to that for hybrid parameters, but now we express the input current and output voltage in terms of the input voltage and output current. This is the inverse of what is done in the hybrid-parameter case; thus we call the set of parameters obtained the *inverse hybrid parameters*. They are represented as $\mathbf{g}_{ij}$. Note that the $\mathbf{g}$ terms do *not* represent conductance. The *g*-parameter equations are

$$\mathbf{I}_1(s) = \mathbf{g}_{11}(s)\mathbf{V}_1(s) + \mathbf{g}_{12}(s)\mathbf{I}_2(s) \tag{8-31a}$$

$$\mathbf{V}_2(s) = \mathbf{g}_{21}(s)\mathbf{V}_1(s) + \mathbf{g}_{22}(s)\mathbf{I}_2(s) \tag{8-31b}$$

The *g*-parameter matrix is

$$\hat{\mathbf{g}}(s) = \begin{bmatrix} \mathbf{g}_{11}(s) & \mathbf{g}_{12}(s) \\ \mathbf{g}_{21}(s) & \mathbf{g}_{22}(s) \end{bmatrix} \tag{8-32a}$$

and its determinant is

$$\underset{\mathbf{g}}{\triangle} = \begin{vmatrix} \mathbf{g}_{11}(s) & \mathbf{g}_{12}(s) \\ \mathbf{g}_{21}(s) & \mathbf{g}_{22}(s) \end{vmatrix} = \mathbf{g}_{11}(s)\mathbf{g}_{22}(s) - \mathbf{g}_{12}(s)\mathbf{g}_{21}(s) \tag{8-32b}$$

To measure $\mathbf{g}_{11}(s)$ and $\mathbf{g}_{21}(s)$ we open-circuit the output and apply a voltage generator to the input. This gives us

$$\mathbf{g}_{11}(s) = \left. \frac{\mathbf{I}_1(s)}{\mathbf{V}_1(s)} \right|_{\mathbf{I}_2(s)=0} \tag{8-33a}$$

$$\mathbf{g}_{21}(s) = \left. \frac{\mathbf{V}_2(s)}{\mathbf{V}_1(s)} \right|_{\mathbf{I}_2(s)=0} \tag{8-33b}$$

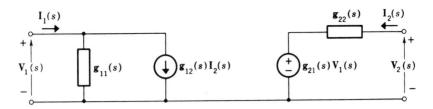

Fig. 8-11   The g-parameter equivalent circuit.   Note that $g_{11}(s)$ is an admittance and $g_{22}(s)$ is an impedance.

Thus $g_{11}(s)$ is called the *open-circuit input driving-point admittance*, and $g_{21}(s)$ is called the *open-circuit forward-transfer-voltage ratio*.

To measure $g_{12}(s)$ and $g_{22}(s)$ we short-circuit the input terminals and apply a current generator to the output terminals.   Thus we obtain

$$g_{21}(s) = \frac{I_1(s)}{I_2(s)}\bigg|_{V_1(s)\,=\,0} \tag{8-33c}$$

$$g_{22}(s) = \frac{V_2(s)}{I_2(s)}\bigg|_{V_1(s)\,=\,0} \tag{8-33d}$$

Hence $g_{21}(s)$ is called the *short-circuit reverse-transfer-current ratio*, and $g_{22}(s)$ is called the *short-circuit output driving-point impedance*.

A *g*-parameter equivalent circuit is shown in Fig. 8-11.

The transmission parameters

Let us now express the input voltage and current in terms of the output voltage and current.   We shall see that this is a particularly useful character-ization to use when networks are cascaded, that is, when the output of one is connected to the input of the next, and so on.   Such connections occur often in electronic equipment.   For instance, the output of a phonograph is con-nected to the input of a preamplifier, the output of the preamplifier is con-nected to the input of the amplifier, and the output of the amplifier is connected to the loudspeaker.   The letters $A(s)$, $B(s)$, $C(s)$, and $D(s)$ are used to repre-sent the *transmission parameters*.   The transmission-parameter equations are

$$V_1(s) = A(s)V_2(s) - B(s)I_2(s) \tag{8-34a}$$

$$I_1(s) = C(s)V_2(s) - D(s)I_2(s) \tag{8-34b}$$

In the case of these parameters it is conventional to call the output current $-I_2(s)$.   The transmission-parameter matrix is

$$\hat{T}(s) = \begin{bmatrix} A(s) & B(s) \\ C(s) & D(s) \end{bmatrix} \tag{8-35}$$

and its determinant is

$$\triangle_T = \begin{vmatrix} \mathbf{A}(s) & \mathbf{B}(s) \\ \mathbf{C}(s) & \mathbf{D}(s) \end{vmatrix} = \mathbf{A}(s)\mathbf{D}(s) - \mathbf{C}(s)\mathbf{B}(s) \tag{8-36}$$

In matrix form we write

$$\begin{bmatrix} \mathbf{V}_1(s) \\ \mathbf{I}_1(s) \end{bmatrix} = \hat{\mathbf{T}} \begin{bmatrix} \mathbf{V}_2(s) \\ -\mathbf{I}_2(s) \end{bmatrix} \tag{8-37}$$

Note that the minus sign is associated with the current, and not with the parameters.

To measure $\mathbf{A}(s)$ and $\mathbf{C}(s)$ we open-circuit the output and alternately apply a voltage generator and current generator to the input. Then

$$\frac{1}{\mathbf{A}(s)} = \frac{\mathbf{V}_2(s)}{\mathbf{V}_1(s)}\bigg|_{\mathbf{I}_2(s)=0} \tag{8-38a}$$

$$\frac{1}{\mathbf{C}(s)} = \frac{\mathbf{V}_2(s)}{\mathbf{I}_1(s)}\bigg|_{\mathbf{I}_2(s)=0} \tag{8-38b}$$

We express these as reciprocals, since it is conventional to write network functions as the ratio of the effect to the cause. Thus $1/\mathbf{A}(s)$ is an *open-circuit transfer-voltage ratio*, and $1/\mathbf{C}(s)$ is an *open-circuit transfer impedance*.

In a similar way, we can determine $\mathbf{B}(s)$ and $\mathbf{D}(s)$ by short-circuiting the output and alternately applying a voltage generator and current generator to the input. Then

$$\frac{1}{\mathbf{B}(s)} = -\frac{\mathbf{I}_2(s)}{\mathbf{V}_1(s)}\bigg|_{\mathbf{V}_2(s)=0} \tag{8-38c}$$

$$\frac{1}{\mathbf{D}(s)} = -\frac{\mathbf{I}_2(s)}{\mathbf{I}_1(s)}\bigg|_{\mathbf{V}_2(s)=0} \tag{8-38d}$$

Hence $1/\mathbf{B}(s)$ is a *short-circuit transfer admittance*, and $1/\mathbf{D}(s)$ is a *short-circuit transfer-current ratio*.

It is not convenient to draw equivalent circuits in terms of the transmission parameters.

Let us demonstrate the advantages of using transmission parameters when networks are cascaded. In Fig. 8-12 we have a twoport which is formed by

Fig. 8-12   A twoport formed by cascading two twoports.

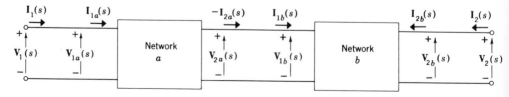

cascading two other twoports. Note that if the overall network behaves as a twoport, then the port conditions will be satisfied at the input port of network a and the output port of network b. Thus networks a and b will behave as twoports (see Sec. 8-1). We shall assume that networks a and b have a transmission-parameter matrix of the form of Eq. (8-35). We use the subscripts a and b to differentiate between the two networks. To obtain the transmission parameters of the overall network we start with the transmission parameters of the subnetworks,

$$\begin{bmatrix} \mathbf{V}_{1a}(s) \\ \mathbf{I}_{1a}(s) \end{bmatrix} = \hat{\mathbf{T}}_a(s) \begin{bmatrix} \mathbf{V}_{2a}(s) \\ -\mathbf{I}_{2a}(s) \end{bmatrix} \tag{8-39a}$$

$$\begin{bmatrix} \mathbf{V}_{1b}(s) \\ \mathbf{I}_{1b}(s) \end{bmatrix} = \hat{\mathbf{T}}_b(s) \begin{bmatrix} \mathbf{V}_{2b}(s) \\ -\mathbf{I}_{2b}(s) \end{bmatrix} \tag{8-39b}$$

However (see Fig. 8-12),

$$\begin{bmatrix} \mathbf{V}_{2a}(s) \\ -\mathbf{I}_{2a}(s) \end{bmatrix} = \begin{bmatrix} \mathbf{V}_{1b}(s) \\ \mathbf{I}_{1b}(s) \end{bmatrix} \tag{8-40}$$

Thus the right-hand side of Eq. (8-39b) can be substituted for the rightmost matrix of Eq. (8-39a). We then obtain

$$\begin{bmatrix} \mathbf{V}_{1a}(s) \\ \mathbf{I}_{1a}(s) \end{bmatrix} = \hat{\mathbf{T}}_a(s)\hat{\mathbf{T}}_b(s) \begin{bmatrix} \mathbf{V}_{2b}(s) \\ -\mathbf{I}_{2b}(s) \end{bmatrix} \tag{8-41}$$

From Fig. 8-12 we have

$$\begin{bmatrix} \mathbf{V}_1(s) \\ \mathbf{I}_1(s) \end{bmatrix} = \begin{bmatrix} \mathbf{V}_{1a}(s) \\ \mathbf{I}_{1a}(s) \end{bmatrix} \tag{8-42}$$

$$\begin{bmatrix} \mathbf{V}_2(s) \\ -\mathbf{I}_2(s) \end{bmatrix} = \begin{bmatrix} \mathbf{V}_{2b}(s) \\ -\mathbf{I}_{2b}(s) \end{bmatrix} \tag{8-43}$$

and substitution in Eq. (8-41) yields

$$\begin{bmatrix} \mathbf{V}_1(s) \\ \mathbf{I}_1(s) \end{bmatrix} = \hat{\mathbf{T}}_a(s)\hat{\mathbf{T}}_b(s) \begin{bmatrix} \mathbf{V}_2(s) \\ -\mathbf{I}_2(s) \end{bmatrix} \tag{8-44}$$

Then comparison of Eqs. (8-44) and (8-37), which define the transmission parameters for the entire network, yields

$$\hat{\mathbf{T}}(s) = \hat{\mathbf{T}}_a(s)\hat{\mathbf{T}}_b(s) \tag{8-45}$$

When twoports are cascaded, the transmission-parameter matrix of the resultant matrix is simply the product of the transmission-parameter matrices of the individual networks. If we characterize networks a and b in terms of other network parameters, then far more complex manipulations must be performed to obtain the parameters of the overall network. The use of the transmission parameters saves work here.

The reverse transmission parameters

At times it is desirable to express the output voltage and current of a twoport in terms of its input voltage and current. The parameters used here are denoted as $\mathcal{C}(s)$, $\mathcal{B}(s)$, $\mathcal{C}(s)$ and $\mathcal{D}(s)$. Thus we have

$$V_2(s) = \mathcal{C}(s)V_1(s) - \mathcal{B}(s)I_1(s) \tag{8-46a}$$

$$I_2(s) = \mathcal{C}(s)V_1(s) - \mathcal{D}(s)I_1(s) \tag{8-46b}$$

It is conventional to use $-I_1(s)$ as the quantity expressed in the equations.

We define a reverse-transmission-parameter matrix as

$$\hat{\mathbf{T}}_R(s) = \begin{bmatrix} \mathcal{C}(s) & \mathcal{B}(s) \\ \mathcal{C}(s) & \mathcal{D}(s) \end{bmatrix} \tag{8-47}$$

and its determinant as

$$\triangle_{\mathbf{T}_R} = \begin{vmatrix} \mathcal{C}(s) & \mathcal{B}(s) \\ \mathcal{C}(s) & \mathcal{D}(s) \end{vmatrix} = \mathcal{C}(s)\mathcal{D}(s) - \mathcal{C}(s)\mathcal{B}(s) \tag{8-48}$$

We determine $\mathcal{C}(s)$ and $\mathcal{C}(s)$ with the input open-circuited and a voltage generator and current generator alternately applied to the output. Hence

$$\frac{1}{\mathcal{C}(s)} = \left.\frac{V_1(s)}{V_2(s)}\right|_{I_1(s)=0} \tag{8-49a}$$

$$\frac{1}{\mathcal{C}(s)} = \left.\frac{V_1(s)}{I_2(s)}\right|_{I_1(s)=0} \tag{8-49b}$$

Thus $1/\mathcal{C}(s)$ is an *open-circuit transfer-voltage ratio*, and $1/\mathcal{C}(s)$ is an *open-circuit transfer impedance*. Similarly, $\mathcal{B}(s)$ and $\mathcal{D}(s)$ are determined with the input short-circuited and a voltage generator and current generator applied to the output. Therefore

$$\frac{1}{\mathcal{B}(s)} = \left.\frac{I_1(s)}{-V_2(s)}\right|_{V_1(s)=0} \tag{8-49c}$$

$$\frac{1}{\mathcal{D}(s)} = \left.\frac{I_1(s)}{-I_2(s)}\right|_{V_1(s)=0} \tag{8-49d}$$

Thus $1/\mathcal{B}(s)$ is a *short-circuit transfer admittance*, and $1/\mathcal{D}(s)$ is a *short-circuit transfer-current ratio*.

8-3 Relations between the twoport parameters: characteristic functions

Usually a twoport can be characterized by any one of the sets of parameters discussed in Sec. 8-2. As a result, we should be able to obtain any set of parameters from any other one. We shall assume that all the parameters exist although this need not be the case (see Sec. 8-4). In this section we shall relate the various parameters and then introduce a new set of functions which make the operation of converting from one set to another less tedious.

The terminal equations of a network can be characterized by Eq. (8-2), (8-20), (8-27), (8-31), (8-34), or (8-46), each of which uses a different set of parameters. To relate these we rearrange one set of equations in the form of the other. For instance, Eqs. (8-2) and (8-20) are

$$\mathbf{V}_1(s) = \mathbf{z}_{11}(s)\mathbf{I}_1(s) + \mathbf{z}_{12}(s)\mathbf{I}_2(s) \tag{8-50a}$$

$$\mathbf{V}_2(s) = \mathbf{z}_{21}(s)\mathbf{I}_1(s) + \mathbf{z}_{22}(s)\mathbf{I}_2(s) \tag{8-50b}$$

and

$$\mathbf{I}_1(s) = \mathbf{y}_{11}(s)\mathbf{V}_1(s) + \mathbf{y}_{12}(s)\mathbf{V}_2(s) \tag{8-51a}$$

$$\mathbf{I}_2(s) = \mathbf{y}_{21}(s)\mathbf{V}_1(s) + \mathbf{y}_{22}(s)\mathbf{V}_2(s) \tag{8-51b}$$

We solve Eqs. (8-50) for the current in terms of the voltage. This yields

$$\mathbf{I}_1(s) = \frac{\mathbf{z}_{22}(s)}{\triangle_z} \mathbf{V}_1(s) - \frac{\mathbf{z}_{12}(s)}{\triangle_z} \mathbf{V}_2(s) \tag{8-52a}$$

$$\mathbf{I}_2(s) = \frac{-\mathbf{z}_{21}(s)}{\triangle_z} \mathbf{V}_1(s) + \frac{\mathbf{z}_{11}(s)}{\triangle_z} \mathbf{V}_2(s) \tag{8-52b}$$

where $\triangle_z$ is defined in Eq. (8-15). Now, Eqs. (8-51) and (8-52) must both give the same values of $\mathbf{I}_1(s)$ and $\mathbf{I}_2(s)$ for *any* given $\mathbf{V}_1(s)$ and $\mathbf{V}_2(s)$. Thus

$$\mathbf{y}_{11}(s) = \frac{\mathbf{z}_{22}(s)}{\triangle_z} \tag{8-53a}$$

$$\mathbf{y}_{12}(s) = -\frac{\mathbf{z}_{12}(s)}{\triangle_z} \tag{8-53b}$$

$$\mathbf{y}_{21}(s) = -\frac{\mathbf{z}_{21}(s)}{\triangle_z} \tag{8-53c}$$

$$\mathbf{y}_{22}(s) = \frac{\mathbf{z}_{11}(s)}{\triangle_z} \tag{8-53d}$$

In matrix form this becomes

$$\begin{bmatrix} \mathbf{y}_{11}(s) & \mathbf{y}_{12}(s) \\ \mathbf{y}_{21}(s) & \mathbf{y}_{22}(s) \end{bmatrix} = \begin{bmatrix} \dfrac{\mathbf{z}_{22}(s)}{\triangle_z} & \dfrac{-\mathbf{z}_{12}(s)}{\triangle_z} \\ \dfrac{-\mathbf{z}_{21}(s)}{\triangle_z} & \dfrac{\mathbf{z}_{11}(s)}{\triangle_z} \end{bmatrix} \tag{8-53e}$$

Note that if $\triangle_z = 0$, the y parameters will not exist.

We can solve Eqs. (8-51) for the voltages in terms of the currents to obtain the z parameters in terms of the y parameters.

To illustrate another calculation let us obtain the h parameters in terms of the z parameters. In this case we wish to manipulate Eqs. (8-50) into the form of Eqs. (8-27). This procedure gives us

$$\mathbf{V}_1(s) = \frac{\triangle_{\mathbf{z}}}{\mathbf{z}_{22}(s)}\, \mathbf{I}_1(s) + \frac{\mathbf{z}_{12}(s)}{\mathbf{z}_{22}(s)}\, \mathbf{V}_2(s) \tag{8-54a}$$

$$\mathbf{I}_2(s) = -\frac{\mathbf{z}_{21}(s)}{\mathbf{z}_{22}(s)}\, \mathbf{I}_1(s) + \frac{1}{\mathbf{z}_{22}(s)}\, \mathbf{V}_2(s) \tag{8-54b}$$

Then, comparing these equations with Eqs. (8-27), we have

$$\hat{\mathbf{h}}(s) = \begin{bmatrix} \mathbf{h}_{11}(s) & \mathbf{h}_{12}(s) \\ \mathbf{h}_{21}(s) & \mathbf{h}_{22}(s) \end{bmatrix} = \begin{bmatrix} \dfrac{\triangle_{\mathbf{z}}}{\mathbf{z}_{22}(s)} & \dfrac{\mathbf{z}_{12}(s)}{\mathbf{z}_{22}(s)} \\ \dfrac{-\mathbf{z}_{21}(s)}{\mathbf{z}_{22}(s)} & \dfrac{1}{\mathbf{z}_{22}(s)} \end{bmatrix} \tag{8-55}$$

Similarly, we can obtain any set of parameters in terms of any other set.

Characteristic functions

To make this operation less tedious let us consider a set of functions which can easily relate all the twoport parameters. These functions will enable us to express twoport parameters and twoport functions in a rather general way. We write each of the z parameters as the ratio of two functions,

$$\begin{bmatrix} \mathbf{z}_{11}(s) & \mathbf{z}_{12}(s) \\ \mathbf{z}_{21}(s) & \mathbf{z}_{22}(s) \end{bmatrix} = \begin{bmatrix} \dfrac{\mathbf{g}(s)}{\mathbf{z}(s)} & \dfrac{\mathbf{r}(s)}{\mathbf{z}(s)} \\ \dfrac{\mathbf{a}(s)}{\mathbf{z}(s)} & \dfrac{\mathbf{h}(s)}{\mathbf{z}(s)} \end{bmatrix} \tag{8-56}$$

One procedure for obtaining these functions, if the z parameters are the ratio of two polynomials, is to place them all over a common denominator. $\mathbf{z}(s)$ is the common denominator, and $\mathbf{g}(s)$, $\mathbf{r}(s)$, $\mathbf{a}(s)$, and $\mathbf{h}(s)$ are the numerators of $\mathbf{z}_{11}(s)$, $\mathbf{z}_{12}(s)$, $\mathbf{z}_{21}(s)$, and $\mathbf{z}_{22}(s)$, respectively. The functions $\mathbf{g}(s)$, $\mathbf{r}(s)$, $\mathbf{a}(s)$, $\mathbf{h}(s)$, $\mathbf{z}(s)$, and one other function, which we shall define $\mathbf{y}(s)$, are called the *characteristic functions* of the network. Note that if all the characteristic functions are multiplied by the *same* function of s, then the z parameters will still be correct. Thus the characteristic functions are not unique until one of them is specified; *then* they are unique.

Now let us obtain the y parameters in terms of the characteristic functions.

Substitution of the z parameters of Eq. (8-56) into Eq. (8-54) yields

$$\begin{bmatrix} \mathbf{y}_{11}(s) & \mathbf{y}_{12}(s) \\ \mathbf{y}_{21}(s) & \mathbf{y}_{22}(s) \end{bmatrix} = \begin{bmatrix} \dfrac{\mathbf{h}(s)}{\mathbf{y}(s)} & \dfrac{-\mathbf{r}(s)}{\mathbf{y}(s)} \\ \dfrac{-\mathbf{a}(s)}{\mathbf{y}(s)} & \dfrac{\mathbf{g}(s)}{\mathbf{y}(s)} \end{bmatrix} \tag{8-57}$$

where

$$\mathbf{y}(s) = \frac{\mathbf{g}(s)\mathbf{h}(s) - \mathbf{a}(s)\mathbf{r}(s)}{\mathbf{z}(s)} \tag{8-58a}$$

or, equivalently,

$$\mathbf{z}(s)\mathbf{y}(s) + \mathbf{a}(s)\mathbf{r}(s) - \mathbf{g}(s)\mathbf{h}(s) = 0 \tag{8-58b}$$

In general, if we solve for any of the sets of parameters in terms of the z parameters and then substitute the characteristic functions of Eq. (8-56), we obtain simple relations (the details of the substitutions are left to the reader):

$$\begin{bmatrix} \mathbf{z}_{11} & \mathbf{z}_{12} \\ \mathbf{z}_{21} & \mathbf{z}_{22} \end{bmatrix} = \begin{bmatrix} \dfrac{\mathbf{g}}{\mathbf{z}} & \dfrac{\mathbf{r}}{\mathbf{z}} \\ \dfrac{\mathbf{a}}{\mathbf{z}} & \dfrac{\mathbf{h}}{\mathbf{z}} \end{bmatrix} \tag{8-59a}$$

$$\begin{bmatrix} \mathbf{y}_{11} & \mathbf{y}_{12} \\ \mathbf{y}_{21} & \mathbf{y}_{22} \end{bmatrix} = \begin{bmatrix} \dfrac{\mathbf{h}}{\mathbf{y}} & -\dfrac{\mathbf{r}}{\mathbf{y}} \\ -\dfrac{\mathbf{a}}{\mathbf{y}} & \dfrac{\mathbf{g}}{\mathbf{y}} \end{bmatrix} \tag{8-59b}$$

$$\begin{bmatrix} \mathbf{h}_{11} & \mathbf{h}_{12} \\ \mathbf{h}_{21} & \mathbf{h}_{22} \end{bmatrix} = \begin{bmatrix} \dfrac{\mathbf{y}}{\mathbf{h}} & \dfrac{\mathbf{r}}{\mathbf{h}} \\ -\dfrac{\mathbf{a}}{\mathbf{h}} & \dfrac{\mathbf{z}}{\mathbf{h}} \end{bmatrix} \tag{8-59c}$$

$$\begin{bmatrix} \mathbf{g}_{11} & \mathbf{g}_{12} \\ \mathbf{g}_{21} & \mathbf{g}_{22} \end{bmatrix} = \begin{bmatrix} \dfrac{\mathbf{z}}{\mathbf{g}} & -\dfrac{\mathbf{r}}{\mathbf{g}} \\ \dfrac{\mathbf{a}}{\mathbf{g}} & \dfrac{\mathbf{y}}{\mathbf{g}} \end{bmatrix} \tag{8-59d}$$

$$\begin{bmatrix} \mathbf{A} & \mathbf{B} \\ \mathbf{C} & \mathbf{D} \end{bmatrix} = \begin{bmatrix} \dfrac{\mathbf{g}}{\mathbf{a}} & \dfrac{\mathbf{y}}{\mathbf{a}} \\ \dfrac{\mathbf{z}}{\mathbf{a}} & \dfrac{\mathbf{h}}{\mathbf{a}} \end{bmatrix} \tag{8-59e}$$

$$\begin{bmatrix} \mathcal{A} & \mathcal{B} \\ \mathcal{C} & \mathcal{D} \end{bmatrix} = \begin{bmatrix} \dfrac{\mathbf{h}}{\mathbf{r}} & \dfrac{\mathbf{y}}{\mathbf{r}} \\ \dfrac{\mathbf{z}}{\mathbf{r}} & \dfrac{\mathbf{g}}{\mathbf{r}} \end{bmatrix} \tag{8-59f}$$

Thus we can easily obtain the characteristic functions for any one given set of parameters, and all the other parameters can then be found by simple substitutions. In general, if one of the characteristic functions is identically zero, then the parameters for which this function is a denominator will not exist.

Let us consider an example of the use of the characteristic functions. Suppose

$$
\begin{bmatrix} \mathbf{z}_{11}(s) & \mathbf{z}_{12}(s) \\ \mathbf{z}_{21}(s) & \mathbf{z}_{22}(s) \end{bmatrix} = \begin{bmatrix} \dfrac{s^2 + 2s + 1}{s^2 + 3s + 2} & \dfrac{s^2 + 1}{s^2 + 3s + 2} \\ \dfrac{s^2 + 1}{s^2 + 3s + 2} & \dfrac{s^2 + 4s + 3}{s^2 + 3s + 1} \end{bmatrix} \tag{8-60}
$$

where we have put the z parameters over a common denominator. Then [see Eq. (8-59a)] we can choose

$$\mathbf{a}(s) = \mathbf{r}(s) = s^2 + 1 \tag{8-61a}$$

$$\mathbf{g}(s) = s^2 + 2s + 1 \tag{8-61b}$$

$$\mathbf{h}(s) = s^2 + 4s + 3 \tag{8-61c}$$

$$\mathbf{z}(s) = s^2 + 3s + 2 \tag{8-61d}$$

Substitution in Eqs. (8-58) yields

$$\mathbf{y}(s) = \frac{(s^2 + 2s + 1)(s^2 + 4s + 3) - (s^2 + 1)^2}{s^2 + 3s + 2} = \frac{6s^3 + 10s^2 + 10s + 2}{s^2 + 3s + 2} \tag{8-61e}$$

Then Eqs. (8-61) can be substituted into any of Eqs. (8-59) to obtain any of the parameters. The characteristic functions are not unique. We can multiply each of them by the same function of s without changing any of the ratios. Note that only ratios of these functions are ever used. In the preceding example, if we had multiplied each characteristic function by $s^2 + 3s + 2$, then each of them would have been a polynomial. This may or may not be an advantage.

8-4 The scattering parameters

In this section we shall consider another set of parameters, called the *scattering parameters*, that can be used to characterize a network. These are different from the parameters discussed in Sec. 8-2 in that they do not directly relate the terminal voltages and currents of the twoports. The scattering parameters were originally used to simplify the analysis of distributed-parameter systems. They relate the incident and reflected waves (see Sec. 6-24). In lumped networks there are no incident and reflected waves, but we can still define scattering parameters. There are instruments that measure the scattering parameters directly. In addition, the scattering parameters always exist for all passive networks (those that do not contain internal power supplies). Note that a network that has a short-circuited input and open-circuited output will not have a z-parameter or a y-parameter matrix. In general, we can produce passive networks for which one or more of the sets of parameters defined in Sec. 8-2 do not exist. If any of the characteristic functions is zero, at least one of the sets of parameters will not exist (if the parameters are infinite, they "do not exist"). Since, as we shall see, the scattering parameters exist for all (nonpathological) passive networks, they are often employed in theoretical studies of such networks.

Consider the twoport of Fig. 8-1. We can write $V_1(s)$ and $I_1(s)$ as the sum and difference of two other terms,

$$V_1(s) = \sqrt{R_{01}} \, [A_1(s) + B_1(s)] \tag{8-62a}$$

$$I_1(s) = \frac{1}{\sqrt{R_{01}}} \, [A_1(s) - B_1(s)] \tag{8-62b}$$

where $\sqrt{R_{01}}$ is called a *normalizing number*. It is arbitrarily chosen. At times the proper choice of R_{01} will simplify computations greatly. In distributed-parameter systems the A_1 and B_1 correspond to incident and reflected components. However, we can consider them as merely two functions defined by Eqs. (8-62) (note that they are not equal to the A and B of the transmission parameters).

Solution of these equations yields

$$A_1(s) = \frac{1}{2} \left(\frac{V_1(s)}{\sqrt{R_{01}}} + \sqrt{R_{01}} \, I_1(s) \right) \tag{8-63a}$$

$$B_1(s) = \frac{1}{2} \left(\frac{V_1(s)}{\sqrt{R_{01}}} - \sqrt{R_{01}} \, I_1(s) \right) \tag{8-63b}$$

Similarly, for port 2 of the network we can define

$$V_2(s) = \sqrt{R_{02}} \, [A_2(s) + B_2(s)] \tag{8-64a}$$

$$I_2(s) = \frac{1}{\sqrt{R_{02}}} \, [A_2(s) - B_2(s)] \tag{8-64b}$$

We can now write these relations in matrix form as

$$\hat{V}(s) = \begin{bmatrix} V_1(s) \\ V_2(s) \end{bmatrix} \tag{8-65a}$$

$$\hat{I}(s) = \begin{bmatrix} I_1(s) \\ I_2(s) \end{bmatrix} \tag{8-65b}$$

$$\sqrt{\hat{R}_0} = \begin{bmatrix} \sqrt{R_{01}} & 0 \\ 0 & \sqrt{R_{02}} \end{bmatrix} \tag{8-65c}$$

$$\hat{A}(s) = \begin{bmatrix} A_1(s) \\ A_2(s) \end{bmatrix} \tag{8-65d}$$

$$\hat{B}(s) = \begin{bmatrix} B_1(s) \\ B_2(s) \end{bmatrix} \tag{8-65e}$$

Then

$$\hat{\mathbf{V}}(s) = \sqrt{\widehat{R_0}}\,[\hat{\mathbf{A}}(s) + \hat{\mathbf{B}}(s)] \tag{8-66a}$$

$$\hat{\mathbf{I}}(s) = \sqrt{\widehat{R_0}}^{-1}\,[\hat{\mathbf{A}}(s) - \hat{\mathbf{B}}(s)] \tag{8-66b}$$

Note that

$$\sqrt{\widehat{R_0}}^{-1} = \begin{bmatrix} \dfrac{1}{\sqrt{R_{01}}} & 0 \\[2ex] 0 & \dfrac{1}{\sqrt{R_{02}}} \end{bmatrix} \tag{8-67}$$

Now we shall define the *scattering matrix* $\mathbf{S}(s)$ which relates the $\mathbf{A}$ and the $\mathbf{B}$ terms as

$$\hat{\mathbf{B}}(s) = \mathbf{S}(s)\hat{\mathbf{A}}(s) \tag{8-68}$$

where

$$\hat{\mathbf{S}}(s) = \begin{bmatrix} \mathbf{S}_{11}(s) & \mathbf{S}_{12}(s) \\ \mathbf{S}_{21}(s) & \mathbf{S}_{22}(s) \end{bmatrix} \tag{8-69}$$

The elements of the scattering matrix are called the *scattering parameters*.

Now, to see how the scattering matrix can be obtained from the network parameters, let us obtain the scattering matrix of the twoport of Fig. 8-1. To *aid in the computations* we form the augmented network shown in Fig. 8-13. That is, we choose values of R_{01} and R_{02}, and then place resistances equal to them in series with the ports 1 and 2, respectively, of the network. Note that the y parameters of this augmented network will always exist for a passive network. In general, the y parameters will not exist if one of them becomes infinite (if, for example, there is a short circuit across one of the ports). This cannot happen in the augmented passive network, because there is a resistance in series with each of the ports (note that in an active network negative resistances are allowed, and the sum of a positive and a negative resistance can be zero).

Fig. 8-13 *The augmented twoport. The generators $\mathbf{V}_{g1}(s)$ and $\mathbf{V}_{g2}(s)$ are not part of the augmented network.*

Let us obtain the y parameters. We define the matrix

$$\hat{\mathbf{V}}_g(s) = \begin{bmatrix} \mathbf{V}_{g1}(s) \\ \mathbf{V}_{g2}(s) \end{bmatrix} \tag{8-70}$$

If $\hat{\mathbf{Y}}_a(s)$ is the y-parameter matrix of the augmented network, then

$$\hat{\mathbf{I}}(s) = \hat{\mathbf{Y}}_a(s)\hat{\mathbf{V}}_g(s) \tag{8-71}$$

We solve for $\mathbf{V}_{g1}(s)$ and $\mathbf{V}_{g2}(s)$ in Fig. 8-13. In matrix form this yields

$$\hat{\mathbf{V}}_g(s) = \hat{\mathbf{V}}(s) + \sqrt{\widehat{R_0}}\sqrt{\widehat{R_0}}\,\hat{\mathbf{I}}(s) \tag{8-72a}$$

Note that this matrix equation actually represents

$$\mathbf{V}_{g1}(s) = \mathbf{V}_1(s) + R_{01}\mathbf{I}_1(s) \tag{8-72b}$$

$$\mathbf{V}_{g2}(s) = \mathbf{V}_2(s) + R_{02}\mathbf{I}_2(s) \tag{8-72c}$$

Substitution of Eqs. (8-66a) and (8-66b) into Eq. (8-72a) yields

$$\hat{\mathbf{V}}_g(s) = \sqrt{\widehat{R_0}}\,[\hat{\mathbf{A}}(s) + \hat{\mathbf{B}}(s)] + \sqrt{\widehat{R_0}}\,[\hat{\mathbf{A}}(s) - \hat{\mathbf{B}}(s)] = 2\sqrt{\widehat{R_0}}\,\hat{\mathbf{A}}(s) \tag{8-73}$$

Dividing both sides of this equation by 2 and then premultiplying by $\sqrt{\widehat{R_0}}^{-1}$ gives us

$$\hat{\mathbf{A}}(s) = \frac{1}{2}\sqrt{\widehat{R_0}}^{-1}\,\hat{\mathbf{V}}_g(s) \tag{8-74}$$

Now we substitute Eq. (8-68) into Eq. (8-66b). This yields

$$\hat{\mathbf{I}}(s) = \sqrt{\widehat{R_0}}^{-1}\,[\hat{\mathbf{A}}(s) - \hat{\mathbf{S}}(s)\hat{\mathbf{A}}(s)] \tag{8-75a}$$

which can be written as

$$\hat{\mathbf{I}}(s) = \sqrt{\widehat{R_0}}^{-1}\,[\hat{\mathbf{U}} - \mathbf{S}(s)]\mathbf{A}(s) \tag{8-75b}$$

where $\hat{\mathbf{U}}$ is the unit matrix. Substituting Eq. (8-74), we obtain

$$\hat{\mathbf{I}}(s) = \frac{1}{2}\sqrt{\widehat{R_0}}^{-1}\,[\hat{\mathbf{U}} - \mathbf{S}(s)]\sqrt{\widehat{R_0}}^{-1}\,\hat{\mathbf{V}}_g(s) \tag{8-76}$$

Comparison with Eq. (8-71) gives us

$$\hat{\mathbf{Y}}_a(s) = \frac{1}{2}\sqrt{\widehat{R_0}}^{-1}\,[\hat{\mathbf{U}} - \hat{\mathbf{S}}(s)]\sqrt{\widehat{R_0}}^{-1} \tag{8-77}$$

Manipulating this equation, we obtain

$$\hat{\mathbf{S}}(s) = \hat{\mathbf{U}} - 2\sqrt{\widehat{R_0}}\,\hat{\mathbf{Y}}_a(s)\sqrt{\widehat{R_0}} \tag{8-78}$$

Thus we have obtained the scattering matrix in terms of the augmented admittance matrix. In addition, Eq. (8-77) gives the augmented admittance matrix in terms of the scattering matrix.

Let us now obtain the z parameters of the network in terms of $\hat{\mathbf{S}}(s)$. The inverse of the y-parameter matrix is the z-parameter matrix [see Eqs. (8-50) and (8-51)]. Thus for the augmented network

$$\hat{\mathbf{z}}_a(s) = \hat{\mathbf{y}}_a(s)^{-1} \tag{8-79}$$

where the subscript a denotes the augmented network. This presupposes that the inverse of $y_a(s)$ exists (that its determinant is not zero). If it does not, then the z-parameter matrix will not exist.

We now determine the relation between the z parameters of the given two-port and that of the augmented one. To determine $\mathbf{z}_{11}(s)$ and $\mathbf{z}_{21a}(s)$ we open-circuit the output [see Eqs. (8-9) and (8-10) and Fig. 8-13]. Thus there will be no current in R_{02}, and it will not affect $\mathbf{z}_{11a}(s)$ and $\mathbf{z}_{12a}(s)$. Since $\mathbf{z}_{11}$ is the driving-point impedance of port 1, with port 2 open-circuited $\mathbf{z}_{11a}$ will just be the sum of $\mathbf{z}_{11}$ and R_{01}. Thus

$$\mathbf{z}_{11a} = \mathbf{z}_{11} + R_{01} \tag{8-80a}$$

To determine $\mathbf{z}_{21a}$ we apply a current generator at the input terminals and determine the open-circuit output voltage (in Fig. 8-13 the voltage generator $\mathbf{V}_{g1}(s)$ is replaced by a current generator, and $\mathbf{V}_{g2}(s)$ is replaced by an open circuit). A resistance in series with the current generator will not affect the current entering the network, so the output voltage will be independent of R_{01}. Therefore

$$\mathbf{z}_{12a} = \mathbf{z}_{12} \tag{8-80b}$$

Similarly we can write

$$\mathbf{z}_{22a} = \mathbf{z}_{22} + R_{02} \tag{8-80c}$$

$$\mathbf{z}_{21a} = \mathbf{z}_{21} \tag{8-80d}$$

In matrix form this is

$$\hat{\mathbf{z}}(s) = \hat{\mathbf{z}}_a(s) - \begin{bmatrix} R_{01} & 0 \\ 0 & R_{02} \end{bmatrix} = \hat{\mathbf{z}}_a(s) - \sqrt{\widehat{R_0}}\,\sqrt{\widehat{R_0}} \tag{8-81}$$

Thus, from Eqs. (8-77), (8-79), and (8-81) we can calculate the z parameters (if they exist) in terms of the scattering parameters.

Although we do not draw a scattering-parameter equivalent circuit, the voltages and currents of the network can be calculated in terms of the scattering parameters. For instance, in Fig. 8-13 suppose we know the scattering parameters of the *twoport in the black box* and have chosen the normalizing numbers equal to R_{01} and R_{02}, respectively (if this is not done, the computations become more tedious). We want to find the currents $\mathbf{I}_1(s)$ and $\mathbf{I}_2(s)$ in terms of the scattering parameters without having to convert them to another set of parameters. From Eqs. (8-74) and (8-68) we have

$$\hat{\mathbf{A}}(s) = \frac{1}{2} \sqrt{\widehat{R_0}}^{-1} \hat{\mathbf{V}}_g(s) \tag{8-82}$$

$$\hat{\mathbf{B}}(s) = \hat{\mathbf{S}}(s)\hat{\mathbf{A}}(s) \tag{8-83}$$

Then, substituting Eqs. (8-82) and (8-83) into Eq. (8-66b), we obtain

$$\hat{\mathbf{I}}(s) = \sqrt{\widehat{R_0}}^{-1} [\hat{\mathbf{U}} - \mathbf{S}(s)]\hat{\mathbf{A}}(s) = \frac{1}{2} \sqrt{\widehat{R_0}}^{-1} [\hat{\mathbf{U}} - \hat{\mathbf{S}}(s)] \sqrt{\widehat{R_0}}^{-1} \hat{\mathbf{V}}_g(s) \tag{8-84}$$

Thus we have obtained the currents in the desired form.

8-5   *n*-port networks

At times the concept of a twoport network can be extended to a network with more than two ports of entry. Such a network with $2n$ terminals is shown in Fig. 8-14. There are port conditions which must be satisfied at each port of the network. That is, if the $2n$-terminal network is to behave as an n-port network, then at each port

$$\mathbf{I}_1(s) = \mathbf{I}_1'(s)$$
$$\mathbf{I}_2(s) = \mathbf{I}_2'(s)$$
$$\cdots \cdots \cdots \tag{8-85}$$
$$\mathbf{I}_n(s) = \mathbf{I}_n'(s)$$

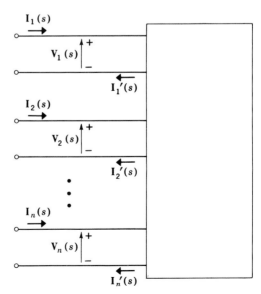

Fig. 8-14   An n-port network.

All the parameters of twoports (including the scattering parameters) can be applied to n ports. For instance, we can write z-parameter equations

$$\hat{\mathbf{V}}(s) = \hat{\mathbf{z}}(s)\hat{\mathbf{I}}(s) \tag{8-86}$$

as in the case of the twoport. However, the indicated matrices must be extended to take into account the fact that there are n ports. That is,

$$\hat{\mathbf{I}}(s) = \begin{bmatrix} \mathbf{I}_1(s) \\ \mathbf{I}_2(s) \\ \cdot \\ \cdot \\ \cdot \\ \mathbf{I}_n(s) \end{bmatrix} \tag{8-87a}$$

$$\hat{\mathbf{V}}(s) = \begin{bmatrix} \mathbf{V}_1(s) \\ \mathbf{V}_2(s) \\ \cdot \\ \cdot \\ \cdot \\ \mathbf{V}_n(s) \end{bmatrix} \tag{8-87b}$$

and

$$\hat{\mathbf{z}}(s) = \begin{bmatrix} \mathbf{z}_{11}(s) & \mathbf{z}_{12}(s) & \cdots & \mathbf{z}_{1n}(s) \\ \mathbf{z}_{21}(s) & \mathbf{z}_{22}(s) & \cdots & \mathbf{z}_{2n}(s) \\ \cdots & \cdots & \cdots & \cdots \\ \mathbf{z}_{n1}(s) & \mathbf{z}_{n2}(s) & \cdots & \mathbf{z}_{nn}(s) \end{bmatrix} \tag{8-88}$$

Proceeding as in the case of the twoport, we can write

$$\mathbf{z}_{ij}(s) = \frac{\mathbf{E}_i(s)}{\mathbf{I}_j(s)} \bigg|_{\mathbf{I}_1(s) = \mathbf{I}_2(s) = \mathbf{I}_{j-1}(s) = \mathbf{I}_{j+1}(s) = \cdots = \mathbf{I}_n(s) = 0} \tag{8-89}$$

If $i \neq j$, then $\mathbf{z}_{ij}(s)$ is an *open-circuit transfer impedance.* If $i = j$, then $\mathbf{z}_{ij}(s)$ is an *open-circuit driving-point impedance.*

In a similar manner, we can define and relate all the other n-port parameters, including the scattering parameters by analogy to the twoport parameters; the details are left to the reader. When we work with parameters that relate input and output quantities (such as h, g, T, and T_r), then half the ports should be designated as input ports and the other half as output ports. Thus n should be an even number.

8-6   Immittance and transfer functions

As an example of the use of the twoport parameters let us obtain some network functions for the network of Fig. 8-15a. We shall use the z parameters, although any of the twoport functions could be used. The z-parameter equivalent circuit for this network is shown in Fig. 8-15b. Its loop equations are

$$V_1(s) = z_{11}(s)I_1(s) + z_{22}(s)I_2(s) \tag{8-90a}$$

$$0 = z_{21}(s)I_1(s) + [z_{22}(s) + Z_L(s)]I_2(s) \tag{8-90b}$$

Now let us solve for the input impedance $Z_{in}(s)$. We have

$$Z_{in}(s) = \frac{V_2(s)}{I_1(s)} \tag{8-91a}$$

Solving Eqs. (8-90) for $I_1(s)$ and substituting in Eq. (8-19a), we obtain

$$Z_{in}(s) = z_{11}(s) - \frac{z_{12}(s)z_{21}(s)}{z_{22}(s) + Z_L(s)} \tag{8-91b}$$

If either $z_{12}(s)$ or $z_{21}(s)$ is zero, then the input impedance is simply $z_{11}(s)$. If either of them is zero, the output circuit does not affect the input.

Let us find the transfer-voltage ratio $V_2(s)/V_1(s)$. From Fig. 8-15 we have

$$V_2(s) = -I_2(s)Z_L(s) \tag{8-92}$$

where the minus sign stems from the assumed direction of $I_2(s)$. We solve Eqs. (8-90) for $I_2(s)$ and substitute in Eq. (8-92) to obtain

$$K_L(s) = \frac{V_2(s)}{V_1(s)} = \frac{z_{21}(s)Z_L(s)}{z_{11}(s)z_{22}(s) - z_{12}(s)z_{21}(s) + Z_L(s)z_{11}(s)} \tag{8-93}$$

Fig. 8-15 (a) An impedance-terminated twoport; (b) an equivalent circuit for this network.

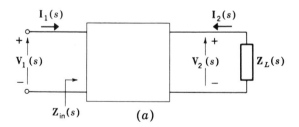

(a)

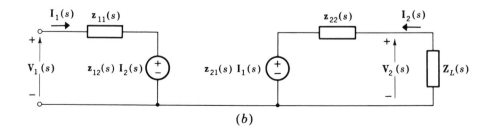

(b)

The transfer-current ratio $\mathbf{I}_2(s)/\mathbf{I}_1(s)$ can be found from Eq. (8-90b) directly;

$$\mathbf{L}_L(s) = \frac{\mathbf{I}_2(s)}{\mathbf{I}_1(s)} = \frac{-\mathbf{z}_{21}(s)}{\mathbf{z}_{22}(s) + \mathbf{Z}_L(s)} \tag{8-94}$$

Note that if $\mathbf{z}_{21}(s)$ is zero, both $\mathbf{K}_L(s)$ and $\mathbf{L}_L(s)$ become zero. That is, $\mathbf{z}_{21}(s)$ indicates the coupling of the input signal to the output in the twoport.

We could have used any of the equivalent circuits developed in Sec. 8-2 to obtain these functions in terms of any of the network parameters. In addition, once they are expressed in terms of one set of parameters, we can express them in terms of the characteristic functions. For instance, substitution of Eq. (8-56) and Eq. (8-58) into Eq. (8-93) gives us

$$\mathbf{K}_L(s) = \frac{\mathbf{a}(s)\mathbf{Z}_L(s)}{\mathbf{y}(s) + \mathbf{g}(s)\mathbf{Z}_L(s)} \tag{8-95}$$

Hence characteristic functions often provide a convenient way of expressing the network relations.

8-7   Some twoport networks

Let us now consider some commonly used network configurations and obtain their network parameters.

Ladder networks

A frequently used network structure is the *ladder network*, shown in Fig. 8-16. We can determine the z parameters of this network by loop, nodal, or cut-set analysis, but the form of the ladder network is such that some simple procedures can also be used.

To determine $\mathbf{z}_{11}(s)$ we find the input impedance of the network when the output is open-circuited. Thus

$$\mathbf{z}_{11}(s) = \mathbf{Z}_1(s) + \mathbf{Z}_a(s) \tag{8-96}$$

Fig. 8-16   A ladder network.

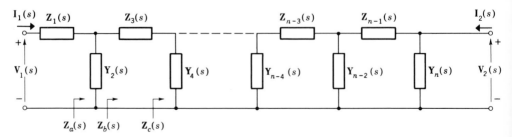

where $\mathbf{Z}_a(s)$ is the impedance as viewed into the network at the point indicated. Consider $\mathbf{Y}_a(s) = 1/\mathbf{Z}_a(s)$. Combining admittances in parallel, we have

$$\mathbf{Y}_a(s) = \mathbf{Y}_2(s) + \frac{1}{\mathbf{Z}_b(s)} \tag{8-97}$$

Substitution in Eq. (8-96) then yields

$$\mathbf{z}_{11}(s) = \mathbf{Z}_1(s) + \frac{1}{\mathbf{Y}_2(s) + 1/\mathbf{Z}_b(s)} \tag{8-98}$$

However,

$$\mathbf{Z}_b(s) = \mathbf{Z}_3(s) + \mathbf{Z}_c(s) \tag{8-99}$$

Thus

$$\mathbf{z}_{11}(s) = \mathbf{Z}_1(s) + \frac{1}{\mathbf{Y}_2(s) + 1/[\mathbf{Z}_3(s) + \mathbf{Z}_c(s)]} \tag{8-100}$$

Continuing in this manner, we obtain

$$\mathbf{z}_{11}(s) = \mathbf{Z}_1(s) + \cfrac{1}{\mathbf{Y}_2(s) + \cfrac{1}{\mathbf{Z}_3(s) + \cfrac{1}{\mathbf{Y}_4(s) + \cfrac{\cdot}{\cdot \cdot \cfrac{1}{\mathbf{Y}_n(s)}}}}} \tag{8-101}$$

This form is called a *Stieljes continued fraction*, and it can be used to calculate $\mathbf{z}_{11}(s)$. We can obtain $\mathbf{z}_{22}(s)$ by proceeding in essentially the same way, but starting at the output side of the network [note that as we have drawn Fig. 8-16 the "first" element encountered is the shunt admittance $\mathbf{Y}_n(s)$].

Now let us find $\mathbf{z}_{21}(s)$. This is given by Eq. (8-10) as

$$\mathbf{z}_{21}(s) = \frac{\mathbf{V}_2(s)}{\mathbf{I}_1(s)} \bigg|_{\mathbf{I}_2(s) = 0} \tag{8-102}$$

Then, in terms of $\mathbf{V}_2(s)$, the current in $\mathbf{Y}_n(s)$ is

$$\mathbf{I}_n(s) = \mathbf{V}_2(s)\mathbf{Y}_n(s) \tag{8-103}$$

This same current must be in $\mathbf{Z}_{n-1}(s)$. Thus the voltage across $\mathbf{Y}_{n-2}(s)$ is

$$\mathbf{V}_{n-2}(s) = \mathbf{V}_2(s) + \mathbf{I}_n(s)\mathbf{Z}_{n-1}(s) = \mathbf{V}_2(s)[1 + \mathbf{Y}_n(s)\mathbf{Z}_{n-1}(s)] \tag{8-104}$$

The current in $\mathbf{Y}_{n-2}(s)$ is

$$\mathbf{I}_{n-2}(s) = \mathbf{Y}_{n-2}(s)\mathbf{V}_{n-2}(s) = \mathbf{V}_2(s)[\mathbf{Y}_{n-2}(s) + \mathbf{Y}_n(s)\mathbf{Z}_{n-1}(s)\mathbf{Y}_{n-2}(s)] \tag{8-105}$$

The current in $\mathbf{Z}_{n-3}(s)$ is $\mathbf{I}_{n-2}(s) + \mathbf{I}_n(s)$. Thus we can calculate the voltage across $\mathbf{Y}_{n-4}(s)$. Continuing in this manner, we can eventually calculate the input current $\mathbf{I}_1(s)$. This will be expressed as $\mathbf{V}_2(s)$ times some function of the immittances of the ladder network. Thus, when we take the ratio $\mathbf{V}_2(s)/\mathbf{I}_1(s)$, we must obtain a function of the immittances.

As an example let us calculate the z parameters of the ladder network shown in Fig. 8-17. Very simple impedances are shown for each of the immittances of Fig. 8-16. We obtain

$$\mathbf{z}_{11}(s) = R_1 + \cfrac{1}{C_2 s + \cfrac{1}{R_3 + \cfrac{1}{C_4 s + \cfrac{1}{R_5 + \infty}}}} \tag{8-106a}$$

Note that the last "resistance" is written as $R_5 + \infty$, since the network is terminated in an open circuit. Manipulating, we have

$$\mathbf{z}_{11}(s) = \frac{R_1 R_3 C_2 C_4 s^2 + (R_1 C_1 + R_1 C_4 + R_3 C_4)s + 1}{R_3 C_4 C_2 s^2 + (C_2 + C_4)s} \tag{8-106b}$$

Similarly,

$$\mathbf{z}_{22}(s) = \frac{R_5 R_3 C_2 C_4 s^2 + (R_5 C_4 + R_5 C_2 + R_3 C_2)s + 1}{R_3 C_2 C_4 s^2 + (C_2 + C_4)s} \tag{8-106c}$$

Now let us determine $\mathbf{z}_{21}(s)$. There is no current in R_5, since the network is open-circuited, so the voltage drop across it is zero. Hence $\mathbf{V}_2(s)$ is the voltage across C_4. Thus the current in it is

$$\mathbf{I}_{C_4}(s) = \mathbf{C}_4 s \mathbf{V}_2(s) \tag{8-107a}$$

This current is also in R_3, so the voltage drop across C_2 is

$$\mathbf{V}_{C_2}(s) = C_4 s \mathbf{V}_2(s) \left(R_3 + \frac{1}{C_4 s} \right) = (R_3 C_4 s + 1)\mathbf{V}_2(s) \tag{8-107b}$$

The current in C_2 is

$$\mathbf{I}_{C_2}(s) = \mathbf{V}_{C_2}(s)C_2(s) = (R_3 C_4 s + 1)C_2 s \mathbf{V}_2(s) \tag{8-107c}$$

The current in R_1 is

$$\mathbf{I}_1(s) = \mathbf{I}_{C_2}(s) + \mathbf{I}_{C_4}(s) = (R_3 C_2 C_4 s^2 + C_2 s + C_4 s)\mathbf{V}_2(s) \tag{8-107d}$$

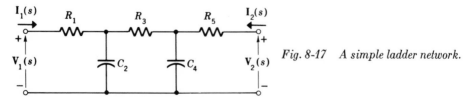

Fig. 8-17   A simple ladder network.

Then

$$\mathbf{z}_{21}(s) = \left.\frac{\mathbf{V}_2(s)}{\mathbf{I}_1(s)}\right|_{\mathbf{I}_2(s)=0} \tag{8-108a}$$

$$\mathbf{z}_{21}(s) = \frac{1}{R_3C_2C_4s^2 + (C_2 + C_4)s}$$

Similarly,

$$\mathbf{z}_{12}(s) = \frac{1}{R_3C_2C_4s^2 + (C_2 + C_4)s} \tag{8-108b}$$

Lattice networks

Somewhat more complex than the ladder network is a network made up of a cascade of networks of the type shown in Fig. 8-18a. This is called a *symmetrical lattice*, since the two impedances $\mathbf{Z}_a(s)$ are equal and the two impedances $\mathbf{Z}_b(s)$ are also equal. A simplified technique for drawing this network is shown in Fig. 8-18b. Solution for the z parameters of this network yields

$$\mathbf{z}_{11}(s) = \mathbf{z}_{22}(s) = \frac{1}{2}\left[\mathbf{Z}_b(s) + \mathbf{Z}_a(s)\right] \tag{8-109a}$$

$$\mathbf{z}_{12}(s) = \mathbf{z}_{21}(s) = \frac{1}{2}\left[\mathbf{Z}_b(s) - \mathbf{Z}_a(s)\right] \tag{8-109b}$$

The y parameters are

$$\mathbf{y}_{11}(s) = \mathbf{y}_{22}(s) = \frac{1}{2}\left[\mathbf{Y}_b(s) + \mathbf{Y}_a(s)\right] \tag{8-110a}$$

$$\mathbf{y}_{21}(s) = \mathbf{y}_{12}(s) = \frac{1}{2}\left[\mathbf{Y}_b(s) - \mathbf{Y}_a(s)\right] \tag{8-110b}$$

where $\mathbf{Y}_a = 1/\mathbf{Z}_a$ and $\mathbf{Y}_b = 1/\mathbf{Z}_b$.

Fig. 8-18   (a) A symmetrical-lattice network; (b) a simplified diagram of this network.

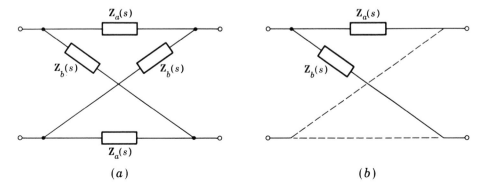

(a)   (b)

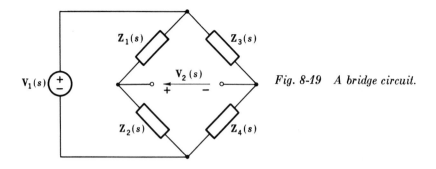

Fig. 8-19   A bridge circuit.

The bridge network

A modification of the lattice network is the *bridge network*, shown in Fig. 8-19. Let us solve for the transfer-voltage ratio of the network.   We have

$$\frac{\mathbf{V}_2(s)}{\mathbf{V}_1(s)} = \frac{\mathbf{Z}_2(s)}{\mathbf{Z}_1(s) + \mathbf{Z}_2(s)} - \frac{\mathbf{Z}_4(s)}{\mathbf{Z}_3(s) + \mathbf{Z}_4(s)} \qquad (8\text{-}111)$$

Now let us adjust the impedances so that the output voltage is zero.   We set Eq. (8-111) equal to zero and manipulate.   This yields

$$\frac{\mathbf{Z}_1(s)}{\mathbf{Z}_2(s)} = \frac{\mathbf{Z}_3(s)}{\mathbf{Z}_4(s)} \qquad (8\text{-}112)$$

If Eq. (8-112) is satisfied, the output voltage will be zero.   In this case the bridge is said to be balanced.

This circuit forms the basis for many impedance-measuring devices.   For instance, consider that $\mathbf{Z}_1$, $\mathbf{Z}_2$, and $\mathbf{Z}_4$ are known, calibrated variable resistors. An unknown resistor $\mathbf{Z}_3$ can be placed in the circuit, and $\mathbf{Z}_1$, $\mathbf{Z}_2$, and $\mathbf{Z}_4$ can be manipulated until the output voltage is zero.   Then $\mathbf{Z}_3$ can be determined from Eq. (8-112).   Such a resistance-measuring bridge circuit is called a *Wheatstone bridge*.   Usually, sinusoidal-steady-state voltages are used in these bridges.   The output voltage is adjusted for a *null*, and the calibrated impedances are used to calculate the impedance of the unknown element at the frequency in question.   Note that when calibrated impedances are used, the bridge circuit can be used to measure impedance as well as resistance.

Twoports in parallel

Let us now consider, not a specific network, but a general configuration that can be used to determine the twoport parameters of many networks.   Consider Fig. 8-20, which consists of two twoports in parallel.   Let us assume that networks a and b both act as twoports and that they are characterized by the

y-parameter matrices $\hat{\mathbf{y}}_a(s)$ and $\hat{\mathbf{y}}_b(s)$, respectively. Then

$$\begin{bmatrix} \mathbf{I}_{1a}(s) \\ \mathbf{I}_{2a}(s) \end{bmatrix} = \hat{\mathbf{y}}_a(s) \begin{bmatrix} \mathbf{V}_{1a}(s) \\ \mathbf{V}_{2a}(s) \end{bmatrix} \tag{8-113a}$$

$$\begin{bmatrix} \mathbf{I}_{1b}(s) \\ \mathbf{I}_{2b}(s) \end{bmatrix} = \hat{\mathbf{y}}_b(s) \begin{bmatrix} \mathbf{V}_{1b}(s) \\ \mathbf{V}_{2b}(s) \end{bmatrix} \tag{8-113b}$$

The overall network is characterized by the y-parameter matrix $\hat{\mathbf{y}}(s)$ and the equation

$$\begin{bmatrix} \mathbf{I}_1(s) \\ \mathbf{I}_2(s) \end{bmatrix} = \hat{\mathbf{y}}(s) \begin{bmatrix} \mathbf{V}_1(s) \\ \mathbf{V}_2(s) \end{bmatrix} \tag{8-113c}$$

We have (see Fig. 8-20)

$$\begin{bmatrix} \mathbf{I}_1(s) \\ \mathbf{I}_2(s) \end{bmatrix} = \begin{bmatrix} \mathbf{I}_{1a}(s) \\ \mathbf{I}_{2a}(s) \end{bmatrix} + \begin{bmatrix} \mathbf{I}_{1b}(s) \\ \mathbf{I}_{2b}(s) \end{bmatrix} \tag{8-114a}$$

$$\begin{bmatrix} \mathbf{V}_1(s) \\ \mathbf{V}_2(s) \end{bmatrix} = \begin{bmatrix} \mathbf{V}_{1a}(s) \\ \mathbf{V}_{2a}(s) \end{bmatrix} = \begin{bmatrix} \mathbf{V}_{1b}(s) \\ \mathbf{V}_{2b}(s) \end{bmatrix} \tag{8-114b}$$

Now we add Eqs. (8-113a) and (8-113b) and then substitute Eqs. (8-114) and factor. This yields

$$\begin{bmatrix} \mathbf{I}_1(s) \\ \mathbf{I}_2(s) \end{bmatrix} = [\mathbf{y}_a(s) + \mathbf{y}_b(s)] \begin{bmatrix} \mathbf{V}_1(s) \\ \mathbf{V}_2(s) \end{bmatrix} \tag{8-115}$$

Comparison with Eq. (8-113c) gives us

$$\hat{\mathbf{y}}(s) = \hat{\mathbf{y}}_a(s) + \hat{\mathbf{y}}_b(s) \tag{8-116}$$

Thus, when twoports are connected in parallel, the y-parameter matrix of the resultant matrix is the sum of the y-parameter matrices of the individual matrices. It should always be verified that the individual networks continue

Fig. 8-20 Two twoports in parallel.

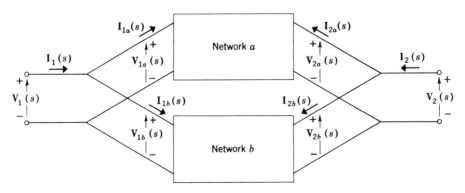

to behave as twoports *after* they are connected in parallel.   Three-terminal twoports, of course, will always behave as twoports, and no verification is necessary.

Bridged-T circuit

As an example of the procedure of the last paragraph let us obtain the y parameters of the network shown in Fig. 8-21a.   It can be considered to be made up of the parallel combination of the three-terminal twoports of Fig. 8-21b and c. The circuit of Fig. 8-21b is called a T *section* because of its shape.   The overall network is called a *bridged*-T *section* because the T section is "bridged" by $\mathbf{Z}_4(s)$.

For the network of Fig. 8-21b network analysis yields

$$\mathbf{y}_{11a}(s) = \frac{\mathbf{Z}_2(s) + \mathbf{Z}_3(s)}{\boxed{\triangle_z}} \tag{8-117a}$$

$$\mathbf{y}_{22a}(s) = \frac{\mathbf{Z}_1(s) + \mathbf{Z}_3(s)}{\boxed{\triangle_z}} \tag{8-117b}$$

$$\mathbf{y}_{12a}(s) = \mathbf{y}_{21a}(s) = - \frac{\mathbf{Z}_3(s)}{\boxed{\triangle_z}} \tag{8-117c}$$

where

$$\boxed{\triangle_z} = \mathbf{Z}_1(s)\,\mathbf{Z}_2(s) + \mathbf{Z}_2(s)\,\mathbf{Z}_3(s) + \mathbf{Z}_3(s)\,\mathbf{Z}_1(s) \tag{8-117d}$$

Fig. 8-21   (a) A bridged-T network; (b) a T-section three-terminal subnetwork of (a); (c) the other three-terminal subnetwork of (a).

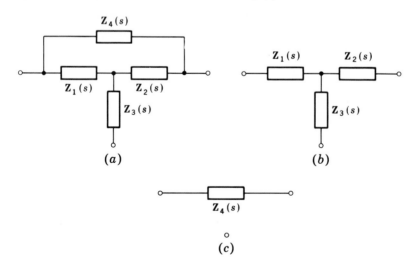

(a) (b)

(c)

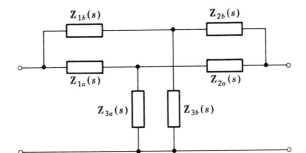

Fig. 8-22   The parallel-T net-work.

For the network of Fig. 8-21*c*

$$\mathbf{y}_{11b}(s) = \mathbf{y}_{22b}(s) = -\mathbf{y}_{12b}(s) = -\mathbf{y}_{21b}(s) = \frac{1}{\mathbf{Z}_4(s)} \tag{8-117e}$$

Thus the *y* parameters for the bridged-T network are

$$\mathbf{y}_{11}(s) = \frac{\mathbf{Z}_2(s) + \mathbf{Z}_3(s)}{\Delta_z} + \frac{1}{\mathbf{Z}_4(s)} \tag{8-118a}$$

$$\mathbf{y}_{22}(s) = \frac{\mathbf{Z}_1(s) + \mathbf{Z}_3(s)}{\Delta_z} + \frac{1}{\mathbf{Z}_4(s)} \tag{8-118b}$$

$$\mathbf{y}_{12}(s) = \mathbf{y}_{21}(s) = -\frac{\mathbf{Z}_3(s)}{\Delta_z} - \frac{1}{\mathbf{Z}_4(s)} \tag{8-118c}$$

The parallel-T network

Another commonly encountered network structure is the *parallel-T section* or the *twin-T network* shown in Fig. 8-22.   It can be analyzed by considering that it consists of two three terminal T sections in parallel; the details are left to the reader.

The parallel-T network has some interesting properties.   Consider that a signal is applied at its input terminals.   It is transmitted through both T sections to the output.   The combination of these two signals produces the actual output.   By an appropriate choice of elements it is possible, at a specific frequency, to have these two signals equal in magnitude but 180° out of phase.   They then cancel, and the output at that frequency is zero.   Hence the parallel-T network is often employed as a filter which effectively rejects a narrow band of frequencies and passes all others.   This type of network, called a *notch filter*, is frequently used to remove interference from a signal. For instance, in a radio receiver interfering stations often produce a 10-kHz interfering signal which is heard as an undesirable whistling sound.   A notch filter can remove this unwanted signal without substantially affecting the desired signal.

Notch filters can also be used in conjunction with feedback amplifiers to produce a filter that rejects all signals except those in a narrow frequency band (by appropriate construction of a feedback device, the frequency response can be made to be essentially the reciprocal of a network in the feedback circuit). This type of filter is used to separate a desired signal from unwanted ones and is called a *bandpass filter* (other forms of bandpass filters and their applications are discussed in Secs. 6-16 to 6-18). For instance, often a weak signal is obscured by interfering *noise*, which consists of random signals of almost all frequencies. If the desired signal and the noise are passed through an appropriate bandpass filter, much of the interfering noise will be rejected by the filter. Thus a bandpass filter can make intelligible a signal that was formerly obscured.

8-8   Linear equivalent circuits for electronic devices

Most electronic devices, such as transistors, are analyzed on the basis of equivalent circuits of the type developed in Sec. 8-2. In general, electronic devices are nonlinear. However, they are often operated so that their voltages and currents vary about some fixed value, called the operating point. When these variations are small and we wish to calculate only the variations, linear equivalent circuits can be used in analyzing the network. The procedures for obtaining these linear circuits, or linear models, were discussed in Sec. 3.8. The word "model" is often used, rather than "equivalent circuit," since the results are only approximate. Models are used by engineers to analyze or design circuits containing elements that are not simply characterized by network functions.

Let us consider the specific example of the transistor and discuss some aspects of its linear-equivalent-circuit (linear-model) analysis. The symbol for the transistor is shown in Fig. 8-23a. It has three leads, called the *emitter*,

Fig. 8-23   (a) The symbol for a transistor; (b) a simple transistor circuit.

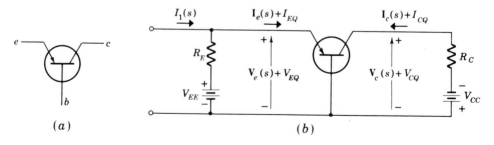

(a)   (b)

the *base*, and the *collector*, labeled e, b, and c, respectively, in the figure. We shall not consider the physics of the transistor here, but shall consider the transistor as just a circuit element. A very simple transistor circuit is shown in Fig. 8-23b. The batteries V_{EE} and V_{CC} produce direct voltages which establish the operating point. $\mathbf{I}_1(s)$ is the Laplace transform of a small time-varying signal. The currents and voltages of the transistor each consist of *time-invariant components* I_{EQ}, I_{CQ}, V_{EQ}, and V_{CQ} and *time-varying*, or *signal, components* $\mathbf{I}_e(s)$, $\mathbf{I}_c(s)$, $\mathbf{V}_e(s)$, and $\mathbf{V}_c(s)$. The signal components are expressed in terms of their Laplace transforms.

If $i_1(t)$ is kept small enough, the variation about the operating point can be characterized by linear relations; that is, the signal components of the current and voltage will be related by linear equations. Since the transistor is a twoport, these equations will take the form of those used in Sec. 8-2 to characterize the various parameters. Thus we can use the same parameters to characterize the behavior of the transistor. Hence, as far as the small-signal components are concerned, the transistor can be approximated by the equivalent circuits of Sec. 8-2. Note that the transistor is a three-terminal twoport, so we do not have to verify that the port conditions are satisfied. Therefore, if the transistor is embedded in a circuit and the signal components are small enough, it can be replaced by its equivalent circuit in an analysis of the signal currents and voltages.

A transistor is not made up of an interconnection of circuit elements, so we cannot use network analysis to obtain its twoport parameters. One way of obtaining them is to make the open- or short-circuit measurements called for in Sec. 8-2 [for the z parameters, for instance, see Eqs. (8-9), (8-10), (8-13), and (8-14)]. However, this presents a problem. These measurements of the signal quantities must be made about the operating point. For instance, in Fig. 8-23b, if we short-circuit the output of the transistor, the direct voltage will also be short-circuited and will become zero. Thus the measurements will not be made with the transistor operating properly. Similarly, if we open-circuit this output, the direct voltage also will not be applied to the transistor The problem can be resolved by using inductors and capacitors as open circuits and short circuits, respectively.

Let us see how this can be done. The signal components usually contain frequencies in a limited band. For instance, in an audio amplifier the input signal may not have frequencies below 20 Hz. There is therefore a minimum signal frequency with which we are concerned. The impedance of an inductor, on a sinusoidal-steady-state basis, is

$$\mathbf{Z}_L(j\omega) = j\omega L \tag{8-119}$$

Thus it is possible to choose an inductor that acts as a very large impedance to all signal frequencies but as a short circuit to direct current (on a sinusoidal-steady-state basis). Similarly, the impedance of a capacitor, on a sinusoidal-

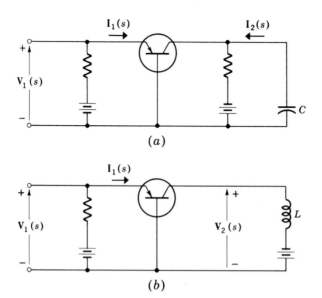

Fig. 8-24 (a) A circuit for short-circuit measurements on the output of transistors; (b) a circuit for open-circuit measurements on the output of a transistor.

steady-state basis, is

$$\mathbf{Z}_C(j\omega) = \frac{1}{j\omega C} \tag{8-120}$$

Hence it is possible to choose a capacitor that acts as a short circuit for the signal components but as an open circuit for direct current.

Let us now consider some circuits that will enable us to make open-circuit and short-circuit measurements without disturbing the direct voltages of the transistor. For a short-circuit output measurement on the transistor consider the circuit of Fig. 8-24a. The capacitor C should be large enough so that it acts as a short circuit for all frequencies of interest. Note that the short-circuit output current is measured in the capacitor branch. The output is short-circuited as far as the signal components are concerned, but on a steady-state basis the capacitor does not affect the direct voltages and currents.

The circuit of Fig. 8-24b is used to make open-circuit output measurements. Here L should be chosen large enough that it acts as an open circuit at all frequencies of interest. Input open-circuit and short-circuit measurements are made with circuits which are essentially the same as those used for the output open-circuit and short-circuit measurements.

We have assumed that a capacitor and an inductor can act as a short circuit and an open circuit, respectively. However, this is only an approximation. In general, if an impedance is to be approximately short-circuited, then an impedance much smaller in magnitude than the given impedance should be placed in parallel with it. Similarly, if an impedance is to be approximately open-circuited, then an impedance much larger than the impedance itself should be placed in series with it. Thus, as a practical matter, it is easier to short-circuit a large impedance than a small one. Similarly, it is easier to open-circuit a small impedance than a large one.

The input impedance of a transistor is relatively low, while its output impedance is relatively high. Therefore we can most accurately make short-circuit output and open-circuit input measurements. The one set of parameters that makes both types of measurement is the set of h parameters [see Eqs. (8-30)]. Hence the transistor is often characterized by an h-parameter equivalent circuit. A typical h-parameter equivalent circuit for the transistor is shown in Fig. 8-25. Assume that its parameters have been determined by the measurements we have discussed. To use this circuit we "remove" the transistor from the circuit diagram under consideration and replace its emitter, base, and collector leads by the leads labeled e, b, and c of Fig. 8-25, respectively. The analysis obtained is valid only for small-signal components. Thus any power supplies should be replaced by impedances which produce only the proper *signal* voltages across their terminals. For instance, an ideal direct-voltage generator has no signal voltage across it, so for small-signal analysis it is replaced by a short circuit. These ideas are illustrated in the example of Fig. 8-26, where Fig. 8-26b is the model of Fig. 8-26a. The circuit of Fig. 8-26b can be analyzed by usual means. This circuit could be used in an audio amplifier. The circuit of Fig. 8-26b can be used to determine its frequency response.

The equivalent circuit that we have developed is called a *common-base equivalent circuit*, because the base is common to both the input and the output (see Fig. 8-24). Similarly, we can obtain *common-emitter equivalent circuits* and *common-collector equivalent circuits*. To distinguish between these, the subscript b, e, or c is sometimes added to the h parameters. To avoid using triple subscripts, the following notation is sometimes used:

$$\begin{bmatrix} \mathbf{h}_{11}(s) & \mathbf{h}_{12}(s) \\ \mathbf{h}_{21}(s) & \mathbf{h}_{22}(s) \end{bmatrix} = \begin{bmatrix} \mathbf{h}_i(s) & \mathbf{h}_r(s) \\ \mathbf{h}_f(s) & \mathbf{h}_o(s) \end{bmatrix} \qquad (8\text{-}121)$$

Fig. 8-25 *An h-parameter equivalent circuit for the transistor. Note that* $\mathbf{h}_{11}(s)$ *is an impedance and* $\mathbf{h}_{22}(s)$ *is an admittance.*

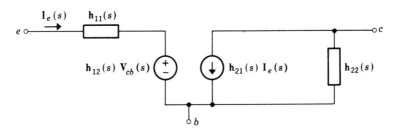

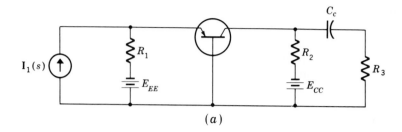

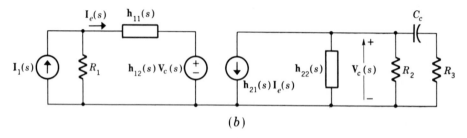

Fig. 8-26   (a) A simple transistor amplifier circuit; (b) an equivalent circuit for this amplifier.   Note that $\mathbf{h}_{11}(s)$ *is an impedance and* $\mathbf{h}_{22}(s)$ *is an admittance.*

These equivalent circuits can also be used on a sinusoidal-steady-state basis if we replace s by $j\omega$ in all the parameters and replace the transforms of the voltages and currents by their phasors (see Sec. 6-2).

The transistor models discussed above are not the only ones that are used. At times equivalent currents are derived on the basis of the physics of the particular device in question.   In addition, other parameters, such as z or y, can be used, and a different equivalent-circuit configuration can result.   The general ideas, however, are the same for all transistor equivalent circuits. In fact, the general concepts of this section are applicable to all linear models of electronic devices.

8-9   The twoport parameters of a transmission line

Let us discuss the length of transmission line shown in Fig. 8-27.   We shall consider it to be a twoport; that is, we shall work with its input and output

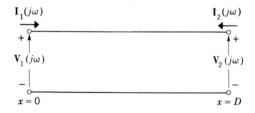

Fig. 8-27   A twoport made up of a transmission line.

terminals only. In addition, we shall assume that the port conditions hold. In this section we shall work on a sinusoidal-steady-state basis, so that s can be replaced by $j\omega$, and the transforms of the voltages and currents can be replaced by their phasors (see Sec. 6-2) in all the developments of this chapter.

Let us determine the z parameters for Fig. 8-27. The voltage and current along this transmission line are given by Eqs. (6-257), where the terminal voltages and currents are

$$\mathbf{V}_1(j\omega) = \mathbf{V}(0,j\omega) \tag{8-122a}$$

$$\mathbf{V}_2(j\omega) = \mathbf{V}(D,j\omega) \tag{8-122b}$$

$$\mathbf{I}_1(j\omega) = \mathbf{I}(0,j\omega) \tag{8-122c}$$

$$\mathbf{I}_2(j\omega) = -\mathbf{I}(D,j\omega) \tag{8-122d}$$

Then, substituting in Eq. (6-257), we obtain

$$\mathbf{V}_1(j\omega) = \mathbf{A}_1 + \mathbf{A}_2 \tag{8-123a}$$

$$\mathbf{V}_2(j\omega) = \mathbf{A}_1 e^{-\theta(j\omega)} + \mathbf{A}_2 e^{\theta(j\omega)} \tag{8-123b}$$

$$\mathbf{Z}_0(j\omega)\mathbf{I}_1(j\omega) = \mathbf{A}_1 - \mathbf{A}_2 \tag{8-124a}$$

$$-\mathbf{Z}_0(j\omega)\mathbf{I}_2(j\omega) = \mathbf{A}_1 e^{-\theta(j\omega)} - \mathbf{A}_2 e^{\theta(j\omega)} \tag{8-124b}$$

where

$$\theta(\omega) = \gamma(j\omega)D$$

and $\gamma(j\omega)$ and $\mathbf{Z}_0(j\omega)$ are defined by Eqs. (6-252) and (6-255), respectively. Now we solve Eqs. (8-124) for $\mathbf{A}_1$ and $\mathbf{A}_2$. This yields

$$\mathbf{A}_1 = \frac{\mathbf{Z}_0(j\omega)[e^{\theta(j\omega)}\mathbf{I}_1(j\omega) + \mathbf{I}_2(j\omega)]}{e^{\theta(j\omega)} + e^{-\theta(j\omega)}} \tag{8-125a}$$

$$\mathbf{A}_2 = \mathbf{Z}_0(j\omega) \frac{e^{-\theta(j\omega)}\mathbf{I}_1(j\omega) + \mathbf{I}_2(j\omega)}{e^{\theta(j\omega)} - e^{-\theta(j\omega)}} \tag{8-125b}$$

and substitution of Eqs. (8-125) into Eqs. (8-123) gives us

$$\mathbf{V}_1(j\omega) = \mathbf{Z}_0(j\omega) \frac{e^{\theta(j\omega)} + e^{-\theta(j\omega)}}{e^{\theta(j\omega)} - e^{-\theta(j\omega)}} \mathbf{I}_1(j\omega) + \frac{2\mathbf{Z}_0(j\omega)}{e^{\theta(j\omega)} - e^{-\theta(j\omega)}} \mathbf{I}_2(j\omega) \tag{8-126a}$$

$$\mathbf{V}_2(j\omega) = \frac{2\mathbf{Z}_0(j\omega)\mathbf{I}_1(j\omega)}{e^{\theta(j\omega)} - e^{-\theta(j\omega)}} + \frac{\mathbf{Z}_0(e^{\theta(j\omega)} + e^{-\theta(j\omega)})}{e^{\theta(j\omega)} - e^{-\theta(j\omega)}} \mathbf{I}_2(j\omega) \tag{8-126b}$$

Using the identities

$$\cosh x = \frac{e^x + e^{-x}}{2} \tag{8-127a}$$

$$\sinh x = \frac{e^x - e^{-x}}{2} \tag{8-127b}$$

Eqs. (8-126) become

$$\mathbf{V}_1(j\omega) = \mathbf{Z}_0(j\omega) \frac{\cosh \theta(j\omega)}{\sinh \theta(j\omega)} \mathbf{I}_1(j\omega) + \frac{\mathbf{Z}_0(j\omega)}{\sinh \theta(j\omega)} \mathbf{I}_2(j\omega) \qquad (8\text{-}128a)$$

$$\mathbf{V}_2(j\omega) = \frac{\mathbf{Z}_0(j\omega)}{\sinh \theta(j\omega)} \mathbf{I}_1(j\omega) + \mathbf{Z}_0(j\omega) \frac{\cosh \theta(j\omega)}{\sinh \theta(j\omega)} \mathbf{I}_2(j\omega) \qquad (8\text{-}128b)$$

Compare these equations with Eqs. (8-2). Both sets of equations express the terminal voltage of a twoport in terms of its terminal currents. Hence both sets of equations give the z parameters. Then, from Eqs. (8-2) and (8-128) we have

$$\begin{bmatrix} \mathbf{z}_{11}(j\omega) & \mathbf{z}_{12}(j\omega) \\ \mathbf{z}_{21}(j\omega) & \mathbf{z}_{22}(j\omega) \end{bmatrix} = \begin{bmatrix} \dfrac{\mathbf{Z}_0(j\omega) \cosh \theta(j\omega)}{\sinh \theta(j\omega)} & \dfrac{\mathbf{Z}_0(j\omega)}{\sinh \theta(j\omega)} \\ \dfrac{\mathbf{Z}_0(j\omega)}{\sinh \theta(j\omega)} & \dfrac{\mathbf{Z}_0(j\omega) \cosh \theta(j\omega)}{\sinh \theta(j\omega)} \end{bmatrix} \qquad (8\text{-}129)$$

and from Eq. (8-59a) we obtain a set of characteristic functions

$$\mathbf{g}(j\omega) = \mathbf{h}(j\omega) = \mathbf{Z}_0(j\omega) \cosh \theta(j\omega) \qquad (8\text{-}130a)$$

$$\mathbf{a}(j\omega) = \mathbf{r}(j\omega) = \mathbf{Z}_0(j\omega) \qquad (8\text{-}130b)$$

$$\mathbf{z}(j\omega) = \sinh \theta(j\omega) \qquad (8\text{-}130c)$$

$$\mathbf{y}(j\omega) = \mathbf{Z}_0{}^2(j\omega) \sinh \theta(j\omega) \qquad (8\text{-}130d)$$

where we have used Eq. (8-58) and the identity

$$\cosh^2 x - \sinh^2 x = 1 \qquad (8\text{-}131)$$

to obtain the last equation. We can now substitute Eqs. (8-130) into Eqs. (8-59) to give us any set of the twoport parameters. These can be used to obtain an equivalent circuit for Fig. 8-27. The z parameters can also be substituted into the relations of Sec. 8-6 to obtain some network functions for the transmission-line network of Fig. 8-27. The transmission line can now be treated like any other twoport.

BIBLIOGRAPHY

Balabanian, N.: "Fundamentals of Circuit Theory," chap. 4, Allyn and Bacon, Inc., Boston, 1961.

Chirlian, P. M.: "Analysis and Design of Electronic Circuits," chap. 3, McGraw-Hill Book Company, New York, 1965.

Chirlian, P. M.: "Integrated and Active Network Analysis and Synthesis," chap. 3, Prentice-Hall, Inc., Englewood Cliffs, N.J., 1967.

Close, C. M.: "The Analysis of Linear Circuits," chap. 12, Harcourt, Brace & World, Inc., New York, 1966.

Friedland, B., O. Wing, and R. Ash: "Principles of Linear Networks," chap. 9, McGraw-Hill Book Company, New York, 1961.

Skilling, H. H.: "Electrical Engineering Circuits," 2d ed., chap. 18, John Wiley & Sons, Inc., New York, 1965.

Van Valkenburg, M. E.: "Network Analysis," 2d ed., chap. 11, Prentice-Hall, Inc., Englewood Cliffs, N.J., 1964.

PROBLEMS

8-1. Discuss why a three-terminal network always behaves as a twoport.

8-2. Discuss why the network of Fig. 8-28 will always behave as a twoport.

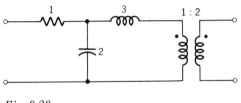

All values are in ohms, henrys, or farads

Fig. 8-28

8-3. Obtain the z parameters of the network of Fig. 8-29.

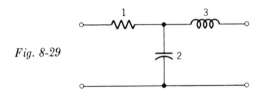

Fig. 8-29

All values are in ohms, henrys, or farads

8-4. Repeat Prob. 8-3 for the network of Fig. 8-30.

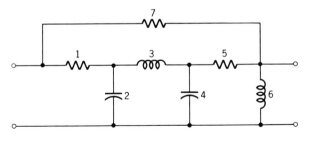

All values are in ohms, henrys, or farads

Fig. 8-30

8-5. Obtain the y parameters for the network of Fig. 8-29.

8-6. Repeat Prob. 8-5 for the network of Fig. 8-30.

8-7. Obtain the h parameters for the network of Fig. 8-29.

8-8. Repeat Prob. 8-7 for the network of Fig. 8-30.

8-9. Obtain the g parameters for the network of Fig. 8-29.

8-10. Repeat Prob. 8-9 for the network of Fig. 8-30.

8-11. Obtain the transmission parameters for the network of Fig. 8-29.

8-12. Repeat Prob. 8-11 for the network of Fig. 8-30.

8-13. Obtain the reserve transmission parameters for the network of Fig. 8-29.

8-14. Repeat Prob. 8-13 for the network of Fig. 8-30.

8-15. Obtain the z parameters for the network of Fig. 8-28.

8-16. Repeat Prob. 8-15, but now obtain the h parameters.

8-17. Obtain the relations between the y parameters and the g parameters.

8-18. Derive Eqs. (8-59).

8-19. Find a set of characteristic functions for the network of Fig. 8-29.

8-20. Repeat Prob. 8-19 for the network of Fig. 8-30.

8-21. Repeat Prob. 8-19 for the network of Fig. 8-28.

8-22. Obtain the scattering parameters for the network of Fig. 8-29 without obtaining them from the other twoport parameters. Use $R_{01} = 2$ and $R_{02} = 3$.

8-23. Repeat Prob. 8-22 for the network of Fig. 8-30.

8-24. Repeat Prob. 8-22 for the network of Fig. 8-28.

8-25. Obtain the z parameters for the network of Fig. 8-31.

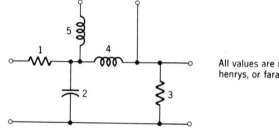

All values are in ohms,   *Fig. 8-31*
henrys, or farads

8-26. Obtain the y parameters for the network of Fig. 8-31.

8-27. Obtain the z parameters in terms of y parameters for a general n-port network.

8-28. Obtain the y parameters in terms of z parameters for a general n-port network.

8-29. Obtain the scattering parameters for the network of Fig. 8-31 Use $R_{01} = 1$, $R_{02} = 2$, and $R_{03} = 1$.

8-30. The network of Fig. 8-29 is terminated in a 5-ohm resistance (at port 2). Find the input impedance, the transfer-voltage ratio, and the transfer-current ratio of this network.

8-31. Repeat Prob. 8-30 for the network of Fig. 8-30.

8-32. Find the y parameters of the network of Fig. 8-30. Consider that a ladder network is connected in parallel with a twoport which consists only of a 7-ohm resistance. Use the procedures of Sec. 8-7 to obtain the y parameters of the ladder network.

8-33. The network of Fig. 8-18 has the element values $\mathbf{Z}_a(s) = s + 1$ and $\mathbf{Z}_b(s) = 1/s$. Find the z parameters of the network.

8-34. Repeat Prob. 8-33, but now find the scattering parameters. Use $R_{01} = R_{02} = 1$.

8-35. In the network of Fig. 8-19 $\mathbf{Z}_2(s) = R_2$, $\mathbf{Z}_4(s) = R_4$, and $\mathbf{Z}_1(s) = R_1 + 1/C_1 s + L_1 s$. If $\mathbf{V}_2(s) = 0$, what is $\mathbf{Z}_3(s)$?

8-36. The transistor of Fig. 8-32 has the following common-base parameters:

$$\mathbf{h}_{ib} = 20 \text{ ohms}$$

$$\mathbf{h}_{rb} = 4 \times 10^{-8}$$

$$\mathbf{h}_{fb} = \frac{-1}{1+s}$$

$$\mathbf{h}_{ob} = 10^{-6} \text{ mho}$$

If

$$\mathbf{Z}_1(s) = 10,000 \text{ ohms}$$

$$\mathbf{Z}_4(s) = 50 \text{ ohms}$$

$$\mathbf{Z}_3(s) = \frac{1,000}{s+1} \text{ ohms}$$

$$\mathbf{Z}_2(s) = 10,000 \text{ ohms}$$

find the transfer-current ratio of this network for small signals.

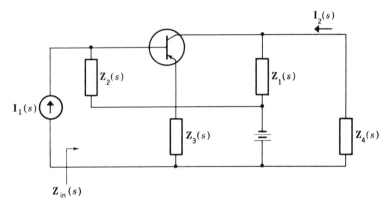

Fig. 8-32

8-37. Find the input impedance $\mathbf{Z}_{\text{in}}(s)$ for the network of Fig. 8-32 on a small-signal basis. Use the parameter and element values of Prob. 8-36.

8-38. Find the h parameters of the transmission-line twoport of Fig. 8-27. Use the terminology of Sec. 8-9.

8-39. Repeat Prob. 8-38, but now find the scattering parameters. Use $R_{01} = R_{02} = R_0$ (assume that the transmission line is lossless and that the characteristic impedance is R_0).

8-40. The network of Fig. 8-27 is terminated (at port 2) in an impedance of $\mathbf{Z}_0(j\omega)$ ohms. Compute the input impedance of the network. Use the terminology of Sec. 8-9.

8-41. Repeat Prob. 8-40, but now find the transfer-voltage ratio.

8-42. Repeat Prob. 8-40, but now use a terminating impedance of $3\mathbf{Z}_0(j\omega)$.

Network Theorems

9

In this chapter we shall discuss some network theorems which in many circumstances greatly simplify network-analysis procedures. We have already considered some simple theorems. For instance, in Sec. 7-2 we demonstrated that a circuit element that is not coupled (by mutual inductance) to another element can be replaced by a voltage generator which produces a voltage equal to the terminal voltage of the element, or that an element can be replaced by a current generator equal to its current. This is called the *substitution theorem*. In Sec. 2-4 and Sec. 5-10 we demonstrated that a current generator in parallel with an impedance can be replaced by a voltage generator in series with an impedance, and vice versa. These theorems proved very helpful, and we shall now discuss some additional ones.

One general comment pertains to many of the network theorems. When one network is replaced by an equivalent one, the behavior of the rest of the circuit is unaffected by this replacement. In general, however, the *internal behavior of the replaced network will be different from that of its equivalent*.

In most of this chapter we shall work with the Laplace transform form of the equations. If the sinusoidal-steady-state response is desired, then we

512

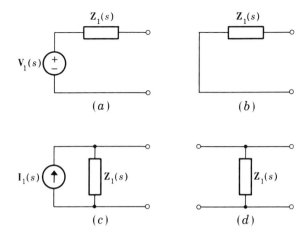

*Fig. 9-1   (a) A voltage gen-
erator; (b) the voltage generator "replaced by its internal
impedance"; (c) a current
generator; (d) the current
generator "replaced by its
internal impedance."*

replace s by $j\omega$ and the transforms of the voltages and currents by their phasors (see Sec. 6-2).

In many of the network theorems we shall make the statement: "Replace the independent generator by its internal impedance." Let us define what we mean by this. Consider the voltage generator of Fig. 9-1a. We wish to make the *generator portion* of this circuit zero (that is, $\mathbf{V}_1 = 0$). Hence the generator itself acts as a short circuit. Thus if $\mathbf{V}_1(s)$ becomes zero, the circuit of Fig. 9-1b results. The impedance $\mathbf{Z}_1(s)$ could be part of the actual generator. That is, $\mathbf{Z}_1(s)$ is internal to the actual generator represented by Fig. 9-1a. Hence we speak of Fig. 9-1b as having "replaced the voltage generator by its internal impedance." If $\mathbf{Z}_1(s)$ is not internal to the actual generator, then Fig. 9-1b still results, since now the generator is replaced by a short circuit (the "ideal generator" is replaced by a short circuit). In Fig. 9-1c a current generator is in parallel with an impedance. If $\mathbf{I}_1(s)$ becomes zero, there is no current in the current-generator branch, and it acts as an open circuit, and Fig. 9-1d results. The impedance $\mathbf{Z}_1(s)$ may be internal to the actual generator. In any event, when we replace the current generator by its internal impedance, Fig. 9-1d results. When we speak of replacing independent generators by their internal impedances, we refer to the operations of Fig. 9-1.

9-1   The superposition theorem

If we are analyzing a linear network containing more than one independent generator, then the *superposition theorem* is often of use. This theorem states that the voltage across or the current through any element can be computed in the following way: replace all the generators except one by their internal impedances and compute the voltage across or the current through the element in question.   Repeat this procedure for *each* independent generator in turn. Then taking the sum of all the calculated voltages across or the currents through the element in question will give the actual voltage across or the current through the element.   That is, the effect of all the generators can be found by obtaining the response considering that each generator in turn acts alone, with all others replaced by their internal impedances, and then adding all the individual responses.

This theorem will be proved in terms of the state-variable characterization of Sec. 7-2.   We shall first consider application of the theorem to those currents and voltages which are the state variables and then extend it to all the currents and voltages of the network.

Let us consider a linear time-invariant network (we shall mention the time-varying case subsequently).   We can characterize its state variables by an equation of the form of Eqs. (7-24) or (7-27).   That is,

$$\frac{d\hat{q}(t)}{dt} = \hat{a}\hat{q}(t) + \hat{b}\hat{y}(t) \tag{9-1}$$

where $\hat{q}(t)$ is a column matrix each element of which is a state variable and $\hat{y}(t)$ is a column matrix each element of which represents a known (independent-generator) quantity.   The elements of the $\hat{a}$ and $\hat{b}$ matrices are constant [these matrices are defined in Eqs. (7-25) and (7-26)] and depend upon the element values and the circuit configuration, *not* upon the values of the independent generators (see Sec. 7-2).   Thus, when any independent generators are replaced by their internal impedances, the $\hat{a}$ and $\hat{b}$ matrices will be unchanged.

To use the superposition theorem we shall consider that *all initial conditions are represented by initial-condition generators* (see Sec. 6-5); these initial-condition generators are treated as though they were independent generators in all subsequent discussions of this theorem.   Thus $\hat{y}(t)$ includes not only the independent generators, but also the initial-condition generators.   (In Sec. 6-5 we represented the initial-condition generators in the Laplace transform domain; to work in the time domain we take the inverse Laplace transform of these generator values.)   It is important to realize that *all* initial conditions are represented by generators, and that these generators are treated like any other independent generator.

In Laplace transform form the solution of Eq. (9-1) is given by Eq. (7-112) as

$$\hat{Q}(s) = [s\mathsf{U} - \hat{a}]^{-1}\hat{b}\hat{Y}(s) \tag{9-2a}$$

where U is the unit matrix of the same order as $\hat{a}$.   Note that the $\hat{q}(0-)$ matrix of Eq. (7-112) is not written here, since we are representing the initial conditions by generators.   To define the various matrices let us write Eq. (9-2a) in an expanded form as

$$
\begin{bmatrix} \mathbf{Q}_1(s) \\ \mathbf{Q}_2(s) \\ \cdot \\ \cdot \\ \cdot \\ \mathbf{Q}_n(s) \end{bmatrix} = \left\{ s \begin{bmatrix} 1 & 0 & \cdots & 0 \\ 0 & 1 & \cdots & 0 \\ \multicolumn{4}{c}{\dotfill} \\ 0 & 0 & \cdots & 1 \end{bmatrix} - \begin{bmatrix} a_{11} & a_{12} & \cdots & a_{1n} \\ a_{21} & a_{22} & \cdots & a_{2n} \\ \multicolumn{4}{c}{\dotfill} \\ a_{n1} & a_{n2} & \cdots & a_{nn} \end{bmatrix} \right\}^{-1}
$$

$$
\times \begin{bmatrix} b_{11} & b_{12} & \cdots & b_{1k} \\ b_{21} & b_{22} & \cdots & b_{2k} \\ \multicolumn{4}{c}{\dotfill} \\ b_{n1} & b_{n2} & \cdots & b_{nk} \end{bmatrix} \begin{bmatrix} \mathbf{Y}_1(s) \\ \mathbf{Y}_2(s) \\ \cdot \\ \cdot \\ \cdot \\ \mathbf{Y}_k(s) \end{bmatrix} \qquad (9\text{-}2b)
$$

We have assumed that there are n state variables and k independent generators, including initial-condition generators.

Now assume that all the independent generators except $\mathbf{Y}_1(s)$ are set equal to their internal impedances. Equation (9-2) is unchanged, except that we set

$$\mathbf{Y}_2(s) = \mathbf{Y}_3(s) = \cdots = \mathbf{Y}_k(s) = 0$$

Thus we can write

$$
\begin{bmatrix} \mathbf{Q}_{11}(s) \\ \mathbf{Q}_{21}(s) \\ \cdot \\ \cdot \\ \cdot \\ \mathbf{Q}_{n1}(s) \end{bmatrix} = \left\{ s \begin{bmatrix} 1 & 0 & \cdots & 0 \\ 0 & 1 & \cdots & 0 \\ \multicolumn{4}{c}{\dotfill} \\ 0 & 0 & \cdots & 1 \end{bmatrix} - \begin{bmatrix} a_{11} & a_{12} & \cdots & a_{1n} \\ a_{21} & a_{22} & \cdots & a_{2n} \\ \multicolumn{4}{c}{\dotfill} \\ a_{n1} & a_{n2} & \cdots & a_{nn} \end{bmatrix} \right\}^{-1}
$$

$$
\times \begin{bmatrix} b_{11} & b_{12} & \cdots & b_{1k} \\ b_{21} & b_{22} & \cdots & b_{2k} \\ \multicolumn{4}{c}{\dotfill} \\ b_{n1} & b_{n2} & \cdots & b_{nk} \end{bmatrix} \begin{bmatrix} \mathbf{Y}_1(s) \\ 0 \\ \cdot \\ \cdot \\ \cdot \\ 0 \end{bmatrix} \qquad (9\text{-}3)
$$

where we have added a second subscript, 1, to $\mathbf{Q}_1(s)$, $\mathbf{Q}_2(s)$, . . . to indicate that they are determined with all independent generators except $\mathbf{Y}_1(s)$ set equal to their internal impedances.

Let us introduce some matrix notation so that we may write these equations in more compact form.   Let

$$\hat{\mathbf{Q}}_{(j)}(s) = \begin{bmatrix} \mathbf{Q}_{1j}(s) \\ \mathbf{Q}_{2j}(s) \\ \cdot \\ \cdot \\ \cdot \\ \mathbf{Q}_{nj}(s) \end{bmatrix} \tag{9-4a}$$

$$\hat{\mathbf{Y}}^{(j)}(s) = \begin{bmatrix} 0 \\ 0 \\ \mathbf{Y}_j(s) \\ 0 \end{bmatrix} \tag{9-4b}$$

where the subscript (j) appends a second subscript to all the $\mathbf{Q}_1(s)$, $\mathbf{Q}_2(s)$, $\cdots$ in the $\hat{\mathbf{Q}}(s)$ matrix and the superscript (j) sets all the elements of $\hat{\mathbf{Y}}(s)$ except $\mathbf{Y}_j(s)$ equal to zero.   Thus Eq. (9-2) can be written as

$$\hat{\mathbf{Q}}_{(1)}(s) = [s\mathsf{U} - \hat{a}]^{-1}\hat{b}\hat{\mathbf{Y}}^{(1)}(s) \tag{9-5a}$$

We now replace all the independent generators but $\mathbf{Y}_2(s)$ by their internal impedances.   Then, proceeding as in the derivation of Eq. (9-5a), we have

$$\hat{\mathbf{Q}}_{(2)}(s) = [s\mathsf{U} - \hat{a}]^{-1}\hat{b}\hat{\mathbf{Y}}^{(2)}(s) \tag{9-5b}$$

We can do this for each independent generator in turn.   For instance, with $\mathbf{Y}_k(s)$ acting with all other generators replaced by their internal impedances we have

$$\hat{\mathbf{Q}}_{(k)}(s) = [s\mathsf{U} - \hat{a}]^{-1}\hat{b}\hat{\mathbf{Y}}^{(k)}(s) \tag{9-5c}$$

Before we sum all these equations, let us consider one summation we will use:

$$\hat{\mathbf{Y}}^{(1)}(s) + \hat{\mathbf{Y}}^{(2)}(s) + \cdots + \hat{\mathbf{Y}}^{(k)}(s) = \hat{\mathbf{Y}}(s)$$

This can be obtained by summing equations of the form of Eq. (9-4b).   Then

$$\sum_{j=1}^{k} \mathbf{Q}_{(j)}(s) = [s\mathsf{U} - \hat{a}]^{-1}\left[\hat{b} \sum_{j=1}^{k} \hat{\mathbf{Y}}^{(j)}(s)\right] \tag{9-6a}$$

Substitution gives us

$$\sum_{j=1}^{k} \hat{\mathbf{Q}}_{(j)}(s) = [s\mathsf{U} - \hat{a}]^{-1}\hat{b}\hat{\mathbf{Y}}(s) \tag{9-6b}$$

Comparing this with Eq. (9-2), we obtain

$$\hat{\mathbf{Q}}(s) = \sum_{j=1}^{k} \hat{\mathbf{Q}}_{(j)}(s) \tag{9-7a}$$

or, equivalently,

$$
\begin{bmatrix} \mathbf{Q}_1(s) \\ \mathbf{Q}_2(s) \\ \cdot \\ \cdot \\ \cdot \\ \mathbf{Q}_n(s) \end{bmatrix} = \begin{bmatrix} \sum_{j=1}^{k} \mathbf{Q}_{1j}(s) \\ \sum_{j=1}^{k} \mathbf{Q}_{2j}(s) \\ \cdot \\ \cdot \\ \cdot \\ \sum_{j=1}^{k} \mathbf{Q}_{nj}(s) \end{bmatrix}
\tag{9-7b}
$$

The individual equations are

$$
\mathbf{Q}_1(s) = \sum_{j=1}^{k} \mathbf{Q}_{1j}(s)
$$

$$
\mathbf{Q}_2(s) = \sum_{j=1}^{k} \mathbf{Q}_{2j}(s)
\tag{9-7c}
$$

$$
\cdots \cdots \cdots
$$

$$
\mathbf{Q}_n(s) = \sum_{j=1}^{k} \mathbf{Q}_{nj}(s)
$$

Thus we have proved the superposition theorem for the state variables of the network.

We have demonstrated that the superposition theorem is valid for those currents and voltages which are characterized by state variables. Let us now show that it is valid for every current and voltage of the network. These are related to the state variables by an equation of the type of Eqs. (7-29) or its matrix equivalent, Eq. (7-32). Taking the Laplace transform of Eq. (7-32), which is just an algebraic equation, we have

$$
\hat{\mathbf{X}}(s) = \hat{c}\hat{\mathbf{Q}}(s) + \hat{d}\hat{\mathbf{Y}}(s)
\tag{9-8}
$$

where the $\hat{\mathbf{X}}(s)$ matrix is a column matrix containing all the desired currents and/or voltages which are not state variables, and the $\hat{c}$ and $\hat{d}$ matrices are constants which depend upon the network configurations and element values but not upon the independent generators (see Sec. 7-2).

In the following development we shall use the matrix notation

$$
\hat{\mathbf{X}}_{(j)}(s) = \begin{bmatrix} \mathbf{X}_{1j}(s) \\ \mathbf{X}_{2j}(s) \\ \cdot \\ \cdot \\ \cdot \\ \mathbf{X}_{nj}(s) \end{bmatrix}
$$

That is, $\hat{\mathbf{X}}_{(j)}(s)$ is the $\hat{\mathbf{X}}(s)$ matrix, with a second subscript (j) added to each term to indicate that all independent generators except $\mathbf{Y}_j(s)$ have been replaced by their internal impedances.

Consider that all independent generators except $\mathbf{Y}_1(s)$ are set equal to their internal impedances. Then Eq. (9-8) becomes

$$\hat{\mathbf{X}}_{(1)}(s) = \hat{c}\hat{\mathbf{Q}}_{(1)}(s) + \hat{d}\hat{\mathbf{Y}}^{(1)}(s) \tag{9-9a}$$

where we have used the notation of Eqs. (9-4). Now assume that all independent generators except $\mathbf{Y}_2(s)$ are replaced by their internal impedances. Thus

$$\hat{\mathbf{X}}_{(2)}(s) = \hat{c}\hat{\mathbf{Q}}_{(2)}(s) + \hat{d}\hat{\mathbf{Y}}^{(2)}(s) \tag{9-9b}$$

We repeat this for each independent generator in turn. For instance, with $\mathbf{Y}_k(s)$ acting with all other generators replaced by their internal impedances we have

$$\hat{\mathbf{X}}_{(k)}(s) = \hat{c}\hat{\mathbf{Q}}_{(k)}(s) + \hat{d}\hat{\mathbf{Y}}^{(k)}(s) \tag{9-9c}$$

Now we sum all these equations,

$$\sum_{j=1}^{k} \hat{\mathbf{X}}_{(j)}(s) = \hat{c} \sum_{j=1}^{k} \hat{\mathbf{Q}}_{(j)}(s) + \hat{d} \sum_{j=1}^{k} \hat{\mathbf{Y}}^{(j)}(s) \tag{9-10a}$$

Substituting Eq. (9-7a) and the expression for $\Sigma\hat{\mathbf{Y}}^{(j)}(s)$, we obtain

$$\sum_{j=1}^{k} \hat{\mathbf{X}}_{(j)}(s) = \hat{c}\hat{\mathbf{Q}}(s) + \hat{d}\hat{\mathbf{Y}}(s) \tag{9-10b}$$

and comparison with Eq. (9-8) gives us

$$\sum_{j=1}^{k} \hat{\mathbf{X}}_j(s) = \hat{\mathbf{X}}(s) \tag{9-10c}$$

We demonstrated from Eqs. (9-7) that any state variable can be found by computing the value when each independent generator in turn acts alone with all the others replaced by their internal impedances, and then summing all the calculated values of the state variable. Now we have shown that the superposition theorem is valid for all voltages and currents, and not only for those expressed as state variables.

If a network contains only resistors, then the equations that characterize it will be algebraic rather than differential, and state-variable equations cannot be written. We can then consider that all the state variables are zero $[\hat{\mathbf{Q}}(s) = 0]$. However, Eq. (9-8) will still be valid; that is, all the currents and voltages will be expressible as linear sums of the independent generator voltages and/or currents, as in Eq. (5-144) (note that in the case of a resistive network the circuit determinant Δ will be composed only of real numbers). The independent generators of Eq. (5-144) are either voltage generators *or* current generators, but if a network contains mixed voltage and current generators, one form can be converted to the other by means of the results of Sec. 5-10. Since Eq. (9-8) is valid, the proof following it is also valid. Thus the superposition theorem can be used for resistive networks.

In the calculations above we have considered that only one independent generator acts at any one time. This need not be the case. For instance, suppose there are five independent generators, $\mathbf{Y}_1(s)$, $\mathbf{Y}_2(s)$, $\mathbf{Y}_3(s)$, $\mathbf{Y}_4(s)$, and $\mathbf{Y}_5(s)$, and we wish to determine the current in an element. We can determine the current with $\mathbf{Y}_3$, $\mathbf{Y}_4$, and $\mathbf{Y}_5$ replaced by their internal impedances, repeat this procedure with $\mathbf{Y}_1$ and $\mathbf{Y}_2$ replaced by their internal impedances, and then add the two currents obtained to obtain the desired current. The validity of this operation follows from Eq. (9-6). Each term in that equation must be present. However, if each of $\mathbf{Y}_1$, $\mathbf{Y}_2$, . . . , $\mathbf{Y}_k$ is assumed to act once, and only once, then every term will be present even if some generators are assumed to act simultaneously. Note that each generator must act only once, and in all other calculations it must be replaced by its internal impedance.

We have proved this theorem using the equations of linear time-invariant networks. However, any linear network can be derived as one whose outputs are linear functions of the independent generators. Thus a linear time-varying network will be characterized by an equation of the *form* of Eq. (9-2); that is,

$$\hat{\mathbf{Q}}(s) = \hat{M}\hat{\mathbf{Y}}(s)$$

Then the proof for linear time-varying networks follows the one just given. Note that it may be necessary to perform a time-domain analysis to obtain $\hat{M}$ because of the difficulty of working with the Laplace transform in time-varying network analysis.

As an example of this procedure let us solve for current in the capacitor C of Fig. 9-2a. The Laplace transform form of this network is given in Fig. 9-2b. Now we apply the superposition theorem. Figure 9-2c shows the network when $v_{ab}(0-)/s$ is replaced by its internal impedance. In this case (see Sec. 8-7) we have a balanced bridge, and the current through the capacitor is zero,

$$\mathbf{I}_{C1}(s) = 0 \tag{9-11a}$$

We replace $\mathbf{V}(s)$ by its internal impedance, and the network of Fig. 9-2d results. Since we wish to determine only $\mathbf{I}_C(s)$, this can be simplified to the circuit of Fig. 9-2e, where the current through the capacitor is

$$\mathbf{I}_{C2}(s) = \frac{v_{ab}(0-)}{s} \frac{1}{R + 1/Cs} = \frac{v_{ab}(0-)/R}{s + 1/RC} \tag{9-11b}$$

Then the transform of the actual current through the capacitor is found by taking the sum of Eqs. (9-11a) and (9-11b). Hence

$$\mathbf{I}_C(s) = \frac{v_{ab}(0-)/R}{s + 1/RC}$$

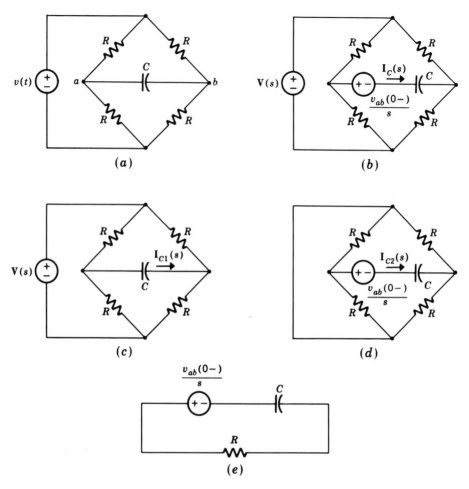

Fig. 9-2   (*a*) *A network;* (*b*) *the transformed form of this network;* (*c*) *the network when* v_{ab} *(0−)/s is replaced by its internal impedance;* (*d*) *the network when* $\mathbf{V}(s)$ *is replaced by its internal impedance;* (*e*) *a simplification of* (*d*).

Thus in this case the superposition theorem allows us to obtain the desired current without having to solve a three-loop circuit.

9-2   Thévenin's theorem

In this section we shall derive an equivalent circuit for any *linear time-invariant* oneport network.   It will enable us, on the basis of some simple measurements or calculations, to replace such a oneport, no matter how complex, by a simple equivalent circuit.   The oneport can be part of a larger network.   Thévenin's

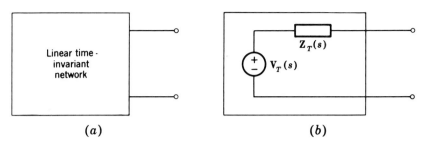

Fig. 9-3 (a) A linear time-invariant network; (b) the Thévenin equivalent circuit for this network.

theorem states that a network of the form of Fig. 9-3a is equivalent, *as far as external conditions are concerned*, to that of Fig. 9-3b if $\mathbf{V}_T(s)$ and $\mathbf{Z}_T(s)$ are chosen properly. $\mathbf{V}_T(s)$ is the Laplace transform of the voltage across the output of the oneport under open-circuit conditions.   That is, it is the voltage when nothing is connected to the black box, as shown in Fig. 9-3a.   The impedance $\mathbf{Z}_T(s)$ is the impedance as viewed into the box when all independent generators, including initial-condition ones, are replaced by their internal impedances.   Let us restate this.   If the network in the black box of Fig. 9-3a is replaced by its Thévenin equivalent circuit of Fig. 9-3b, there are no electrical measurements that we can make to tell them apart.   That is, if either of the circuits of Figs. 9-3a and b is connected into a network, the effect on that network will be identical.   It should be stressed that the equivalence of Figs. 9-3a and b is valid *only* for conditions *external* to the oneport.

The only conditions we impose upon the oneport are that its elements be linear and time invariant and that there be no coupling through the walls of the box (such as mutual inductance).   The circuit into which the oneport is connected can be nonlinear and time varying (we shall add some restrictions later in the use of nonlinear networks).

Now let us prove Thévenin's theorem.   We must demonstrate that in Figs. 9-4a and b the terminal voltage and current $\mathbf{V}(s)$ and $\mathbf{I}(s)$ are the same

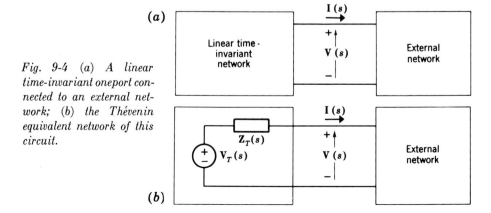

Fig. 9-4 (a) A linear time-invariant oneport connected to an external network; (b) the Thévenin equivalent network of this circuit.

for the actual network and for the Thévenin equivalent circuit.   If the input voltage and current are the same for the external network, then all conditions are the same for it.   The *external network* can contain independent generators, or dependent generators, or be nonlinear or time varying.   We need only assume that the voltage across its terminals is some function of the current entering them.

If $\mathbf{I}(s)$ is the Laplace transform of the current entering the terminals and $\mathbf{V}(s)$ is the Laplace transform of the voltage across the terminals, then we assume that $\mathbf{V}(s)$ can be written as

$$\mathbf{V}(s) = f[\mathbf{I}(s)] \qquad (9\text{-}12)$$

Note that this function is due to the *external network*.   [In the case of non-linear networks we may, in *theory*, have to obtain an infinite catalog to obtain Eq. (9-12); that is, for each $i(t)$ compute a $v(t)$ and then take the Laplace transforms to obtain Eq. (9-12).]

Now we treat the external network as just a single element which is characterized by Eq. (9-12) and perform a loop analysis on the circuit of Fig. 9-4a. This is shown in Fig. 9-5a.   We choose loop currents so that the only loop current into the external network is $\mathbf{I}_n(s)$.   Then the loop-current equations are of the form

$$\mathbf{V}_1(s) = \mathbf{Z}_{11}(s)\mathbf{I}_1(s) + \mathbf{Z}_{12}(s)\mathbf{I}_2(s) + \cdots + \mathbf{Z}_{1n}(s)\mathbf{I}_n(s)$$
$$\mathbf{V}_2(s) = \mathbf{Z}_{21}(s)\mathbf{I}_1(s) + \mathbf{Z}_{22}(s)\mathbf{I}_2(s) + \cdots + \mathbf{Z}_{2n}(s)\mathbf{I}_n(s)$$
$$\cdots\cdots\cdots\cdots\cdots\cdots\cdots\cdots\cdots\cdots\cdots\cdots\cdots \qquad (9\text{-}13)$$
$$\mathbf{V}_n(s) = \mathbf{Z}_{n1}(s)\mathbf{I}_1(s) + \mathbf{Z}_{n2}(s)\mathbf{I}_2(s) + \cdots + \mathbf{Z}_{nn}(s)\mathbf{I}_n(s) + \mathbf{V}(s)$$

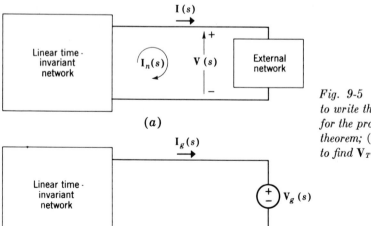

Fig. 9-5   A circuit used to write the loop equations for the proof of Thévenin's theorem; (b) a circuit used to find $\mathbf{V}_T(s)$ and $\mathbf{Z}_T(s)$.

where $\mathbf{I}_1(s) \cdots \mathbf{I}_{n-1}(s)$ are in the linear time-invariant network. Note that the external network does not "couple" to any of the loop currents. It enters into the equations only as a voltage drop in the nth loop. Now we solve for $\mathbf{I}_n(s)$, which is equal to $\mathbf{I}(s)$ [consider that $\mathbf{V}(s)$ is brought over to the left-hand side of the last equation]. We have

$$\mathbf{I}(s) = \frac{\mathbf{\Delta}_{1n}}{\mathbf{\Delta}}\mathbf{V}_1(s) + \frac{\mathbf{\Delta}_{2n}}{\mathbf{\Delta}}\mathbf{V}_2(s) + \cdots + \frac{\mathbf{\Delta}_{nn}}{\mathbf{\Delta}}\mathbf{V}_n(s) - \frac{\mathbf{\Delta}_{nn}}{\mathbf{\Delta}}\mathbf{V}(s) \qquad (9\text{-}14a)$$

This can be written in more compact form as

$$\mathbf{I}(s) = \sum_{k=1}^{n} \frac{\mathbf{\Delta}_{kn}}{\mathbf{\Delta}}\mathbf{V}_k(s) - \frac{\mathbf{\Delta}_{nn}}{\mathbf{\Delta}}\mathbf{V}(s) \qquad (9\text{-}14b)$$

where

$$\mathbf{\Delta} = \begin{vmatrix} \mathbf{Z}_{11}(s) & \mathbf{Z}_{12}(s) & \cdots & \mathbf{Z}_{1n}(s) \\ \mathbf{Z}_{21}(s) & \mathbf{Z}_{22}(s) & \cdots & \mathbf{Z}_{2n}(s) \\ \cdots & \cdots & \cdots & \cdots \\ \mathbf{Z}_{n1}(s) & \mathbf{Z}_{n2}(s) & \cdots & \mathbf{Z}_{nn}(s) \end{vmatrix} \qquad (9\text{-}15)$$

Equations (9-14) consist of one equation with two unknowns, $\mathbf{V}(s)$ and $\mathbf{I}(s)$. Equation (9-12) is another equation with these two unknowns. Hence we can solve for $\mathbf{V}(s)$ and $\mathbf{I}(s)$. There is one assumption that we must make about the external network: if it is nonlinear, Eqs. (9-12) and (9-14) must be such that they yield a unique solution for $\mathbf{V}(s)$ and $\mathbf{I}(s)$.

If Fig. 9-4b is to be equivalent for external conditions to Fig. 9-4a, then $\mathbf{V}(s)$ and $\mathbf{I}(s)$ calculated from Fig. 9-4b must be the same as those calculated from Fig. 9-4a. We apply loop analysis to Fig. 9-4b and solve for $\mathbf{I}(s)$. This yields

$$\mathbf{I}(s) = \frac{\mathbf{V}_T(s)}{\mathbf{Z}_T(s)} - \frac{\mathbf{V}(s)}{\mathbf{Z}_T(s)} \qquad (9\text{-}16)$$

This equation, in conjunction with Eq. (9-12), can also be solved for $\mathbf{V}(s)$ and $\mathbf{I}(s)$. Thus, if Figs. 9-4a and 9-4b are to be equivalent, then Eqs. (9-14) and (9-16) must be identical. If they are identical, then comparison of Eqs. (9-14) and (9-16) yields

$$\mathbf{Z}_T(s) = \frac{\mathbf{\Delta}}{\mathbf{\Delta}_{nn}} \qquad (9\text{-}17)$$

$$\mathbf{V}_T(s) = \sum_{k=1}^{n} \frac{\mathbf{\Delta}_{kn}}{\mathbf{\Delta}_{nn}}\mathbf{V}_k(s) \qquad (9\text{-}18)$$

According to Thévenin's theorem, $\mathbf{V}_T(s)$ must be the open-circuit voltage of the network and $\mathbf{Z}_T(s)$ must be the impedance as viewed into the network, with all generators replaced by their internal impedances. If we prove that $\mathbf{V}_T(s)$ and $\mathbf{Z}_T(s)$ given by Eqs. (9-17) and (9-18) are such quantities, then we have proved Thévenin's theorem.   Let us see if Eqs. (9-17) and (9-18) satisfy these requirements.

One procedure for determining the open-circuit voltage is to apply a voltage generator to the oneport, as shown in Fig. 9-5*b*. We adjust the voltage $\mathbf{V}_g(s)$ until the current into the network is zero.   If there is no current from the oneport, then the voltage across its terminals must be its open-circuit voltage (note that any element can be replaced by a current generator equal to its current, and a current generator of zero can be replaced by an open circuit).   Equation (9-14) will characterize the network of Fig. 9-5*b* if we replace $\mathbf{I}(s)$ by $\mathbf{I}_g(s)$ and $\mathbf{V}(s)$ by $\mathbf{V}_g(s)$. We then set $\mathbf{I}_g(s) = 0$, and $\mathbf{V}_g(s)$ becomes the open-circuit voltage $\mathbf{V}_{oc}(s)$.   Thus

$$\sum_{k=1}^{n} \frac{\mathbf{\Delta}_{kn}}{\mathbf{\Delta}} \mathbf{V}_k(s) - \frac{\mathbf{\Delta}_{nn}}{\mathbf{\Delta}} \mathbf{V}_{oc}(s) = 0 \tag{9-19a}$$

or, equivalently,

$$\mathbf{V}_{oc}(s) = \sum_{k=1}^{n} \frac{\mathbf{\Delta}_{kn}}{\mathbf{\Delta}_{nn}} \mathbf{V}_k(s) \tag{9-19b}$$

Comparison with Eq. (9-18) shows that

$$\mathbf{V}_T(s) = \mathbf{V}_{oc}(s) \tag{9-20}$$

Thus $\mathbf{V}_T(s)$ is as it should be.

Now let us compute the impedance viewed into the oneport, with all independent generators replaced by their internal impedances. We can again use Fig. 9-5*b*, with all the internal independent generators (in the black box) set equal to their internal impedances.   We have

$$\mathbf{Z}_{in}(s) = - \frac{\mathbf{V}_g(s)}{\mathbf{I}_g(s)} \bigg|_{\mathbf{V}_1(s) = \mathbf{V}_2(s) = \cdots = \mathbf{V}_n(s) = 0} \tag{9-21}$$

where the minus sign results from the assumed direction of $\mathbf{I}_g(s)$.   Then, substituting in Eq. (9-14), we have

$$\mathbf{Z}_{in}(s) = \frac{\mathbf{\Delta}}{\mathbf{\Delta}_{nn}} \tag{9-22}$$

Comparison with Eq. (9-17) shows that

$$\mathbf{Z}_T(s) = \mathbf{Z}_{in}(s)$$

Then $\mathbf{Z}_T(s)$ is as it should be, and we have proved the theorem.

We have seen that the external network can be nonlinear. As a practical matter, however, we do not use Laplace transforms to solve nonlinear circuit problems.   This may seem to limit the utility of Thévenin's theorem since $\mathbf{V}_{oc}(s)$ and $\mathbf{Z}_T(s)$ are in Laplace transform form, but at times the internal impedance is purely resistive, and we can use Thévenin's theorem on a time-domain

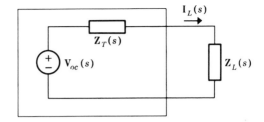

Fig. 9-6 A circuit that can be used to determine $\mathbf{Z}_T(s)$ when a short-circuit measurement cannot be made.

basis. That is, we take the inverse transform of $\mathbf{V}_T(s)$; call it $v_T(t)$. This, then, is the Thévenin voltage generator. The Z_T is simply the resistive imped-ance. Even if the impedance is not purely resistive, we can at times synthesize, or construct, an impedance which is equivalent to it and can be put in series with the time-domain voltage generator. This impedance can be obtained from the impedance configuration that results when all the independent gen-erators are replaced by their internal impedances. This assumes that the Thévenin equivalent circuit is obtained from a circuit diagram. If it is obtained from open- and short-circuit measurements, there are other tech-niques available to synthesize the impedance (such techniques are beyond the scope of this book). Once a valid Thévenin equivalent circuit has been obtained, any valid analysis procedure can be used to study the network.

One word of caution is needed. This theorem is valid on a sinusoidal-steady-state basis if s is replaced by $j\omega$ and the transforms of the generators are replaced by phasors. If we are dealing with a sinusoidal steady state, in general, we *cannot* work with nonlinear or time-varying networks. Thus, in the sinusoidal steady state the external network should be linear and time invariant.

Let us consider another procedure for obtaining the Thévenin equivalent circuit. Suppose we place a short circuit across the output of the oneport of Fig. 9-3. The short-circuit current will be

$$\mathbf{I}_{sc}(s) = \frac{\mathbf{V}_{oc}(s)}{\mathbf{Z}_T(s)} \tag{9-23a}$$

or, equivalently,

$$\mathbf{Z}_T(s) = \frac{\mathbf{V}_{oc}(s)}{\mathbf{I}_{sc}(s)} \tag{9-23b}$$

Thus, by making two simple measurements, an open-circuit voltage measure-ment and a short-circuit current measurement, the Thévenin equivalent circuit can be obtained, no matter how complex the oneport. At times a network will be damaged by a short-circuit measurement. In such cases we can place a known impedance $\mathbf{Z}_L(s)$ across the terminal and measure the cur-rent (see Fig. 9-6). In addition to the open-circuit voltage, we measure $\mathbf{I}_L(s)$.

Then

$$\mathbf{I}_L(s) = \frac{\mathbf{V}_{oc}(s)}{\mathbf{Z}_T(s) + \mathbf{Z}_L(s)} \tag{9-24}$$

and we can determine $\mathbf{Z}_T(s)$.

As an example, suppose we wish to make a Thévenin circuit measurement of an electric outlet. A short circuit placed across the outlet would "blow" the fuse or circuit breaker. Thus a short-circuit current measurement cannot be made. However, the measurement defined in Eq. (9-24) can be used to determine $\mathbf{I}_L(s)$ [or $\mathbf{I}_L(j\omega)$ on a sinusoidal-steady-state basis]. For reasons of accuracy, the magnitude of $\mathbf{Z}_L$ should be the smallest one that can be used without producing a value of $\mathbf{I}_L$ which overloads the circuit. Note that two simple measurements are used to obtain a Thévenin equivalent circuit which represents an *entire* power system. Such a system can extend over an area of a thousand square miles or more. It could have a circuit diagram that has thousands of meshes and nodes. However, two simple measurements characterize it as far as conditions at the outlet in question are concerned. If the system changes after the measurement is made, then the Thévenin equivalent circuit must also be changed (the measurements must be repeated).

Let us consider an example of Thévenin's theorem. We shall find the Thévenin equivalent circuit for the Laplace transformed network of Fig. 9-7a.

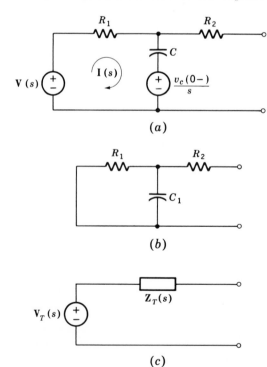

(a)

(b)

(c)

Fig. 9-7 (a) A network to be replaced by the Thévenin equivalent circuit; (b) a circuit used to compute $\mathbf{Z}_T(s)$; (c) the Thévenin equivalent circuit

$$\mathbf{V}_T(s) = \frac{\mathbf{V}(s) - V_c(0-)/s}{RCs + 1} + \frac{v_c(0-)}{s}$$

$$\mathbf{Z}_T(s) = R_2 + \frac{R_1}{1 + R_1Cs}$$

The open-circuit voltage is given by

$$\mathbf{V}_{oc}(s) = \frac{\mathbf{I}(s)}{Cs} + \frac{v_c(0-)}{s}$$

and

$$\mathbf{I}(s) = \frac{\mathbf{V}(s) - v_c(0-)/s}{R_1 + 1/Cs}$$

Thus

$$\mathbf{V}_{oc}(s) = \frac{\mathbf{V}(s) - v_c(0-)/s}{1 + R_1Cs} + \frac{v_c(0-)}{s} \tag{9-25}$$

When we replace the generators by their internal impedances, the circuit of Fig. 9-7b results. Hence

$$\mathbf{Z}_T(s) = R_2 + \frac{R_1}{1 + R_1Cs} \tag{9-26}$$

The Thévenin equivalent circuit is shown in Fig. 9-7c. Suppose we connect different impedances, in turn, to the terminals of the circuit of Fig. 9-7. The current in each of these can now be obtained by solving a one-loop circuit. If we had not used Thévenin's theorem, a two-loop circuit would have had to be solved each time. If the network of Fig. 9-7a were more complex, the saving in work would be still greater.

In deriving Thévenin's theorem we did not use the superposition theorem, as is often done. This was to demonstrate that Thévenin's theorem is independent of the superposition theorem.

9-3 Norton's theorem

In Sec. 5-10 we saw that a voltage generator in series with an impedance is equivalent to a current generator in shunt with an impedance as far as external conditions are concerned. Thus the Thévenin equivalent circuit can be replaced by a current-generator circuit. This is called a *Norton equivalent circuit*. Thus the two circuits, shown in Fig. 9-8, are equivalent if

$$\mathbf{I}_N(s) = \frac{\mathbf{V}_T(s)}{\mathbf{Z}_T(s)} \tag{9-27}$$

From Eq. (9-23a) we have

$$\mathbf{I}_N(s) = \mathbf{I}_{sc}(s) \tag{9-28}$$

Thus the current generator in the Norton equivalent circuit is equal to the short-circuit current of the oneport. The impedance is equal to the Thévenin impedance.

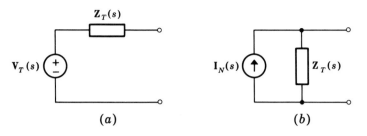

Fig. 9-8   (a) A Thévenin equivalent circuit; (b) a Norton equivalent circuit, where $\mathbf{I}_N(s) = \mathbf{V}_T(s)/\mathbf{Z}_T(s)$.

9-4   The maximum-power-transfer theorem

Often we wish the power delivered to a load impedance to be maximized. This is usually done on a sinusoidal-steady-state basis, and the power is the average power. In this section we shall work on such a basis. We wish to determine the value of the maximum power that a oneport can deliver to any impedance, and the value of load impedance that results in this maximum power. We shall use Thévenin's theorem here.

Assume that the network supplying power to the load impedance is replaced by Thévenin's theorem, as shown in Fig. 9-9a, and the load impedance $\mathbf{Z}_L(j\omega)$ is to be adjusted so that maximum power is supplied to it. In Fig. 9-9b the impedances are broken up into their resistive and reactive components (we are working at a single frequency on a sinusoidal-steady-state basis). Then, for Fig. 9-9b

$$\mathbf{I} = Ie^{j\phi} = \frac{V_T}{R_T + R_L + j(X_T + X_L)} = \frac{V_T}{\sqrt{(R_T + R_L)^2 + (X_T + X_L)^2}}\, e^{j\phi} \tag{9-29}$$

The phasors are given on an rms basis.

Fig. 9-9   (a) A Thévenin equivalent circuit with a load impedance; (b) the circuit of (a) with the impedance broken up into resistive and reactive components.

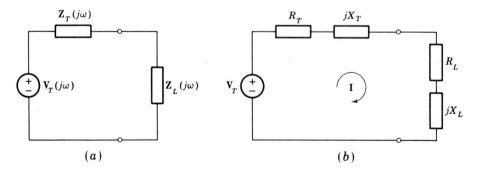

The power dissipated in the load is just the power dissipated in the resistive portion of the load. No average power is dissipated in a reactance; hence

$$P = I^2 R_L = \frac{V_T^2 R_L}{(R_T + R_L)^2 + (X_T + X_L)^2} \tag{9-30}$$

Now, suppose we vary X_L. If we set

$$X_L = -X_T \tag{9-31}$$

then Eq. (9-30) will be maximized regardless of the value of R_T or R_L. Let us do this (note that X_L will be positive if the load is inductive and negative if it is capacitive). Thus

$$P = \frac{V_T^2 R_L}{(R_T + R_L)^2} \tag{9-32}$$

Now we differentiate with respect to R_L and set the derivative equal to zero. This yields

$$\frac{V_T^2 (R_T + R_L)(R_T - R_L)}{(R_T + R_L)^3} = 0 \tag{9-33}$$

We shall restrict ourselves to passive loads, so R_L will be positive. We shall assume that R_T is also positive. If R_L approaches infinity, then Eq. (9-32) will be satisfied. However, this results in $P = 0$. Hence it is not a maximum. Therefore, for maximum power dissipated in the load impedance

$$R_L = R_T \tag{9-34}$$

(It is left to the reader to verify that this value of R_L does not give a minimum or a point of inflection.)

Equations (9-31) and (9-34) give the requirement on $\mathbf{Z}_L$ such that maximum power be supplied to it. When they are satisfied, the load is said to be *matched* for maximum power transfer. Let us compute the maximum power. Substituting Eqs. (9-31) and (9-34) into Eq. (9-30), we obtain

$$P_{\max} = \frac{V_T^2}{4R_T} \tag{9-35}$$

This is the maximum power that the oneport can supply to any passive load.

At times $\mathbf{Z}_L$ and $\mathbf{Z}_T$ are purely resistive, but neither can be varied. To obtain maximum power transfer in such cases the impedance-matching properties of a transformer can be used [see Eq. (6-238)]. A transformer is inserted between the load and the oneport, as shown in Fig. 9-10, and the turns ratio is adjusted so that

$$R_T = \left(\frac{n_1}{n_2}\right)^2 R_L \tag{9-36}$$

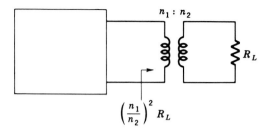

$\left(\dfrac{n_1}{n_2}\right)^2 R_L$

Fig. 9-10   The use of an ideal transformer to impedance-match a oneport.

Maximum power is then transferred to the ideal transformer. Since it is lossless, the power is then transferred to the load.   Even if Z_T and Z_L are not resistive, this procedure can be used if a reactance X_L can be inserted between the oneport and the transformer.   The value of X_L should be such that $(n_1/n_2)^2 Z_L + jX_L$ has a reactance equal to the negative of X_T.

There is one fact that should be noted carefully since it often causes trouble. Consider Fig. 9-9, but now assume that Z_T is variable and that its variation does not affect V_T.   In addition, assume that Z_L is fixed.   Now let us maximize the power.   Since R_T does not enter into the numerator of Eq. (9-30), the power is maximized when

$$X_T = -X_L \tag{9-37a}$$

$$R_T = 0 \tag{9-37b}$$

This gives different results from those when the load is adjustable.   It is usually not possible to vary Z_T, but these comments are included because the idea of a varying Z_T often causes confusion.

9-5   The reciprocity principle

Many networks exhibit a property which we shall term *reciprocity*.   Let us define it and then determine the network characteristics that produce it. Initially our discussion will be confined to the networks that have only one independent generator, with the assumption that all initial conditions are zero.

Consider the circuit of Fig. 9-11a, which represents a network with one voltage generator. $\mathbf{I}_j(s)$ is the current in some branch j of the network in response to the voltage generator $\mathbf{V}_k(s)$ in branch k.   In Fig. 9-11b the voltage generator has been placed in branch j; it is now called $\mathbf{V}_j(s)$.   Let us determine the current in branch k.   The voltage generator has been replaced by a short circuit in branch k.   If the network is reciprocal, then

$$\frac{\mathbf{I}_j(s)}{\mathbf{V}_k(s)} = \frac{\mathbf{I}_k(s)}{\mathbf{V}_j(s)} \tag{9-38}$$

We can state this in the following way.   In a reciprocal network the ratio

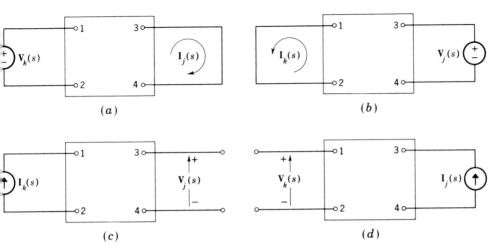

Fig. 9-11 *Reciprocal networks:* (a) $\mathbf{I}_j(s)/\mathbf{V}_k(s) = \mathbf{Y}_{T_1}(s)$; (b) $\mathbf{I}_k(s)/\mathbf{V}_j(s) = \mathbf{Y}_{T_2}(s)$; (c) $\mathbf{V}_j(s)/\mathbf{I}_k(s) = \mathbf{Z}_{T_1}(s)$; (d) $\mathbf{V}_k(s)/\mathbf{I}_j(s) = \mathbf{Z}_{T_2}(s)$. *If the network is reciprocal,* $\mathbf{Y}_{T_1}(s) = \mathbf{Y}_{T_2}(s)$ *and* $\mathbf{Z}_{T_1}(s) = \mathbf{Z}_{T_2}(s)$.

of the transform of the current in a short circuit at one part of a network to the transform of the voltage generator connected at another part of the network does not change if the position of the generator and short circuit are interchanged. Note that the generator is considered to be ideal; that is, it has no internal impedance. Also, the current is in a short circuit. This is no limitation, since any element can be considered to have a zero-resistance wire connected to it, as illustrated in Fig. 9-12a.

Reciprocity also applies to current generators and a voltage response across an open circuit. For instance, consider Figs. 9-11c and d. If the network is reciprocal, then

$$\frac{\mathbf{V}_j(s)}{\mathbf{I}_k(s)} = \frac{\mathbf{V}_k(s)}{\mathbf{I}_j(s)} \qquad\qquad (9\text{-}39)$$

Fig. 9-12 (a) *A short circuit (between terminals ab) in series with an impedance;* (b) *an open circuit across an impedance.*

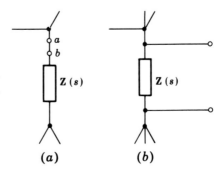

Note that there does not have to be a specific open circuit. We can always place one across any impedance (see Fig. 9-12b). Thus the statement of reciprocity can be extended: the ratio of the transform of the current (voltage) in a short circuit (across an open circuit) of a network to the transform of a voltage (current) generator applied at another part of the network is unchanged if the positions of the generators and short circuit (open circuit) are interchanged. Note that in so far as reciprocity is concerned, the response to a voltage generator is a current and the response to a current generator is a voltage. Reciprocity *does not have any implications* for a voltage in response to a voltage generator or a current in response to a current generator.

Let us now consider a general class of networks and demonstrate that such networks are reciprocal. This class consists of any network made up only of resistors, inductors, capacitors, and mutual inductors. Loop-analysis equations of such circuits will generally be of the form

$$\mathbf{V}_1(s) = \mathbf{Z}_{11}(s)\mathbf{I}_1(s) + \mathbf{Z}_{12}(s)\mathbf{I}_2(s) + \cdots + \mathbf{Z}_{1n}(s)\mathbf{I}_n(s)$$
$$\mathbf{V}_2(s) = \mathbf{Z}_{21}(s)\mathbf{I}_1(s) + \mathbf{Z}_{22}(s)\mathbf{I}_2(s) + \cdots + \mathbf{Z}_{2n}(s)\mathbf{I}_n(s)$$
$$\cdots \cdots \cdots \cdots \cdots \cdots \cdots \cdots \cdots \cdots \cdots \cdots \cdots \cdots$$ (9-40)
$$\mathbf{V}_n(s) = \mathbf{Z}_{n1}(s)\mathbf{I}_1(s) + \mathbf{Z}_{n2}(s)\mathbf{I}_2(s) + \cdots + \mathbf{Z}_{nn}(s)\mathbf{I}_n(s)$$

If the network contains only resistors, inductors, capacitors, and mutual inductors, then

$$\mathbf{Z}_{ij}(s) = \mathbf{Z}_{ji}(s)$$ (9-41)

[this is discussed in the paragraph following Eq. (3-16)]. Let us assume that there are zero initial conditions and that the circuit contains only one independent voltage generator. Let this be in the *j*th loop. Also, let us assume that loop currents are chosen so that the generator lies only in this loop. Now let us solve for $\mathbf{I}_k(s)$. We choose loop currents so that $\mathbf{I}_k(s)$ is the current in the branch in question; call this branch *k*. From Cramer's rule [see Eq. (5-144)] we obtain

$$\mathbf{I}_k(s) = \frac{\mathbf{\Delta}_{jk}\mathbf{V}_j(s)}{\mathbf{\Delta}}$$ (9-42a)

or

$$\frac{\mathbf{I}_k(s)}{\mathbf{V}_j(s)} = \frac{\mathbf{\Delta}_{jk}}{\mathbf{\Delta}}$$ (9-42b)

where

$$\mathbf{\Delta} = \begin{vmatrix} \mathbf{Z}_{11}(s) & \mathbf{Z}_{12}(s) & \cdots & \mathbf{Z}_{1n}(s) \\ \mathbf{Z}_{21}(s) & \mathbf{Z}_{22}(s) & \cdots & \mathbf{Z}_{2n}(s) \\ \cdots & \cdots & \cdots & \cdots \\ \mathbf{Z}_{n1}(s) & \mathbf{Z}_{n2}(s) & \cdots & \mathbf{Z}_{nn}(s) \end{vmatrix}$$ (9-43)

Now suppose the generator is placed in branch k; we shall now call it $\mathbf{V}_k(s)$. It is replaced by a short circuit in loop j. Note that this does not change $\mathbf{\Delta}$, since all the impedances are unchanged by this substitution. Then, in Eq. (9-40) all the voltage generators except $\mathbf{V}_k(s)$ are zero (note that branch k lies only in loop k). Thus

$$\mathbf{I}_j(s) = \frac{\mathbf{\Delta}_{kj}\mathbf{V}_k(s)}{\mathbf{\Delta}} \tag{9-44a}$$

or

$$\frac{\mathbf{I}_j(s)}{\mathbf{V}_k(s)} = \frac{\mathbf{\Delta}_{kj}}{\mathbf{\Delta}} \tag{9-44b}$$

If the network is reciprocal, then Eqs. (9-42b) and (9-44b) are equal. If this is to be so, then

$$\mathbf{\Delta}_{jk} = \mathbf{\Delta}_{kj} \tag{9-45}$$

A general study of determinants will indicate that this relation holds if the determinant is symmetrical ($\mathbf{Z}_{ij} = \mathbf{Z}_{ji}$). We have demonstrated that it is [see Eq. (9-41)]. Hence Eq. (9-45) is valid, and

$$\frac{\mathbf{I}_k(s)}{\mathbf{V}_j(s)} = \frac{\mathbf{I}_j(s)}{\mathbf{V}_k(s)} \tag{9-46}$$

We could prove the second statement of the reciprocity theorem, involving current generators and voltages across elements, by working analogously with nodal or cut-set analysis. The details of this analysis, which parallel those we have just considered for loop analysis, are left to the reader. We have demonstrated that networks composed of only resistors, inductors, capacitors, and mutual inductors are reciprocal.

Let us see the effect of reciprocity on twoport parameters. We shall begin with the z parameters. Consider Eqs. (8-10) and (8-13), which give $\mathbf{z}_{21}(s)$ and $\mathbf{z}_{12}(s)$, respectively, as

$$\mathbf{z}_{21}(s) = \left.\frac{\mathbf{V}_2(s)}{\mathbf{I}_1(s)}\right|_{\mathbf{I}_2(s)\,=\,0} \tag{9-47a}$$

$$\mathbf{z}_{12}(s) = \left.\frac{\mathbf{V}_1(s)}{\mathbf{I}_2(s)}\right|_{\mathbf{I}_1(s)\,=\,0} \tag{9-47b}$$

However, from Eq. (9-39), these two equations are equal in reciprocal networks. Thus

$$\mathbf{z}_{12}(s) = \mathbf{z}_{21}(s) \tag{9-48}$$

in a reciprocal network. Then, from Eq. (8-59a) we see that for the characteristic functions

$$\mathbf{a}(s) = \mathbf{r}(s) \tag{9-49}$$

Hence [see Eq. (8-59*b*)]

$$\mathbf{y}_{12}(s) = \mathbf{y}_{21}(s) \tag{9-50}$$

From Eqs. (8-59*e*) and (8-58) we have

$$\mathbf{A}(s)\mathbf{D}(s) - \mathbf{B}(s)\mathbf{C}(s) = \frac{\mathbf{g}(s)\mathbf{h}(s) - \mathbf{y}(s)\mathbf{z}(s)}{\mathbf{a}(s)} = \frac{\mathbf{r}(s)}{\mathbf{a}(s)} \tag{9-51}$$

Then, substituting Eq. (9-49), we see that in a reciprocal network

$$\mathbf{A}(s)\mathbf{D}(s) - \mathbf{B}(s)\mathbf{C}(s) = 1 \tag{9-52}$$

Often, but not always, networks containing dependent generators are non-reciprocal. For instance, consider Eqs. (3-48), (3-51), and (5-141), which are loop and nodal equations for circuits containing dependent generators. Note that the equations are not symmetrical [for example, in Eq. (5-141) $\mathbf{Z}_{ij} \neq \mathbf{Z}_{ji}$ for all $\mathbf{Z}_{ij}$].

We have thus far considered only one independent generator in the reciprocal network. If there are more, then the superposition theorem can be applied. Thus we can consider subnetworks each of which has only one independent generator, and the reciprocity theorem can be applied to each of these subnetworks.

9-6   The compensation theorem

Often an element will change value in a network from such causes as heating or aging, and we wish to calculate the effect of this change on the currents and voltages of the network. An analogous problem occurs when a network is initially designed and built. The values of the actual elements will be somewhat different from the designed values owing to the tolerance of the components; thus we can consider that the actual elements have "changed" from their designed values.

Let us assume that a single element has changed value. To calculate the effect of this change on any current or voltage, we could perform a loop, nodal, or cut-set analysis upon the network in question and calculate the new current or voltage. This can be very tedious, especially if we wish to calculate the effect of several changes in the element value. In this section we shall consider a procedure that lessens the tedium.

Consider the network representation of Fig. 9-13*a*. The impedance which can vary is $\mathbf{Z}(s)$. It has a current $\mathbf{I}_1(s)$ in it. We wish to study the effect of the change in impedance on the current $\mathbf{I}_k(s)$, which is some current in the network. In Fig. 9-13*b* the change in $\mathbf{Z}(s)$ is represented by $\delta\mathbf{Z}(s)$. The currents change to $\mathbf{I}_1(s) + \delta\mathbf{I}_1(s)$ and $\mathbf{I}_k(s) + \delta\mathbf{I}_k(s)$, etc., when the impedance changes. The voltage drop across $\delta\mathbf{Z}(s)$ is

$$\mathbf{V}_{\delta Z}(s) = \delta\mathbf{Z}(s)\,[\mathbf{I}_1(s) + \delta\mathbf{I}_1(s)] \tag{9-53}$$

We can replace any element by a voltage generator equal to the voltage across it (see Sec. 7-2). Thus we can replace Fig. 9-13b by Fig. 9-14a. If both voltage generators $\delta\mathbf{Z}(s)\,\mathbf{I}_1(s)$ and $\delta\mathbf{Z}(s)\,\delta\mathbf{I}_1(s)$ are replaced by short circuits, then the original network, with the original currents, results. Thus application of the superposition theorem to Fig. 9-14a yields Fig. 9-14b. This figure can be used to calculate the changes in any current due to a change in $\mathbf{Z}(s)$.

The only problem here is that we must know $\delta\mathbf{I}_1(s)$ to find one generator voltage. Thus we must consider the original circuit, with $\mathbf{Z}(s)$ replaced by $\mathbf{Z}(s) + \delta\mathbf{Z}(s)$, and solve it for $\mathbf{I}_1(s) + \delta\mathbf{I}_1(s)$. It would save work if we just solved this circuit directly for $\mathbf{I}_k(s) + \delta\mathbf{I}_k(s)$ and did not use the compensation theorem. This difficulty can be resolved in the following way. The current in the voltage generator $\delta\mathbf{Z}(s)\,\delta\mathbf{I}_1(s)$ is $\delta\mathbf{I}_1(s)$. If this generator were replaced by an impedance $\delta\mathbf{Z}(s)$, the same voltage drop would be obtained, and the circuit would be equivalent. This is done in Fig. 9-14c. Thus we no longer need to solve for $\delta\mathbf{I}_1(s)$ and hence we need only solve for the current in the one generator network of Fig. 9-14c to obtain the change in any current caused by a change in $\mathbf{Z}(s)$ (note that when the independent generators are replaced by their internal impedances, a simpler network may result).

The circuit of Fig. 9-13c is satisfactory, but it can be improved upon somewhat. Often we wish to calculate the effect of many different changes in $\mathbf{Z}(s)$. The impedance $\delta\mathbf{Z}(s)$ changes with each calculation. This changes the circuit determinant, and hence a new determinant must be evaluated for each calculation. The generator $\delta\mathbf{Z}(s)\,\mathbf{I}_1(s)$ also changes, but this does not complicate the situation because, in general, $\delta\mathbf{Z}(s)\,\mathbf{I}_1(s)$ enters into the solution only as

Fig. 9-13 (a) *A network containing an impedance* $\mathbf{Z}(s)$ *which will change by an amount* $\delta\mathbf{Z}(s)$ *and a current* $\mathbf{I}_K(s)$ *to be studied;* (b) *the network after* $\mathbf{Z}(s)$ *has changed. The currents have changed by* $\delta\mathbf{I}(s)$.

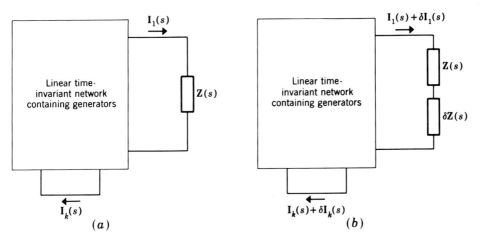

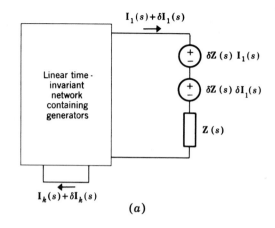

(a)

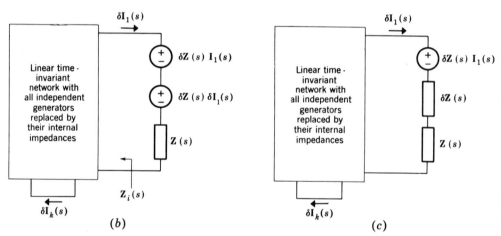

(b)   (c)

Fig. 9-14   (a) A network equivalent to Fig. 9-13b, with $\delta\mathbf{Z}(s)$ replaced by a voltage generator; (b) a network that can be used to calculate $\delta\mathbf{I}_k(s)$; (c) an alternative representation of (b).

a multiplying factor [see Eq. (9-42a) for the solution of a circuit with only one voltage generator].   To improve the situation, we must calculate $\mathbf{Z}_i(s)$, the impedance viewed into the network, as shown in Fig. 9-14b.   This involves one additional calculation, but it will save us many calculations if many values of $\delta\mathbf{Z}$ are to be used.

Suppose we have calculated $\mathbf{Z}_i(s)$.   Then the current $\delta\mathbf{I}_1(s)$ is given by (see Fig. 9-14b)

$$\delta\mathbf{I}_1(s) = \frac{-\delta\mathbf{Z}(s)\,\mathbf{I}_1(s) - \delta\mathbf{Z}(s)\,\delta\mathbf{I}_1(s)}{\mathbf{Z}(s) + \mathbf{Z}_i(s)} \qquad (9\text{-}54a)$$

Then, solving for $\delta\mathbf{I}_1(s)$, we obtain

$$\delta\mathbf{I}_1(s) = -\frac{\delta\mathbf{Z}(s)\,\mathbf{I}_1(s)}{\mathbf{Z}_i(s) + \mathbf{Z}(s) + \delta\mathbf{Z}(s)} \tag{9-54b}$$

Using Eq. (9-54b) to obtain a voltage equal to the sum of that produced by the two generators of Fig. 9-14b, we obtain

$$\delta\mathbf{Z}(s)\,\mathbf{I}_1(s) + \delta\mathbf{Z}(s)\,\delta\mathbf{I}_1(s) = \delta\mathbf{Z}(s)\,\mathbf{I}_1(s)\,\frac{\mathbf{Z}_i(s) + \mathbf{Z}(s)}{\mathbf{Z}_i(s) + \mathbf{Z}(s) + \delta\mathbf{Z}(s)} \tag{9-55}$$

Thus the two voltage generators of Fig. 9-14b can be replaced by one whose voltage is given by Eq. (9-55); this is shown in Fig. 9-15.   Now the characteristic determinant is the same as that of the original network.   Thus it need only be calculated once, even if we make calculations involving many $\delta\mathbf{Z}(s)$.

Let us consider an example of this procedure.   Let us determine the change in the generator current caused by a change in R_3 in Fig. 9-16.   We calculate $\mathbf{I}_1(s)$ from the network of Fig. 9-16.   This entails solving the loop equations

$$0 = \left(R_2 + R_3 + \frac{1}{Cs}\right)\mathbf{I}_1(s) - \frac{1}{Cs}\,\mathbf{I}_2(s) \tag{9-56a}$$

$$\mathbf{V}(s) = -\frac{1}{Cs}\,\mathbf{I}_1(s) + \left(R_1 + \frac{1}{Cs}\right)\mathbf{I}_2(s) \tag{9-56b}$$

Hence

$$\mathbf{I}_1(s) = \frac{\mathbf{V}(s)/Cs}{(R_1 + 1/Cs)(R_2 + R_3 + 1/Cs) - 1/(Cs)^2}$$

$$= \frac{\mathbf{V}(s)}{R_1 + R_2 + R_3 + (R_1R_2 + R_1R_3)Cs} \tag{9-57}$$

Fig. 9-15   A network equivalent to Fig. 9-14b which should be used for calculations involving several different values of $\delta\mathbf{Z}(s)$.

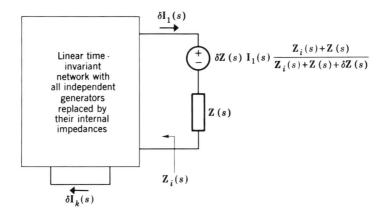

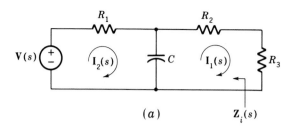

(a)

$Z_i(s)$

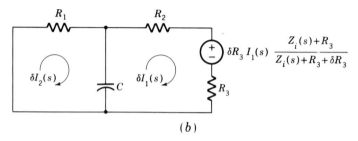

(b)

*Fig. 9-16   (a) A two-loop circuit.   Note that $Z_i(s)$ calculated with
$V(s)$ replaced by a short circuit; (b) the circuit used to calculate the
changes in the currents caused by a change in R_3.*

Now we calculate $Z_i(s)$, with $V(s)$ replaced by a short circuit, as

$$Z_i(s) = R_2 + \frac{R_1}{1 + R_1 Cs} \tag{9-58}$$

The circuit of Fig. 9-16b is used to compute the change in current for any value
of δR_3.   The value of $I_1(s)$ and $Z_i(s)$ are given in Eqs. (9-57) and (9-58).
Writing loop equations for this circuit, we have

$$-\delta R_3\, I_1(s)\, \frac{Z_i(s) + R_3}{Z_i(s) + R_3 + \delta R_3} = \left(R_2 + R_3 + \frac{1}{Cs}\right)\delta I_1(s) - \frac{1}{Cs}\,\delta I_2(s) \tag{9-59a}$$

$$0 = -\frac{1}{Cs}\,\delta I_1(s) + \left(R_1 + \frac{1}{Cs}\right)\delta I_2(s) \tag{9-59b}$$

Solving these simultaneous equations and substituting Eqs. (9-57) and (9-58),
we have

$$\delta I_2(s) = \frac{-\delta R_3\, V(s)}{[R_1 + R_2 + R_3 + R_1(R_2 + R_3)Cs]\,\{R_1 + R_2 + R_3(1 + \delta) \atop\qquad\qquad\qquad + [R_2 + R_3(1 + \delta)]\,R_1 Cs\}}$$

$$\tag{9-59c}$$

Note that the characteristic determinant is the same as for Eqs. (9-56).
Hence it has already been evaluated and need not be solved again.   It now

becomes a matter of simple substitution in Eq. (9-59c) to obtain the effect of many different changes in R_3.

If δ is small, Eq. (9-59c) can be simplified. If $\delta \ll 1$, then we have

$$\delta \mathbf{I}_2(s) \approx -\delta R_3 \frac{\mathbf{V}(s)}{[(R_1 + R_2 + R_3) + R_1(R_2 + R_3)Cs]^2} \tag{9-59d}$$

In this case the change in $\mathbf{I}_2(s)$ is the change in R_3 multiplied by a function which is independent of δR_3.

9-7 Duality

The equations of loop analysis and those of nodal or cut-set analysis are very similar in form. Many times we have proved a statement by loop analysis and then noted that a similar result would follow analogously using nodal or cut-set analysis. That is, usually the voltages and currents behave analogously in electric networks. This is termed *duality*. For instance, one form of the reciprocity principle (see Sec. 9-5) involves a current in a short circuit in response to a voltage generator. The dual form of the theorem involves the voltage across an open circuit in response to a current generator.

We can also speak of *dual networks*. Two networks are said to be duals if the loop equations of one are the *same* as the nodal or cut-set equations of the other, except that the functions of voltage and current have been interchanged. For example, loop equations for the circuit of Fig. 9-17a are

$$\mathbf{V}_{g1}(s) = \left(R + \frac{1}{Cs}\right) \mathbf{I}_1(s) - \frac{1}{Cs}\,\mathbf{I}_2(s) \tag{9-60a}$$

$$\mathbf{V}_{g2}(s) = -\frac{1}{Cs}\,\mathbf{I}_1(s) + \left(Ls + \frac{1}{Cs}\right) \mathbf{I}_2(s) \tag{9-60b}$$

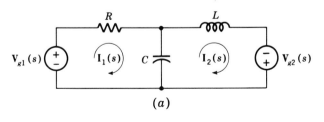

Fig. 9-17 (a) A two-loop network; (b) its dual if $R_1 = 1/R$, $L_1 = C$, $C_1 = L$, $\mathbf{I}_{g1}(s) = \mathbf{V}_{g1}(s)$, and $\mathbf{I}_{g2}(s) = \mathbf{V}_{g2}(s)$.

(a)

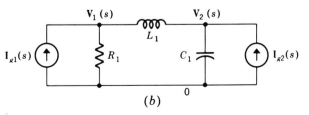

(b)

and nodal equations for the network of Fig. 9-17*b* are

$$\mathbf{I}_{g1}(s) = \left(\frac{1}{R_1} + \frac{1}{L_1 s} \right) \mathbf{V}_1(s) - \frac{1}{L_1 s} \mathbf{V}_2(s) \tag{9-61a}$$

$$\mathbf{I}_{g2}(s) = -\frac{1}{L_1 s} \mathbf{V}_1(s) + \left(C_1 s + \frac{1}{L_1 s} \right) \mathbf{V}_2(s) \tag{9-61b}$$

Now let us assume that

$$R_1 = \frac{1}{R} \tag{9-62a}$$

$$L_1 = C \tag{9-62b}$$

$$C_1 = L \tag{9-62c}$$

$$\mathbf{I}_{g1}(s) = \mathbf{V}_{g1}(s) \tag{9-62d}$$

$$\mathbf{I}_{g2}(s) = \mathbf{V}_{g2}(s) \tag{9-62e}$$

Substituting these values into Eq. (9-61), we obtain

$$\mathbf{V}_{g1}(s) = \left(R + \frac{1}{Cs} \right) \mathbf{V}_1(s) - \frac{1}{Cs} \mathbf{V}_2(s) \tag{9-63a}$$

$$\mathbf{V}_{g2}(s) = -\frac{1}{Cs} \mathbf{V}_1(s) + \left(Ls + \frac{1}{Cs} \right) \mathbf{V}_2(s) \tag{9-63b}$$

Equations (9-60) and (9-63) are the same, except that the functions of the unknown voltages and currents are interchanged. Thus, if Eqs. (9-62) hold, Figs. 9-17*a* and 9-17*b* are duals.

We shall now discuss without proof, a procedure whereby the dual of any *planar network* can be obtained. A planar network is one that can be drawn on a plane without any wires crossing (see Fig. 3-41 for an example of a *non-planar* network). We shall consider this procedure in general terms, but using the specific example of Fig. 9-18. The technique consists of a sequence of rules.

1. Identify each windowpane loop of the network (each area enclosed by circuit elements) and put a small circle inside each one. Number these in sequence, beginning with 1. Place a small circle outside the network and number it zero.

2. At the place where the dual network is to be drawn, put small circles corresponding to the ones drawn in the original network, including the zero circle (typical spacing is shown in Fig. 9-18*b*). These circles will be the nodes of the dual network. The node 0 is called the *datum* node.

3. Draw dashed lines between *all* the circles in the original diagram. Each dashed line should start at one circle and end at another, and should pass through one, and only one, element or generator. Draw as many dashed lines as possible.

4. Inspect each dashed line. If a dashed line is drawn between points *i*

and j, then in the dual network draw an element between nodes i and j (this includes the datum node). If the element "cut" by the dashed line is a resistance of R ohms, then the element drawn in the dual network should be a resistance of $1/R$ ohms; if the element cut by the dashed line is an inductance of L henrys, then the element in the dual network should be a capacitor of L farads; and if the element cut by the dashed line is a capacitor of C farads, then the element drawn in the dual network should be an inductance of C henrys. If the cut element is a voltage generator, of $\mathbf{V}(s)$ volts, then the element drawn in the dual should be a current generator of $\mathbf{V}(s)$ amp; and if the element cut is a current generator of $\mathbf{I}(s)$ amp, then the element drawn in the dual should be a voltage generator of $\mathbf{I}(s)$ volts [note that R, L, and C represent numbers; $\mathbf{V}(s)$ and $\mathbf{I}(s)$ are functions of s].

This technique can also be used in the time domain. If the element cut is an open (or closed) switch, we replace it by a closed (open) switch.

An example of this procedure is shown in Fig. 9-18. Note that if one of the cut elements is a zero-resistance wire, then the element in the dual will be an open circuit; that is, no connection is made in the dual. Hence we do not draw dashed lines through zero-resistance elements.

Fig. 9-18 The procedure for obtaining the dual of a planar network: (a) a network; (b) its dual if $R_1 = 1/R$, $C_1 = L$, $L_1 = C$, $\mathbf{I}_{g1}(s) = \mathbf{V}_{g1}(s)$, and $\mathbf{I}_{g2}(s) = \mathbf{V}_{g2}(s)$.

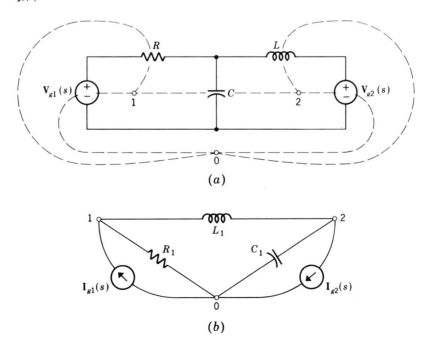

(a)

(b)

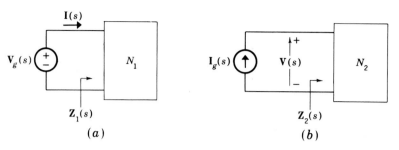

Fig. 9-19   (a) A network; (b) its dual.   The networks within the black boxes do not contain any independent generators (including initial-condition generators).

As an example of dual networks let us demonstrate how to find an impedance which is the reciprocal of a given one.   Consider Figs. 9-19a and b, where the two networks are duals.   The circuit determinant written on a loop basis for network N_1 is identical to the circuit determinant written on a nodal basis for N_2.   Thus

$$\frac{\mathbf{I}(s)}{\mathbf{V}_g(s)} = \frac{\mathbf{V}(s)}{\mathbf{I}_g(s)} \tag{9-64}$$

For these networks

$$\mathbf{Z}_1(s) = \frac{\mathbf{V}_g(s)}{\mathbf{I}(s)} \tag{9-65a}$$

$$\mathbf{Z}_2(s) = \frac{\mathbf{V}(s)}{\mathbf{I}_g(s)} \tag{9-65b}$$

Hence

$$\mathbf{Z}_1(s) = \frac{1}{\mathbf{Z}_2(s)} \tag{9-66}$$

In this case $\mathbf{Z}_1(s)$ and $\mathbf{Z}_2(s)$ are called *reciprocal impedances*.   In many network-design procedures both an impedance and its reciprocal must be synthesized.   The use of this reciprocal-network procedure allows the network designer to obtain the second network with a minimum amount of work.

9-8   Mechanical analogs

Electric networks are characterized by integral-differential equations.   The solution of these networks consists of the solution of these equations.   We have developed many techniques in Chaps. 4 to 8 which can be used to solve these equations. If a *nonelectrical* system has the same type of integral-differential equations, then we can use the techniques developed for the solution of electrical systems to solve the equations of this other system. In this section we shall briefly consider some mechanical systems and demonstrate that their equations are analogous to electrical ones. Thus we can apply our analysis techniques to these networks. In control systems electric circuits are often used to operate mechanical devices. Thus a knowledge of some aspects of such devices is important to electrical engineers.

We shall discuss the mechanical integral-differential equations in terms of the simple mechanical system of Fig. 9-20*a*, where a force f moves a mass M, which is restrained by a spring of spring constant k and by friction of constant B. We shall assume that the system is linear. That is, if y is the velocity of the mass, then the force due to friction is

$$f_B = yB \tag{9-67}$$

and the spring's force is

$$f_K = K \int y \, dt \tag{9-68}$$

The force due to the mass is

$$f_M = M \frac{dy}{dt} \tag{9-69}$$

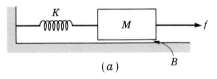

(a)

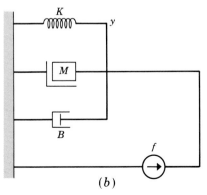

*Fig. 9-20   (a) A simple mechanical system;
(b) its mechanical circuit diagram.*

(b)

Thus the integral-differential equation for the entire system is

$$f = M \frac{dy}{dt} + By + K \int y \, dt \tag{9-70}$$

Note that in this problem the velocity of each component with respect to the reference is the one used. Equation (9-70) can be represented by the mechanical circuit diagram drawn in Fig. 9-20b. Here each component is connected between the reference and a bar which moves at a velocity y. Note that the velocity of a mass is *always* referred to the reference. That is why it is drawn as the "two-terminal" element shown. The symbol for friction is the *dashpot* shown in the figure. When a force is not applied as in Fig. 9-20a, it can be considered to be applied between the reference and the point of application. Thus Fig. 9-20b shows a "force generator."

Equation (9-70) can be solved by the procedures we have developed. An alternative procedure would be to obtain an electric network which had the same equations and solve it. We can write the equation

$$i = C \frac{dv}{dt} + Gv + \frac{1}{L} \int v \, dt \tag{9-71}$$

This will be the same as Eq. (9-70) if we set

$$i = f \tag{9-72a}$$

$$C = M \tag{9-72b}$$

$$G = B \tag{9-72c}$$

$$L = \frac{1}{K} \tag{9-72d}$$

$$v = y \tag{9-72e}$$

A circuit characterized by Eq. (9-71) is shown in Fig. 9-21a. It has essentially the same form as the mechanical network of Fig. 9-20b.

We can also write the electrical equation as

$$v_1 = L_1 \frac{di_1}{dt} + R_1 i_1 + \frac{1}{C_1} \int i_1 \, dt \tag{9-73}$$

This will also be analogous to Eq. (9-70) if

$$v_1 = f \tag{9-74a}$$

$$L_1 = M \tag{9-74b}$$

$$R_1 = B \tag{9-74c}$$

$$C_1 = \frac{1}{K} \tag{9-74d}$$

$$i_1 = y \tag{9-74e}$$

An electric circuit which has this equation is shown in Fig. 9-21*b*. It is the dual of Fig. 9-21*a*.

Analogs characterized by Eqs. (9-72) or (9-74) can be used to characterize mechanical systems. The analog of Eq. (9-72) is most convenient, since the mechanical and electrical systems will have essentially the same form. This is the one we shall use.

Let us discuss this analog further. In general, if we make voltage analogous to velocity and current analogous to force, then the equations of the voltages across a capacitor, an inductor, and a resistor in terms of their currents will be the same as the equations of the force applied to a mass, a spring, and a dashpot in terms of their velocities (that is, the relative velocities of the ends of the spring and dashpot). Thus these elements will be analogous. Note that each mechanical parameter can be considered to be a "two-terminal" device. There are two ends to a spring, and its displacement is proportional to the integral of the difference between the velocities of the ends. A similar statement can be made about the dashpot. In the case of mass the velocity is always referred to the reference. Thus it can also be represented as a two-terminal device. In the mechanical circuit diagram the ends of the two-terminal device are connected to points which move at the proper velocities. A force can be applied between two moving points in the system. A "force generator" can be connected between these points in the mechanical circuit. If the force is as indicated in Fig. 9-20, the "force generator" can be assumed to be applied between the reference and the point of application. We can now draw a mechanical circuit diagram. The electrical analog, based on Eqs. (9-72), can be drawn by making the substitutions indicated in those equations. In the mechanical diagram, for example, for each mass we substitute a capacitor. The topology of the two diagrams will be the same.

Fig. 9-21 Electrical analogs for the mechanical system of Fig. 9-20: (a) an analog if i = f, C = M, R = 1/B, L = 1/K, and v = y; (b) an analog if $v_1 = f$, $L_1 = M$, $R_1 = B$, $C_1 = 1/K$, and $i_1 = y$.

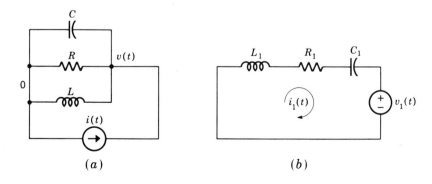

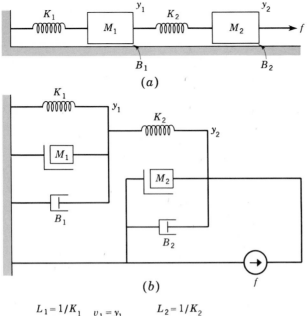

(a)

(b)

Fig. 9-22 (a) A mechanical system; (b) its mechanical circuit diagram; (c) its electrical analog based on Eqs. (9-72).

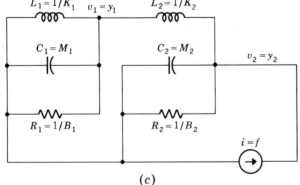

(c)

As a further illustration consider the example of Fig. 9-22a. The mechanical circuit diagram is drawn in Fig. 9-22b. Note that the forces of all elements except the spring K_2 depend upon their velocity with respect to the reference. The force of the spring K_2 depends upon the difference between y_1 and y_2. Thus K_2 is drawn between bars which move at these velocities. The electrical analog can be drawn simply by substituting elements as given in Eq. (9-72). This is shown in Fig. 9-22c. These equations for this network, and thus for the mechanical system, can be obtained by nodal analysis.

We have considered linear time-invariant mechanical systems. If the systems are nonlinear or time varying, then nonlinear or time-varying differential equations result. The electrical analogs are nonlinear and time varying.

In such cases the procedures developed for solving such electrical systems can be applied to the mechanical systems.

9-9 Some network equivalences: T-pi transformation

Three terminal networks can always be considered to act as twoports (see Sec. 8-1).   Thus the circuits of Figs. 8-6, 8-9, 8-10, and 8-11 can all be considered equivalent as far as external conditions are concerned if the twoport parameters used in obtaining them are all equivalent.   That is, they are all based on the same set of characteristic functions [see Eqs. (8-59)].   A special case of interest occurs when the three-terminal twoports are reciprocal.   Thus [see Eqs. (9-48) and (9-50)] $z_{12} = z_{21}$ and $y_{12} = y_{21}$.   In this case the dependent generators of Figs. 8-6b and 8-9b can be eliminated.   The resulting circuits are drawn in Figs. 9-23a and 9-23b, respectively.   The network of Fig. 9-23a is called a T or Y section because it can be drawn so that it resembles the letter T or Y.   The network of Fig. 9-23b is called a delta or pi section since it can be drawn so that it resembles the Greek letters Δ or π.   Comparing Figs. 9-23a and 8-6b, we have

$$\mathbf{Z}_1(s) = \mathbf{z}_{11}(s) - \mathbf{z}_{12}(s) \tag{9-75a}$$

$$\mathbf{Z}_2(s) = \mathbf{z}_{22}(s) - \mathbf{z}_{12}(s) \tag{9-75b}$$

$$\mathbf{Z}_3(s) = \mathbf{z}_{12}(s) \tag{9-75c}$$

Similarly, comparing Figs. 9-23b and 8-9b, we obtain

$$\mathbf{Y}_a(s) = \mathbf{y}_{11}(s) + \mathbf{y}_{12}(s) \tag{9-76a}$$

$$\mathbf{Y}_b(s) = \mathbf{y}_{22}(s) + \mathbf{y}_{12}(s) \tag{9-76b}$$

$$\mathbf{Y}_c(s) = -\mathbf{y}_{12}(s) \tag{9-76c}$$

Fig. 9-23   (a) A T or Y section; (b) a delta or pi section.

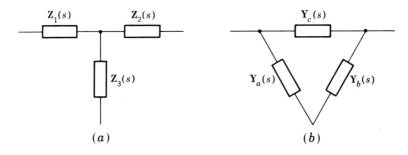

(a) (b)

Thus, if we wish to convert a T section to a pi section, we compute its y parameters and substitute in Eqs. (9-76) to obtain the element values. Analogously, a pi section can be converted to a T section by computing the z parameters and substituting in Eqs. (9-75). It should be stressed that these circuits are equivalent only for conditions *external* to the T or pi networks.

BIBLIOGRAPHY

Ley, B. S., S. G. Lutz, and C. F. Rehberg: "Linear Circuit Analysis," chaps. 5 and 9, McGraw-Hill Book Company, New York, 1959.

Peskin, E.: "Transient and Steady State Analysis of Electric Networks," chap. 6, D. Van Nostrand Company, Inc., Princeton, N.J., 1961.

Skilling, H. H.: "Electrical Engineering Circuits," 2d ed., chap. 11, John Wiley & Sons, Inc., New York, 1965.

Van Valkenburg, M. E.: "Network Analysis," 2d ed., chap. 9, Prentice-Hall, Inc., Englewood Cliffs, N.J., 1964.

PROBLEMS

9-1. Use the superposition theorem to solve for the current in and the voltages across the elements of the network of Fig. 4-22. Use the Laplace transform form of the network. Assume that only one generator, including the initial-condition generators, acts at a time.

9-2. Repeat Prob. 9-1 for the network of Fig. 4-23.

9-3. Repeat Prob. 9-1 for the network of Fig. 4-24.

9-4. Repeat Prob. 9-1 for the network of Fig. 4-25 and for the network of Fig. 4-26.

9-5. Repeat Prob. 9-1 for the network of Fig. 4-27. The dependent generators should be treated as circuit elements. They should not be "replaced" by their internal impedances.

9-6. Obtain the Thévenin equivalent circuit for the network of Fig. 9-24. If a 1-ohm resistor is connected to the terminals of this circuit, what will be the current in it? Repeat this calculation for a 1-farad capacitor connected to the circuit.

Fig. 9-24

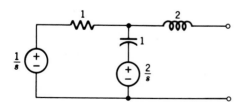

All values are in volts, ohms, henrys, or farads

9-7. Repeat Prob. 9-6 for the network of Fig. 9-25.

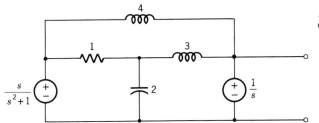

All values are in volts, ohms, henrys, or farads

Fig. 9-25

9-8. Repeat Prob. 9-6 for the network of Fig. 9-26.

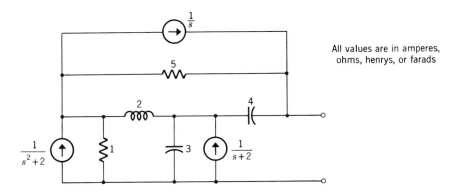

All values are in amperes, ohms, henrys, or farads

Fig. 9-26

9-9. Repeat Prob. 9-6 for the network of Fig. 9-27.

Fig. 9-27

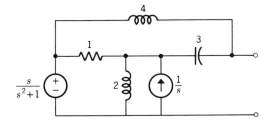

All values are in volts, amperes, ohms, henrys, or farads

9-10. Repeat Prob. 9-6 for the network of Fig. 9-28.

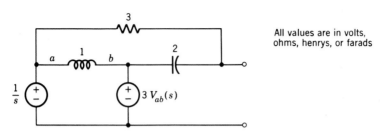

All values are in volts, ohms, henrys, or farads

Fig. 9-28

9-11. Repeat Prob. 9-6, but now obtain the Norton equivalent circuit.
9-12. Repeat Prob. 9-7, but now obtain the Norton equivalent circuit.
9-13. Repeat Prob. 9-8, but now obtain the Norton equivalent circuit.
9-14. Repeat Prob. 9-9, but now obtain the Norton equivalent circuit.
9-15. Repeat Prob. 9-10, but now obtain the Norton equivalent circuit.
9-16. Compute the maximum power that the network of Fig. 9-29 can deliver to any passive load.   What should be the value of the load impedance?

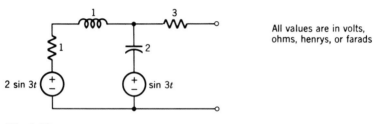

All values are in volts, ohms, henrys, or farads

Fig. 9-29

9-17. What should be the turns ratio of the ideal transformer of Fig. 9-30 if maximum power is to be delivered to the 4-ohm load?

Fig. 9-30

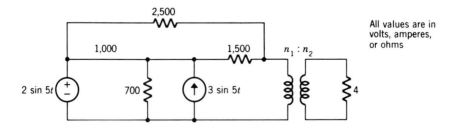

All values are in volts, amperes, or ohms

9-18. The network of Fig. 9-31*a* contains no independent generators except the one independent voltage generator shown. The output current is $3/s$ amp. Compute the current $\mathbf{I}(s)$ is Fig. 9-31*b*. The networks in the black boxes are the same.

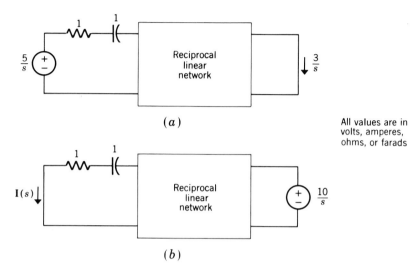

(*a*)

All values are in volts, amperes, ohms, or farads

(*b*)

Fig. 9-31

9-19. Use Fig. 9-32 to demonstrate the validity of the reciprocity principle Use the open circuit shown.

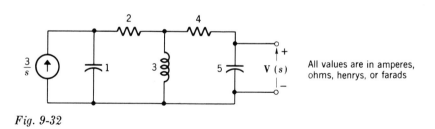

All values are in amperes, ohms, henrys, or farads

Fig. 9-32

9-20. If the 3-henry inductor of Fig. 4-23 changes to a 4-henry inductor, what is the change in the current through the 1-ohm resistor? Work in the Laplace transform domain.

9-21. Repeat Prob. 9-20, but now assume that the 3-henry inductor changes to a 2-henry inductor.

9-22. If the $\frac{1}{2}$-ohm resistance of Fig. 4-24 changes to a 2-ohm resistor, what is the change in voltage across the 1-ohm resistor? Work in the Laplace transform domain.

9-23. Repeat Prob. 9-22, but now assume that the ½-ohm resistor becomes a short circuit.

9-24. Obtain the dual of the network of Fig. 4-22.

9-25. Repeat Prob. 9-24 for the network of Fig. 4-23.

9-26. Repeat Prob. 9-24 for the network of Fig. 4-24.

9-27. Repeat Prob. 9-24 for the network of Fig. 4-25.

9-28. Write the integral differential equations for the mechanical system of Fig. 9-33.

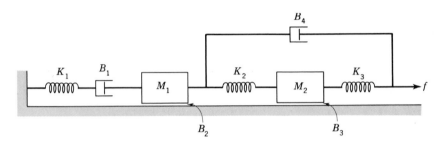

Fig. 9-33

9-29. Figures 9-23*a* and *b* are to be equivalent.   Determine $\mathbf{Z}_1(s)$, $\mathbf{Z}_2(s)$, and $\mathbf{Z}_3(s)$ in terms of $\mathbf{Y}_a(s)$, $\mathbf{Y}_b(s)$, and $\mathbf{Y}_c(s)$.

9-30. Repeat Prob. 9-29, but now determine $\mathbf{Y}_a(s)$, $\mathbf{Y}_b(s)$ and $\mathbf{Y}_c(s)$ in terms of $\mathbf{Z}_1(s)$, $\mathbf{Z}_2(s)$, and $\mathbf{Z}_3(s)$.

Signal-flow Graphs

10

In this chapter we shall introduce a technique for representing and solving a set of linear simultaneous equations graphically. This representation is called a *signal-flow graph* or *signal-flow diagram*.[1] Such a pictorial representation often provides insight into the equations which the equations themselves do not provide. More important, signal-flow graphs drawn for an entire system clarify the functions and relative importance of the elements of the system. The signal-flow graph can be used to represent state-variable equations. As we shall discuss, this signal-flow-graph representation can be used to program an analog computer for solution of the state-variable equations.

In much of this chapter we shall work with the Laplace transform form of equations. The procedures of Sec. 6-2 can be used to obtain the same results on a sinusoidal-steady-state basis. With operator notation we can also work in the time domain.

10-1 Signal-flow graphs: definitions and equations

A signal-flow graph is a graphical representation of a set of simultaneous equations. A typical one is shown in Fig. 10-1. Let us begin with some rules and definitions from which we shall be able to determine the simul-

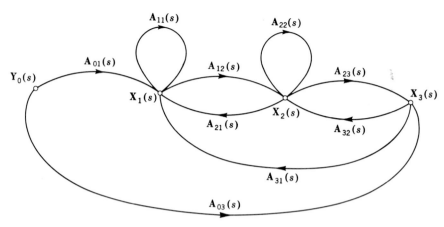

Fig. 10-1   A signal-flow graph.

taneous equations of the signal-flow graph.   In Fig. 10-1 the small circles are
called *nodes*.   The node values, such as $Y_0(s)$ and $X_1(s)$, represent the variables of the equations.   Some may be dependent variables; others are independent variables.   The lines are called *branches*.   They are assigned a
direction.   Each branch has a value $A_{ij}(s)$, called the *branch gain* or *branch
transmittance*.   The arrow of a branch points from its *input end* toward its
output end.   The *signal transmission* along a branch is defined as the *product*
of the node value at the *input end* of the branch and the branch transmittance.
A branch is said to be *incident* on a node if it is connected to it and its arrow
points toward the node.   If a branch is connected to a node and its arrow
points away from it, then the branch is said to *leave* the node.

   With the aid of these definitions, we can now state a rule which will enable
us to write the equations of a signal-flow graph: any node value is equal to the
sum of all the signal transmissions of all the branches *incident* on that node.
This, then, defines the equations of a signal-flow graph.   For instance, in
Fig. 10-1 we can write for each node

$$X_1(s) = A_{01}(s)Y_0(s) + A_{11}(s)X_1(s) + A_{21}(s)X_2(s) + A_{31}(s)X_3(s) \qquad (10\text{-}1a)$$
$$X_2(s) = 0Y_0(s) + A_{12}(s)X_1(s) + A_{22}(s)X_2(s) + A_{32}(s)X_3(s) \qquad (10\text{-}1b)$$
$$X_3(s) = A_{03}(s)Y_0(s) + 0X_1(s) + A_{23}(s)X_2(s) + 0X_3(s) \qquad (10\text{-}1c)$$

Note that the variable $Y_0(s)$ is not dependent on any of the other variables,
since all the branches leave its node.   Thus $Y_0(s)$ is an *independent variable*.
A node which has all its branches leaving it is called a *source node*.   In general,
all independent variables are associated with source nodes.

   A branch can run from a node to itself; this is called a *self-loop*.   The
signal transmission of a self-loop follows the same rules as any other branch
[for example, $A_{11}(s)X_1(s)$ in Eq. (10-1a)].

A node with only branches incident upon it is called a *sink node*.

One way of solving for the unknowns $X_1(s)$, $X_2(s)$, and $X_3(s)$ is to manipulate Eqs. (10-1) into a form suitable for solution; that is,

$$-A_{01}(s)Y_0(s) = [A_{11}(s) - 1]X_1(s) + A_{21}(s)X_2(s) + A_{31}(s)X_3(s) \qquad (10\text{-}2a)$$

$$0 = A_{12}(s)X_1(s) + [A_{22}(s) - 1]X_2(s) + A_{32}(s)X_3(s) \qquad (10\text{-}2b)$$

$$-A_{03}(s)Y_0(s) = 0X_1(s) + A_{23}(s)X_2(s) - X_3(s) \qquad (10\text{-}2c)$$

The usual procedures can be used to solve these equations. In Sec. 10-4 we shall discuss a graphical procedure for solving signal-flow graphs.

10-2 The signal-flow graph of a set of simultaneous equations

Suppose we have a set of simultaneous equations

$$Y_1(s) = \alpha_{11}(s)X_1(s) + \alpha_{12}(s)X_2(s) + \cdots + \alpha_{1n}(s)X_n(s)$$

$$Y_2(s) = \alpha_{21}(s)X_1(s) + \alpha_{22}(s)X_2(s) + \cdots + \alpha_{2n}(s)X_n(s) \qquad (10\text{-}3)$$

$$\cdots\cdots\cdots\cdots\cdots\cdots\cdots\cdots\cdots\cdots\cdots\cdots\cdots\cdots$$

$$Y_n(s) = \alpha_{n1}(s)X_1(s) + \alpha_{n2}(s)X_2(s) + \cdots + \alpha_{nn}(s)X_n(s)$$

and we wish to represent these by a signal-flow graph. In other words, we would like to put them in a form similar to that of Eqs. (10-1), with each variable set equal to a linear combination of the other variables, including itself and the known quantities. To do this we bring the known quantities over to the right-hand side of Eqs. (10-3); then we add $X_1(s)$ to both sides of the first equation, $X_2(s)$ to both sides of the second equation, and so on. Proceeding in this way, we obtain a set of equations that can be used to draw the signal-flow graph:

$$X_1(s) = -Y_1(s) + [\alpha_{11}(s) + 1]X_1(s) + \alpha_{12}(s)X_2(s) + \cdots$$
$$+ \alpha_{1n}(s)X_n(s)$$

$$X_2(s) = -Y_2(s) + \alpha_{21}(s)X_1(s) + [\alpha_{22}(s) + 1]X_2(s) + \cdots$$
$$+ \alpha_{2n}(s)X_n(s) \qquad (10\text{-}4)$$

$$\cdots\cdots\cdots\cdots\cdots\cdots\cdots\cdots\cdots\cdots\cdots\cdots\cdots\cdots$$

$$X_n(s) = -Y_n(s) + \alpha_{n1}(s)X_1(s) + \alpha_{n2}(s)X_2(s) + \cdots$$
$$+ [\alpha_{nn}(s) + 1]X_n(s)$$

To illustrate the drawing of a signal-flow graph let us consider the specific set of equations

$$Y_1 = \alpha_{11}X_1 + \alpha_{12}X_2 + \alpha_{13}X_3 \qquad (10\text{-}5a)$$

$$Y_2 = \alpha_{21}X_1 + \alpha_{22}X_2 + \alpha_{23}X_3 \qquad (10\text{-}5b)$$

$$Y_3 = \alpha_{31}X_1 + \alpha_{32}X_2 + \alpha_{33}X_3 \qquad (10\text{-}5c)$$

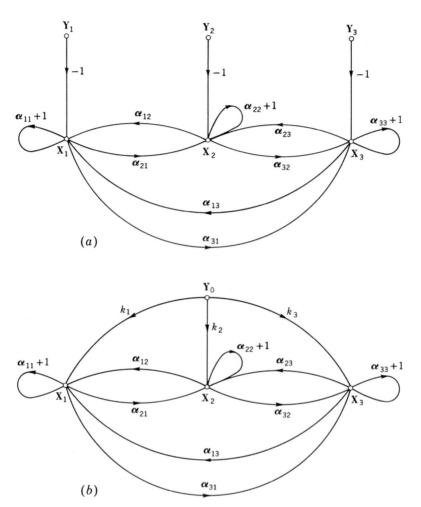

Fig. 10-2   (a) The signal-flow graph of Eqs. (10-5); (b) an alternative representation when the independent variables can be expressed as in Eqs. (10-7).

Proceeding as for Eqs. (10-4), we obtain

$$X_1 = -Y_1 + (\alpha_{11} + 1)X_1 + \alpha_{12}X_2 + \alpha_{13}X_3 \qquad (10\text{-}6a)$$

$$X_2 = -Y_2 + \alpha_{21}X_1 + (\alpha_{22} + 1)X_2 + \alpha_{23}X_3 \qquad (10\text{-}6b)$$

$$X_3 = -Y_3 + \alpha_{31}X_1 + \alpha_{32}X_2 + (\alpha_{33} + 1)X_3 \qquad (10\text{-}6c)$$

The signal-flow graph for this set of equations is shown in Fig. 10-2a.

Some networks have only one independent generator. In this case the independent variables can all be expressed as constants times this generator voltage or current. For instance, there may be only one independent voltage generator, but it may lie in more than one loop. Hence there is more than one loop voltage [that is, $\mathbf{Y}_k(s)$] that will not be zero.   Then, if there is only one independent generator, we can write:

$$\mathbf{Y}_1 = -k_1\mathbf{Y}_0 \tag{10-7a}$$

$$\mathbf{Y}_2 = -k_2\mathbf{Y}_0 \tag{10-7b}$$

$$\mathbf{Y}_3 = -k_3\mathbf{Y}_0 \tag{10-7c}$$

Now the variables $\mathbf{Y}_1$, $\mathbf{Y}_2$, and $\mathbf{Y}_3$ in Eqs. (10-6) can be replaced by the values given in Eqs. (10-7), and the signal-flow graph of Fig. 10-2a can then be drawn as in Fig. 10-2b.

10-3   Simplifications of signal-flow graphs

In this section we shall consider some procedures for simplifying a signal-flow graph without changing the values of any of the variables.   That is, when the equations of the modified signal-flow graph are solved, the values of the variables will be the same as in the original signal-flow graph.   These modifications can help in the solution for the unknown independent variables.   In general, a signal-flow graph can be characterized by a set of equations of the form

$$\mathbf{X}_1 = \mathbf{B}_{11}\mathbf{Y}_1 + \mathbf{B}_{21}\mathbf{Y}_2 + \cdots + \mathbf{B}_{k1}\mathbf{Y}_k + \mathbf{A}_{11}\mathbf{X}_1 + \mathbf{A}_{21}\mathbf{X}_2 \\ + \cdots + \mathbf{A}_{n1}\mathbf{X}_n$$

$$\mathbf{X}_2 = \mathbf{B}_{12}\mathbf{Y}_1 + \mathbf{B}_{22}\mathbf{Y}_2 + \cdots + \mathbf{B}_{k2}\mathbf{Y}_k + \mathbf{A}_{12}\mathbf{X}_1 + \mathbf{A}_{22}\mathbf{X}_2 \\ + \cdots + \mathbf{A}_{n2}\mathbf{X}_n \quad (10\text{-}8)$$

$$\cdots \cdots \cdots \cdots \cdots \cdots \cdots \cdots \cdots \cdots \cdots \cdots \cdots$$

$$\mathbf{X}_n = \mathbf{B}_{1n}\mathbf{Y}_1 + \mathbf{B}_{2n}\mathbf{Y}_2 + \cdots + \mathbf{B}_{kn}\mathbf{Y}_k + \mathbf{A}_{1n}\mathbf{X}_1 + \mathbf{A}_{2n}\mathbf{X}_2 \\ + \cdots + \mathbf{A}_{nn}\mathbf{X}_n$$

where the $\mathbf{A}$ and $\mathbf{B}$ terms represent coefficients which may be functions of s. The $\mathbf{Y}$ terms are the independent variables and the $\mathbf{X}$ terms are the dependent variables.

In a signal-flow graph a node value is only *directly* affected by the branches *incident* on that node.   Thus, if we change the branches incident on a node in such a way that the node value is unchanged, then *all* the node values will be unchanged.   In general, a modification of the signal-flow graph will change its equations.   If we are not to change the values of the variables, then the modifications must be consistent with Eqs. (10-8).

Elimination of a self-loop

In the next section we shall see that a self-loop can present problems when signal-flow graphs are to be solved for unknown quantities.   Let us demonstrate how we can eliminate a self-loop without changing any of the node values.   Assume that node x_j has a self-loop of transmittance $\mathbf{A}_{jj}$.   Then the jth equation of Eq. (10-8) will be

$$\mathbf{X}_j = \mathbf{B}_{1j}\mathbf{Y}_1 + \mathbf{B}_{2j}\mathbf{Y}_2 + \cdots + \mathbf{B}_{kj}\mathbf{Y}_k + \mathbf{A}_{1j}\mathbf{X}_1 + \cdots + \mathbf{A}_{(j-1)j}\mathbf{X}_j$$
$$+ \mathbf{A}_{jj}\mathbf{X}_j + \mathbf{A}_{(j+1)j}\mathbf{X}_{j+1} + \cdots + \mathbf{A}_{nj}\mathbf{X}_n \quad (10\text{-}9)$$

Now assume that

$$\mathbf{A}_{jj} \neq 1 \qquad\qquad\qquad\qquad\qquad (10\text{-}10)$$

We bring the $\mathbf{A}_{jj}\mathbf{X}_j$ term to the left-hand side of the equation and solve for $\mathbf{X}_j$. This yields

$$\mathbf{X}_j = \frac{\mathbf{B}_{1j}\mathbf{Y}_1}{1 - \mathbf{A}_{jj}} + \cdots + \frac{\mathbf{B}_{kj}\mathbf{Y}_k}{1 - \mathbf{A}_{jj}} + \frac{\mathbf{A}_{1j}}{1 - \mathbf{A}_{jj}}\mathbf{X}_1 + \cdots + \frac{\mathbf{A}_{(j-1)j}}{1 - \mathbf{A}_{jj}}\mathbf{X}_{j-1}$$
$$+ \frac{\mathbf{A}_{(j+1)j}}{1 - \mathbf{A}_{jj}}\mathbf{X}_{j+1} + \cdots + \frac{\mathbf{A}_{nj}}{1 - \mathbf{A}_{jj}}\mathbf{X}_j \quad (10\text{-}11)$$

Equations (10-11) and (10-9) are equivalent.   Thus we could substitute Eq. (10-11) for Eq. (10-9) in Eqs. (10-8).   Thus none of the variables of the signal-flow graph would be changed.   However, Eq. (10-11) does not indicate a self-loop term, so the signal-flow graph characterized by the new set of equations would not have a self-loop at node $\mathbf{X}_j$.   Let us see what other modifications have been made in the signal-flow graph.   All the equations of Eq. (10-8) except the jth one are unchanged.   Thus all the branches *incident* on nodes *other* than $\mathbf{X}_j$ are *unchanged*.   Equation (10-11) shows that in the new signal-flow graph the transmittances of the branches incident on $\mathbf{X}_j$ are given by the old transmittances multiplied by $1/(1 - \mathbf{A}_{jj})$.   The self-loop branch is removed.   For example, consider the signal-flow graph of Fig. 10-3a.   In Fig. 10-3b we have eliminated the self-loop of node $\mathbf{X}_2$.

Combination of parallel branches

If two branches are *both incident* on the *same* node and *both leave* the same node, then they can be combined into a single branch whose transmittance is the sum of the transmittances of the individual branches.   Consider the left-hand signal-flow graph of Fig. 10-4a.   The signal transmission from node $\mathbf{X}_i$ to node $\mathbf{X}_j$ is $\mathbf{A}_{ij1}\mathbf{X}_i + \mathbf{A}_{ij2}\mathbf{X}_i$, but this is equal to $(\mathbf{A}_{ij1} + \mathbf{A}_{ij2})\mathbf{X}_i$.   It can be represented as the signal transmission along a branch of transmittance $\mathbf{A}_{ij1} + \mathbf{A}_{ij2}$ incident on node $\mathbf{X}_j$ and leaving node $\mathbf{X}_i$.   Thus the equivalence of Fig. 10-4a is valid.

Node splitting

At times it is desirable to represent a particular node as a sink or a source node. This can be done by replacing the node by two nodes, one with all the incident branches and the other with all the leaving branches.   The node value of the first node will be unchanged, since all the signal transmissions to it are unchanged. The second node is merely *defined* to have the same value as the first. Thus all the signal transmissions away from the node will be proper. This is called *node splitting*, and is illustrated in Fig. 10-4b.

Shift of the input end of a branch

The only way in which a branch affects a signal-flow graph is by the signal transmitted along it. Thus, *if* we can shift the input end of the branch and adjust the branch transmittance so that the signal transmission remains unchanged, then the node value will be unchanged. An illustration of this is shown in Fig. 10-4c. The signal transmission along branch A_{ki} is $X_k A_{ki}$. However,

$$X_k = A_{jk}X_j \tag{10-12}$$

Hence we can state that the signal transmission along branch A_{ki} is $A_{ki}A_{jk}X_j$.

Fig. 10-3   (a) A signal-flow graph; (b) a modification of this in which all the node values are unchanged and the self-loop of node X_2 is eliminated.

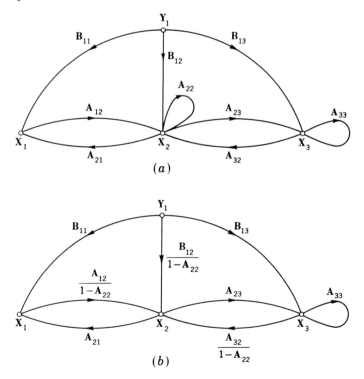

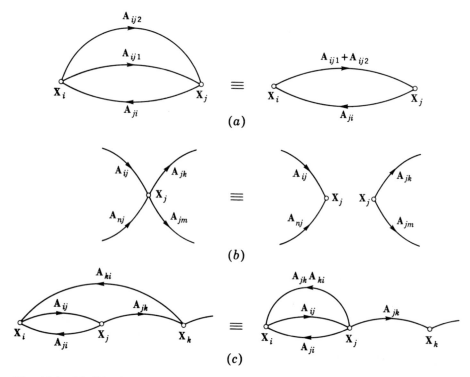

Fig. 10-4   Modifications of a signal-flow graph which do not change any of the node values: (a) combination of parallel branches; (b) node splitting; (c) shift of the input end of a branch.

If we shift the input end of this branch from node X_k to node X_j and change the branch transmittance to $A_{ki}A_{jk}$, its signal transmission will be unchanged. Thus the node values will be unchanged. This shift is shown in Fig. 10-4c. Such shifts are not always possible. For instance, if there were another branch incident on node X_k, we could not make such a shift.

10-4   Reduction of signal-flow graphs

A signal-flow graph represents a set of simultaneous equations. The solution of this set of equations consists of a single unknown expressed in terms of the known quantities. In the case of a signal-flow graph this occurs if there is only one unknown node, with no self-loop, and all the other nodes are source nodes. For instance, in Fig. 10-5 the equation for node X_k is

$$\mathbf{X}_k = \mathbf{B}_{1k}\mathbf{Y}_1 + \mathbf{B}_{2k}\mathbf{Y}_2 + \mathbf{B}_{3k}\mathbf{Y}_3 \tag{10-13}$$

Thus the unknown we wish to find is expressed in terms of known quantities.

One procedure for solving signal-flow graphs consists of eliminating a node without changing any other of the node values; it is called *node pulling.* If this procedure is applied to each unknown node in turn, it eventually results in a signal-flow graph with only one unknown node. Then, as in Fig. 10-5, the signal-flow graph can easily be solved for this unknown.

To develop this procedure we shall work with Eqs. (10-8), which characterize a signal-flow graph. Suppose we wish to eliminate node X_j from the signal-flow graph, and this node has no self-loop. If it has, we eliminate the self-loop by the procedure of Sec. 10-3 (we shall discuss the case $A_{jj} = 1$ subsequently). Then the equation for X_j in Eq. (10-8) will be

$$X_j = B_{1j}Y_1 + \cdots + B_{kj}Y_k + A_{1j}X_1 + \cdots + A_{(j-1)j}X_{j-1} + 0X_j$$
$$+ A_{(j+1)j}X_{j+1} + \cdots + A_{nj}X_n \quad (10\text{-}14a)$$

or, in more compact form,

$$X_j = \sum_{r=1}^{k} B_{rj}Y_r + \sum_{\substack{r=1 \\ r \neq j}}^{n} A_{rj}X_r \quad (10\text{-}14b)$$

Now we remove this equation from those that characterize the signal-flow graph. In addition, we use Eqs. (10-14) to eliminate X_j from all the remaining signal-flow-graph equations. Thus we have a valid set of equations, but with one fewer node.

In Eqs. (10-8) a typical variable (other than X_j) is

$$X_h = \sum_{r=1}^{k} B_{rh}Y_r + \sum_{r=1}^{n} A_{rh}X_r \quad (10\text{-}15)$$

This can be written as

$$X_h = \sum_{r=1}^{k} B_{rh}Y_r + \sum_{\substack{r=1 \\ r \neq j}}^{n} A_{rh}X_h + A_{jh}X_j \quad (10\text{-}16)$$

where we have removed the X_j term from the summation. To eliminate the X_j term we substitute Eq. (10-14b) into Eq. (10-16). Then, after manipulating, we obtain

$$X_h = \sum_{r=1}^{k} (B_{rh} + B_{rj}A_{jh})Y_r + \sum_{r=1}^{n} (A_{rh} + A_{rj}A_{jh})X_r \quad (10\text{-}17)$$

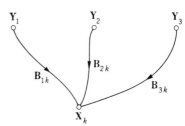

Fig. 10-5 A signal-flow graph with only one unknown node.

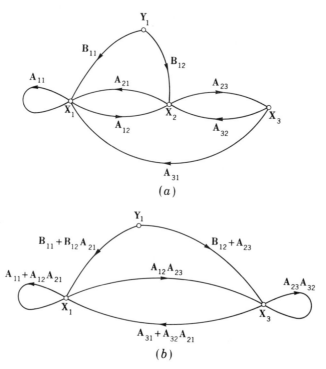

Fig. 10-6 (a) A signal-flow graph; (b) an equivalent signal-flow graph with node X_2 eliminated.

Let us discuss the significance of Eq. (10-17). Consider the signal transmission from node X_r to node X_h. The original branch transmittance A_{rh} is still there, but we have now added the transmittance $A_{rj}A_{jh}$; that is, we have added the product of the branch transmittances from X_r to X_j and X_j to X_h. This can be considered to be the transmittance from node X_r to node X_h through node X_j (note that there can be no other node intervening). When a node is eliminated, it is replaced by branches which provide all possible transmission paths from one node to another through the eliminated node. A transmission path through a node consists of one branch entering the node and another branch leaving the node. Figure 10-6 illustrates this procedure. Note that node pulling can change (or create) self-loops as well as other branch transmittances.

A node that has a self-loop cannot be eliminated [note that X_j cannot appear on the right-hand side of Eq. (10-14)]. The procedure of Sec. 10-3 can be used to eliminate a self-loop unless $A_{jj} = 1$. If $A_{jj} = 1$, then we pull another node. The process of node pulling may change the value of A_{jj} so that its self-loop can be eliminated. If every unknown node has a unity self-loop, then the procedure cannot continue. However, it can be shown in this case that the simultaneous equations characterized by the signal-flow graph are linearly dependent and hence do not have a solution. Therefore the signal-flow graph cannot have a solution. It can also be shown[2] that if the set of simultaneous equations characterized by the signal-flow graph is linearly independent, then a solution to the signal-flow graph will always exist.

As an example let us solve Fig. 10-7a for X_3. Real numbers are used for the branch transmittance to make the arithmetic easier. Since X_1 does not have a self-loop, we shall eliminate it [see Eq. (10-17) and the discussion following it]; the signal-flow graph of Fig. 10-7b results. Now we eliminate the self-loop of node X_2 by dividing all branches incident on it by $1 - 3 = -2$; the resulting signal-flow graph is shown in Fig. 10-7c. After eliminating node X_2, we obtain the signal-flow graph of Fig. 10-7d. The final signal-flow graph is shown in Fig. 10-7e, where we have eliminated the self-loop of node X_3. Thus we have

$$X_3 = -\frac{7}{10} Y_1 - \frac{3}{10} Y_2 \qquad (10\text{-}18)$$

Fig. 10-7 The reduction of a signal-flow graph: (a) the signal-flow graph; (b) node X_1 removed; (c) the self-loop of node X_2 removed; (d) node X_2 removed; (e) the self-loop of node X_3 removed.

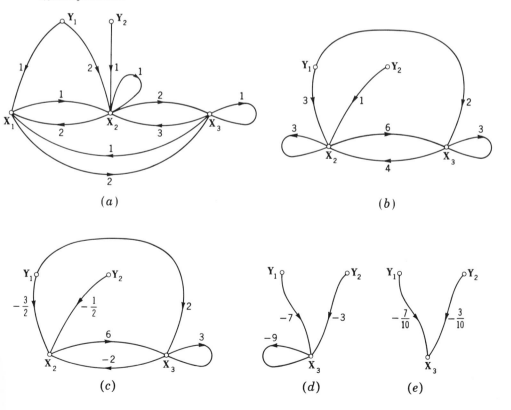

(a)

(b)

(c)

(d)

(e)

If we wish to find additional unknowns, we do not have to repeat the entire solution procedure. For instance, if we also want to find $\mathbf{X}_2$, we substitute the value of $\mathbf{X}_3$ given by Eq. (10-18) into Fig. 10-7c. The value of $\mathbf{X}_2$ can then be obtained without any further signal-flow-graph reductions.

10-5 The signal-flow graph of an electric network

We shall now discuss a procedure for obtaining a signal-flow graph which characterizes a network. One procedure is just to take the loop, nodal, or cut-set simultaneous equations and draw the signal-flow graph for them. However, there is another procedure we can use which is based upon the topology of the circuit. In Sec. 3-1 we demonstrated that all the network branch voltages could be expressed in terms of the tree-branch voltages, and all the branch currents could be expressed in terms of the chord currents. Thus the network voltages and currents are completely characterized by the tree-branch voltages and the chord currents. These will be our node variables.

In this procedure we choose a tree in the following way. All voltage generators should be chosen to be in the tree branches and any current generator in the chords. This will usually be possible. If a loop contains only voltage generators then this procedure fails. However, usually one of these voltage generators must be expressible in terms of the other (see Fig. 10-8). Thus one generator can be removed without affecting its terminal voltage, and thus without changing the network currents. If one of the voltage generators cannot be expressed in terms of the others, then an infinite current will circulate around the loop ($I = V/Z$ and $Z = 0$). We shall not allow this case. Since there will be no loops composed only of voltage generators, we shall always be able to include all these generators in the tree branches. Similarly, we shall rule out cut sets composed only of current generators. Thus we shall always be able to choose the current-generator branches as chords.

The procedure for drawing the signal-flow graphs is as follows:

1. Choose a tree as outlined above.

2. Express the tree-branch currents in terms of the chord currents and the chord-branch voltages in terms of the tree-branch voltages (Kirchhoff's laws can be used here and in 1). The *desired variables* are the *tree-branch voltages* and the *chord currents*.

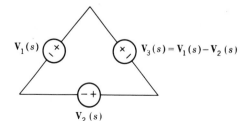

Fig. 10-8 A loop of voltage generators.

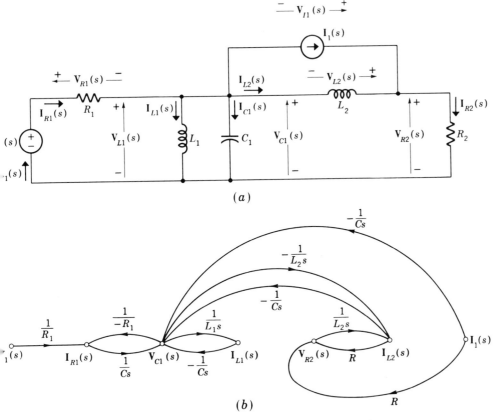

Fig. 10-9 (a) A network; (b) a signal-flow graph for this network.

3. Use the expression that relates the voltage across an impedance to the current through it to eliminate any undesired variable from step 2 (the chord voltages and the tree-branch currents). The resulting set of equations will characterize the signal-flow graph.

Let us illustrate this procedure with the network of Fig. 10-9a. We shall choose the tree consisting of the branches containing $V_1(s)$, C_1, and R_2. We express the chord voltages in terms of the tree-branch voltages as

$$\mathbf{V}_{R1}(s) = \mathbf{V}_1(s) - \mathbf{V}_{C1}(s) \qquad (10\text{-}19a)$$

$$\mathbf{V}_{L1}(s) = \mathbf{V}_{C1}(s) \qquad (10\text{-}19b)$$

$$\mathbf{V}_{L2}(s) = \mathbf{V}_{R2}(s) - \mathbf{V}_{C1}(s) \qquad (10\text{-}19c)$$

$$\mathbf{V}_{I1}(s) = \mathbf{V}_{R2}(s) - \mathbf{V}_{C1}(s) \qquad (10\text{-}19d)$$

Now we express the tree-branch currents in terms of the chord currents as

$$\mathbf{I}_{V1}(s) = \mathbf{I}_{R1}(s) \tag{10-20a}$$

$$\mathbf{I}_{C1}(s) = \mathbf{I}_{R1}(s) - \mathbf{I}_{L1}(s) - \mathbf{I}_{L2}(s) - \mathbf{I}_1(s) \tag{10-20b}$$

$$\mathbf{I}_{R2}(s) = \mathbf{I}_{L2}(s) + \mathbf{I}_1(s) \tag{10-20c}$$

Then we eliminate the undesired variables which consist of the left-hand side of Eqs. (10-19) and (10-20).

If a current in an impedance is an undesired variable, we can express it as the quotient of the voltage across the impedance divided by the impedance. Similarly, if the voltage across an impedance is an undesired variable, we can express it as the product of the current through the impedance and the impedance. Note that the voltage across the impedance and the current through it cannot *both* be undesirable variables (either a chord current or a tree-branch voltage is a desired variable). Thus for Eqs. (10-19) and (10-20) we have

$$R_1 \mathbf{I}_{R1}(s) = \mathbf{V}_1(s) - \mathbf{V}_{C1}(s) \tag{10-21a}$$

$$L_1 s \mathbf{I}_{L1}(s) = \mathbf{V}_{C1}(s) \tag{10-21b}$$

$$L_2 s \mathbf{I}_{L2}(s) = \mathbf{V}_{R2}(s) - \mathbf{V}_{C1}(s) \tag{10-21c}$$

$$C s \mathbf{V}_{C1}(s) = \mathbf{I}_{R1}(s) - \mathbf{I}_{L1}(s) - \mathbf{I}_{L2}(s) - \mathbf{I}_1(s) \tag{10-21d}$$

$$\frac{\mathbf{V}_{R2}(s)}{R} = \mathbf{I}_{L2}(s) + \mathbf{I}_1(s) \tag{10-21e}$$

We have not written the equations for the voltages across the current generator and the current through the voltage generator. These can be written as

$$\mathbf{V}_{I1}(s) = \mathbf{V}_{L2}(s) = \mathbf{V}_{R2}(s) - \mathbf{V}_{C1}(s) \tag{10-22a}$$

$$\mathbf{I}_{V1}(s) = \mathbf{I}_{R1}(s) \tag{10-22b}$$

They merely add sink nodes to the signal-flow graph: hence they will not affect any other values. Now, manipulating Eqs. (10-21), we have

$$\mathbf{I}_{R1}(s) = \frac{1}{R_1} \mathbf{V}_1(s) - \frac{1}{R_1} \mathbf{V}_{C1}(s) \tag{10-23a}$$

$$\mathbf{I}_{L1}(s) = \frac{1}{L_1 s} \mathbf{V}_{C1}(s) \tag{10-23b}$$

$$\mathbf{I}_{L2}(s) = \frac{1}{L_2 s} \mathbf{V}_{R2}(s) - \frac{1}{L_2 s} \mathbf{V}_{C1}(s) \tag{10-23c}$$

$$\mathbf{V}_{C1}(s) = \frac{1}{Cs} \mathbf{I}_{R1}(s) - \frac{1}{Cs} \mathbf{I}_{L1}(s) - \frac{1}{Cs} \mathbf{I}_{L2}(s) - \frac{1}{Cs} \mathbf{I}_1(s) \tag{10-23d}$$

$$\mathbf{V}_{R2}(s) = R \mathbf{I}_{L2}(s) + R \mathbf{I}_1(s) \tag{10-23e}$$

These equations characterize the signal-flow graph shown in Fig. 10-9*b*.

Note that the addition of Eqs. (10-22) would merely add two sink nodes. If a sink node is pulled, it does not affect the rest of the network, since no branches leave it. Thus we do not bother to draw the sink nodes. In general, the voltage across a current generator and the current in a voltage generator will lead to sink nodes. This flow graph can be solved for any of the dependent variables in terms of $V_1(s)$ and $I_1(s)$.

If there are initial conditions present, then the initial-condition generators are treated as independent generators in this procedure.

This procedure is similar to that used in Sec. 7-2 to obtain the state variables for a *linear* network. If a proper tree exists (see Sec. 7-2), and it is used in the procedure, then the variables will be the state variables plus others. The nodes corresponding to the other unknowns can be pulled to yield a signal-flow graph whose unknowns are the state variables. This procedure will not be directly applicable to nonlinear or time-varying networks.

10-6 State-variable equations: analog-computer simulation and signal-flow graphs

In this section we shall determine the signal-flow graph of a set of state-variable equations. As we shall see, this signal-flow graph is a great help in solving state-variable equations with an analog computer. Digital computers can be used to solve problems with an extremely high degree of accuracy. In many circumstances, however, only two to four significant figures are needed for sufficient accuracy, and in such cases the analog computer is often far simpler and less costly to use than the digital computer. Analog computers can be used to solve the equations of many types of systems. These do not have to be characterized by a state-variable form, but the state-variable form is especially simple to use with analog computers.

Before we proceed any further, let us discuss analog computers. In analog computation a circuit is set up whose integral-differential equation is made to be the same as the equation under study. The response of the circuit is then recorded or observed on an oscilloscope, and the solution of the desired equation is obtained. Programming the analog computer so that its integral-differential equation is the same as the desired one may be a relatively complex matter. The use of signal-flow graphs can reduce the complexity. If we represent a set of state-variables equations by a signal-flow graph, then in many circumstances the analog-computer circuits can be immediately obtained from it.

An analog computer is made up of basic building blocks, each of which will be discussed in turn. Their signal-flow graphs will also be given. We shall see later that the signal-flow graph of the set of state-variable equations contains elements that are the same as the signal-flow graphs of the building blocks of the analog computer. This will enable us to determine the appropri-

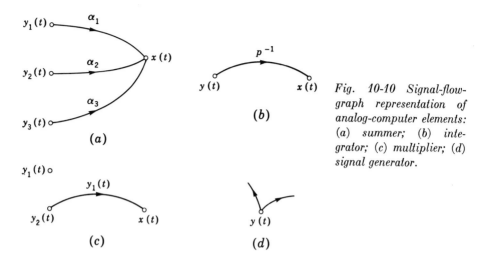

Fig. 10-10 Signal-flow-graph representation of analog-computer elements: (a) summer; (b) integrator; (c) multiplier; (d) signal generator.

ate interconnection of the building blocks (to program the computer). We shall consider the mathematical characteristics of these building blocks; a discussion of their actual circuits is beyond the scope of this book.

Summers and amplifiers

A *summer* is a device which has two or more inputs. The output signal is the sum of all the input signals, each of which can be multiplied by an arbitrary constant. A signal-flow-graph representation of a summer is shown in Fig. 10-10a. In this case

$$x(t) = \alpha_1 y_1(t) + \alpha_2 y_2(t) + \alpha_3 y_3(t) \tag{10-24}$$

This particular summer is built with a four-port network; it has three input ports and one output port. An *amplifier* is a special case of a summer. It has only one input, and the output is a constant times this input. If the inputs y_2 and y_3 were not present in Fig. 10-10a, this network would be an amplifier, where the constant α_1 was the *gain* of the amplifier.

Integrators

An *integrator* is a twoport circuit which produces an output equal to the definite integral of the input plus an arbitrary constant. That is, if the input of an integrator is $y(t)$, then the output is

$$x(t) = x(0-) + \int_{0-}^{t} y(\tau)\, d\tau \tag{10-25}$$

Circuitry within the integrator is such that the initial value $x(0-)$ can be adjusted to any desired value (within practical limits). Thus the input to an integrator is the derivative of the output. The signal-flow-graph representation is shown in Fig. 10-10b, where the operator notation of Eq. (3-13) is used. In this case $x(t)$ is given by Eq. (10-25). Alternatively, we can state that

$$y(t) = \frac{dx(t)}{dt} \tag{10-26}$$

where $x(0-)$ is specified.

Multipliers

A *multiplier* is a threeport device (two input ports and one output port) whose output is the product of its two inputs. For instance, if the inputs are $y_1(t)$ and $y_2(t)$, then the output is

$$x(t) = y_1(t)y_2(t) \tag{10-27}$$

A signal-flow-graph representation of a multiplier is shown in Fig. 10-10c. The branch transmittance is set equal to one of the variables (note that the transmittance may be a function of time). Many nonlinear functions can be generated by means of multipliers. For instance, if the same variable $y(t)$ is applied to both inputs, then the output will be $y^2(t)$.

Signal generators

A *signal generator* is different from the previously discussed computer elements in that it does *not* produce an output in response to an input. Instead, it generates an arbitrary function; that is, it is used to represent an independent variable. As such, it is drawn as a source node in the signal-flow diagram. This is illustrated in Fig. 10-10d. The actual signal generator is a voltage or current generator.

Let us consider a very simple state-variable equation and draw its signal-flow graph. We shall demonstrate that this is made up of the analog-computer building blocks. Thus it can represent the signal-flow graph of the analog computer which can be used to compute the state variables. The equation we shall use is

$$\frac{dq_1(t)}{dt} = q_1(t) + by(t) \tag{10-28}$$

The signal-flow graph is shown in Fig. 10-11a. At the start call one node $dq_1(t)/dt$ and make this the input node of an integrator. Then the output of the "integrator branch" is $q_1(t)$. The $y(t)$ is equal to the given function $y(t)$. If we write the equation for the node $dq_1(t)/dt$, we obtain Eq. (10-28). Thus Fig. 10-11a can be said to be the signal-flow graph for Eq. (10-28).

Now let us consider an actual analog-computer circuit which can be used to solve Eq. (10-28) for $q_1(t)$. Each signal-flow-graph branch of Fig. 10-11a also represents an actual analog-computer building block. We can build the computer by using the signal-flow graph to indicate the interconnections of these building blocks. Such a circuit is shown in Fig. 10-11b. The networks

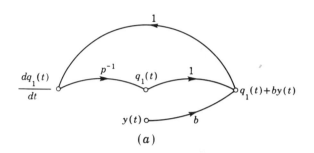

(a)

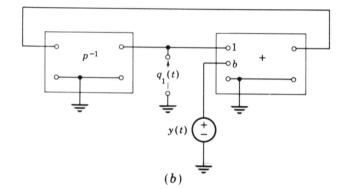

(b)

Fig. 10-11 (a) A signal-flow-graph representation of Eq. (10-28); (b) the block diagram of an analog computer that can be used to compute $q_1(t)$; all the grounded terminals are interconnected.

enclosed in the black boxes are an integrator and a summer. The terminals marked with the ground symbol (the three parallel lines of differing length) are all connected to a common point (to simplify the diagram this connection is not shown). The generator $y(t)$ is one that produces the desired "driving signal." The output voltage $q_1(t)$ is measured between the appropriately marked pair of terminals. In practice, the integrating circuit is adjusted to supply the proper initial value of $q_1(t)$ at $t = 0-$. In addition, $y(t)$ is applied at $t = 0$. A recorder or oscilloscope is connected to the $q_1(t)$ terminals. Thus $q_1(t)$ can be determined and recorded.

Now let us draw the signal-flow graph, or analog-computer configuration, for a more general set of state-variable equations. We shall now consider not only the state variables, as given in Eq. (7-27), but also the other variables of the system as expressed in Eq. (7-32). A typical set of equations will be of the form

$$\frac{dq_1(t)}{dt} = a_{11}q_1(t) + a_{12}q_2(t) + b_{11}y_1(t) + b_{12}y_2(t) \tag{10-29a}$$

$$\frac{dq_2(t)}{dt} = a_{21}q_1(t) + a_{22}q_2(t) + b_{21}y_1(t) + b_{22}y_2(t) \tag{10-29b}$$

$$x_1(t) = c_{11}q_1(t) + c_{12}q_2(t) + d_{11}y_1(t) + d_{12}y_2(t) \tag{10-30a}$$

$$x_2(t) = c_{21}q_1(t) + c_{22}q_2(t) + d_{21}y_1(t) + d_{22}y_2(t) \tag{10-30b}$$

To draw the signal-flow graph we first draw nodes for each of the state variables, their derivatives, each $y(t)$, and each $x(t)$.   Then we connect the derivatives of the state variables to their corresponding state variables by integrator branches.   The remaining interconnections are made in accordance with the given equations.   The signal-flow-graph representation of Eqs. (10-29) and (10-30) is given in Fig. 10-12.   Note that $y_1(t)$ and $y_2(t)$ are source nodes, while $x_1(t)$ and $x_2(t)$ are sink nodes.   We have chosen the number of $x(t)$ variables to be equal to the number of state variables.   This need not be the case.   For instance, we could have considered that there were three $x(t)$ variables, $x_1(t)$, $x_2(t)$, and $x_3(t)$.   This was not done to avoid cluttering the diagram.

Time-varying systems

The state-variable equation of time-varying networks can also be represented by signal-flow graphs.   The branch transmittances will now be functions of time.   If an analog computer is to be constructed, then the building blocks of the computer must be time varying.   In practice, such elements may at times be difficult to obtain.

Fig. 10-12   The signal-flow-graph representation of Eqs. (10-29) and (10-30).

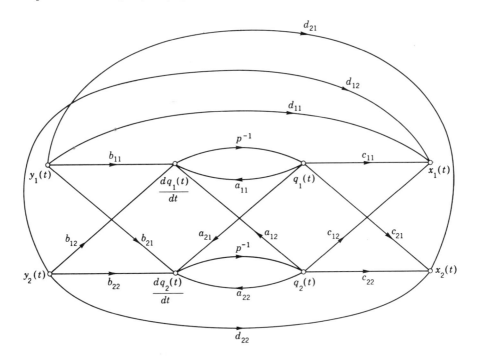

Let us draw the signal-flow diagram for the time-varying system whose state variables are given in Eqs. (7-60b) and (7-61) as

$$\frac{di_L(t)}{dt} = -\frac{1}{L(t)}\left[R_1 + \frac{dL(t)}{dt}\right]i_L(t) - \frac{1}{L(t)}v_C(t) + \frac{1}{L(t)}v(t) \tag{10-31a}$$

$$\frac{dv_C(t)}{dt} = \frac{1}{C(t)}i_L(t) - \frac{1}{C(t)}\left[\frac{1}{R_2} + \frac{dC(t)}{dt}\right]v_C(t) \tag{10-31b}$$

The signal-flow diagram for these equations is given in Fig. 10-13. Note that it is drawn in essentially the same way as for the time-invariant case, except that now the branch transmittances are time varying. The analog-computer configuration is obtained from the signal-flow graph in the same way as for a time-invariant network. As a practical matter, it may be difficult to obtain time-varying computer elements. At times multiplying circuits are used to obtain time-varying branch transmittances (see Fig. 10-10c).

Nonlinear systems

Some (but not all) nonlinear systems can be represented by signal-flow graphs by adding the multipliers of Fig. 10-10c to those elements we have already used. Consider the nonlinear state-variable equations

$$\frac{dq_1(t)}{dt} = \alpha_1 q_1(t) + q_2{}^2(t) + \beta_1 y_1(t) \tag{10-32a}$$

$$\frac{dq_2(t)}{dt} = \alpha_2 q_1(t)q_2(t) + q_2{}^2(t) + \beta_2 y_1(t)y_2(t) \tag{10-32b}$$

Fig. 10-13   The signal-flow-graph representation of Eqs. (10-31).

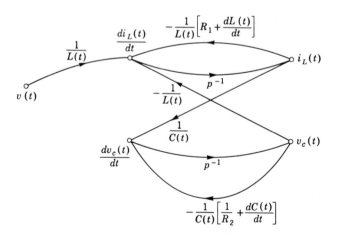

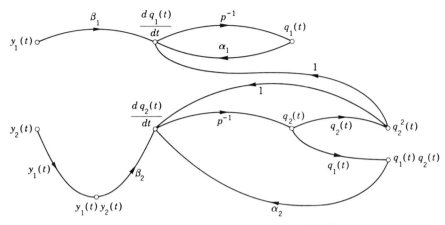

Fig. 10-14   The signal-flow-graph representation of Eqs. (10-32).

The signal-flow-graph representation of these equations is given in Fig. 10-14. The branches labeled $q_1(t)$, $q_2(t)$, and $y_1(t)$ represent multipliers in an analog computer. The branches labeled 1 are direct connections.

We cannot draw signal-flow graphs or set up analog-computer configurations for all nonlinear systems with the elements of Fig. 10-10. For instance, consider Eqs. (7-78) and (7-79), where terms involving the state variables appear in the denominators of algebraic fractions. The elements of Fig. 10-10 *cannot* be used to obtain such functions. The addition of a branch (and computer element) whose output is the reciprocal of the input could be used to obtain such fractions in the equations of a signal-flow graph. At times nonlinear elements with characteristics which match those of commonly occurring systems are incorporated into analog computers. This is often a help in solving nonlinear equations.

REFERENCES

[1] S. J. Mason, Feedback Theory: Some Properties of Signal Flow Graphs, *Proc. IRE*, vol. 41, pp. 1144–1156, 1953; Feedback Theory: Further Properties of Signal Flow Graphs, *Proc. IRE*, vol. 44, pp. 920–926, 1956.

[2] S. Seshu and N. Balabanian, "Linear Network Analysis," p. 415, John Wiley & Sons, Inc., New York, 1959.

BIBLIOGRAPHY

Chirlian, P. M.: "Analysis and Design of Electronic Circuits," chap. 9, McGraw-Hill Book Company, New York, 1965.

Kuo, B. C.: "Linear Networks and Systems," chap. 7, McGraw-Hill Book Company, New York, 1967.

Mason, S. J.: Feedback theory: Some properties of signal flow graphs, *Proc. IRE*, vol. 41, pp. 1145–1156, 1953.

————: Feedback theory: Further properties of signal flow graphs, *Proc. IRE*, vol. 44, pp. 920–926, 1956.

Mason, S. J., and H. J. Zimmerman: "Electronic Circuits, Signals and Systems," chaps. 4 and 5, John Wiley & Sons, Inc., New York, 1960.

Peskin, E.: "Transient and Steady State Analysis of Electric Networks," chap. 8, D. Van Nostrand Company, Inc., Princeton, N.J., 1961.

Seshu, S., and N. Balabanian: "Linear Network Analysis," pp. 407–425, John Wiley & Sons, Inc., New York, 1959.

Truxal, J. G.: "Automatic Feedback Control System Synthesis," pp. 88–113, McGraw-Hill Book Company, New York, 1955.

PROBLEMS

10-1. Obtain a signal-flow graph that represents the equations

$$X_1 = Y_1 - 3Y_2 + 3X_1 - 3X_2 + X_3$$
$$X_2 = -Y_1 + 5Y_2 + 3X_1 - X_2 + 4X_3$$
$$X_3 = 0Y_1 + 2Y_2 - X_1 + 7X_2 + 9X_3$$

10-2. Repeat Prob. 10-1 for the equations

$$X_1 = Y_1 - \frac{3}{s+1}Y_2 + \frac{2}{s}X_1 - 3X_2$$

$$X_2 = sY_1 + 0Y_2 + \frac{2s^2}{s^2+4}X_1 - \frac{3}{s+1}X_2$$

10-3. Find a set of equations that characterize the signal-flow graph of Fig. 10-15.

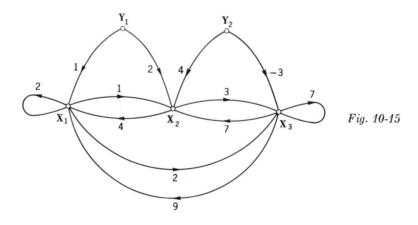

Fig. 10-15

10-4. Repeat Prob. 10-3 for the network of Fig. 10-16.

10-5. Obtain a signal-flow graph that represents the set of simultaneous equations

$$\mathbf{Y}_1 = 2\mathbf{X}_1 + 4\mathbf{X}_2 + \mathbf{X}_3$$
$$\mathbf{Y}_2 = 3\mathbf{X}_1 + 7\mathbf{X}_2 - \mathbf{X}_3$$
$$\mathbf{Y}_3 = 9\mathbf{X}_1 + 4\mathbf{X}_2 + 7\mathbf{X}_3$$

10-6. Obtain a signal-flow graph that represents the set of simultaneous equations

$$\mathbf{Y}_1 = \frac{s}{s+1}\mathbf{X}_1 + \mathbf{X}_2 + \frac{1}{s}\mathbf{X}_3$$
$$\frac{1}{s^2}\mathbf{Y}_2 = \frac{s}{2s+3}\mathbf{X}_1 + \frac{1}{s}\mathbf{X}_2 + \mathbf{X}_3$$
$$\mathbf{Y}_3 = \mathbf{X}_1 + \frac{s}{s^2+4}\mathbf{X}_2 + \mathbf{X}_3$$

10-7. Eliminate all self-loops from the signal-flow graph of Fig. 10-15.

10-8. Repeat Prob. 10-7 for the signal-flow graph of Fig. 10-16.

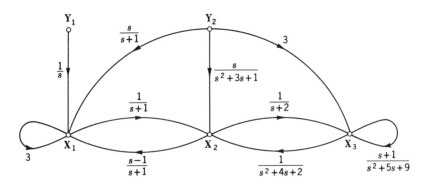

Fig. 10-16

10-9. Use signal-flow-graph-reduction techniques to solve Fig. 10-15 for $\mathbf{X}_3$ in terms of $\mathbf{Y}_1$ and $\mathbf{Y}_2$.

10-10. Repeat Prob. 10-9 for the network of Fig. 10-16.

10-11. Use signal-flow-graph-reduction techniques to solve Fig. 10-9*b* for $\mathbf{V}_{R2}(s)$ in terms of the independent-generator quantities.

10-12. Use signal-flow-graph-reduction techniques to solve the simultaneous equations of Prob. 10-5 for $\mathbf{X}_3$ in terms of $\mathbf{Y}_1$, $\mathbf{Y}_2$, and $\mathbf{Y}_3$.

10-13. Repeat Prob. 10-12 for the equations of Prob. 10-6.

10-14. Use the procedures of Sec. 10-5 to obtain a signal-flow graph for the network of Fig. 4-22. Work in the Laplace transform domain.

10-15. Repeat Prob. 10-14 for the network of Fig. 4-23.

10-16. Repeat Prob. 10-14 for the network of Fig. 4-24.
10-17. Repeat Prob. 10-14 for the network of Fig. 4-25.
10-18. Repeat Prob. 10-14 for the network of Fig. 4-26.
10-19. Repeat Prob. 10-14 for the network of Fig. 10-17.

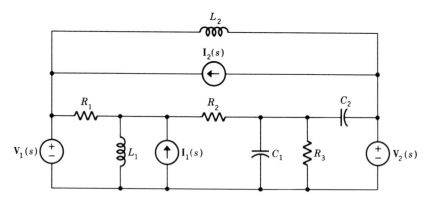

Fig. 10-17

10-20. Draw the signal-flow graph for the state-variable equations of Prob. 7-3.

10-21. Repeat Prob. 10-20 for the equation of Prob. 7-4.
10-22. Repeat Prob. 10-20 for the equation of Prob. 7-5.
10-23. Repeat Prob. 10-20 for the equation of Prob. 7-6.
10-24. Repeat Prob. 10-20 for the equation of Prob. 7-8.
10-25. Repeat Prob. 10-20 for the equation of Prob. 7-11.
10-26. Repeat Prob. 10-20 for the equation of Prob. 7-12.
10-27. Repeat Prob. 10-20 for the equation of Prob. 7-13.
10-28. Repeat Prob. 10-20 for the equation of Prob. 7-14.

Fourier Series and Fourier Integral

11

In this chapter we shall consider a procedure for representing a nonsinusoidal function of time as a combination of sinusoids. This will allow us to use sinusoidal-steady-state analysis to solve for the currents and voltages of a linear network whose excitations are not sinusoidal. Initially we shall discuss nonsinusoidal *periodic* functions and develop a procedure for expressing these functions as a sum of sinusoids. We shall then discuss circuit analysis using these functions. Subsequently, we shall generalize this procedure to nonperiodic functions of time. These procedures are closely related to the Laplace transform; in Sec. 11-11 we shall discuss this relationship in detail.

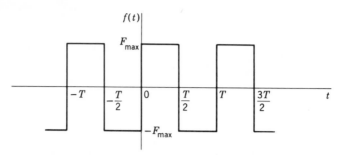

Fig. 11-1   A square wave.

11-1   Fourier series

A periodic function is one that repeats itself every T sec; that is, it can be expressed as

$$f(t + T) = f(t) \qquad -\infty \leq t \leq \infty \tag{11-1}$$

A typical periodic function, called a *square wave*, is shown in Fig. 11-1. T is called the *period* of the function.   As in the case of sinusoids (see Sec. 6-1),

$$f_0 = \frac{1}{T} \tag{11-2}$$

is called the *frequency* of the function, measured in hertz, and

$$\omega_0 = 2\pi f_0 = \frac{2\pi}{T} \tag{11-3}$$

is the *angular frequency*.   We shall assume that the periodic functions with which we work satisfy the conditions that there can be only a finite number of finite maxima or minima in any one period, there can be only a finite number of jump discontinuities in any one period, and the integral

$$\int_{-T/2}^{T/2} |f(t)| \, dt$$

is finite.   These are called the *Dirichlet conditions*.   In general, all the functions that we wish to consider will satisfy these conditions.

It can be shown that any periodic function that satisfies the Dirichlet conditions can be expanded in an infinite series of the form

$$f(t) = a_0 + a_1 \cos \omega_0 t + a_2 \cos 2\omega_0 t + a_3 \cos 3\omega_0 t$$
$$+ \cdots + b_1 \sin \omega_0 t + b_2 \sin 2\omega_0 t + b_3 \sin 3\omega_0 t + \cdots \tag{11-4a}$$

where the a and b terms are constants.   This is called a *Fourier series*.   That is, the periodic function consists of a sum of sinusoids and cosinusoids. The frequency of these terms is an *integral* multiple of the frequency of the periodic function itself. f_0 is called the *fundamental frequency;* its integral multiples are called *harmonics.* Any periodic function satisfying the Dirichlet conditions can be expressed as in Eq. (11-4a) (it is beyond the scope of this chapter to prove this). We can rewrite Eq. (11-4a) as

$$f(t) = a_0 + \sum_{k=1}^{\infty} (a_k \cos k\omega_0 t + b_k \sin k\omega_0 t) \tag{11-4b}$$

We must now develop a procedure whereby, given a periodic $f(t)$, we can find the constant a's and b's of Eq. (11-4). Since they are constants, if we can evaluate them in any way, we know that they are valid for all time. If we integrate a sinusoid or cosinusoid for one period (or an integral number of periods), its average value (or integral) is zero,

$$\int_{-T/2}^{T/2} \sin \omega_0 t \, dt = 0 \tag{11-5}$$

$$\int_{-T/2}^{T/2} \cos \omega_0 t \, dt = 0 \tag{11-6}$$

where ω_0 and T are related as in Eq. (11-3). Now we integrate Eq. (11-4b). This yields

$$\int_{-T/2}^{T/2} f(t) \, dt = \int_{-T/2}^{T/2} a_0 \, dt + \int_{-T/2}^{T/2} \sum_{k=1}^{n} (a_k \cos k\omega_0 t + b_k \sin k\omega_0 t) \, dt \tag{11-7a}$$

We shall assume that the functions are such that the order of summation and integration can be interchanged. Thus

$$\int_{-T/2}^{T/2} f(t) \, dt = a_0 \int_{-T/2}^{T/2} dt$$
$$+ \sum_{k=1}^{\infty} \left(a_k \int_{-T/2}^{T/2} \cos k\omega_0 t \, dt + b_k \int_{-T/2}^{T/2} \sin k\omega_0 t \, dt \right) \tag{11-7b}$$

Each of the integrals in the summation will be zero [see Eqs. (11-5) and (11-6)]. Note that if $k = 2, 3, \ldots$, the integral is over $2, 3, \ldots$ cycles. Hence the integrals are zero, and Eq. (11-7) yields

$$a_0 = \frac{1}{T} \int_{-T/2}^{T/2} f(t) \, dt \tag{11-8}$$

Thus a_0 is the *average value* of $f(t)$ over one period.

To evaluate the other constants we proceed in a similar manner and make use of the integral relations

$$\int_{-T/2}^{T/2} \cos m\omega_0 t \cos n\omega_0 t \, dt = \begin{cases} 0 & m \neq n \\ \dfrac{T}{2} & m = n \end{cases} \tag{11-9}$$

$$\int_{-T/2}^{T/2} \sin m\omega_0 t \sin n\omega_0 t \, dt = \begin{cases} 0 & m \neq n \\ \dfrac{T}{2} & m = n \end{cases} \tag{11-10}$$

$$\int_{-T/2}^{T/2} \sin m\omega_0 t \cos n\omega_0 t \, dt = 0 \tag{11-11}$$

where n and m are integers. To evaluate a_m we multiply both sides of Eq. (11-4) by $\cos m\omega_0 t \, dt$ and integrate from $-T/2$ to $T/2$. After interchanging the order of summation and integration, which we assume can be done, we obtain

$$\int_{-T/2}^{T/2} f(t) \cos m\omega_0 t \, dt = a_0 \int_{-T/2}^{T/2} \cos m\omega_0 t \, dt$$
$$+ \sum_{k=1}^{\infty} a_k \int_{-T/2}^{T/2} \cos m\omega_0 t \cos k\omega_0 t \, dt$$
$$+ \sum_{k=1}^{\infty} b_k \int_{-T/2}^{T/2} \cos m\omega_0 t \sin k\omega_0 t \, dt \tag{11-12}$$

The first integral on the right-hand side is zero [see Eq. (11-6)]. Every term in the first summation will be zero, except where $k = m$ [see Eq. (11-9)], and all terms of the third summation will be zero [see Eq. (11-11)]. Carrying out the integration, we obtain

$$a_m = \frac{2}{T} \int_{-T/2}^{T/2} f(t) \cos m\omega_0 t \, dt \tag{11-13}$$

If we proceed in a similar manner, but multiply both sides of Eq. (11-4) by $\sin m\omega_0 t$, we obtain

$$b_m = \frac{2}{T} \int_{-T/2}^{T/2} f(t) \sin m\omega_0 t \, dt \tag{11-14}$$

As an example let us obtain the Fourier series of the square wave of Eq. (11-1). Substituting in Eqs. (11-8) and (11-13), we obtain

$$a_0 = \frac{1}{T} \int_{-T/2}^{0} -F_{\max} \, dt + \frac{1}{T} \int_{0}^{T/2} F_{\max} = 0 \tag{11-15a}$$

$$a_m = \frac{2}{T} \int_{-T/2}^{0} -F_{\max} \cos m\omega_0 t \, dt + \frac{2}{T} \int_{0}^{T/2} F_{\max} \cos m\omega_0 t \, dt = 0 \tag{11-15b}$$

(note that in each case the integrand in the first integral is positive while, in the second integral, it is negative and the sum of the two integrals is zero).

Substituting in Eq. (11-14), we have

$$b_m = \frac{2}{T} \int_{-T/2}^{0} -F_{\max} \sin m\omega_0 t \, dt + \frac{2}{T} \int_{0}^{T/2} F_{\max} \sin m\omega_0 t \, dt$$

$$= \frac{4}{T} \int_{0}^{T/2} \sin m\omega_0 t \, dt = \frac{2}{\pi m} F_{\max} (1 - \cos m\pi) \quad (11\text{-}15c)$$

Thus the Fourier series for the square wave of Fig. 11-1 is

$$f(t) = \frac{2}{\pi} F_{\max} \sum_{k=1}^{\infty} \frac{1}{k} (1 - \cos k\pi) \sin k\omega_0 t \qquad (11\text{-}16a)$$

Since

$$1 - \cos m\pi = \begin{cases} 2 & m = 1,\, 3,\, 5,\, 7,\, \dots \\ 0 & m = 2,\, 4,\, 6,\, 8,\, \dots \end{cases}$$

then

$$f(t) = \frac{4}{\pi} F_{\max} (\sin \omega_0 t + \tfrac{1}{3} \sin 3\omega_0 t + \tfrac{1}{5} \sin 5\omega_0 t + \cdots) \qquad (11\text{-}16b)$$

The exponential form of the Fourier series

Let us now manipulate the Fourier series so that we can write it in a more compact form. We shall also introduce phasor notation (see Sec. 6-1) which will simplify the solution of electric network problems when the excitation is a nonsinusoidal periodic function. The Fourier series is of the form

$$f(t) = a_0 + \sum_{k=1}^{\infty} (a_k \cos k\omega_0 t + b_k \sin k\omega_0 t) \qquad (11\text{-}17)$$

We use Euler's relation to rewrite the sine and cosine [see Eq. (6-20)] as

$$\sin k\omega_0 t = \frac{e^{jk\omega_0 t} - e^{-jk\omega_0 t}}{2j} \qquad (11\text{-}18)$$

$$\cos k\omega_0 t = \frac{e^{jk\omega_0 t} + e^{-jk\omega_0 t}}{2} \qquad (11\text{-}19)$$

Substituting these equations in Eq. (11-17) and combining terms, we have

$$f(t) = a_0 + \sum_{k=1}^{\infty} \frac{a_k - jb_k}{2} e^{jk\omega_0 t} + \frac{a_k + jb_k}{2} e^{-jk\omega_0 t} \qquad (11\text{-}20)$$

If we let

$$\mathbf{C}_s = \frac{a_k - jb_k}{2} \qquad (11\text{-}21)$$

and substitute Eqs. (11-13) and (11-14) into Eq. (11-21), we have

$$C_k = \frac{1}{T} \int_{-T/2}^{T/2} f(t)(\cos k\omega_0 t - j \sin k\omega_0 t) \, dt \tag{11-22}$$

However,

$$e^{-jx} = \cos x - j \sin x \tag{11-23}$$

Hence

$$C_k = \frac{1}{T} \int_{-T/2}^{T/2} f(t)e^{-jk\omega_0 t} \, dt \tag{11-24}$$

Now let us consider Eqs. (11-13) and (11-14) with m replaced by $-m$. Note that

$$\cos(-x) = \cos x \tag{11-25a}$$
$$\sin(-x) = -\sin x \tag{11-25b}$$

Then

$$a_{-m} = a_m \tag{11-26a}$$
$$b_{-m} = -b_m \tag{11-26b}$$

That is, if we simply replace m by $-m$ in Eqs. (11-13) and (11-14), Eqs. (11-26) result. Then, substituting in Eq. (11-21), we have

$$C_{-k} = \frac{a_k + jb_k}{2} \tag{11-27}$$

where C_{-k} can be obtained from Eq. (11-24) by replacing k by $-k$. Substituting Eqs. (11-21) and (11-27) into Eq. (11-20), we obtain

$$f(t) = a_0 + \sum_{k=1}^{\infty} C_k e^{jk\omega_0 t} + \sum_{k=-1}^{-\infty} C_k e^{jk\omega_0 t} \tag{11-28}$$

Note that the minus sign has been removed from the exponent and subscript in the second summation, because k takes on negative values. Evaluating Eq. (11-24) for $k = 0$, we have

$$C_0 = \frac{1}{T} \int_{-T/2}^{T/2} f(t) \, dt \tag{11-29}$$

Comparison with Eq. (11-8) gives us

$$C_0 = a_0 \tag{11-30}$$

and substituting this into Eq. (11-28), we obtain

$$f(t) = \sum_{k=-\infty}^{\infty} C_k e^{jk\omega_0 t} \tag{11-31}$$

Thus we can write the Fourier series in a very compact form. Note that for all k we have

$$\mathbf{C}_k = \frac{1}{T} \int_{-T/2}^{T/2} f(t) e^{-jk\omega_0 t}\, dt \tag{11-32}$$

The form of the Fourier series given by Eq. (11-31) is called the *exponential form*. That given by Eq. (11-4) is called the *sine-and-cosine form*.

Let us discuss the significance of the constant $\mathbf{C}_k$. We use a procedure similar to that of Eqs. (6-12) to (6-16) to take the sum $a_k \cos k\omega_0 t + b_k \sin k\omega_0 t$, which consists of the sum of all the terms at the frequency $k\omega_0$,

$$a_k \cos k\omega_0 t + b_k \sin k\omega_0 t = d_k \cos (k\omega_0 t + \phi_k) \tag{11-33a}$$

where

$$d_k = \sqrt{a_k{}^2 + b_k{}^2} \tag{11-33b}$$

$$\phi_k = -\tan^{-1}\frac{b_k}{a_k} \tag{11-33c}$$

(Note that we have used a cosine rather than a sine here.) From Eq. (11-21) we obtain

$$\mathbf{C}_k = \frac{a_k - jb_k}{2} = \frac{1}{2}\sqrt{a_k{}^2 + b_k{}^2}\, e^{-j\tan^{-1}(b_k/a_k)} \tag{11-34}$$

Comparison of Eqs. (11-33) and (11-34) shows that $\mathbf{C}_k$ is a phasor whose magnitude is half the magnitude of the total cosinusoid at the frequency $k\omega_0$. The phase angle of $\mathbf{C}_k$ is the phase angle of the cosinusoid. The factor $\frac{1}{2}$ comes about because both $\mathbf{C}_k e^{jk\omega_0 t}$ and $\mathbf{C}_{-k} e^{-jk\omega_0 t}$ contribute components at the frequency $k\omega_0$.

As an example let us obtain the Fourier series of the square wave of Fig. 11-1. From Eq. (11-32) we have

$$\mathbf{C}_k = \frac{1}{T} \int_{-T/2}^{0} -F_{\max} e^{-jk\omega_0 t}\, dt + \frac{1}{T} \int_{0}^{T/2} F_{\max} e^{-jk\omega_0 t}\, dt \tag{11-35a}$$

and substitution of Eq. (11-3) gives us

$$\mathbf{C}_k = \frac{F_{\max}}{2\pi jk}(1 - e^{jk\pi}) - \frac{F_{\max}}{2\pi jk}(-1 + e^{-jk\pi}) = j\frac{F_{\max}}{2\pi k}(e^{jk\pi} + e^{-jk\pi} - 2) \tag{11-35b}$$

Thus

$$f(t) = j\frac{F_{\max}}{2\pi} \sum_{k=-\infty}^{\infty} \frac{1}{k}(e^{-jk\pi} + e^{jk\pi} - 2)e^{jk\omega_0 t}$$

$$= j\frac{F_{\max}}{\pi} \sum_{k=-\infty}^{\infty} \frac{(\cos k\pi - 1)e^{jk\omega_0 t}}{k} \tag{11-36}$$

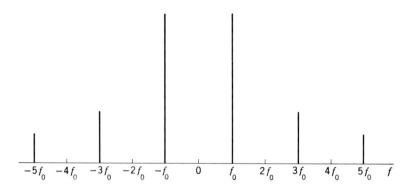

Fig. 11-2 Part of the frequency spectrum of a square wave.

Note that if $k = 0, \pm 2, \pm 4, \ldots$, then $\mathbf{C}_k = 0$, and if $k = \pm 1, \pm 3, \pm 5,$ $\ldots$, then $\mathbf{C}_k = -2jF_{max}/\pi k$.   If these values are substituted into Eq. (11-36) and the terms for positive and negative k are combined, the series of Eq. (11-16) results.

In general, $f(t)$ will be a real function of time.   Thus the imaginary terms in the exponential form of the Fourier series will always cancel each other.

Discrete Fourier spectrum

At times we wish to represent the magnitude of the frequencies present in a waveform.   We can do this by plotting a frequency axis.   Along the axis we put vertical lines, the length of which indicate the magnitudes of $\mathbf{C}_k$.   This is called a *discrete-frequency spectrum*.   Figure 11-2 shows a discrete-frequency spectrum for the square wave.   Sometimes both positive and negative frequencies are plotted.   These correspond to positive and negative values of k (such as $\mathbf{C}_k$ and $\mathbf{C}_{-k}$).

11-2   Waveform symmetries

If the waveform of the periodic function that we are expanding in a Fourier series has certain symmetries, then some of the coefficients will be zero. Recognition of this will be helpful, since we will not have to evaluate them. We shall consider each of these symmetries in turn.

Even and odd functions

A function is called an *even function* if it satisfies the relation

$$f(t) = f(-t) \tag{11-37}$$

That is, if t is replaced by $-t$, the function is unchanged. An even function is shown in Fig. 11-3a. If

$$f(t) = -f(-t) \tag{11-38}$$

then $f(t)$ is called an *odd function* of time. An odd function is shown in Fig. 11-3b. In general, we can show that any function of time can be expressed as the sum of an even function and an odd function. That is,

$$f(t) = f_e(t) + f_o(t) \tag{11-39}$$

where $f_e(t)$ is an even function of time and $f_o(t)$ is an odd function of time.

For instance, consider the sum $f(t) + f(-t)$. Taking this sum and substituting Eqs. (11-37) and (11-38), we have

$$f_e(t) = \frac{f(t) + f(-t)}{2} \tag{11-40a}$$

If we replace t by $-t$, the same function results. Hence this is an even function. Similarly,

$$f_o(t) = \frac{f(t) - f(-t)}{2} \tag{11-40b}$$

If we take the sum of Eqs. (11-40a) and (11-40b), we obtain $f(t)$. Thus we see that any $f(t)$ can be expressed as the sum of an even $f(t)$ and an odd $f(t)$.

The product of *two even* functions and *two odd* functions will be *even*. This follows from the rule for the multiplication of negative numbers. Similarly, the product of an *even* function and an *odd* function is *odd*.

Now let us consider the integral of an even function over symmetric limits; thus

$$\int_{-a}^{a} f_e(t) \, dt = \int_{-a}^{0} f_e(t) \, dt + \int_{0}^{a} f_e(t) \, dt \tag{11-41a}$$

We replace t by $-t$ in the first integral on the right-hand side,

$$\int_{-a}^{a} f_e(t) \, dt = - \int_{a}^{0} f_e(-t) \, dt + \int_{0}^{a} f_e(t) \, dt = 2 \int_{0}^{a} f(t) \, dt \tag{11-41b}$$

Fig. 11-3   (a) An even function of time; (b) an odd function of time.

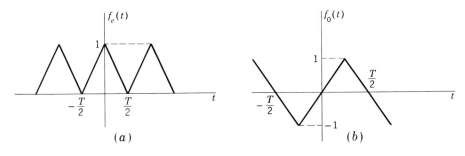

where we have substituted Eq. (11-39).   The integration of an odd function over symmetric limits is

$$\int_{-a}^{a} f_o(t)\, dt = \int_{-a}^{0} f_o(t)\, dt + \int_{0}^{a} f_o(t)\, dt = -\int_{a}^{0} f_o(-t)\, dt + \int_{0}^{a} f_o(t)\, dt$$

and substituting Eq. (11-38), we obtain

$$\int_{-a}^{a} f_o(t)\, dt = 0 \tag{11-42}$$

Now let us consider the Fourier series of even and odd functions of time. We shall study the even one first.   From Eqs. (11-8) and (11-13) we have

$$a_0 = \frac{1}{T} \int_{-T/2}^{T/2} f_e(t)\, dt = \frac{2}{T} \int_{0}^{T/2} f_e(t)\, dt \tag{11-43}$$

$$a_n = \frac{2}{T} \int_{-T/2}^{T/2} f_e(t)\, \cos n\omega_0 t\, dt = \frac{4}{T} \int_{0}^{T/2} f_e(t)\, \cos n\omega_0 t\, dt \tag{11-44}$$

The last integral is obtained by noting that $\cos x$ is an even function of time [see Eq. (11-25a)].   Thus the integrand is even, and we can apply Eq. (11-41b). From Eq. (11-14) we have

$$b_n = \frac{2}{T} \int_{-T/2}^{T/2} f_e(t)\, \sin n\omega_0 t\, dt = 0 \tag{11-45}$$

This is obtained by observing that the integrand is an odd function of time and then applying Eq. (11-42).   Thus an even function of time contains only a constant term and cosine terms in its Fourier series.   The constants $\mathbf{C}_k$ [see Eq. (11-21)] are real numbers.

If we proceed in essentially the same manner for an odd function, we have

$$a_k = 0 \qquad k = 0, 1, 2, \ldots$$

$$b_k = \frac{4}{T} \int_{0}^{T/2} f_o(t)\, \sin k\omega_0 t\, dt \tag{11-46}$$

Thus an odd function of time has a Fourier series which contains only sine terms.   The constant $\mathbf{C}_k$ is a pure imaginary number.

At times we work with a function of time that can be expressed as an odd function plus a constant.   For example, in the case

$$f(t) = K + f_o(t) \tag{11-47}$$

we expand $f(t) - K$ in a Fourier series of sine terms and then add the constant K to obtain the Fourier series of $f(t)$.

In general, we can express any function as a sum of even and odd parts. Each of these can be expanded separately, and then the two series can be added to obtain the series for the entire function.   As an example consider the square wave of Fig. 11-1 is an odd function of time.   Its Fourier series [see Eq. (11-16)] contains only sine terms.

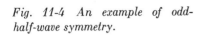

Fig. 11-4 An example of odd-half-wave symmetry.

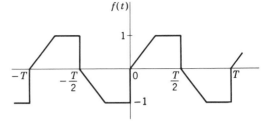

Odd-half-wave symmetry

Suppose now that $f(t)$ is characterized by

$$f(t) = -f\left(t + \frac{T}{2}\right) \tag{11-48}$$

A typical waveform of this type is shown in Fig. 11-4. Note that the second half of the period repeats the first half, except that it is multiplied by -1. This is called *odd-half-wave symmetry*. Evaluating $\mathbf{C}_k$, given by Eq. (11-32), we have

$$\mathbf{C}_k = \frac{1}{T}\int_{-T/2}^{0} f(t)e^{-jk\omega_0 t}\, dt + \frac{1}{T}\int_{0}^{T/2} f(t)e^{-jk\omega_0 t}\, dt \tag{11-49a}$$

In the first integral we let

$$t = t_1 + \frac{T}{2}$$

Then

$$\mathbf{C}_k = \frac{1}{T}\int_{0}^{T/2} f\left(t_1 + \frac{T}{2}\right) e^{-jk\omega_0 t_1}e^{-jk\omega_0(T/2)}\, dt_1 + \frac{1}{T}\int_{0}^{T/2} f(t)e^{-jk\omega_0 t}\, dt \tag{11-49b}$$

Substituting Eq. (11-48) and combining terms, we have

$$\mathbf{C}_k = \frac{1}{T}\int_{0}^{T/2} f(t)e^{-jk\omega_0 t}(1 - e^{-jk\omega_0 T/2})\, dt \tag{11-49c}$$

and substituting Eq. (11-3), we have

$$\mathbf{C}_k = \frac{1}{T}\int_{0}^{T/2} f(t)e^{-jk\omega_0 t}(1 - e^{-jk\pi})\, dt \tag{11-49d}$$

Consider the term $1 - e^{jk\pi}$. If $k = 0, 2, 4, 6, \ldots$, then $e^{jk\pi} = 1$. Thus

$$1 - e^{jk\pi} = 0 \qquad k = 0, 2, 4, 6, \ldots \tag{11-50}$$

Hence

$$\mathbf{C}_k = 0 \qquad k = 0, 2, 4, 6, \ldots \tag{11-51}$$

Therefore waveforms that exhibit *odd-half-wave symmetry* have *no even harmonics.*   For example, consider the square wave of Fig. 11-1, whose Fourier series is given by Eqs. (11-16) and (11-36).

In the case of the odd harmonics we can generally simplify Eq. (11-49d). If k is odd, then $1 - e^{jk\pi} = 2$.   Thus

$$\mathbf{C}_k = \frac{2}{T} \int_0^{T/2} f(t)e^{-jk\omega_0 t}\, dt \qquad k = 1, 3, 5, \ldots \tag{11-52}$$

Even-half-wave symmetry

A function with even-half-wave symmetry is characterized by

$$f(t) = f\left(t + \frac{T}{2}\right) \tag{11-53}$$

If we studied this function, we would see that, analogous to the case of odd-half-wave symmetry, the Fourier series contains only even harmonics.   Actually, this is really not a special case: compare Eq. (11-53) and Eq. (11-1).   In this case $f(t)$ is a periodic function with period $T/2$.   If Eq. (11-53) is true for a function, we have identified the period improperly.   Thus the fundamental frequency is $2/T = 2f_0$.   This is why there are only even harmonics (note that we will obtain the correct Fourier series if we use a period that is twice the actual one).

11-3   Finite Fourier series: errors and Gibb's phenomenon

The Fourier series of a general periodic function of time consists of an infinite number of terms.   As a practical matter, we cannot, in general, sum an infinite number of terms.   Hence we *truncate* the series; that is, we terminate it after a finite number of terms.   This introduces an error.   For instance, in Eq. (11-16) we have the Fourier series of the square wave of Fig. 11-1,

$$f(t) = \frac{2F_{\max}}{\pi} \sum_{k=1}^{\infty} \frac{1}{k} (1 - \cos k\pi) \sin k\omega_0 t \tag{11-54a}$$

$$f(t) = \frac{2F_{\max}}{\pi} \left(\sin \omega_0 t + \frac{1}{3} \sin 3\omega_0 t + \frac{1}{5} \sin 5\omega_0 t + \frac{1}{7} \sin 7\omega_0 t + \cdots\right)$$

$$\tag{11-54b}$$

In practice, we can work with only a finite number of terms, such as

$$f_5(t) = \frac{2F_{\max}}{\pi} \left(\sin \omega_0 t + \frac{1}{3} \sin 3\omega_0 t + \frac{1}{5} \sin 5\omega_0 t\right) \tag{11-55}$$

Thus an error results.   This is given by

$$\epsilon(t) = f(t) - f_5(t) \tag{11-56}$$

Note that the coefficients fall off as frequency increases. This leads to the hope that we can truncate the series without introducing too much error.

In general, we can write

$$f(t) = a_0 + \sum_{k=1}^{\infty} (a_n \cos k\omega_0 t + b_n \sin \omega_0 t) \tag{11-57}$$

If we terminate the series after N terms, we have

$$f_N(t) = \alpha_0 + \sum_{k=1}^{N} (\alpha_n \cos k\omega_0 t + \beta_n \sin \omega_0 t) \tag{11-58}$$

Note that we have changed the coefficients; the reason for this is that we may reduce the error by changing the coefficients.

Let us now consider the optimum choice of coefficients in a finite Fourier series. We define the error as

$$\epsilon(t) = f(t) - f_N(t) \tag{11-59}$$

This is a function of time. In general, for a fixed N there is no choice of the α and β terms which will minimize the error for all time [a given choice may decrease $\epsilon(t)$ at one time and increase it at another]. Thus we must choose an error criterion that will give us a single number which characterizes the error. We then choose the α and β terms to minimize this number.

One criterion might be to minimize the maximum error $|\epsilon(t)|_{\max}$. However, there are many circumstances in which the maximum error does not change with the choice of coefficients. Another choice would be to minimize the average error,

$$\epsilon_{av} = \int_{-T/2}^{T/2} |\epsilon(t)|\, dt \tag{11-60}$$

Note that the *magnitude* of $\epsilon(t)$ is integrated; otherwise the positive and negative errors would cancel. That is, if $\epsilon(t)$ is large and negative at one time and large and positive at another time, then we should not adopt an error criterion that allows these to cancel each other. A third error criterion that is often used is the mean-square error,

$$\epsilon_{ms} = \int_{-T/2}^{T/2} [f(t) - f_N(t)]^2\, dt \tag{11-61}$$

Here we square the error to prevent negative errors from canceling positive ones.

Ideally, the error criterion should be chosen on the basis of the use to which the series is being put. However, it is difficult to integrate magnitudes, since we do not know when the function will change signs. Note that α_n and β_n in Eq. (11-58) are unknowns. It is also difficult to determine the maximum error when α_n and β_n are unknowns. As a practical matter, the mean-square error is the simplest one to use and is used as an error criterion in many applications.

Note that convenience, rather than the fact that it is the best error criterion, often dictates its use.

Now let us determine the constants of Eq. (11-58) such that the mean-square error is minimized. From Eq. (11-61) we have

$$\epsilon_{ms} = \int_{-T/2}^{T/2} \left\{ f(t) - \left[\alpha_0 + \sum_{k=1}^{N} (\alpha_k \cos k\omega_0 t + \beta_k \sin k\omega_0 t) \right] \right\}^2 dt \qquad (11\text{-}62)$$

Let us minimize this with respect to a specific α_k. We differentiate Eq. (11-62) with respect to α_k and set the derivative equal to zero (it is left to the reader to show that this is a maximum and not a minimum, etc.). Note that $f(t)$ is *not* a function of α_k. We shall assume that the functions are such that the order of differentiation and integration can be interchanged. Thus

$$\frac{\partial \epsilon_{ms}}{\partial \alpha_k} = \int_{-T/2}^{T/2} 2 \left\{ f(t) - \left[\alpha_0 + \sum_{k=1}^{N} (\alpha_k \cos k\omega_0 t + \beta_k \cos k\omega_0 t) \right] \right\} \cos k\omega_0 t \, dt$$

$$= 0 \qquad (11\text{-}63a)$$

Now, carrying out the integration and making use of Eqs. (11-6), (11-9), and (11-11) we obtain

$$\int_{-T/2}^{T/2} f(t) \cos k\omega_0 t = \alpha_k \int_{-T/2}^{T/2} \cos^2 k\omega_0 t \, dt = \frac{\alpha_k T}{2} \qquad (11\text{-}63b)$$

or

$$\alpha_k = \frac{2}{T} \int_{-T/2}^{T/2} f(t) \cos k\omega_0 t \, dt \qquad (11\text{-}63c)$$

Comparison with Eq. (11-13) yields

$$\alpha_k = a_k \qquad (11\text{-}64)$$

Independently of all other α and β terms, then, to minimize the error with respect to the chosen α_k we set $\alpha_k = a_k$. Since this is independent of k and the other coefficients, we can generalize for all $k = 1, 2, \ldots, N$ and set

$$\alpha_k = a_k \qquad k = 1, 2, \ldots, N \qquad (11\text{-}65)$$

to minimize the error. Similarly, by differentiating with respect to α_0 and then β_k, we obtain

$$\alpha_0 = a_0 \qquad (11\text{-}66)$$

$$\beta_k = b_k \qquad k = 1, 2, \ldots, N \qquad (11\text{-}67)$$

In other words, to minimize the mean-square error we set the coefficients of the finite Fourier series equal to the corresponding ones in the infinite series; that is, we just truncate the infinite series after N terms and do not change the coefficients.

It should be emphasized that the results of Eqs. (11-65) through (11-67)

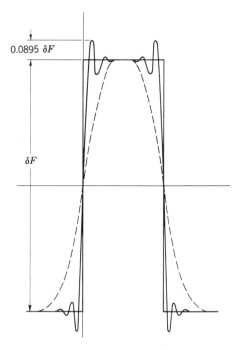

0.0895 δF

δF

Fig. 11-5 An example of Gibb's phenomenon. The dashed curve shows a response free of Gibb's phenomenon.

are applicable only for a mean-square-error criterion. If another error criterion is used, different coefficients would be obtained. In general, if we used a different error criterion, we could not obtain a general expression for the coefficients; they could be obtained only on a trial-and-error basis.

Let us now consider the waveform of truncated Fourier series in some special cases. If we take the Fourier series for the square wave and terminate it after a finite number of terms, a response of the type shown in Fig. 11-5 results. When the square wave jumps, the response does not follow it, but after a short time overshoots and oscillates in a damped fashion about the top of the pulse. The maximum overshoot is 8.95 percent of the jump δF in the square wave. If we add more terms to the Fourier series, the oscillation falls off at a faster rate and occurs at a higher frequency. However, the maximum overshoot of 8.95 percent *does not change*. The fact that the oscillation occurs at a higher frequency and falls off faster indicates that the mean-square error is decreasing as the number of terms is increased (ϵ_{ms} approaches zero as N approaches infinity). In general, if we terminate the Fourier series of any function that has a jump discontinuity, the resultant waveform will have an overshoot of 8.95 percent of the jump. This is called *Gibb's phenomenon*. The series converges exactly to the function only when it contains all its terms (an infinite number).

In discussing the convergence of the Fourier series in the vicinity of a discontinuity we considered overshoots and undershoots that occurred before and after the actual discontinuity. Let us now discuss the convergence of the Fourier series *at* the actual point of discontinuity. Suppose this occurs at $t = t_0$. We shall use the following notation. Just prior to $t = t_0$ the function in question is given by $f(t_{0-})$, and just after t_0 the function is given by $f(t_{0+})$. The jump discontinuity is equal to $f(t_{0-}) - f(t_{0+})$. At the point of discontinuity it can be shown that the Fourier series will converge to

$$f_0 = \frac{f(t_{0-}) + f(t_{0+})}{2}$$

That is, it will converge to the average of the values before and after the discontinuity. The Fourier series thus overshoots by an amount $0.0895[f(t_{0-}) - f(t_{0+})]$ prior to t_0, passes through f_0 at $t = t_0$, and then undershoots by $0.0895[f(t_{0-}) - f(t_{0+})]$ after $t = t_0$.

Gibb's phenomenon can be eliminated if we change the coefficients of the finite Fourier series. This will increase the mean-square error. If the highest frequency in the truncated Fourier series is $N\omega_0$, we multiply a_k and b_k or $\mathbf{C}_k$ by

$$1 - \frac{k}{N+1} \qquad k = 0, 1, 2, \ldots, N$$

This will eliminate Gibb's phenomenon. As N approaches infinity, this factor becomes unity for all finite coefficients. Thus the series will converge to the proper value. This factor will also reduce the magnitude of the high-frequency terms. The rapid changes of $f(t)$ with time are due to the high-frequency terms, which also change rapidly with time. Thus reduced speed of response, as well as increased mean-square error, are the price paid for eliminating Gibb's phenomenon. The dashed curve of Fig. 11-5 illustrates a typical square-wave response when this is done.

In the next section we shall see that the response of a network to a periodic signal can be obtained using the Fourier series. Often we wish to determine by means of network analysis if this response has an overshoot when the input signal has discontinuities. In analyzing the network it is desirable that the input signal itself not contain any overshoot. If it does, then we cannot ascertain whether the overshoot in the output is due to the network or is a response to the overshoot in the input signal. Thus, in using a Fourier series of a discontinuous function in such an analysis, the procedure discussed above should be used to eliminate Gibb's phenomenon.

11-4   Periodic-steady-state network analysis

We shall now consider the response of a network to generators that produce periodic waveforms. We are concerned here with the periodic-steady-state response, which is analogous to the sinusoidal-steady-state response discussed in Sec. 6-2. That is, the response to an applied periodic signal will contain some components that decay exponentially with time and some that do not. After several periods have elapsed, the decaying component usually becomes negligible. The remaining response is the *periodic-steady-state response* (alternatively, we can consider that the periodic waveform is applied at $t = -\infty$). If we want to find the total response to a function applied at $t = 0$, then we can use the Laplace transform (see Sec. 5-17 for a discussion of the Laplace transforms of semiperiodic functions).

Suppose we have a periodic voltage whose Fourier series is

$$v(t) = \sum_{k=-\infty}^{\infty} \mathbf{C}_k e^{jk\omega_0 t} \tag{11-68}$$

where

$$\mathbf{C}_k = C_k e^{j\phi_k} \tag{11-69}$$

The physical interpretation of Eq. (11-69) is that there is a sum of cosinusoid generators of the form

$$v(t) = V_0 + \sum_{k=1}^{\infty} \sqrt{2}\, V_k \cos(\omega t + \phi_k) \tag{11-70}$$

where [see Eqs. (11-33) and (11-34)]

$$V_k = \sqrt{2} C_k \qquad k \neq 0 \tag{11-71a}$$

$$V_0 = C_0 \tag{11-71b}$$

Note that $\mathbf{C}_0 = a_0$ [see Eq. (11-30)]. The voltage $v(t)$ of Eq. (11-70) can be considered to be produced by an infinite number of voltage generators all connected in series. Such an interconnection is shown in Fig. 11-6a. If we had used a current generator instead of a voltage generator, then the various current subgenerators would be connected in *parallel*.

To analyze a linear circuit with a voltage generator of the type shown in Fig. 11-6a we can apply the superposition theorem. That is, we consider that only one generator acts at a time. Since we are interested only in the periodic-steady-state response here, we need only find the sinusoidal-steady-state response. Thus we can use the generator of Fig. 11-6b, where the sinusoidal generators are replaced by their phasors. In the case of the direct-voltage generator, to obtain the steady-state response we consider that all inductors are short circuits and all capacitors are open circuits; that is, let ω approach zero.

As an example of this procedure let us obtain the voltage $v(t)$ in the network of Fig. 11-7a. The current generator produces a square wave whose waveform is shown in Fig. 11-1. The Fourier series for this waveform is given in Eq. (11-16) as

$$i(t) = \frac{4I_{\max}}{\pi} \left(\sin \omega_0 t + \frac{1}{3} \sin 3\omega_0 t + \frac{1}{5} \sin 5\omega_0 t + \cdots \right) \tag{11-72}$$

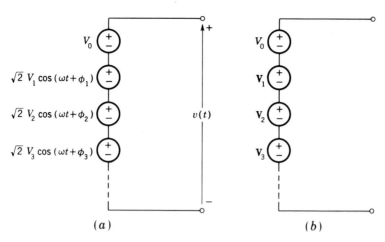

(a)   (b)

Fig. 11-6 (a) *A voltage generator that will produce the voltage v(t) of Eq. (11-70); (b) a phasor representation of this generator,* $\mathbf{V}_k = v_k e^{-j\phi k}$.

Fig. 11-7 (a) *A network with a square-wave signal; (b) a phasor network that can be used to calculate the periodic-steady-state output* $\mathbf{I}_k = 2\sqrt{2}\,I_{\max}/\pi k$ $(k = 1,3,5, \ldots);$ *(c) the network in (b) with only one generator applied. The superposition theorem is used here.*

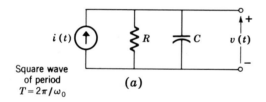

(a)

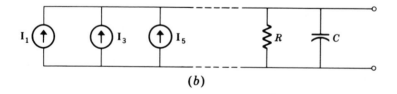

(b)

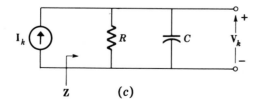

(c)

Each of these components can be represented by a generator, as shown in Fig. 11-7b. Note that the rms value of each component is $2\sqrt{2}\,I_{\max}/k\pi$ ($k = 1, 3, 5, \ldots$). We can now apply the superposition theorem and assume that only one generator acts at one time. The others are replaced by their internal impedances, which are open circuits. This is shown in Fig. 11-7c. Note that the frequency of operation of each generator is $k\omega_0$. Thus, on a sinusoidal-steady-state basis the impedance $\mathbf{Z}$ at a frequency $k\omega_0$ is

$$\mathbf{Z} = \frac{R}{1 + jk\omega_0 CR} \tag{11-73}$$

Hence

$$\mathbf{V}_k = \frac{2\sqrt{2}\,I_{\max}}{\pi k}\,\frac{R}{1 + jk\omega_0 CR} = \frac{2\sqrt{2}\,I_{\max}R}{\pi k\,\sqrt{1 + k^2\omega_0^2 C^2 R^2}}\,e^{-j\tan^{-1}k\omega_0 CR}$$
$$k = 1, 3, 5, \ldots \tag{11-74}$$

Thus each component in the voltage in the Fourier series of the output will be

$$v_k(t) = \frac{4I_{\max}R}{\pi k\,\sqrt{1 + k^2\omega_0^2 C^2 R^2}}\,\sin\left[k\omega_0 t - \tan^{-1}(k\omega_0 CR)\right]$$
$$k = 1, 3, 5, \ldots \tag{11-75}$$

Therefore

$$v(t) = \frac{4I_{\max}R}{\pi}\,\sum_{k=1}^{\infty}\frac{1}{k\,\sqrt{1 + (2k-1)^2\omega_0^2 C^2 R^2}}\,\sin\{(2k-1)\omega_0 t$$
$$-\tan^{-1}[(2k-1)\omega_0 CR]\} \tag{11-76}$$

where we have replaced k by $2k - 1$, so that only the odd terms are present.

If the circuit contains more than one periodic generator, we can treat *each* one by the procedure we have discussed. If there are several generators, then it is possible that there will be several harmonic generators which operate at the same frequency. These can be used simultaneously in the analysis.

11-5 The effective value of a Fourier series

In Sec. 6-8 we discussed the effective value of an arbitrary waveform. Now let us determine the effective value of a periodic function in terms of its Fourier series. We shall consider a voltage of the form

$$v(t) = V_0 + \sqrt{2}\,\sum_{k=1}^{\infty} V_k \sin\left(k\omega_0 t + \phi_k\right) \tag{11-77}$$

To determine its effective value we substitute in Eq. (6-126) to obtain

$$V_{\text{eff}} = \sqrt{\frac{1}{T}\int_{-T/2}^{T/2}\left[V_0 + \sqrt{2}\,\sum_{k=1}^{\infty} V_k \sin\left(k\omega_0 t + \phi_k\right)\right]^2 dt} \tag{11-78}$$

Note that we have shifted the limits of integration from zero to T to $-T/2$ to $T/2$. This will not change the value of the integral. In fact, we can use any limits of integration, as long as we integrate over one full cycle. Squaring as indicated and noting that the integrals of many terms are zero, when the order of summation and integration are interchanged (which we assume can be done), we obtain [see Eqs. (11-5), (11-6), and (11-9) to (11-11)]

$$V_{\text{eff}} = \sqrt{\frac{1}{T} \int_{-T/2}^{T/2} \left[V_0{}^2 + \sum_{k=1}^{\infty} 2V_k \sin^2 \left(k\omega_0 t + \phi_k \right) \right] dt} \qquad (11\text{-}79)$$

Note that to use Eqs. (11-5), (11-6), and (11-9) to (11-11) we expand $\sin (\omega_0 t + \phi_k)$ as

$$\sin (\omega_0 t + \phi_k) = \sin \omega_0 t \cos \phi_k + \cos \omega_0 t \sin \phi_k$$

Interchanging the order of summation and integration and integrating Eq. (11-79), we obtain

$$V_{\text{eff}} = \sqrt{V_0{}^2 + \sum_{k=1}^{\infty} V_k{}^2} \qquad (11\text{-}80)$$

That is, the effective value of the Fourier series is obtained by taking the square root of the sum of the squares of the individual effective values. The magnitudes V_k usually fall off sufficiently rapidly with increasing k that V_{eff} is bounded even though there are an infinite number of terms in Eq. (11-80).

11-6   The Fourier integral

Use of the Fourier series to express periodic functions as a sum of sinusoids has enabled us to use sinusoidal-steady-state response to analyze circuits on a periodic-steady-state basis. In this section we shall generalize our results so that we can represent nonperiodic waveforms in terms of sinusoidal components. The procedure by which we shall do this is called the *Fourier integral* or *Fourier transform*. We shall again restrict ourselves to functions that satisfy the Dirichlet conditions (see Sec. 11-1). In the case of nonperiodic functions these conditions are generalized as follows: (1) the function $f(t)$ must have a finite number of finite maxima and minima for $-\infty \le t \le \infty$, (2) the function must have a finite number of finite jump discontinuities for $-\infty \le t \le \infty$, and (3) the integral

$$\int_{-\infty}^{\infty} |f(t)| \, dt$$

must exist.

We shall develop the Fourier integral from the Fourier series by means of limit processes. Our procedures will be heuristic here, rather than completely rigorous. Distribution theory[1] can be used to develop the Fourier transform rigorously. However, this development is beyond the scope of our discussion.

We shall start our development with the exponential form of the Fourier series given by Eqs. (11-31) and (11-32). Before we rewrite these equations, let us multiply Eq. (11-32) by T with the constant TC_k, written as $\mathbf{C}'_k$. Thus

$$\mathbf{C}'_k = TC_k = \int_{-T/2}^{T/2} f(t)e^{-jk\omega_0 t}\, dt \tag{11-81}$$

Then, writing Eq. (11-31) in terms of $\mathbf{C}'_k$, we have

$$f(t) = \frac{1}{T} \sum_{k=-\infty}^{\infty} \mathbf{C}'_k e^{jk\omega_0 t} \tag{11-82}$$

In Eq. (11-82) we can replace $1/T$ by $\omega_0/2\pi$ [see Eq. (11-3)]. ω_0 represents the fundamental angular frequency. However, it also represents the spacing between the harmonics. To indicate this we shall write $\omega_0 = \delta\omega$, or

$$\frac{1}{T} = \frac{\delta\omega}{2\pi} \tag{11-83}$$

Thus Eq. (11-82) becomes

$$f(t) = \frac{1}{2\pi} \sum_{k=-\infty}^{\infty} \mathbf{C}'_k e^{jk\omega_0 t}\, \delta\omega \tag{11-84}$$

The constants $\mathbf{C}'_k$ are complex functions of frequency [see Eq. (11-81)]. To indicate this let us make the substitution

$$\mathbf{C}'_k = \mathbf{F}(jk\omega_0) \tag{11-85}$$

where we have included the j because it appears with ω_0 [see Eq. (11-81)]. Thus we can write

$$\mathbf{F}(jk\omega_0) = \int_{-T/2}^{T/2} f(t)e^{-jk\omega_0 t}\, dt \tag{11-86}$$

$$f(t) = \frac{1}{2\pi} \sum_{k=-\infty}^{\infty} \mathbf{F}(jk\omega_0)e^{jk\omega_0 t}\, \delta\omega \tag{11-87}$$

We shall use these relations to obtain the Fourier integral.

If a function is periodic, it repeats itself every T sec. If it is not periodic, then we can consider it to be a periodic function whose period is infinite; that is, it does not repeat itself until an infinite time has elapsed. Let us study the summation of Eq. (11-87) and consider what happens as T approaches infinity. The spacing between the harmonics approaches zero [see Eq. (11-83)], so we can state that $\delta\omega$ approaches $d\omega$. The quantity $k\omega_0$ represents the frequency of a particular harmonic. The harmonics become arbitrarily close together. We shall call the angular frequency of any "harmonic" ω. Then

$$k\omega_0 = \omega \tag{11-88}$$

As $\delta\omega$ approaches $d\omega$, the summation of Eq. (11-87) just becomes the definition of the Riemann integral.   Hence

$$f(t) = \frac{1}{2\pi} \int_{-\infty}^{\infty} \mathbf{F}(j\omega) e^{j\omega t} \, d\omega \tag{11-89}$$

That is, instead of summing an infinite number of harmonics which are spaced a finite frequency apart, we integrate over a continuum of frequency terms. Now let us obtain $\mathbf{F}(j\omega)$ from $\mathbf{F}(jk\omega_0)$. $\mathbf{F}(jk\omega_0)$ is given by Eq. (11-86).   To obtain $\mathbf{F}(j\omega)$ all we need do is let T approach infinity.   Then Eq. (11-86) becomes [see Eq. (11-88)]

$$\mathbf{F}(j\omega) = \int_{-\infty}^{\infty} f(t) e^{-j\omega t} \, dt \tag{11-90}$$

Equations (11-89) and (11-90) are called the *Fourier transform pairs.* Equation (11-90) converts a function of time into a function of frequency, while Eq. (11-89) does the converse. $\mathbf{F}(j\omega)$ is called the *Fourier spectrum* or *Fourier transform* of $f(t)$.   We shall use the notation $\mathbf{F}(j\omega) = \mathfrak{F}[f(t)]$.   Similarly, $f(t)$ can be called the *inverse Fourier transform* of $\mathbf{F}(j\omega)$.   We can write $f(t) = \mathfrak{F}^{-1}[\mathbf{F}(j\omega)]$.   Instead of having a set of discrete harmonics, as we do in the Fourier series, we now have a continuum of frequencies.

Let us consider the amplitude of any one frequency.   In the Fourier series [see Eq. (11-87)] the amplitude of a single harmonic is given by

$$\frac{\mathbf{F}(jk\omega_0) \, \delta\omega}{2\pi}$$

In general, the integral of Eq. (11-90) will be bounded.   Thus $\mathbf{F}(jk\omega_0)$ will be bounded.   Then, as T approaches infinity, $\delta\omega$ approaches zero.   Hence the energy contained at any one frequency is differentially small.   If we consider a finite band of frequencies, then this can contain finite energy.   Thus the Fourier spectrum $\mathbf{F}(\omega)$ does not give the magnitude of the components as a function of frequency. $\mathbf{F}(\omega) \, d\omega/2\pi$ gives this magnitude.   This is in contrast to the discrete Fourier spectrum (see Sec. 11-1), where the actual magnitudes are plotted.   The function $\mathbf{F}(\omega)$ is said to be in the *frequency domain*, while $f(t)$ is said to be in the *time domain.*

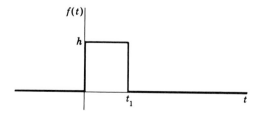

Fig. 11-8   *A flat-topped pulse.*

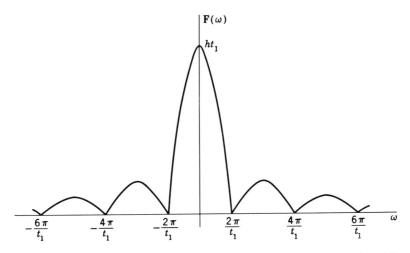

Fig. 11-9   The magnitude of the Fourier spectrum of the waveform of Fig. 11-8.

As an example of the Fourier integral let us obtain $\mathbf{F}(\omega)$ for the pulse shown in Fig. 11-8. Substituting this $f(t)$ into Eq. (11-90), we have

$$\mathbf{F}(j\omega) = h \int_0^{t_1} e^{-j\omega t} \, dt \tag{11-91a}$$

$$\mathbf{F}(j\omega) = \frac{h(1 - e^{-j\omega t_1})}{j\omega} = \frac{h(e^{j\omega t_1/2} - e^{-j\omega t_1/2})}{j\omega} \, e^{-j\omega t_1/2} \tag{11-91b}$$

This can be written as

$$\mathbf{F}(j\omega) = h t_1 \frac{\sin (\omega t_1/2)}{\omega t_1/2} \, e^{-j\omega t_1/2} \tag{11-91c}$$

A plot of the magnitude of this function is shown in Fig. 11-9. Note that $\mathbf{F}(j\omega)$ decreases as ω increases. For sufficiently large ω we can often assume that $\mathbf{F}(j\omega)$ is zero without introducing too much error. This is analogous to truncating a Fourier series. The statements in Sec. 11-3 about mean-square error and Gibb's phenomenon also apply here. Note (see Fig. 11-9) that if t_1 is decreased, then the value of $\mathbf{F}(j\omega)$ stays large for higher frequencies. That is, the higher-frequency components become more important as the period becomes shorter. In general, the shorter a pulse, the more important its high-frequency response.

We can obtain the Fourier integral in a somewhat different form. Let us write $\mathbf{F}(j\omega)$ in terms of its real and imaginary components as

$$\mathbf{F}(j\omega) = \mathbf{a}(\omega) - j\mathbf{b}(\omega) \tag{11-92}$$

Substitution in Eq. (11-89) yields

$$f(t) = \int_{-\infty}^{\infty} [\mathbf{a}(\omega) - j\mathbf{b}(\omega)](\cos \omega t + j \sin \omega t)\, d\omega \tag{11-93a}$$

$$f(t) = \int_{-\infty}^{\infty} [\mathbf{a}(\omega) \cos \omega t + \mathbf{b}(\omega) \sin \omega t]\, dt$$

$$+ j \int_{-\infty}^{\infty} [\mathbf{a}(\omega) \sin \omega t - \mathbf{b}(\omega) \cos \omega t]\, dt \tag{11-93b}$$

where we have expanded $e^{j\omega t}$ by Euler's relation. If $f(t)$ is real, as it must be in any actual problem, then the imaginary components of Eq. (11-93b) must be zero. That is, when the second integral of Eq. (11-93b) is evaluated, it will be zero. Thus

$$f(t) = \int_{-\infty}^{\infty} \mathbf{a}(\omega) \cos \omega t\, d\omega + \int_{-\infty}^{\infty} \mathbf{b}(\omega) \sin \omega t\, d\omega \tag{11-94}$$

To obtain $\mathbf{a}(\omega)$ and $\mathbf{b}(\omega)$ directly we rewrite Eq. (11-90) by Euler's relation as

$$\mathbf{F}(j\omega) = \mathbf{a}(\omega) - j\mathbf{b}(\omega) = \int_{-\infty}^{\infty} f(t)(\cos \omega t - j \sin \omega t)\, dt \tag{11-95}$$

Then, equating the real and imaginary components, we obtain

$$\mathbf{a}(\omega) = \int_{-\infty}^{\infty} f(t) \cos \omega t\, dt \tag{11-96a}$$

$$\mathbf{b}(\omega) = \int_{-\infty}^{\infty} f(t) \sin \omega t\, dt \tag{11-96b}$$

Equations (11-94) and (11-96) are analogous to the sine and cosine form of the Fourier series (see Sec. 11-1).

11-7   Transient responses of networks

Let us determine the response of a network to a generator (or generators) whose output is an arbitrary function of time. We desire the *entire* response, not just a steady-state form. The Fourier integral can be of use here. The development of this section will be heuristic rather than rigorous. Let us assume that the generator produces the time function $f(t)$. Then, from Eq. (11-90) we can obtain its Fourier transform, $\mathbf{F}(j\omega)$, which we assume exists.

Now let us consider the *physical* interpretation of Eq. (11-89), which gives $f(t)$ in terms of $\mathbf{F}(\omega)$. At a single pair of frequencies $\pm\omega$ the term

$$\mathbf{F}(j\omega)e^{j\omega t} + \mathbf{F}(-j\omega)e^{-j\omega t}$$

can be considered to be a sinusoid of frequency ω. This is also shown in terms of the real and imaginary components of $\mathbf{F}(j\omega)$ by Eq. (11-94). Then Eq. (11-89) consists of an "infinite sum" of all these sinusoidal components. Thus a function of time can be considered to consist of an infinite sum of sinusoidal terms. Note that these sinusoids are assumed to be present for all time $(-\infty \leq t \leq \infty)$. This is true even if $f(t)$ is zero for $t < 0$. For $t < 0$ the integral of Eq. (11-89) merely evaluates to zero (the "infinite sum" is zero for $t < 0$). Thus we can consider $f(t)$ to be composed of a "summation of sinusoids," and with the superposition theorem we can obtain the response to each of these. We then "sum" these responses to obtain the complete response to $f(t)$. This "summation" is actually an integral in the case of the Fourier integral.

The sinusoids are applied at $t = -\infty$. The response to any one of them will consist of decaying exponentials plus sinusoidal-steady-state terms (we assume that the exponential terms are decaying, that is, that all poles lie in the left half plane). Thus for all

$$-T_1 < t \leq \infty \tag{11-97}$$

where T_1 is any finite number, the damped exponential terms will become negligible. (Note that the sinusoids are applied at $t = -\infty$.) Hence to obtain the response for all times of interest we need only determine the sinusoidal-steady-state response to the sinusoidal components of $\mathbf{F}(j\omega)$ and then integrate them by means of Eq. (11-89), where $\mathbf{F}(j\omega)$ is replaced by the response to it. Note that the Fourier integral allows us to use sinusoidal-steady-state analysis to obtain the total response to an arbitrary $f(t)$.

The actual frequency component that we work with [see Eq. (11-94)] is

$$\mathbf{a}(\omega) \cos \omega t + \mathbf{b}(\omega) \sin \omega t = \sqrt{\mathbf{a}^2(\omega) + \mathbf{b}(\omega)^2} \cos [\omega t + \phi(\omega)] \tag{11-98}$$

where

$$\phi(\omega) = -\tan^{-1} \frac{\mathbf{b}(\omega)}{\mathbf{a}(\omega)} \tag{11-99}$$

From Eq. (11-92) we have

$$\mathbf{F}(j\omega) = \sqrt{\mathbf{a}^2(\omega) + \mathbf{b}(\omega)^2}\, e^{-j \tan^{-1} [\mathbf{b}(\omega)/\mathbf{a}(\omega)]} \tag{11-100}$$

Thus $\mathbf{F}(j\omega)$ is the phasor that can represent the generator. Note that [see Eqs. (11-96)]

$$\mathbf{a}(\omega) = \mathbf{a}(-\omega) \tag{11-101a}$$

$$\mathbf{b}(\omega) = -\mathbf{b}(-\omega) \tag{11-101b}$$

Thus

$$\mathbf{F}(-j\omega) = \mathbf{F}^*(j\omega) \tag{11-102}$$

The Fourier integral will include both $\mathbf{F}(j\omega)$ and $\mathbf{F}(-j\omega)$, since the integral is from minus infinity to plus infinity. Thus we shall also have a generator component due to a phasor $\mathbf{F}(-j\omega)$. Hence we can consider that $\mathbf{F}(j\omega)$ is the generator phasor without introducing any error (integration from minus infinity to infinity will include all the required terms).

To actually analyze the network we proceed as in Sec. 11-4. That is, we

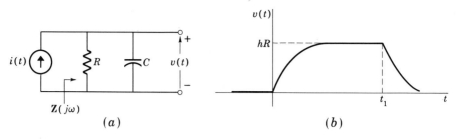

Fig. 11-10   (a) An RC network; (b) the response of this network to the pulse of Fig. 11-8, where RC ≪ t_1.

represent the input signal as an infinite sum of generators, with their phasors given by $\mathbf{F}(j\omega)$ (one for each value of ω). This requires an infinite number of generators in any finite frequency range. We sum them mathematically by integrating. Note that in Sec. 11-4 the generator phasor was $2\mathbf{C}_k$. However, there we considered only frequencies from zero to infinity. Here we consider frequencies from minus infinity to infinity. Thus we shall not use the factor of 2.

If we consider the "input generators" to have phasors given by $\mathbf{F}(j\omega)$, then sinusoidal-steady-state analysis yields an output signal composed of phasors $\mathbf{G}(j\omega)$ (we shall see an example of this subsequently). Then substitution into Eq. (11-89) gives us the desired response $g(t)$. Note that this procedure is similar to that of Sec. 11-4, where the sinusoidal-steady-state analysis was used to obtain the Fourier series coefficients, which were then substituted into the Fourier series expression.

As an example of this procedure let us compute the output voltage $v(t)$ of the network of Fig. 11-10. The input current is the pulse given in Fig. 11-8. From Eq. (11-91b) its Fourier transform is

$$\mathbf{I}(j\omega) = \frac{h(1 - e^{-j\omega t_1})}{j\omega} \tag{11-103}$$

The impedance $\mathbf{Z}(j\omega)$ is given by

$$\mathbf{Z}(j\omega) = \frac{R}{1 + j\omega RC} \tag{11-104}$$

Consider that $\mathbf{I}(j\omega)$ represents a single-frequency phasor. Thus the voltage phasor will be

$$\mathbf{V}(j\omega) = \mathbf{I}(j\omega)\,\mathbf{Z}(j\omega) = \frac{h(1 - e^{-j\omega t_1})}{j\omega}\,\frac{R}{1 + j\omega RC} \tag{11-105}$$

By treating ω as a variable, we can evaluate this for all frequencies and then substitute $\mathbf{V}(j\omega)$ into Eq. (11-89) to obtain $v(t)$. This yields

$$v(t) = \frac{1}{2\pi} \int_{-\infty}^{\infty} \frac{h(1 - e^{-j\omega t_1})}{j\omega} \frac{R}{1 + j\omega RC} e^{j\omega t} \, d\omega \tag{11-106a}$$

or

$$v(t) = \frac{h}{2\pi} \int_{-\infty}^{\infty} \frac{1}{j\omega} \frac{R}{1 + j\omega RC} e^{j\omega t} \, d\omega - \frac{h}{2\pi} \int_{-\infty}^{\infty} \frac{1}{j\omega} \frac{R}{1 + j\omega RC} e^{j\omega(t - t_1)} \, d\omega \tag{11-106b}$$

Let us consider the first integral,

$$v_1(t) = \frac{h}{2\pi} \int_{-\infty}^{\infty} \frac{1}{j\omega} \frac{R}{1 + j\omega RC} e^{j\omega t} \, d\omega \tag{11-107a}$$

This can be written as

$$v_1(t) = \frac{h}{2\pi} \int_{-\infty}^{\infty} \frac{R(1 - j\omega RC)}{j\omega(1 + \omega^2 R^2 C^2)} (\cos \omega t + j \sin \omega t) \, d\omega \tag{11-107b}$$

Since $v(t)$ is real, we can eliminate the imaginary component. Thus

$$v_1(t) = \frac{h}{2\pi} \int_{-\infty}^{\infty} \frac{-R^2 C}{1 + \omega^2 R^2 C^2} \cos \omega t \, d\omega + \frac{h}{2\pi} \int_{-\infty}^{\infty} \frac{R}{\omega(1 + \omega^2 R^2 C^2)} \sin \omega t \, d\omega \tag{11-107c}$$

If we integrate and evaluate, we obtain

$$v_1(t) = \frac{hR}{2} [-1 + 2u(t)(1 - e^{-t/RC})] \tag{11-108}$$

where $u(t)$ is the unit-step function. Let us consider why $u(t)$ appears. The first integral is equal to an even function of time $-(hR/2)e^{-|t|/RC}$, while the second is an odd function of time, part of which is equal to $-(hR/2)e^{-t/RC}$ for $t > 0$. Thus for $t < 0$ it is $(hR/2)e^{-|t|/RC}$, which cancels the $-(hR/2)e^{-|t|/RC}$ term. Note that $(hR/2)[-1 + 2u(t)]$ is another odd function of time included in the second integral of Eq. (11-107c).

The second integral of Eq. (11-106b) is the same as the first, except that t is replaced by $t - t_1$. Thus we can obtain its solution by replacing t by $t - t_1$ in Eq. (11-108). After some terms are canceled, the total $v(t)$ is given as

$$v(t) = hR[u(t)(1 - e^{-t/RC}) - u(t - t_1)(1 - e^{-(t-t_1)/RC})] \tag{11-109}$$

A sketch of the function is shown in Fig. 11-10b.

In some instances splitting an integral into two, as in Eq. (11-106b), produces two integrals that do not exist, although the single integral does exist. Thus care should be taken with the procedure.

We could have studied this problem in terms of the Laplace transform. In general, if a network circuit diagram is given, the Laplace transform is more convenient to use and allows us to incorporate initial conditions easily. However, the Fourier transform is useful for general theoretical analyses. It also provides us with insight into the relationships of the frequency and time responses. We shall discuss this further in Sec. 11-11.

11-8   Transfer functions: unit-impulse response and unit-step response

Suppose now that we wish to determine the response of a twoport to an input signal. We shall illustrate this problem with a transfer-voltage ratio, but the discussion applies to any transfer function. Thus in Fig 11-11*a* we shall determine $v_2(t)$ in response to the input $v_1(t)$. The twoport is assumed to be linear and time invariant, with zero initial conditions.

We can apply a sinusoidal generator to the input, as shown in Fig. 11-11*b*, and then, with sinusoidal-steady-state analysis or actual measurement, we can obtain $\mathbf{V}_2(j\omega)$ for all frequencies. The network is characterized by a transfer function

$$\mathbf{W}(j\omega) = \frac{\mathbf{V}_2(j\omega)}{\mathbf{V}_1(j\omega)} \tag{11-110}$$

Thus we can obtain the output phasor for any input phasor from Eq. (11-110).

Now assume that the input function $v_1(t)$ has a Fourier transform given by Eq. (11-90) as

$$\mathbf{V}_1(j\omega) = \int_{-\infty}^{\infty} v_1(t)e^{-j\omega t}\, dt \tag{11-111}$$

Thus (see Sec. 11-7) $v_2(t)$ will have a Fourier transform which is

$$\mathbf{V}_2(j\omega) = \mathbf{W}(j\omega)\mathbf{V}_1(j\omega) \tag{11-112}$$

Then we can obtain $v_2(t)$ by substituting this into Eq. (11-89):

$$v_2(t) = \frac{1}{2\pi} \int_{-\infty}^{\infty} \mathbf{W}(j\omega)\mathbf{V}_1(j\omega)e^{j\omega t}\, d\omega \tag{11-113}$$

Thus we can calculate the output voltage. We shall next see that $\mathbf{W}(j\omega)$ is the Fourier transform of the unit-impulse response.

Fig. 11-11   (*a*) *A twoport network illustrating a transfer-voltage ratio;* (*b*) *the same twoport showing a sinusoidal-steady-state-measurement circuit.*

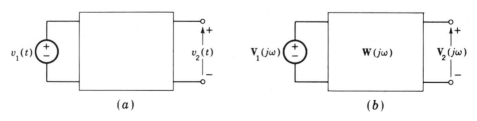

(*a*)   (*b*)

Unit-impulse response

Let us assume that the input signal is the unit impulse $\delta(t)$ (see Sec. 5-14). Its Fourier transform is [see Eq. (11-90)]

$$\mathcal{F}[\delta(t)] = \int_{-\infty}^{\infty} \delta(t) \, e^{-j\omega t} \, d\omega \qquad (11\text{-}114a)$$

Then from Eq. (5-224) we obtain

$$\mathcal{F}[\delta(t)] = 1 \qquad (11\text{-}114b)$$

Let us call $w(t)$ the response of a network to the unit impulse. Then, substituting in Eq. (11-113), we have

$$w(t) = \int_{-\infty}^{\infty} \mathbf{W}(j\omega)e^{j\omega t} \, d\omega \qquad (11\text{-}115)$$

Thus the response to a unit impulse takes on a simple form. This result is similar to the results obtained with the Laplace transform (see Sec. 5-15) and shows that $\mathbf{W}(j\omega)$ is the Fourier transform of $w(t)$.

Unit-step response

Now let us obtain the unit-step response. We must attempt to obtain the Fourier transform of $u(t)$. Substitution in Eq. (11-90) yields

$$\mathcal{F}[u(t)] = \int_{0}^{\infty} e^{-j\omega t} \, dt = \int_{0}^{\infty} (\cos \omega t - j \sin \omega t) \, dt \qquad (11\text{-}116)$$

We cannot evaluate this integral in the usual sense, because $\lim_{t \to \infty} e^{-j\omega t}$ or $\lim_{t \to \infty} \cos \omega t$ or $\lim_{t \to \infty} \sin \omega t$ do not exist. At times the Fourier transform of $u(t)$ is obtained by considering it as a limit of another function [for example, $u(t) - \lim_{a \to 0} u(t)e^{-at}$]. Actually, the only rigorous way to evaluate $\mathcal{F}[u(t)]$ is by means of distribution theory, which is beyond the scope of this chapter. However, we shall state $\mathcal{F}[u(t)]$ here as

$$\mathcal{F}[u(t)] = \pi \, \delta(\omega) + \frac{1}{j\omega} \qquad (11\text{-}117)$$

Note that this contains a delta function. The unit step contains a finite amount of energy at zero frequency. Thus (see Sec. 11-6) the continuous Fourier spectrum is infinite at that *one* frequency. To obtain the unit-step response $a(t)$ we substitute $\mathcal{F}[u(t)]$ into Eq. (11-113). Hence

$$a(t) = \frac{1}{2\pi} \int_{-\infty}^{\infty} \left[\pi \, \delta(\omega) + \frac{1}{j\omega} \right] \mathbf{W}(\omega)e^{j\omega t} \, d\omega \qquad (11\text{-}118a)$$

Then, from Eq. (5-224) we have

$$a(t) = \frac{1}{2} \mathbf{W}(0) + \frac{1}{2\pi} \int_{-\infty}^{\infty} \frac{\mathbf{W}(\omega)}{j\omega} e^{j\omega t} \, d\omega \qquad (11\text{-}118b)$$

The use of the Fourier transform allows us to correlate the sinusoidal-steady-state response with the transient response of a network. In fact, we see that the two are interrelated; if we know one, we can usually determine the other. Equation (11-113) allows us to determine the time-domain response in terms of the frequency-domain response. Similarly, if we know the transient response [such as $v_1(t)$ and $v_2(t)$], we can take their Fourier transforms and substitute in Eq. (11-110) to obtain $\mathbf{W}(j\omega)$. This presupposes $\mathbf{V}_1(j\omega) \neq 0$ for any ω.

In Sec. 5-15 we discussed the various criteria used to rate the unit-step response. It should be noted that these criteria are somewhat limited. Let us consider them in terms of the frequency response. Actually, we cannot make definite statements, but if we study a great many networks, we can obtain some general ideas. The 10 to 90 percent rise time is reduced as the high-frequency response of the network is increased. In general, speaking heuristically, the high-frequency components are the ones that tend to produce rapid changes of $f(t)$ with time. Note that these components themselves change rapidly. Then, for a fast response it is necessary that the high-frequency components make a substantial contribution to the response. A very large low-frequency component can also lead to rapid responses. In general, this can lead to a large overshoot. (This is not the usual overshoot.) Overshoot of the usual type is also related to the falloff in frequency response. Overshoot can be considered somewhat analogous to Gibb's phenomenon, which results when a Fourier series is truncated. In network response the "truncation" is caused by the falloff in $\mathbf{W}(j\omega)$ with ω. Note that if $\mathbf{W}(j\omega) = 0$ for $|\omega| > \omega_0$, then the integral of Eq. (11-113) becomes an integral from $-\omega_0$ to ω_0. This is equivalent to truncating the Fourier series. In general, if the high-frequency falloff is too rapid, overshoot will occur.

11-9   The time-shift theorem

Let us assume that we have the Fourier transform of $f(t)$,

$$\mathcal{F}[f(t)] = \mathbf{F}(j\omega) \tag{11-119}$$

and we wish to find the Fourier transform of $f(t - t_1)$, or $f(t)$ delayed by t_1 sec. We shall designate it as

$$\mathcal{F}[f(t - t_1)] = \mathbf{F}_1(\omega)$$

Substituting in Eq. (11-90), we have

$$\mathbf{F}_1(j\omega) = \int_{-\infty}^{\infty} f(t - t_1)e^{-j\omega t}\,dt \tag{11-120}$$

Let

$$t - t_1 = x \tag{11-121}$$

Then

$$\mathbf{F}_1(j\omega) = \int_{-\infty}^{\infty} f(x)e^{-j\omega x}e^{-j\omega t_1}\, dx \qquad (11\text{-}122)$$

We remove $e^{-j\omega t_1}$ from the integral,

$$\mathbf{F}_1(j\omega) = e^{-j\omega t_1}\int_{-\infty}^{\infty} f(x)e^{-j\omega x}\, dx \qquad (11\text{-}123)$$

and the integral is now just the definition of $\mathbf{F}(j\omega)$,

$$\mathbf{F}_1(j\omega) = e^{-j\omega t_1}\mathbf{F}(j\omega) \qquad (11\text{-}124)$$

This result is very similar to the time-shift theorem for the Laplace transform (see Sec. 5-16).

11-10   Convolution

In this section we shall prove a theorem very similar to the time-convolution theorem for the Laplace transform (see Sec. 5-20). Many of the details of the proof follow closely those of the time-convolution theorem. The convolution theorem we are about to prove will enable us to obtain the inverse Fourier transform when we can identify $\mathbf{F}(j\omega)$ as the product of two functions whose Fourier transforms are known. The theorem states that if

$$\mathfrak{F}[g(t)] = \mathbf{G}(j\omega) \qquad (11\text{-}125a)$$
$$\mathfrak{F}[h(t)] = \mathbf{H}(j\omega) \qquad (11\text{-}125b)$$

and

$$\mathfrak{F}[f(t)] = \mathbf{G}(j\omega)\mathbf{H}(j\omega) \qquad (11\text{-}126)$$

then

$$f(t) = \int_{-\infty}^{\infty} g(\tau)h(t - \tau)\, d\tau \qquad (11\text{-}127)$$

To prove this we shall take the Fourier transform of $f(t)$ and show that it is given by Eq. (11-126).

In general, if two functions have the same Fourier transforms, they are equal, except possibly at a finite number of points, where they can differ by a finite amount. This is analogous to the uniqueness of the Laplace transform (see Sec. 5-1). Substituting Eq. (11-127) into Eq. (11-90), we have

$$\mathbf{F}(\omega) = \int_{-\infty}^{\infty}\int_{-\infty}^{\infty} g(\tau)h(t - \tau)\, d\tau\, e^{-j\omega t}\, dt \qquad (11\text{-}128)$$

We shall assume that $g(t)$ and $h(t)$ are such that the order of integration can be interchanged. Then

$$\mathbf{F}(\omega) = \int_{-\infty}^{\infty} g(\tau)\int_{-\infty}^{\infty} h(t - \tau)e^{-j\omega t}\, dt\, d\tau \qquad (11\text{-}129)$$

The inner integral is just the Fourier transform of $h(t)$ delayed by τ sec.

Then, applying Eq. (11-124), we have

$$\mathbf{F}(\omega) = \int_{-\infty}^{\infty} g(\tau)\mathbf{H}(j\omega)e^{-j\omega t}\,d\tau \tag{11-130}$$

Note that $\mathbf{H}(j\omega)$ is a constant as far as the integration is concerned. Thus it can be removed from the integral. The remaining integral is just $\mathfrak{F}[g(t)]$. Thus

$$\mathbf{F}(\omega) = \mathbf{G}(j\omega)\mathbf{H}(j\omega) \tag{11-131}$$

and we have proved the theorem.

The integral of Eq. (11-127) is called the *convolution* of $g(t)$ and $h(t)$ (see Sec. 5-20), written as $g(t) * h(t)$; thus

$$\mathfrak{F}[g(t) * h(t)] = \mathbf{G}(j\omega)\mathbf{H}(j\omega) \tag{11-132}$$

Because of the similarity of the form of Eqs. (11-89) and (11-90), we can write

$$\mathfrak{F}[g(t)h(t)] = \frac{1}{2\pi}\,\mathbf{G}(j\omega) * \mathbf{H}(j\omega) = \frac{1}{2\pi}\int_{-\infty}^{\infty} \mathbf{G}(jx)\mathbf{H}[j(\omega - x)]\,dx \tag{11-133}$$

The details are left to the reader.

As an example of the convolution theorem let us obtain the response of a network in terms of its impulse response. In Sec. 11-8 we demonstrated that if a voltage $v_1(t)$ with Fourier transform $\mathbf{V}_1(j\omega)$ is applied to a network whose impulse response $w(t)$ has a Fourier transform $\mathbf{W}(j\omega)$, then the output voltage is [see Eq. (11-113)]

$$v_2(t) = \int_{-\infty}^{\infty} W(j\omega)\mathbf{V}_1(j\omega)e^{j\omega t}\,d\omega \tag{11-134}$$

We have taken the input and the output to be voltages. Actually, either or both could be currents. Equation (11-134) was derived after showing that the Fourier transform of $v_2(t)$ is $\mathbf{W}(j\omega)\mathbf{V}_1(j\omega)$. Thus [see Eq. (11-132)]

$$v_2(t) = w(t) * v_1(t) = \int_{-\infty}^{\infty} w(\tau)v_1(t - \tau)\,d\tau \tag{11-135}$$

Since $\mathbf{W}(j\omega)\mathbf{V}_1(j\omega) = \mathbf{V}_1(j\omega)\mathbf{W}(j\omega)$, we can also write

$$v_2(t) = \int_{-\infty}^{\infty} v_1(\tau)w(t - \tau)\,d\tau \tag{11-136}$$

These equations are essentially the same as Eqs. (5-203) and (5-303), which were derived with the Laplace transform. Remember that in Sec. 5-20 the function of time was zero for t less than zero.

11-11   The relation between the Fourier transform and the Laplace transform

In this section we shall obtain the Laplace transform from the Fourier transform. This will give us some insight into both these transforms. The derivation will be heuristic at times. The fact that the Laplace transform can be derived from the Fourier transform does not mean that the Fourier transform is more general. In fact, we shall see that many functions which do not possess Fourier transforms do have Laplace transforms.

We shall start our discussion with the Fourier transform pair of Eqs. (11-89) and (11-90),

$$\mathbf{F}(j\omega) = \int_{-\infty}^{\infty} f(t)e^{-j\omega t}\, dt \tag{11-137}$$

$$f(t) = \frac{1}{2\pi} \int_{-\infty}^{\infty} \mathbf{F}(j\omega)e^{j\omega t}\, d\omega \tag{11-138}$$

Now, as is usually the case in practical problems, we shall restrict ourselves to functions of time which are zero for $t < 0$; that is, we shall work with $f(t)u(t)$. Equation (11-137) becomes

$$\mathbf{F}(j\omega) = \int_{0}^{\infty} f(t)e^{j\omega t}\, d\omega \tag{11-139}$$

Now let us consider another function of time, $f_a(t)$, defined as

$$f_a(t) = u(t)f(t)e^{-\sigma t} \tag{11-140}$$

We obtain its Fourier transform,

$$\mathbf{F}_a(j\omega) = \int_{0}^{\infty} f(t)e^{-\sigma t}e^{-j\omega t}\, dt \tag{11-141a}$$

or, equivalently,

$$\mathbf{F}_a(j\omega) = \int_{0}^{\infty} f(t)e^{-(\sigma+j\omega)t}\, dt \tag{11-141b}$$

Let us express the inverse Fourier transform of $\mathbf{F}_a(j\omega)$ so that $f(t)$ is obtained directly. Note that $f(t)e^{-\sigma t}u(t)$ often has a Fourier transform, while $f(t)u(t)$ does not. For instance, $u(t)e^{+3t}$ does not have a Fourier transform because the integral of Eq. (11-137) will not converge. However, then Eq. (11-141) will converge if $\sigma > 3$, since $f_a(t)$ falls off exponentially with time. Similarly, a function such as $u(t)$ must be treated by distribution theory, while $u(t)e^{-\sigma t}$, ($\sigma > 0$) presents no problems.

Now we take the inverse Fourier transform of $\mathbf{F}_a(j\omega)$. Substituting in Eq. (11-138), we have

$$f(t)u(t)e^{-\sigma t} = f_a(t) = \frac{1}{2\pi} \int_{-\infty}^{\infty} \mathbf{F}_a(j\omega)e^{j\omega t}\, d\omega \tag{11-142}$$

Multiplying through by $e^{\sigma t}$, we obtain

$$f(t)u(t) = \frac{1}{2\pi} \int_{-\infty}^{\infty} \mathbf{F}_a(j\omega)e^{(\sigma+j\omega)t}\, d\omega \tag{11-143}$$

We can now consider that we have a new transform pair given by Eqs. (11-141) and (11-143),

$$\mathbf{F}_a(j\omega) = \int_0^\infty f(t)e^{-(\sigma+j\omega)t}\,dt \tag{11-144}$$

$$f(t)u(t) = \frac{1}{2\pi}\int_{-\infty}^\infty \mathbf{F}_a(j\omega)e^{(\sigma+j\omega)t}\,d\omega \tag{11-145}$$

Now let us make the substitution

$$s = \sigma + j\omega \tag{11-146}$$

Then Eqs. (11-144) and (11-145) become

$$\mathbf{F}_1(s) = \int_0^\infty f(t)e^{-st}\,dt \tag{11-147}$$

$$f(t)u(t) = \frac{1}{2\pi j}\int_{\sigma-j\infty}^{\sigma+j\infty} \mathbf{F}_1(s)e^{st}\,ds \tag{11-148}$$

where we have used the notation

$$\mathbf{F}_1(s) = \mathbf{F}_a(j\omega) \tag{11-149}$$

since s now acts as the variable. Comparison of Eqs. (11-147) and (11-148) with Eqs. (5-14), which define the Laplace transform pair, shows that they are essentially the same. Note that in the Laplace transform σ is restricted ($\sigma > \sigma_0$); this is to make the integral of Eq. (5-14a) converge. The same statement can be made about Eq. (11-147). Thus the Laplace transform can be considered to be the Fourier transform with the convergence factor $e^{-\sigma t}$ added. This makes the Laplace transform somewhat more versatile, since many functions will have Laplace transforms whereas they will not have Fourier transforms. That is, for certain functions the integral of Eq. (11-137) will not exist, while that of Eq. (11-147) will exist if σ is large enough [for example, $e^{2t}u(t)$]. Note that there are functions that have neither Fourier nor Laplace transforms, such as $u(t)e^{t^2}$.

The Laplace transform is also ideally suited to treating initial conditions In general, if a network diagram or equivalent circuit is available, it is usually easier to work with the Laplace transform than with the Fourier transform. Conversely, the Fourier transform gives better insight into the relation between frequency response and transient response. It is often used in theoretical studies which correlate the time-domain and the frequency-domain responses. Often the frequency response of a network has been measured experimentally. In such a case it is usually easier to use the Fourier transform to calculate the time-domain response. The Laplace transform is more useful in providing insight between time-domain response and the pole-zero location.

The development of this section indicates some of the physical meaning of the Laplace transform variable s. When Re $s = \sigma = 0$, then $s = j\omega$. This corresponds to ω in the Fourier transform. Thus it is the real frequency variable.

One fact should be noted. The Fourier transform cannot be obtained from the Laplace transform simply by replacing s by $j\omega$. If the Laplace transform has poles in the right half plane, then the function of time will contain increasing exponentials, and the Fourier transform will not exist. If the Laplace transform has poles that lie only in the left half plane, then the time function will be exponentially damped. Thus the Fourier transform integral will converge, and the Fourier transform *can* be obtained from the Laplace transform just be replacing s by $j\omega$. If the Laplace transform has poles on the $j\omega$ axis, then the Fourier transform will exist. However, the time functions lead to special cases (which must be treated by distribution theory). In such circumstances the Fourier transform cannot be obtained from the Laplace transform simply by replacing s by $j\omega$; for instance, $\mathcal{L}[u(t)] = 1/s$, while $\mathcal{F}[u(t)] = \pi\delta(\omega) + 1/j\omega$ [see Eq. (11-117)]. In general, any functions that are zero for $t < 0$ and have a Fourier transform will also have a Laplace transform.

The preceding discussion applies to functions of time. In contrast, when we obtain network transfer functions or immittances, their Fourier domain and Laplace domain representations are more closely related, if we assume zero initial conditions. For instance, the impedance of a capacitor on a Laplace transform basis is

$$\mathbf{Z}(s) = \frac{1}{sC}$$

If we work on a Fourier transform basis, then the sinusoidal-steady-state response would be used, and the impedance in question would be

$$\mathbf{Z}(j\omega) = \frac{1}{j\omega C}$$

In general, the sinusoidal-steady-state network transfer function or immittance can be obtained from the Laplace transform form of the transfer function or immittance by replacing s by $j\omega$. Note that this applies to transfer functions or immittances which are the ratio of the transforms of two time functions. It does not apply to the time functions themselves.

The Laplace transform has been restricted to functions of time which are zero for $t < 0$. Actually, a *two-sided Laplace transform* exists with which we can treat functions which are nonzero for $-\infty \le t \le \infty$. In general, for the types of problems we consider this is not as practical as the one-sided Laplace transform that we have studied.

REFERENCE

[1] L. Schwartz, "Théorie des distributions," vols. I and II, Actualités scientifiques et industrielles, Hermann and Cie, Paris, 1957, 1959.

BIBLIOGRAPHY

Clement, P. R., and W. C. Johnson: "Electrical Engineering Science," chap. 16, McGraw-Hill Book Company, New York, 1960.

Close, C. M.: "The Analysis of Linear Circuits," chap. 9, Harcourt, Brace & World, Inc., New York, 1966.

Javid, M., and E. Brenner: "Analysis, Transmission, and Filtering of Signals," chaps. 5 and 6, McGraw-Hill Book Company, New York, 1963.

Ley, B. J., S. G. Lutz, and C. F. Rehberg: "Linear Circuit Analysis," chaps. 6 and 7, McGraw-Hill Book Company, New York, 1959.

Manning, L. A.: "Electrical Circuits," chaps. 20 and 21, McGraw-Hill Book Company, New York, 1966.

Peskin, E.: "Transient and Steady State Analysis of Electrical Networks," chap. 2, D. Van Nostrand Company, Inc., Princeton, N.J., 1961.

Skilling, H. H.: "Electrical Engineering Circuits," 2d ed., chaps. 14 and 15, John Wiley & Sons, Inc., New York, 1965.

PROBLEMS

11-1. Obtain the sine and cosine form of the Fourier series for the function of time of Fig. 11-3a.

11-2. Repeat Prob. 11-1 for the waveform of Fig. 11-3b.

11-3. Repeat Prob. 11-1 for the waveform of Fig. 11-4.

11-4. Obtain the sine and cosine form of the Fourier series of $f(t) = \sin^2 \omega_0 t$.

11-5. Obtain the sine and cosine form of the Fourier series of $f(t) = |\sin \omega_0 t|$.

11-6. Repeat Prob. 11-1, but now obtain the exponential form of the Fourier series. Draw the discrete Fourier spectrum.

11-7. Repeat Prob. 11-2, but now obtain the exponential form of the Fourier series. Draw the discrete Fourier spectrum.

11-8. Repeat Prob. 11-3, but now obtain the exponential form of the Fourier series. Draw the discrete Fourier spectrum.

11-9. Repeat Prob. 11-5, but now obtain the exponential form of the Fourier series. Draw the discrete Fourier spectrum.

11-10. Plot four Fourier series for the square wave given in Eq. (11-16). Use 1, 3, 7, and 11 terms. Discuss error and Gibb's phenomenon in terms of this example.

11-11. Repeat Prob. 11-10, but modify the coefficients to eliminate Gibb's phenomenon.

11-12. The current generator of Fig. 11-7 produces the waveform of Fig. 11-3a. Compute $v(t)$.

11-13. Repeat Prob. 11-12, but now use the waveform of Fig. 11-3b.

11-14. Repeat Prob. 11-12, but now use the waveform of Fig. 11-4.

11-15. Repeat Prob. 11-12, but now use the waveform of Prob. 11-4.

11-16. Repeat Prob. 11-12, but now use the waveform of Prob. 11-5.

11-17. The current generator of Fig. 11-12 produces the waveform of Fig. 11-3a. Compute $v(t)$.

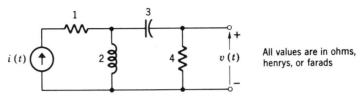

Fig. 11-12

11-18. Repeat Prob. 11-17 for the waveform of Fig. 11-3b.

11-19. Repeat Prob. 11-17 for the waveform of Fig. 11-4.

11-20. Repeat Prob. 11-17 for the waveform of Prob. 11-5.

11-21. Compute the rms value of the waveform of Fig. 11-3a.

11-22. Repeat Prob. 11-21 for the waveform of Fig. 11-3b.

11-23. Find the Fourier transform of the waveform $f(t) = e^{-|t|}$. Draw the continuous spectrum.

11-24. Repeat Prob. 11-23 for $f(t) = u(t)e^{-t}$.

11-25. Repeat Prob. 11-23 for $f(t) = u(t) \sin t - u(t - 2\pi) \sin (t - 2\pi)$.

11-26. Repeat Prob. 11-23 for the pulse of Fig. 11-13.

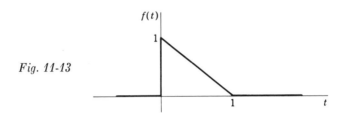

Fig. 11-13

11-27. Repeat Prob. 11-23 for the pulse of Fig. 11-14.

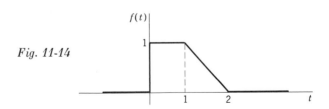

Fig. 11-14

11-28. The current generator of Fig. 11-7 produces the waveform of Prob. 11-23. Find $v(t)$. Use $R = C = 1$. There is no initial storage of energy in the capacitor or inductor.

11-29. Repeat Prob. 11-28 for the waveform of Prob. 11-24.

11-30. Repeat Prob. 11-28 for the waveform of Prob. 11-25

11-31. Repeat Prob. 11-28 for the waveform of Fig. 11-13.

11-32. Repeat Prob. 11-28 for the waveform of Fig. 11-14.

11-33. Find the unit-impulse response of the network of Fig. 11-7. Use $R = C = 1$.

11-34. Find the unit-step response of the network of Fig. 11-12.

11-35. For the network of Fig. 11-11 $\mathbf{W}(j\omega) = 1/(j\omega + 2)$. Find its unit-impulse response.

11-36. Repeat Prob. 11-35, but now find the unit-step response.

11-37. Find the Fourier transform of the pulse of Fig. 11-13 if it is delayed for 2 sec. Use the results of Prob. 11-26 here.

11-38. Find the Fourier transform of the pulse of Fig. 11-14 if it is delayed by 5 sec. Use the result of Prob. 11-27 here.

11-39. Use the convolution theorem to find $f(t)$ when its Fourier transform is

$$\mathbf{F}(j\omega) = \frac{1}{2 + j\omega} \frac{1}{5 + j\omega}$$

11-40. Use the convolution theorem to find $\mathbf{F}(j\omega)$, the Fourier transform of $f(t)$, when $f(t) = e^{-a|t|}e^{-b|t|}$.

11-41. Repeat Prob. 11-40 for $f(t) = e^{-at}e^{-bt} \sin t\, u(t)$.

11-42. Express the response of the network of Prob. 11-35 to an arbitrary input in terms of its unit-impulse response.

Index

DATE DUE

4/oc			
GAYLORD			PRINTED IN U.S A.